SUBSTANCE USE
AND MISUSE

SUBSTANCE USE AND MISUSE

Everything Matters

Third Edition

Rick Csiernik

CANADIAN SCHOLARS

Toronto | Vancouver

Substance Use and Misuse: Everything Matters, Third Edition
Rick Csiernik

First published in 2021 by
Canadian Scholars, an imprint of CSP Books Inc.
425 Adelaide Street West, Suite 200
Toronto, Ontario
M5V 3C1

www.canadianscholars.ca

Library and Archives Canada Cataloguing in Publication

Title: Substance use and misuse : everything matters / Rick Csiernik.
Other titles: Substance use and abuse
Names: Csiernik, Rick, author.
Description: Third edition. | Previous editions published under title: Substance use and abuse. | Includes bibliographical references and index.
Identifiers: Canadiana (print) 20210101296 | Canadiana (ebook) 20210101318 | ISBN 9781773382296 (softcover) | ISBN 9781773382302 (PDF) | ISBN 9781773382319 (EPUB)
Subjects: LCSH: Substance abuse—Canada. | LCSH: Substance abuse—Treatment—Canada. | LCSH: Drug abuse—Canada. | LCSH: Drug abuse—Treatment—Canada. | LCSH: Psychotropic drugs. | LCSH: Drug addiction.
Classification: LCC HV5840.C2 C75 2021 | DDC 362.290971—dc23

Page layout by S4Carlisle Publishing Services
Cover design by Em Dash

Printed and bound in Ontario, Canada

Canadä

Contents

Tables, Figures, and Boxes

TABLES

FIGURES

BOXES

Preface

The preface of the first edition of *Substance Use and Abuse: Everything Matters*, published in 2011, began with this statement to contextualize drug use in our society:

Select any day of any week, of any month, of any year and read any major media source on any continent, save Antarctica, and you will find at least one article, typically within the first three pages, or first five minutes of a broadcast, pertaining to psychoactive drugs:

> *Addict's body to be exhumed for new tests*
> —*The Guardian*, Manchester, United Kingdom, Saturday, February 14, 2004

> *'War on drugs' not meant to be won*
> —*Norwich Bulletin*, Connecticut, United States, Monday, June 6, 2005

> *West Africa new hub for drug-trafficking networks*
> —*Mail and Guardian*, Johannesburg, South Africa, Saturday, May 13, 2006

> *Prince uses speech to talk about his alcohol problem*
> —*The Japan Times*, Tokyo, Japan, Sunday, July 8, 2007

> *Authorities smash drug ring with Hezbollah ties*
> —*Colombia Reports*, Medellin, Colombia, Tuesday, October 21, 2008

> *Australians arrested in global drug swoop*
> —*Sydney Morning Herald*, Sydney, Australia, Thursday, April 9, 2009

> *Quebec's landmark heroin study in jeopardy*
> —*The Globe and Mail*, Toronto, Canada, Wednesday, August 26, 2009

Unfortunately, the same could be done just as easily for the second edition, published in 2016, only this time there was also an article from Antarctica:

> *Nigeria: Still on the Tobacco Control Bill*
> —*All Africa*, Johannesburg, South Africa, Sunday, March 15, 2015

> *Saudi Arabia beheads four men for smuggling drugs*
> —*Aljazeera*, Doha, Qatar, Monday, August 18, 2014

Drug treatment court is proof people care
  —*The Spectator*, Hamilton, Canada, Tuesday, February 17, 2015

Senate bill would end federal prohibition on medical marijuana
  —*The Washington Post*, Washington, United States, Wednesday, March 11, 2015

Ban alcohol firms from sponsoring sports clubs and events, doctors urge
  —*The Guardian*, London, United Kingdom, Thursday, December 25, 2014

Drugs bound for Future Music Festival seized by Queensland anti-bikie squad
  —*The Sydney Morning Herald*, Sydney, Australia, Friday, March 6, 2015

Ottawa rejects marijuana firm CEN Biotech's licence application
  —*The Globe and Mail*, Toronto, Canada, Saturday, February 14, 2015

Are researchers in Antarctica on thin ice for abusing alcohol?
  —*Today.com*, Monday, October 26, 2015

… and yet again for this third edition, but this time collected all in the span of one week:

Japanese man detained in Cambodia for alleged drug possession
  —*The Japan Times*, Tokyo, Japan, Monday, February 17, 2020

Higher alcohol taxes to fund NHS would benefit poor—study
  —*The Guardian*, London, United Kingdom, Tuesday, February 18, 2020

Ethiopia passes landmark smoking excise bill
  —*All Africa*, Johannesburg, South Africa, Wednesday, February 19, 2020

NFL free agents Greg Robinson, Quan Bray arrested with 157 pounds of weed
  —*New York Daily News*, New York, United States, Thursday, February 20, 2020

Aussie businessman handed 27-year jail term over $1.5b cocaine importation
  —*The Sydney Morning Herald*, Sydney, Australia, Friday, February 21, 2020

12-step cured him, but it was the music that kept him going
  —*The Hamilton Spectator*, Hamilton, Canada, Saturday, February 22, 2020.

When it comes to addiction, everything does truly matter. Everything is connected and thus has an impact on the drugs we use, and misuse. The "everything" includes our physiology and biological makeup, our psychological well-being, our connections to our immediate environment, how much money our parents earned in the labour market, whether we were raised in a single-parent family, the immediate community in which we live and work, our sense of spirituality and hopefulness, and even the continent of our birth. All these items and more factor into what we deem to be appropriate, legal, licit, functional, and necessary when it comes to taking or avoiding psychoactive substances. Psychoactive drugs are an integral part of the human experience. They were in use before we as a species even had any formal written language, and once we learned to read and write, their use became a topic as prominent in literature and media as aggression and sexuality. Drugs define us in so many ways but extend even beyond the scope of humanity, as illustrated by the infamous YouTube video of a drunken elephant (https://www.youtube.com/watch?v=AIDJ-sTuoO8) and, closer to home, drunken squirrels (https://www.youtube.com/watch?v=4ikH9ZRcF2Q).

As evidenced by the sample of media headlines above, taken from every continent including Antarctica, psychoactive drugs are a global phenomenon. Every culture we know of has had or does have a very specific relationship with one or more psychoactive drugs, and most include some level of tragedy directly related to the use of these substances. The contemporary global drug trade keeps some national economies afloat. In some developed nations, significant economies have evolved around both rehabilitation and incarceration. Historically, drugs have been a component of the slave trade, been responsible for the creation of national boundaries, and been instrumental in the creation of cultural identities. Psychoactive substances sustain us. They provide us with euphoria. They are integral to our concepts of recreation and celebration. And they ease the pain of our loved ones when they are terminally ill yet can shorten our lifespan such that issues of aging are never even a consideration. Thus, what can our response be in the 21st century to something as integrated into our lives and culture as is the use of drugs?

In forming our response, our first step must be to enhance our knowledge of this global phenomenon. This book attempts to provide a fundamental working knowledge of the world of psychoactive drugs. *Substance Use and Misuse: Everything Matters* will introduce you to the foundational knowledge you need to understand the bio-psycho-social phenomenon that is addiction, its prevalence, why it arises, the range of psychoactive drugs ingested, and how they affect substance users and their environments. Ideas on how to prevent the development of substance misuse precede the section that presents a range of treatment options, from pharmacological treatments to harm reduction to self-help mutual aid, as our prevention initiatives have historically been underfunded and inconsistently delivered. An examination of treatment resources required to comprehensively and holistically assist those with addiction issues precedes a review of legal, ethical, and competency issues of which those working in the addiction field need to be cognizant. Throughout the book, you will be introduced not only to how everything matters when it comes to the process of developing an addiction, but also to how everything matters with regard to how we respond to the issues raised by this process.

Rick Csiernik
Hamilton, Ontario
September 2020

Acknowledgements

I would like to begin by acknowledging all of you who have the desire to do this difficult work in a field and with a population that remains marginalized and oppressed, even in the most open and affluent of societies. I want to thank the other addiction educators who are also using this resource for having faith that this work can aid them in teaching this difficult topic. I also wish to thank Dr. Susan Silva-Wayne for her support for the development of the first edition of this book, along with all the staff at Canadian Scholars over the years for turning thoughts and ideas into substance, especially Natalie Garriga, Emma Melnyk, and Sarah Powell. I would also like to thank past commentators for their kind words: Kristen Buscaglia, Phil Durrant, Tom Gabriel, Christie McGaghran, and Heidi Stanley, along with the anonymous reviewers across all three editions who provided insightful feedback and recommendations to enhance and refine the manuscript. Finally, thank you to Dr. Derek Chechak for his assistance with revisions to the second edition, Andrée Schuller for co-writing Chapter 23 of this edition, and to Emma W. Johnson for her incredible editing that allows this manuscript to be readable. And of course, Deborah, Alex, and Ben for giving me the space and time to do the work and for their ongoing, often unintended inspiration.

In closing, a goal for you not only as you read this book but as you navigate the complex world you live in: Be the fish that sees the water you swim in.

SECTION I

FUNDAMENTAL CONCEPTS

Drugs may be employed not only to treat pathological conditions; reduce pain, suffering, agitation and anxiety, but also to enhance the normal state—increase pleasure, facilitate learning and memory, reduce jealousy and aggressiveness. Hopefully, such pharmacological developments will come about as an accompaniment of, and not as a substitute for, a more ideal society.
  —Stanley Jarvik, 1967, p. 18

The Nixon campaign in 1968, and the Nixon White House after that, had two enemies: the antiwar Left, and black people. You understand what I am saying? We knew we couldn't make it illegal to be either against the war or black. But by getting the public to associate the hippies with marijuana and blacks with heroin and then criminalizing both heavily, we could disrupt those communities. We could arrest their leaders, raid their homes, break up their meetings, and vilify them night after night on the evening news. Did we know we were lying about the drugs? Of course we did.
  —John Ehrlichman, Counsel and Assistant to President Nixon as told to Dan Baum, 2016

Are you the fish that can see the water that you swim in?

Do we live in a drug culture? This question is moot, for if one examines the history of humanity, we as a species have so incorporated psychoactive drugs into every aspect of our civilization—celebration, medicine, escapism, sport, entertainment, survival, relaxation, day-to-day living, and even pandemic response—that to ask if there is a drug culture is synonymous with asking if there is a human culture. So, are you the fish that can see the water that you swim in?

A decade ago, the United Nations Office on Drugs and Crime (2011) estimated that the annual illicit drug trade was worth $1.1 trillion CAD, which was equivalent to 1.5 percent of global gross domestic product (GDP), with the cocaine trade alone accounting for $110 billion CAD alone. This is greater than the annual revenues of all but 15 national economies. This means that the drug trade produces more revenue than the paid work in Argentina, Saudi Arabia, Nigeria, or Switzerland and is far greater than the revenue produced by the world's largest multinationals, such as Walmart, Nestlé, Procter & Gamble, China National Petroleum, or Sony. In the United States alone, more than $85 billion CAD worth of illegal drugs are sold every year, yet only a tiny fraction is intercepted and seized by law enforcement agents. This has led the former director of the National Drug Control Policy, Michael Botticelli, to state that the United States could no longer attempt to arrest itself out of its drug problem (Lopez, 2014).

Herein lies the core problem. As a species, humans have a fascination with any drug that alters our basic perception of our environment, our interactions with and reactions to the external world, and thus to our own internal world. Anthropologists have postulated that a primary motivation for the shift from hunting and gathering societies to agrarian-based cultures was to allow for the regular and systematic cultivation of intoxicating beverages. This may explain, in part, why Indigenous Peoples in Canada were among the few groups never to use psychoactive drugs for recreational purposes until contact with outsiders. Archaeological evidence at multiple sites around the world indicates that the regular use of psychoactive substances dates back 10,000 years (Hayen et al., 2013; Merlin, 2003). In ancient Egypt, hieroglyphics illustrate gods holding and using different hallucinogenic drugs (Bertol et al., 2004). The use of drugs to produce altered states of consciousness is connected to many early peoples' belief systems, and it has been argued that psychoactive substances have been central to the evolution of human culture globally (Guerra-Doce, 2015). Unfortunately, the use and misuse of these psychoactive substances have an indisputable cost in terms of individual suffering, not only financially, but also personally, and to us all as a society and a species (Nutt et al., 2007).

Psychoactive drug use is not a strange anomaly of the 21st century, but rather a historical part of human civilization. Despite the perpetual historic discouragement of drug use, this behaviour has become an integral part of cultures worldwide, and it is unlikely that it will subside in the near future, if ever. A more realistic and pragmatic goal is a move toward wellness, harm reduction, and the abatement of misuse in lessening the extent to which persons are harmed and cause harm to others because of psychoactive drugs.

This opening section provides an overview of the fundamental concepts needed to understand substance use and misuse, including definitions of addiction and related concepts and pharmacological foundations, along with the prevalence and economic impacts of drug use.

CHAPTER 1

Conceptualizing Addiction

WHAT IS A PSYCHOACTIVE DRUG?

To a pharmacologist, a psychoactive drug is either a chemical not naturally found in the body or is a body chemical administered in a larger dose than is normal to the body. A specific person, via some mode of administration (see Table 2.1), takes the substance in a given amount (the dose level) on a particular frequency (the schedule of use) for a certain period of time. It is administered with the intent of producing a change in behaviour by specifically altering the central nervous system (CNS), but also has a profound effect on the larger peripheral nervous system, particularly the autonomic nervous system (ANS). The Le Dain Commission (1973), which produced the landmark body of work examining drugs in a scientific manner for the first time in Canada, defined a psychoactive drug as any substance, natural or synthesized, that by its chemical nature alters structure or function of the body or mind in the living organism. At the beginning of this century, the Canadian parliamentary Special Committee on Non-Medical Use of Drugs (2002) further defined a psychoactive drug as a substance that, when ingested, alters mental processes such as cognition or affect. Psychoactive drugs are substances that alter brain functioning by increasing, decreasing, or disrupting CNS activity. This in turn produces changes in mood, perception, sensation, need, consciousness, and other psychological functions and ultimately produces changes in behaviour. In addition, these substances influence a great number of physiological functions mediated by the ANS that are outside the realm of conscious control, such as respiration, cardiovascular function, hormonal balance, sexual arousal, and the critical fight/flight response. Psychoactive agents are used for both medical and non-medical purposes and may be either licit or illicit, depending on the place and time they are being used.

Drug misuse can apply to the occasional improper or inappropriate use of either a social or a prescription drug leading to outcomes ranging from intoxication to a hangover to criminal charges arising from impaired driving to ongoing problematic use of any drug that leads to a state of addiction. Adverse effects associated with drug misuse can also include medical complications, behavioural alterations, difficulties with social relationships, and medical, legal, and vocational issues. Thus, in this context, misuse refers to the use of any psychoactive drug to the extent that it interferes with a person's health or with economic or social adjustment. However, both legal and illegal drugs are employed for a range of reasons without the user ever developing a dependency or an addiction. This can range from the occasional and recreational use of alcohol, cannabis, ecstasy, or khat, to the therapeutic use of Valium, Ritalin, or morphine, to the functional use of coca leaves to help with strenuous labour in the Andes, to the use of opium to counteract the effects of dysentery and hunger in the Middle East.

ADDICTION

The term addiction derives from the Latin word *addicto*, meaning "bound or devoted or bondage to a practice." This is tied to the story of a Roman slave named Addictus, who, after a long period of servitude, was finally set free by his master. However, Addictus had become used to being chained and to following his master's commands. Even though Addictus was now allowed to remove what had bound him throughout his life, he had become so accustomed to the pain that, when the chains were unlocked, he could not bring himself to remove them.

The word "addiction" has been used so casually in so many ways and in so many different contexts that in practical terms it has lost its actual meaning. Many definitions begin with the narrow observation that addiction is the behaviour engaged in by compulsive drug users in search of their substance(s) of choice. At the turn of the 20th century, the term "addiction" had a strong behavioural connotation. It referred to compulsive drug seeking and the loss of personal control to drugs. It also involved a breakdown in lifestyle, including family, work, and leisure activities. In the 1950s and 1960s, addiction began to gain a closer association with the unpleasant physical reactions that occurred with the stoppage of drug administration. Those who were labelled as addicted continued to take the drug to avoid the negative bodily reactions that occurred when the drug cleared the system, that is, the withdrawal process. In 1964, the World Health Organization (WHO) moved away from the increasingly nebulous term "addiction" and began to use the more precise and narrower concept of "dependence," categorizing it by distinct physical and psychological components. However, the idea of addiction for many people continues to be overly narrow, often relating more to the exhibition of psychological dependence rather than sufficiently considering the equally important physical dependency on a chemical agent. This is further highlighted in Koob's (2008) definition, which only views addiction as a chronic relapsing disorder characterized by impulsivity and compulsivity with a neurobiological basis. Unfortunately, even when integrated, these two ideas do not provide us with an adequate, holistic conceptualization of this complex idea.

The standpoint provided by one's education also plays a vital role in how an idea is conceptualized. The classic example is the American Society of Addiction Medicine

(2019), whose very detailed definition of addiction has evolved over time but is still enveloped in a unidimensional standpoint:

> Addiction is a treatable, chronic medical disease involving complex interactions among brain circuits, genetics, the environment, and an individual's life experiences. People with addiction use substances or engage in behaviors that become compulsive and often continue despite harmful consequences. Prevention efforts and treatment approaches for addiction are generally as successful as those for other chronic diseases.

Unfortunately, this definition, like interpretations focused on behaviour, still misses a crucial element inherent in the holistic nature of addiction. Noted psychologist, addiction theorist, and pundit Stanton Peele (1983, 1985, 1989, 2000, 2016) has been among the most vigorous opponents of any strictly medical definition of addiction. Peele claims that addiction is not a chemical reaction. Rather, it is a social experience that in and of itself can bring about dependency to a substance in an otherwise healthy individual. People become dependent to a particular state of body and mind. According to Peele, no substance is inherently addictive, nor is substance addiction a single phenomenon. It occurs along a continuum, and even those at the extremes of addictiveness show the capacity to act in other than an addicted way under the right circumstances.

Anthropologists state that drinking alcohol is generally a social act that is performed in a socially recognized setting. Human geographers illustrate that the consumption of alcohol typically takes place at a specific time and in a specific place, with the affective potential of bringing people together in urban places in the evenings and at night (Oksanen, 2013). A dramatic 20th-century example of the importance of the social dimension of addiction involved conscripted American soldiers fighting communist forces in Vietnam as part of the ongoing Cold War conflict between the United States and Russia. As the outcome of a 1971 congressional visit to Vietnam, the United States Department of Defence set up a urine-screening program to detect heroin use in all combat troops at the time of their departure from Vietnam. These veterans, most of whom were still under the age of 21, were then to be detoxified. In one study, 75 percent of ground troops who engaged in combat and who tested positive for heroin use claimed they became addicted in Vietnam. One-third of these soldiers continued using, but less than 10 percent showed signs of what could be classified as dependency on returning to the United States (Roffman, 1976).

A second follow-up study of Vietnam veterans was also commissioned to determine the long-term consequences of their heroin use. Eight to twelve months after returning from Southeast Asia, interviews were conducted with approximately 900 males who had seen active combat duty. The sample was randomly selected from the 14,000 army-enlisted men who returned to the United States in September 1971, the first month in which the urine-screening and detoxification system was operating uniformly throughout Vietnam.

Men who had been detected as drug-positive at departure were over-sampled, so the full sample included a large number of men who would be at high risk after their return. In 1974, 617 former soldiers with an average age of 24 were re-interviewed. In this follow-up group, it was discovered that the sample was no more likely to be using heroin regularly or daily, if at all, than either marijuana or amphetamines. Despite their initial addiction, the majority of former soldiers had managed to quit on their own. As well, some were even able to return to casual use without becoming dependent again. While treatment was certainly vital in aiding some individuals to become abstinent, these studies clearly indicated there were other factors involved in addiction. The importance of environmental and social factors that precipitate and support drug use were clearly demonstrated. A major difference in this sample and clinical samples of heroin users from the United States entering treatment was not only that the Vietnam group had been exposed to a far more generous supply and superior quality of the drug for one year, but the exposure was in an extraordinary setting that featured the constant threat of death. Further, for those veterans who continued to use heroin in the United States two to three years after returning from active duty in Vietnam, only one in six came to treatment (Becoña, 2018; Robins et al., 2010).

Drugs produce societal harm in multiple ways: through damage to family and social life; through additional costs to the health, social services, and criminal justice systems; through decreased workplace productivity; through property damage; and, of course, through violence and the costs of organized crime (Nutt et al., 2007). For Peele and Brodsky (1992), the social context for addiction required:

- a readily available substance;
- stress in a severe form, including misery, danger, and discomfort;
- alienation;
- emotional and/or vocational deprivation; and
- a lack of control over one's life.

When considering what addiction entails, the larger social, environmental, and cultural factors that surround an individual need to be considered, for we human beings are fundamentally social creatures (Oksanen, 2013). This concept was further underscored by the longitudinal work done by Hallam Hurt and her colleagues beginning in 1989 at the height of the "crack baby" epidemic. They followed a cohort of children exposed to cocaine while in utero, along with a comparison group of children exposed to non-gestational cocaine who also lived in the inner city of a large American urban centre and came from low-income, predominantly African American, single-parent-led families. Over time, they found no difference in school performance, grade point average, reading level, or standardized reading and math test scores between the two groups. Nor were there differences in IQ, executive brain functioning, or general cognitive abilities. However, both groups had lower scores than the average for American children their age across all of the variables. Ongoing evaluations examining environmental factors of all participants found that 81 percent of the children had seen someone arrested; 35 percent had seen someone shot; and 19 percent had seen a dead body in their neighbourhood by the age of seven. Those children who reported a high exposure to violence were also the most likely to have symptoms of depression and anxiety, and to have lower self-esteem. Hallam's conclusion was that poverty and adverse childhood experiences were a far more powerful influence on the academic outcomes of inner-city children than gestational exposure to cocaine (Avants et al., 2007; Farah et al., 2008; Hurt et al., 2005, 2008, 1997, 2001).

Dr. Robert DuPont (1994), then head of the Institute for Behavioural Health in Rockville, Maryland, stated that addiction needs to be considered in terms of how it disorganizes and creates crises in individuals' lives. Recently the term *addiction* has finally begun to encompass a greater social orientation rather than a purely biomedical or bio-psycho one. When one views pharmacological data and literature in the light of its social and legal history, the tendency by the medical community to explain drug misuse and addiction becomes, at best, suspect. Likewise, when only compulsion and compulsive behaviours are considered as leading to addiction, both the biological and social dimensions are improperly minimized. Addiction may well be a dependent state acquired over an extended period of time by a predisposed person in an attempt to correct a chronic stress condition in a conscious, deliberate, self-satisfying, selective manner. However, there is also extensive evidence that social, economic, and situational factors play key roles in initiating addiction (Kallant, 2009, 2015). Thus, addiction needs to be viewed in a holistic manner and as a process that integrates three constituent components: biological, psychological, and social. Or, to properly and holistically conceptualize it: addiction is a bio-psycho-social phenomenon.

DEPENDENCY

When considering both addiction and its sub-component, dependency, it is useful to specify what it is that is being depended on and for what reasons, and then to identify the consequences of its presence or absence. The social and moral significance of dependency changes considerably if the drug is relied on for a societally deemed legitimate reason, for example, taking Dilaudid (hydromorphone) for pain relief from cancer, as opposed to using the same drug for escape from an unpleasant or intolerable social situation, such as violence in an interpersonal relationship. Psychoactive drug-related problems tend to arise because of both a psychological and physical dependence on a certain drug, not either or.

Physical Dependency

Physical dependence is a physiological state of cellular adaptation that occurs when the body becomes so accustomed to a drug that it can only function normally when the drug is present. Without the drug, the user will experience physical disturbances or illness, known as withdrawal. Withdrawal symptoms can be prevented or promptly relieved by the administration of a sufficient quantity of the original drug or, often, by one with similar pharmacological properties, such as a benzodiazepine like Xanax in place of alcohol. However, in the latter case, in which one psychoactive drug is used to prevent withdrawal symptoms from another, cross-dependence to the new drug can easily develop.

The development of physical dependence is important in the maintenance of drug taking, not only because of its negative reinforcement, but also because administration, either to alleviate or to prevent withdrawal, can lead to additional positive reinforcement. Instead of a return to a neutral body state, or homeostasis, there may be an overshooting effect, resulting in further positive reinforcement. Physical dependence is usually preceded by serious personal, psychological, social, and even physiological complications. Physical dependence can occur with chronic use of most depressants, opioids, and stimulants. Among the hallucinogens, physical dependence has not yet been demonstrated, except with cannabis. It is also the component missing from behaviours that are mistakenly labelled as addiction.

Psychological Dependency

Psychological dependence occurs when a drug becomes so important to a person's thoughts or activities that the person believes that they[1] cannot manage without the substance. Psychological dependence may range from a mild wish to a compelling emotional need for periodic or continuous use of a drug and may escalate to feelings of loss or desperation if the drug is unattainable. In the case of psychological dependence, a person begins to feel and eventually believe that they need the drug to cope with a variety of life situations. The feelings of either relaxation or arousal become required because individuals believe they cannot get through a day or a situation without these affects.

In many instances, the psychological aspects are considerably more important than physical dependence in maintaining chronic drug use and can last far longer. While physical withdrawal can be managed in weeks or even days in some limited cases, psychological cravings can lead to drug use months and even years after the last actual administration. Subtle yet persistent psychological and social factors are more than adequate to maintain the behaviour of drug consumption even after a successful detoxification process.

The Diagnostic and Statistical Manual of Mental Disorders (DSM) constitutes the guidelines developed by the American Psychiatric Association (APA) to inform its members, and other helping professionals, on how to diagnosis mental health issues. In the fourth edition of the DSM (APA, 2000), dependence was defined as a maladaptive pattern of substance use leading to clinically significant impairment or distress. However, in the fifth edition (APA, 2013), a new conceptualization relating to alcohol and other psychoactive drugs was created. Problems relating to psychoactive drug use became classified as substance-related disorders, with separate listings for alcohol, caffeine, cannabis, hallucinogens, inhalants, opioids, sedative-hypnotics (benzodiazepines and barbiturates), stimulants, and tobacco, with a final category entitled "other or unknown." As well, at the very end of the section, one new area was added: non-substance-related disorders, which has only one subtype: gambling.

In the development of DSM-V, the working group also had extensive discussions regarding the use of the term *addiction*. There was general agreement that *dependence* as a label for compulsive, out-of-control drug use was problematic, and that the idea had confused many physicians and psychiatrists. This confusion resulted in individuals with normal tolerance and withdrawal being labelled with the stigmatizing and oppressive term *addict*. This also resulted in the withholding of adequate doses of opioids from patients suffering severe pain because of the physician's fear of producing addiction. Thus, the term *dependence* was removed, and in its place, each of the drugs, including the "other" grouping, is now described in detail under the following headings: use, intoxication, and withdrawal.

WHAT IS NOT AN ADDICTION

Toward the end of the 20th century, an evident shift toward the medicalization of behaviour occurred, with a broad range of non-medical problems becoming defined and treated as such (Szasz, 2007). These newly medicalized behaviours simultaneously became intertwined with both the creation and manufacturing of mental illness, partially because in the United States, under its corporate health care model, insurance companies would only pay for medical or psychiatric treatment if the situation could be medically framed. No DSM diagnosis, no treatment—and thus slowly all types of behaviours began to be conceptualized as addictions (Greenberg, 2010; Watters, 2010). Life problems were increasingly transformed into pathologies, with addiction becoming one of the most popular, incorrectly, and overused medical terms. This has further allowed pharmaceutical companies to market not to alleviate or mitigate illness but to treat behaviours (Conrad, 2007). Thus, it is not surprising that the popular though problematic label of addiction has been placed on these behavioural issues.

Compulsive Conditions

Compulsive conditions or behaviours, or simply compulsions, are most commonly referenced in anxiety literature, and are found in part in the obsessive-compulsive section of the DSM. In the purest sense, compulsions are repetitive behaviours performed in an effort to minimize an anxiety or control or prevent an obsessive thought, which may or may not be related to the behaviour. For instance, a person may repeatedly wash their hands because of an obsessive fear of germs or because the person feels that the action is necessary to prevent some unrelated harm. In Goodman's (1990) early conceptualization of addiction, compulsions were an integral component, along with reward-seeking behaviour, designed to evade or avoid internal discomfort but only part of the condition of addiction. What some have labelled as behavioural addiction, including gambling or shopping, are better understood as compulsions that involve:

- spontaneous desires to act a particular way,
- a subjective sense of feeling temporarily out of control,
- psychological conflict pertaining to the driving behaviour, and
- a disregard for negative consequences (Sussman & Sussman, 2011).

Everitt and Robbins (2005) view addiction as a progression from a loss of control to a developed habit to an eventual compulsion. Although their conceptualization emphasizes the change in the brain that can foster an actual addiction to psychoactive drugs, the end point of compulsion recognizes the dependent nature, and not necessarily goal-directed state, of the process. For instance, a compulsive internet gamer is not playing just to win but also to avoid other life issues. They are gaming for the action, excitement, or emotional affect (Nakken, 1996). Whereas a habit develops as people become accustomed to using a psychoactive substance, the compulsion defines continuous and often escalating drug-seeking behaviours (Everitt & Robbins, 2005). Pickard (2012) defines compulsion as "an urge, impulse or desire that is irresistible: so strong that it is impossible for it not to lead to action" (p. 41).

Those who label compulsive conditions as an addiction point to the mood modification, tolerance, and salience (Kuss & Griffiths, 2012) that arises when a person engages in the action. However, they always omit examining the effect on the autonomic nervous system that distinguishes addiction to psychoactive agents, necessitating distinct treatment, treatment systems, and policies. As well, the social context is rarely considered, with attention primarily focused upon the psychological state. For example, in Kuss and Griffiths's (2012) systemic review of internet gaming addiction, the cause is simply the internal factors of personality traits and motivations for playing, combined with structural game characteristics. Likewise, Ryding and Kaye (2017) define internet addiction as involving "intense preoccupation with using the Internet, difficulty managing time on the Internet, becoming irritated if disturbed whilst online, and decreased social interaction in the real world" (p. 226). This is not to diminish the serious impact that these and other compulsive conditions produce; in fact, by distinguishing these as distinct concepts, distinct treatments, treatment systems, and policy approaches are required rather than a homogenous response to everything labelled an addiction.

In 1990, Isaac Marks introduced the construct of non-chemical addictions. This substantively contributed to the proliferation of human behaviours becoming pathologized and labelled as an addiction, such as:

- aggression (Golden & Shaham, 2018)
- consumer brands (Cui et al., 2018; Mrad & Cui, 2017)
- eating/food (Hauck et al., 2019; Naish et al., 2018; Shell & Firmin, 2017)

- entrepreneurship (Spivack & McKelvie, 2018)
- exercising (Jee, 2016; Landolfi, 2013)
- gambling (Murch & Clark, 2016; Zack et al., 2019)
- gaming (Kuss & Griffiths, 2012; Starcevic & Aboujaoude, 2017)
- internet use (Ryding & Kaye, 2017; Starcevic & Aboujaoude, 2017; Thorsteinsson & Davey, 2014), including
  - Facebook (Andreassen et al., 2012; Jafri, 2015)
  - pornography (Duffy et al., 2016; Love et al., 2015; Short et al., 2012)
  - selfitis (taking selfies) (Balakrishnan & Griffiths, 2018; Begum, 2019)
  - social networking sites (Wang, Wang et al., 2018)
  - YouTube (Balakrishnan & Griffiths, 2017)
- love (Costa et al., 2019; Sanches & John, 2019)
- maladaptive daydreaming (Pietkiewicz et al., 2018)
- news (Ishaq et al., 2017)
- non-suicidal self-injury (Blasco-Fontecilla et al., 2016; Victor et al., 2012)
- sex (Barrilleaux, 2016; Hall, 2014)
- shopping/buying (Manchiraju et al., 2017; Uzarska et al., 2019)
- smartphones [nomophobia] (De-Sola Gutiérrez et al., 2016; Panova & Carbonell, 2018; Sagar, 2019)
- studying (Atroszko et al., 2015, 2016a, 2016b)
- sugar (DiNicolantonio et al., 2018; Throsby, 2019)
- ultraviolet indoor tanning (Becirevic et al., 2017; Reed, 2015)
- video games (Ferguson & Colwell, 2019; Hellman et al., 2013)
- work (Atroszko et al., 2019; Orosz et al., 2016)

However, the majority of these compulsive conditions only have shared psychological characteristics with addiction, specifically the inability to resist an urge or drive that harms oneself (Grant et al., 2013).

Billieux and colleagues (2015) argue that research in the behavioural addiction field that has led to the propagation of these new addictions is extremely weak. For some conditions, the foundation is based on older research that was used to validate other disorders that themselves do not meet the full criteria of an addiction, such as gambling. This has led many behavioural addictions to simply being descriptions of traits, with empirical support failing to explain functional impairment, the biological impact beyond the role of dopamine (see Chapter 2), or the social context to any extent. Another criticism of current diagnostic approaches is that they fail to account for elevated and repeated engagement that is not always problematic nor always associated with adverse consequences. Again, most of these behavioural addictions do not have a distinct physical or social dimension as part of their conceptualization (Deleuze et al., 2018). Konkolÿ Thege and colleagues (2015a) reported that the natural course and impact of behaviours such as exercising, gaming, and compulsive sexual activity is often transient and context dependent.

Benson and Eisenach (2013) provide a clear distinction between a compulsive condition or activity and an addiction in their discussion of compulsive buying. They begin by citing the standardized criteria first presented by McElroy and colleagues (1994), which defined the disorder as a maladaptive preoccupation with shopping, whether impulses or behaviour, that either (a) is irresistible, intrusive, and/or senseless, or (b) results in frequent buying of more than can be afforded, frequent buying of items that are not needed, or shopping for longer periods of time than intended. First documented early in the 20th century by psychiatrists Emil Kraepelin and Eugen Bleuler, whose primary focus was on studying schizophrenia, the underlying issue is a preoccupation with shopping and then impulse buying that leads to feelings of distress that interferes with social and/or occupational functioning. As well, this behaviour can lead to significant debt, family issues, and feelings of shame, guilt, depression, hopelessness, and anger. Benson and Eisenach (2013) first pointed out that this was not a universal condition, but rather a behaviour that only arises in cultures with widely accessible credit and unlimited buying opportunities—primarily Western cultures. As well, unlike an addiction, there is no distinct biological dimension, no chemically induced change to the central nervous system, no change to the brain itself as occurs with psychoactive drugs, no fight/flight response, and no other secondary effects to the autonomic nervous system.

A counsellor working with a service user who wishes to use the language of addiction when examining compulsive conditions needs to make a choice. While the correct conceptualization remains compulsive gaming or compulsive shopping or overworking, what remains more important is engaging with the person and developing a therapeutic alliance (see Section V). In deciding to use the service user's language rather than the correct terminology, the counsellor needs to determine if using the accurate term will aid in formulating appropriate treatment plans or goals or if the distinction is not important at the beginning of the change process but can be introduced later during counselling. Perhaps most importantly, the counsellor needs to assess if the use of the label *addict* actually helps or further stigmatizes the service user.

Food

Food addiction and eating disorders are distinct entities. Eating disorders are complex mental health conditions whose etiologies still remain poorly understood and that have a substantive premature mortality rate, particularly anorexia nervosa (Fichter & Quadflieg, 2016). Generally speaking, eating disorders involve either insufficient or excessive food intake, which is detrimental to both physical and psychological health. The most common categories are:

- anorexia nervosa: extreme food restriction interfering with maintaining adequate weight associated with extensive distorted body image;
- bulimia nervosa: food restriction followed by binge eating followed by purging;

- avoidant and restrictive food intake disorder: limiting food intake but without the distorted body image associated with anorexia nervosa; and,
- binge eating disorder: consuming excessive amounts of food followed by periods of guilt for consuming such large quantities (Heller, 2003).

Food addiction is not related to the mental health issue categorized as eating disorders, though like eating disorders food addiction has garnered increasing attention in recent years. Some authors have noted marked similarities between binge eating and substance dependence disorders, including issues of tolerance and withdrawal (Cassin & von Ranson, 2007), which is also noted in the DSM-V. However, food addiction is quite distinct from these disorders. In the mid-20th century in the United States, medical thought regarding obesity reinterpreted being overweight and obese as the consequence of addiction drawing on the psychodynamic theory (see Chapter 6) of oral fixation, a psychological manifestation. This idea quickly became popular, enhancing the stigma and oppression associated with weight gain that in turn produced further negative physical and emotional effects for those labelled as overweight, often called body shaming. The conceptualization of food as an addiction became even more prominent when Wang and colleagues (2001) reported that the "availability of dopamine D_2 receptor was decreased in obese individuals in proportion to their BMI (body mass index). Dopamine modulates motivation and reward circuits and hence dopamine deficiency in obese individuals may perpetuate pathological eating as a means to compensate for decreased activation of these circuits" (p. 354).

Not surprisingly, given the fundamental need to eat, there are several issues with labelling eating an addiction, regardless of the impact of dopamine. The premise that food produces an addiction has been perpetuated and advanced by recent neurobiological findings regarding how certain foods are processed in the brain. Food addiction proponents claim that foods high in sugar, salt, and fat create an addiction because they overstimulate dopamine receptors compared to fruits, vegetables, and protein (Pai, 2016). However, a 2009 symposium held to evaluate the notion of food addiction concluded that, although highly palatable foods can promote changes to the body under the right conditions, they do not meet the core criteria of an addiction (Corwin & Grigson, 2009). More importantly, dopamine is activated regardless of the type of food that is eaten. Dopamine may be more activated by specific foods that humans did not have as ready access to during the evolution of our species and when available aided in early survival, like salt and sugar; however, dopamine activation is not limited to those substances alone (Wieland, 2019). In fact, you can see dopamine activation when water is given to a thirsty subject (Galistu & Paolo, 2012).

Further neurobiological research indicates that the release of dopamine that occurs when engaging in eating and other compulsive activities is insufficient to produce adequate reinforcement to obsessively engage in these activities, especially when compared to the dopamine release produced by psychoactive drugs such as cocaine or methamphetamine.

Dopamine release from eating does not occur to the same degree in the same parts of the brain that are primarily activated by psychoactive drugs (Berridge & Kringelbach, 2015). As well, neither tolerance nor withdrawal reactions to food have ever been demonstrated (Wilson, 2000).

While there are numerous limitations to the Diagnostic and Statistical Manual of Mental Disorders, the DSM does not recognize the category of food addiction. Further, given that eating is necessary to sustain life, the application of the addiction concept contributes to an ineffective policy response to the epidemiological findings regarding obesity's consequences. In turn, calling eating a disease, or eating disorders an addiction, distracts from public health initiatives. Rather than looking at broader societal patterns, calling someone a food addict changes the focus to correcting individual eating behaviour or encouraging individuals to simply attend non-professional self-help groups similar to Alcoholics Anonymous, thus negating the necessity of engaging in population-level interventions (Rasmussen, 2014). However, the major distinction between food and psychoactive drugs is that food is essential for survival and psychoactive drugs are not. If reoccurrence (relapse) to drugs indicates a return to previous drug use, what then does a relapse to eating entail?

Gambling

Gambling was added to the DSM classification system in 1980 as an impulse control disorder. However, in 2013 the issue of addiction, compulsive conditions, and impulse control disorders became further muddled by the 141 American psychiatrists who determined what constituted a mental disorder, 69 percent of whom had financial connections with different pharmaceutical companies (Cosgrove & Krimsky, 2012). The outcome of the group deliberations that developed the DSM-V dramatically altered the addiction landscape in North America. For the first time, a non-substance use condition, gambling, was placed together with substance-use disorders in a new category entitled "Substance-Related and Addictive Disorder." In contrast, the International Classification of Disease, Eleventh Revision (ICD-11), the medical coding developed by the World Health Organization (2019a), continues to classify gambling as an impulse control disorder.

As Blaszczynski and Nower (2002) note, "there is no single conceptual theoretical model of gambling that adequately accounts for the multiple biological, psychological and ecological variables contributing to the development of pathological gambling" (p. 487). In part, this is because of the unique phenomenon that is problem gambling. Problem gambling's most prominent characteristic is that of impulsivity, and that winning is a desirable outcome not for the gains made but so that the person can continue to engage in the activity at the exclusion of all others (Clarke, 2006; Derevensky et al., 2017; Lawrence et al., 2009). Grassi and colleagues (2019) conducted a study comparing individuals given a diagnosis of obsessive-compulsive disorder (OCD), individuals with a gambling disorder, and a group of control subjects exhibiting neither condition. Those individuals who were diagnosed as having a gambling disorder had more similarities than differences to those who had been given the diagnosis of OCD compared to the control group: impulsivity, decision making, and reward system response.

Models of problematic gambling that have emerged over time are based on a wide range of theories: behavioural (Anderson & Brown, 1984; McConaghy et al., 1983); cognitive (Sharpe & Tarrier, 1993; Ladouceur & Walker, 1996); psychobiological (Blaszczynski et al., 1986; Carlton & Goldstein, 1987; Comings et al., 1996; Lesieur & Rosenthal, 1991; Rugle, 1993); psychodynamic (Bergler, 1958; Rosenthal, 1992; Wildman, 1997); and sociological (Rosecrance, 1985; Ocean & Smith, 1993). These perspectives are not mutually exclusive, but rather reflect the different authors' attempts to classify this unique and non-substance-related dysfunctional behaviour. Authors have also attempted to classify types of problem gambling. For instance, Blaszczynski and Nower (2002) describe three categories: (1) behaviourally conditioned, (2) emotionally focused, and (3) antisocial-impulsivist. People who comprise each category may vary on coping skills/styles, co-morbid mental health conditions, and thrill-seeking/arousal. All groups are influenced by various ecological factors, such as availability and accessibility, but there is substantial variation in terms of biological, emotional, and personality traits. As well, unlike with addiction, there is no direct biological trigger with problem gambling nor direct health risks that arise with excessive gambling, and no risk of overdose or physical harm from withdrawal, which is a major issue with addiction to psychoactive drugs. Also important to consider is that once the gambling ends, so does the relief associated with the activity, unlike psychoactive drugs where the effects can last hours.

Sex

Patrick Carnes (1996) championed the term *sex addict* at a time when the idea of behavioural addiction was still nascent. However, his education and training exclusively in counselling is evident in his interpretation of addiction as it applies to human sexuality:

> (Sex) addicts do not perceive themselves as worthwhile persons. Nor do they believe that other people would care for them or meet their needs if everything was known about them, including the addiction. Finally, they believe that sex is their most important need. Sex is what makes isolation bearable. If you do not trust people, one thing that is true about sex—and alcohol, food, gambling, and risk—is that it always does what it promises—for the moment. Thus, as in our definition of addiction, the relationship is with sex—and not people. (Carnes, 2001, p. 16)

What is common among many behaviours labelled as addictive is that the term has found meaning in popular culture rather than in evidence-informed research. However, unlike most other behavioural addictions, there is a definite biological reward to some compulsive sexual behaviours, though the underlying motivation is not typically achieving an orgasm, which produces a dopamine release in the CNS. In the DSM-V there is no mention of sexual addiction, while in the World Health Organization's ICD-11 it is classified as a compulsive behaviour:

> Compulsive sexual behaviour disorder is characterized by a persistent pattern of failure to control intense, repetitive sexual impulses or urges resulting in repetitive sexual behaviour. Symptoms may include repetitive sexual activities becoming a central focus of the person's life to the point of neglecting health and personal care or other interests, activities and responsibilities; numerous unsuccessful efforts to significantly reduce repetitive sexual behaviour; and continued repetitive sexual behaviour despite adverse consequences or deriving little or no satisfaction from it. The pattern of failure to control intense, sexual impulses or urges and resulting repetitive sexual behaviour is manifested over an extended period of time (e.g., 6 months or more), and causes marked distress or significant impairment in personal, family, social, educational, occupational, or other important areas of functioning. Distress that is entirely related to moral judgments and disapproval about sexual impulses, urges, or behaviours is not sufficient to meet this requirement. (World Health Organization, 2019a)

The academic literature contains similar conceptualizations that also use the more accurate term *compulsive sexual behaviour* rather than sex addiction. For example, Kraus and colleagues (2016) conceptualize compulsive sexual behaviour as a condition when individuals have difficulty controlling inappropriate or excessive sexual fantasies, urges/ cravings, or behaviours that generate subjective distress or impairment in their daily functioning. Others who recognize that this behaviour does not meet all the criteria of addiction use terms such as sexual compulsivity (Quadland, 1985) and sexual impulsivity (Barth & Kinder, 1987), or simply categorize it as a variant of obsessive-compulsive disorder (Coleman et al., 2003). Early on in the debate over what language to use, Schmidt (1992) stated that there are no scientific data to support a concept of sexual behaviour that can be considered addictive. Despite this, therapists continue to argue for common ground with an addiction, though these arguments remain focused on only psychological and behavioural features, such as impulsivity, tolerance, and compulsivity producing harmful consequences, that reduce anxiety while also producing pleasure or gratification (Carnes, 2001; Carnes & Adams, 2019; Goodman, 2001).

A subset of compulsive sexual activity is pornography addiction, which has taken on the acronym SPPA: self-perceived pornography addiction. As is the case with other compulsive conditions that have been labelled as addiction, SPPA has no agreed upon definition, is not recognized as a formal psychological disorder, and there remains debate if it is even a phenomenon, given that sexual activity is an innate human drive. Duffy and colleagues (2016) undertook a systematic review of quantitative and qualitative peer-reviewed journal articles and found that SPPA was typically defined as excessive pornography use that produced negative consequences. Those that suffer from SPPA generally have relationship issues and experience increased feelings of isolation, though there are questions of the cause and effect relationship between the variables.

Sex is a common reinforcer, just as food is, with both being natural processes. Thus, while increases in dopamine transmission in the nucleus accumbens (a key part of the brain responsible for the perception of pleasure and reward) certainly do occur and often in large amounts with these processes, unlike with psychoactive substances, their effect is regulated by reward predictability and habituation (Heinz et al., 2019). One final important treatment issue to consider is that the act of simply labelling compulsive sexual activity as an addiction can diminish the impact that childhood sexual abuse and childhood adverse experiences play on problematic adult sexual behaviour (Aaron, 2012).

NOTE

1. The singular *they* will be used throughout the book in instances when a gender-neutral singular pronoun is needed.

CHAPTER 2

Pharmacological Foundatio

DRUG GROUPS

Psychoactive drugs can be placed into one of four large families: depressants (including opioids), stimulants, hallucinogens, and psychotherapeutic agents. Depressants produce a reduction of arousal and activity in the central nervous system. These drugs are used therapeutically as anaesthetics, aids for sleeping, anti-anxiety agents, and sedatives. For the most part, the non-medical use of these agents results from their ability to produce disinhibition and to artificially relieve feelings of anxiety (Chapter 8). Opioids are a specific subgroup of CNS depressants. The distinct attribute that differentiates these psychoactive agents from other CNS depressants is their ability to mask pain and also to suppress cough. While depressants initially affect the neurotransmitter gamma-aminobutyric acid (GABA), opioids mimic endorphin neurotransmitters found in all brains (Chapter 9).

Stimulants produce a general increase in the activity of the cerebral cortex, creating mood elevation, increased vigilance, and the postponement of fatigue. Some stimulants are also used as appetite suppressants and decongestants, and to treat attention-deficit/hyperactivity disorder (ADHD). These drugs produce changes through their effect primarily upon dopamine (Chapter 10).

Hallucinogens are a family of psychoactive agents that affect the CNS in a much different manner than do depressants and stimulants. Hallucinogens produce a generalized disruption in the brain, especially of perception, cognition, and mood. Several of them, such as ecstasy, have secondary CNS stimulant effects. The most frequently used hallucinogen, cannabis, has an associated pharmacological effect more closely associated with CNS depressants, as do dissociative anaesthetics including PCP (phencyclidine) and ketamine. Hallucinogens primarily affect serotonin, though cannabis has its own unique neurotransmitter, the endocannabinoids, particularly anandamide (Chapter 11).

Psychotherapeutic agents are substances primarily employed to treat people with specific forms of mental health issues: depression, bipolar disorder, and psychosis. Many produce unpleasant side effects in persons without the condition as well as in those with a mental health issue. Thus, compliance has historically been of greater concern than misuse, though more recently synthesized members of this group of psychoactive drugs tend to have fewer negative side effects. As these psychoactive drugs do not produce a rapid state of mood enhancement in users, they are not generally subject to non-medical use. More recent additions to this category, though, such as the selected serotonin reuptake inhibitors (SSRIs), an example of which is Prozac, have raised new controversies and concerns (Chapter 12).

NEUROPHYSIOLOGY

In order to gain an understanding of how psychoactive agents affect the central nervous system, one must have a basic understanding of the process that underlies the functioning of the brain and spinal cord. This field is known as neurophysiology. Of the billions of cells of which the brain is composed, it is only the neuron, or nerve cell, that processes information. Messages travel within each cell as electrical transmissions, but as one neuron has no direct physical contact with another, electrical transmission between cells cannot occur. Thus, information between nerve cells must be communicated chemically. A neuron consists of the cell body, or soma, where metabolic activity occurs featuring the nucleus and dendrites. Dendrites are the extension of the soma that receive messages from the axons of adjoining cells. The axon is the part of the neuron along which signals are transmitted to adjoining cells that terminate in axon terminals. It is in the axon terminals where the various neurotransmitters such as dopamine, endorphins, and serotonin are found. The gap across which the neurotransmitters must travel is referred to as the synaptic cleft. The synaptic cleft is typically 10–20 nanometers across. This is such a tiny space that it takes only 0.1 milliseconds for a neurotransmitter to drift, or defuse, across the gap to the next axon (see Figure 2.1).

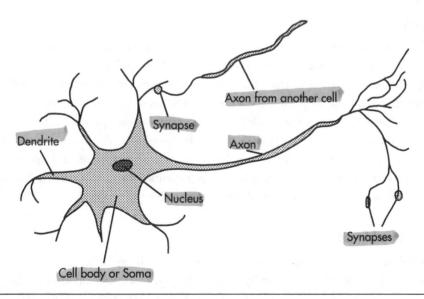

Figure 2.1: A Neuron

During early brain development, which occurs from the third trimester of pregnancy to the third year of life, there is an overproduction of neuronal tissue. As well, during adolescence, many synapses and neurons are altered and even eliminated in a second reshaping of the brain. These processes are partially influenced by interactions with the environment, with substance use or misuse being one of the most critical external influencing factors of this development. The most powerful alterations occur in the frontal lobes, responsible for higher order thinking, which are still maturing until a person is in their mid-20s. The temporal lobes, which are critically involved in memory formation, reach their maximum grey matter volume slightly earlier, at the age of 16 to 17. Thus, due to these maturation processes, adolescents are more vulnerable to the effects of many psychoactive drugs than are older adults (White et al., 2002).

NEUROTRANSMITTERS

Neurotransmitters are chemicals found in the brain that are used to relay, amplify, and modulate signals between neurons that produce physical actions, feelings, and behaviours. There are over 50 known neurotransmitters that carry chemical information between cells. Despite the fact that different psychoactive drugs affect different neurotransmitters, most drugs of misuse have been linked to their ability to directly or indirectly increase dopamine activity, particularly within the mesolimbic dopaminergic system, which is the key component of the reward system portion of the brain (European Monitoring Centre for Drugs and Drug Addiction, 2009b). Along with dopamine, the most prominent neurotransmitters include endocannabinoids, endomorphins, GABA, glutamate, norepinephrine, and serotonin.

Dopamine

This neurotransmitter is a member of the monoamine catecholamine family of neurotransmitters, which also includes epinephrine and norepinephrine. Dopamine stimulates the nerve receptors in the brain, creating sensations of power, energy, and, most importantly, euphoria. Dopamine has a specific function in terms of regulating mood and affect and also plays a prominent role in motivation and reward processes. There are several dopamine systems in the brain. However, the mesolimbic dopamine system appears to be the most important for motivational and reinforcement processes and the system on which most psychoactive drugs produce their behavioural effects. CNS stimulants such as amphetamines and cocaine act directly on the dopamine systems in the brain.

Endocannabinoids

Cannabis acts on two specific receptors in the brain, CB_1 and CB_2. It is believed that cannabis affects neuronal function by causing the psychoactive component of the drug, tetrahydrocannabinol (THC), to bind to CB_1 receptors that are located primarily in the cerebral cortex, cerebellum, and hippocampus. It is thought to be responsible for the euphoria, time distortion, and minor hallucinogenic effects. As well, when THC binds to THC-specific receptors on a neighbouring terminal of a dopaminergic neuron, this sends a signal to the dopamine terminal to release more dopamine into the synaptic cleft.

Endorphins

Natural endorphins in the body are mimicked in nature and through synthesis by the opioid family of psychoactive drugs. Endorphins bind to opioid receptors, which are located on post-synaptic cells as well as on the terminals of other neurons. Endorphins, along with blocking the perception of pain, modulate dopamine transmission in the brain. Thus, users not only have the sensation of pain masked by taking drugs such as Demerol, OxyContin, and heroin, but they also obtain an artificially induced sense of euphoria.

Gamma-Aminobutyric Acid (GABA)

GABA is an amino acid that acts as a depressant transmitter that counters feelings of anxiety, which is the natural resting state of all humans. Anxiety is a vital human response created in the brain that alerts humans to the dangers and threats in our environments. GABA works by occupying receptor sites and preventing their stimulation. The message that GABA transmits is an inhibitory one: it tells the neurons that it contacts to slow down or stop firing, and thus for us to become less anxious. As approximately 40 percent of the millions of neurons throughout the brain respond to GABA, this means that GABA has a general quietening influence on the entire brain, working as the body's natural calming agent. As well, when GABA molecules are inhibited by CNS depressants such as alcohol, barbiturates, and benzodiazepines, an increased amount of dopamine is released, which produces the sensation of euphoria.

Glutamate

Glutamic acid or glutamate is an excitatory neurotransmitter. It is the base chemical from which GABA, an inhibitory neurotransmitter, is synthesized. Thus, the two balance each other. Glutamate itself is linked to memory and learning, and an association has been made between glutamate modulation and the development of attention-deficit/hyperactivity disorder (Petroff, 2002).

Norepinephrine

Norepinephrine, also referred to as noradrenaline, is like dopamine, a monoamine catecholamine. It is released by the adrenal gland and acts not only as a neurotransmitter, but also as a hormone. In its hormonal form, it works in conjunction with epinephrine (adrenaline) to provide a boost to the body in stressful situations. Norepinephrine has more of an effect on blood vessels, while epinephrine affects the heart more, though both are active in the body's fight-flight response to stress producing a burst of energy at times of threat or potential danger. Individuals who experience repeated or ongoing bursts of norepinephrine due to an activated fight/flight response will feel anxious and hyperactive and can have their sense of hunger suppressed. Norepinephrine's function as a neurotransmitter relates to both depression and mania. Inhibiting the reuptake of norepinephrine aids in alleviating depression, while elevated levels of this neurotransmitter can lead to mania.

Serotonin

Serotonin is referred to by some as the happiness transmitter. It too is a monoamine, but it belongs to the indolamine group. This neurochemical is responsible for reducing depression, alleviating anxiety, elevating mood, and increasing feelings of self-worth. It is closely associated with a new group of antidepressant drugs that include Prozac, Paxil, Zoloft, Luvox, Lexapro, and Celexa. However, excessive amounts of serotonin can produce hallucinations.

PHARMACODYNAMICS

Tolerance and withdrawal are two key components related to physical dependency that fall under the broader category of pharmacodynamics, which is an examination of what drugs do to the body.

Tolerance

Even though the DSM-V classified tolerance as simply another criterion to describe substance use disorders, it remains a significant contributing factor in the process of addiction development. After repeated use of a drug, the user may become more resistant to its effects. This loss of sensitivity is known as tolerance. Tolerance simply means that the body has adapted to the presence of the drug. With many chemical agents, the brain becomes used to the substance and the original effects of the drug diminish over time. Tolerant individuals may appear to walk and talk with no impairment but more complex and less observable behaviours, such as precise judgment or fine motor skills, will still be negatively affected. Tolerance may occur to both the desired effects of the drug of choice as well as to its adverse effects. Tolerance typically occurs after a period of chronic exposure, though for some drugs, like hallucinogens, it can occur after a single use.

Acute tolerance is evidenced in those persons who appear to become less intoxicated the more they drink. For these persons, there is a greater degree of impairment at the start of a drinking session than at its conclusion. With the chronic use of drugs such as alcohol, the liver also becomes slightly more efficient in breaking down the substance, requiring more to be taken to obtain the desired effect. The most common example of tolerance is the person who can "really hold their liquor." This is merely one indication of an individual who consumes alcohol on a regular basis. While tolerant individuals' behaviours may become less impaired, the physical damage escalates with increased drug administration.

Tolerance can be categorized as either dispositional, when the liver is able to process the drug more efficiently and excrete it faster from the body, or functional, also known as metabolic or pharmacodynamic tolerance. Functional tolerance occurs when actual physical changes take place in the body's receptors or when receptor sensitivity is altered. Drug sensitivity may also decrease over the course of a small number of administrations.

Functional tolerance development depends on a variety of factors, including:

- the pharmacological properties of the drug that is administered;
- the effect being measured;
- the selected dose, as generally the greater the dose, the faster the rate of tolerance development;
- previous drug history, for if a person has been tolerant to a drug in the past, tolerance will develop much more quickly on subsequent drug exposures, not only to the drug but related drugs;
- behavioural demands—if drug users are required to handle complex tasks during periods of intoxication, they will quickly develop tolerance to those drug effects that adversely affect their performance of that particular task; and
- the setting in which use takes place—if a person administers a drug in the same room each day, the person's body learns to expect the substance in that room; conditioned compensatory changes occur in the brain that reduce the intensity of the experienced effect—if the same amount is consumed in a different environment, the person can overdose (Sproule, 2004).

In many instances, once an individual becomes tolerant to the effects of one drug, the person will also show tolerance to other psychoactive drugs with similar effects on the central nervous system. This is called cross-tolerance. A phenomenon often referred to as reverse tolerance or sensitization has been noted with some drugs, notably hallucinogens, in which the desired effects may reportedly be achieved with smaller doses after the initial experience with the drug. Learning, environmental, and pharmacological mechanisms have been suggested to underlie this process. Finally, there is tachyphylaxis, a term derived from the Greek *tachys*, meaning "rapid," and *phylaxis*, meaning "protection," but which equates to nearly complete tolerance. This sudden decline in a drug effect could follow either one administration of that drug or multiple administrations of small doses. The underlying cause of this phenomenon might be a significant decrease of the neurotransmitter that mediates the drug effects or an acute downgrading of the available drug or neurotransmitter receptors. This downgrading could be due to the saturation of these receptors and commonly occurs with most hallucinogens, save cannabis, after only two or three days of consecutive use. It can also occur with psychotherapeutic agents, and if these are being used to help regulate a person's emotional state or behaviour, the consequences can be substantive.

Withdrawal

Withdrawal is the development of physical disturbances or physical illness when drug use is suddenly discontinued. It is the rebound effect that is a component of the process of physical dependence. When a drug ceases to be administered, the compensatory mechanisms cause a temporary overactivity of the cells; this overactivity, or rebounding, is the basis for withdrawal symptoms. The severity of the withdrawal reaction after stopping drug use is not necessarily related to the severity of dependence. Withdrawal from depressants generally results in symptoms of acute and toxic hyperactivation and physiological arousal, while the pattern following intense stimulant use usually involves sedation, depression, and extensive sleep to compensate for the artificially produced overarousal that stimulants produce in the central and autonomic nervous systems. Withdrawal symptoms can be prevented or promptly relieved by the use of the original drug, or one that is pharmacologically equivalent: the hair of the dog.

PHARMACOKINETICS

Pharmacokinetics is the part of pharmacology that deals with what the body does to a drug: how a drug gets from the external world into the body and to the specific site in the brain where it produces its effect. It involves the study of how a psychoactive drug is administered, absorbed, distributed, metabolized, and finally eliminated by the body. This is an extremely complex process, with a variety of factors being responsible for the effect, if any, that a psychoactive drug has. Three critical pharmacokinetics factors are:

1. how we get the drug into our body or the route of administration;
2. distribution of the drug by the circulating blood to the various parts of the body; and
3. the eventual breakdown of the drug into an inactive compound: metabolization and elimination.

Routes of Administration

Drugs can be administered in a variety of ways that determine both how quickly and how intense the reaction will be:

*   oral administration—through the mouth to the stomach and the intestines
*   across mucous membranes—in the nose, gums, rectum, and vagina
*   injection—directly into the vein, muscle, or under the skin
*   inhalation—through the lungs
*   transdermal—across the skin (see Table 2.1)

Oral Administration

In this commonly used process of drug administration, the substance is swallowed and is turned into a fluid in the stomach, if it is not already in that form. From the stomach, the psychoactive agent moves to the small intestine, where it penetrates the lining. It then passes into the bloodstream, after being processed by the liver, and eventually reaches the central and autonomic nervous systems. How much of the drug is absorbed depends on its solubility—how efficiently it is turned into liquid in the stomach—and its permeability—how well it passes through the lining of the intestine—as well as by the presence or absence of food in the digestive tract. The more food that is present, the slower the entire process.

Alcohol is a pharmacological exception. Ethyl alcohol, that is, beverage alcohol, is absorbed directly through the stomach wall into the bloodstream and then moved to the central nervous system once it has been processed by the liver. This is faster than the route through the intestinal lining, especially on an empty stomach. However, when the stomach is full, the alcohol is absorbed by the food and is then processed by the intestine, slowing the rate of absorption.

Drugs administered orally in a liquid form are absorbed more rapidly than tablets or capsules. Sometimes drugs in tablet form, especially illicit ones, are poorly manufactured. They may not dissolve at all or become encapsulated by food and will pass through both the stomach and the intestine and be excreted without ever being absorbed into the bloodstream. They thus never affect the central nervous system. There are several significant disadvantages with oral administration:

- losing the drug through vomiting,
- stomach discomfort,
- inability to accurately calculate the amount of the drug absorbed, and
- slowness of the process relative to other options.

When administered orally, enzymes in the stomach and intestine can destroy some non-psychoactive drugs, such as insulin, before they can be absorbed. Likewise, cocaine, when administered orally, is metabolized in such a way that little if any psychoactive effect is produced in the central nervous system.

Across Mucous Membranes

Fewer layers of cells exist in mucous membrane areas than in other parts of the body, allowing for the quick absorption of psychoactive agents. Mucous membrane is found in the nose, lips, gums, vagina, and rectum. Drugs that can be sniffed, such as cocaine hydrochloride, stick to the nasal membranes and are transferred into the bloodstream and then to the central nervous system, while also affecting the autonomic nervous system. Nicotine from chewing tobacco and pipe smoke crosses the mouth membrane into the blood and then moves to the CNS and ANS. Drugs administered in the form of suppositories are useful if a person is vomiting, unconscious, or unable to swallow. However, absorption is irregular and unpredictable across all mucous membranes, and many psychoactive drugs administered in this manner irritate the mucous membranes. More substantive long-term issues associated with this method of administration include the development of a deviated septum and oral cancers of the mouth and gums.

Injection

Natural biological barriers are bypassed by directly injecting a drug into the body. There are three ways to inject drugs:

1. Intravenously: Injecting the drug directly into a vein is the fastest of the three injection options, with the initial effect generally perceived within 10–15 seconds.
2. Subcutaneous: Injecting the drug just under the skin is also referred to as skin popping. The effect takes place 5–50 minutes after the injection, depending on how quickly the drug penetrates the walls of the blood vessels and the rate of blood flow through the skin. Some users have been known to inject the drug between their toes to minimize the puncture marks that accumulate with multiple injections.
3. Intramuscular: Injecting the drug into the skeletal muscle of the arms, legs, or buttocks is the slowest of the three injection methods, taking between 10–15 minutes to produce a psychoactive effect. However, this method of absorption is still quicker than when the drug is processed through the stomach. Absorption after an intramuscular injection is also dependent on the rate of blood flow to that muscle.

Advantages of injecting psychoactive drugs include the quickness and accuracy of dosage. The drawbacks include the lack of time to respond to an unexpected reaction or overdose, the painfulness of an injection, and the inability to recall the drug. The necessity of a sterile needle, especially in light of HIV and hepatitis C risks, is a significant factor to consider, especially when injecting street drugs.

Inhalation

Gases such as nitrous oxide pass through the lung membranes and into the blood and to the CNS extremely quickly, in as little as eight to ten seconds. The almost immediate effect is a direct result of the large surface area of the lungs. Nicotine in cigarettes and THC, the psychoactive agent found in cannabis smoke, act somewhat differently. These drugs are contained in small particles carried in the smoke, and although absorption is still quick, not all the drug particles get through. Thus, absorption is not as efficient as with other gases. Cocaine, which has anaesthetic properties, in the crack form is absorbed faster through the lungs than across the mucous membranes of the nose, even faster than when it is directly injected into a vein.

Table 2.1: Routes of Administration

Method	Example of Drug	Time Needed for Effect	Advantages of Route	Disadvantages of Route
oral	alcohol	30–60 minutes	convenient	slow, irregular
inhalation	nicotine	8 seconds	fast	lung damage
intravenous injection	heroin	15 seconds	fast	overdose infections
mucous membrane	cocaine	1–2 minutes	convenient	local tissue damage
subcutaneous injection	heroin	5–10 minutes	safer and easier than intravenous	infection
intramuscular injection	morphine	10–15 minutes	controlled	painful
transdermal	nicotine	15–20 minutes	convenient	limited application

Transdermal

This is the least common method of administration, as few psychoactive substances are able to pass through the skin and reach the central nervous system via this organ. Also, as transdermal administration is a relatively slow means of producing an effect in the CNS, it is not a primary means of ingesting drugs for recreational purposes. The primary psychoactive substances that can be used transdermally are opioids, used with individuals in chronic pain or who are terminally ill, nicotine in the form of a nicotine patch, and occasionally LSD, though the latter is primarily ingested orally.

Distribution of Drugs throughout the Body

Substances are distributed throughout the body by the circulation of the blood. Once a psychoactive drug is absorbed into the blood, it is carried to most parts of the body, including the central and autonomic nervous systems, within a minute. However, psychoactive drugs create their effects by reaching specific cells found only in the CNS. To do so, the drug molecule must be small enough to pass through the pores in capillaries from the veins and then through the cell walls. Drug molecules must also be lipid (fat) soluble. The greater the lipid solubility of a drug, the easier the drug passes from the blood into the brain. The vast majority of psychoactive drugs are highly lipid soluble, meaning they pass easily into the brain to produce their effects. Ionization, which is the positive or negative charge a drug carries, is also a factor. Drugs with little ionization pass through lipid (fat) membranes more easily. The lower the ionization of a drug, either positive or negative, the more likely it will alter the CNS.

Breakdown and Elimination

The liver is the body's detoxification centre. For a drug to be removed from the blood-stream and to no longer affect the CNS or ANS, it must be metabolized by enzymes in the liver and eliminated from the body primarily in the form of urine or feces. Drugs must first be metabolized or changed so that they cannot pass from the kidney back into the blood. Anaesthetic gases and volatile drugs are eliminated through the lungs, as is approximately 5 percent of all beverage alcohol consumed. Other sites of elimination are the sweat glands, saliva, and, importantly, breast milk.

After a drug is totally absorbed into the body, the concentration in the blood soon starts to fall. This drop is initially rapid because of the movement of the drug from the bloodstream into the body's tissues. The rate of decline slows as excretion begins. The rate of decline depends on both the type of drug and the concentration of the drug in the blood. The higher the drug concentration, the faster metabolism and excretion will proceed. This variability makes it difficult to compare the rate of metabolism of one drug to that of another. To address this difficulty, the concept of half-life was borrowed from nuclear physics. Half-life is a measure of the rate of metabolism of a drug. It indicates the length of time required for a drug's blood concentration to fall by one-half. By knowing the half-life of a drug, one can better assess the appropriate dosage, frequency, and amount required to treat a specific medical condition. In the later stages of metabolism and excretion, the half-life of a drug is constant, no matter how high the concentration actually is. The half-life of many drugs increases with the user's age. This may be due to increased amounts of body fat, which acts as a reservoir for highly lipid soluble drugs, or from impaired liver or kidney function. Ethyl alcohol, however, does not have a half-life, but rather is eliminated at a constant rate from the body (Sproule, 2004).

CHAPTER 3

Drug Use and Its Economic Implications

GLOBAL DRUG USE

It is estimated that, worldwide, half the adult population uses psychoactive drugs on a regular basis, far more if caffeine is included in the totals. Between 1990 and 2016, the global prevalence of all substance use disorders increased for both men and women (Degenhardt et al., 2018). The United Nations Office on Drugs and Crime (UNODC) (2019), through a global study, estimated that 271 million people, or 5.5 percent of the world's population aged 15 to 64, had used illegal drugs in the previous year. This is a 30 percent increase over the past decade, a period in which the global population aged 15 to 64 grew 10 percent. The number of people who are believed to have addiction-related issues is 35.3 million, though only a small proportion have ready access to evidence-informed treatment options. Despite having the most access to treatment options, North Americans still have the greatest mortality rate from illicit drugs in the world, at 155.8 per 1 million for those aged 15 to 64 (International Narcotics Control Board, 2019).

While illicit opioid use is a global issue, it is in North America where the rate of use is greatest at 4.0 percent of the population, compared to Asia where the rate is estimated at 1.6 percent, though there are more users in that region of the world due to differences in population. Across North America, the issue has not only been the increasing number of opioid users but the dramatic increase in drug poisonings in both Canada and the United States, an increase of 13 percent between 2016 and 2017 in the United States. Over the past two decades, drug overdose has more than tripled to become the leading cause of injury deaths in the United States, outnumbering deaths from motor vehicle accidents and homicides. The age-adjusted rate of drug overdose deaths in the United States increased from 6.1 per 100,000 in 1999 to 21.7 in 2017, though it did drop slightly in 2018 to 20.7 percent. Drug poisoning death rates increased for all age groups, with the greatest percentage increase among adults aged 55 to 64, most of whom were men. The states with the greatest per capita rates of death from opioids were West Virginia, Delaware, Maryland, Pennsylvania, Ohio, and New Hampshire. There were over 130,000 opioid related overdose deaths between 2017 and 2018 alone, contributing to why the United States has the

Table 3.1: Daily Doses of Opioids in the 20 Most Populous Countries, 2013–2015

Country	Daily Dose of Opioids per Million People
United States	47,580
Germany	30,780
Japan	1,220
Vietnam	1,100
Turkey	700
Iran	460
Brazil	460
China	240
Thailand	170
Mexico	160
Russia	120
Egypt	93
Ethiopia	49
Indonesia	44
Bangladesh	36
India	21
Philippines	20
Pakistan	2
Nigeria	1
DR Congo	1

Source: Data from https://theatlas.com/charts/rJJ-98IUz.

lowest life expectancy among high-income nations (Hedegaard et al., 2020; Ho, 2019). However, as Table 3.1 illustrates, it is not only illicit use that is greater in the United States, but also licit use.

Another issue associated with but not exclusive to opioid use is the method of administration: injection. People who inject drugs (PWID) experience multiple negative health consequences. They are at an increased risk of fatal overdose and are disproportionately impacted by HIV and hepatitis C. Forty-three percent of all PWID reside in three nations: China, Russia, and the United States. Roughly one in eight people, 1.4 million globally, who inject drugs live with HIV. Hepatitis C is likewise a significant health issue for PWID, with 5.6 million PWID diagnosed with hepatitis C. More than half of the illicit drug–related deaths worldwide are the result of untreated hepatitis C leading to liver cancer and cirrhosis (UNODC, 2019).

The UNODC (2019) also estimates that 18 million people used cocaine during the past year, with North Americans again being the most prominent users, as they are with methamphetamine, also approximately 18 million people, or 2.1 percent of the population aged 15 to 64. The difference is that while premature deaths due to stimulant use remain far fewer compared to those produced by alcohol, tobacco, or opioids, there was a 10-fold increase in the United States in a decade, from 1,300 in 2007 to over 10,000 in 2017.

The most commonly used hallucinogen globally, after cannabis, with an estimated 21 million users, is MDMA (ecstasy). However, it is cannabis that remains the most administered illicit drug globally, with an estimated 188 million users worldwide. While relative use remains low at 3 to 5 percent of the global population, it is estimated that nearly 20 (10.6 percent) million people globally are dependent on that drug. The greatest per capita use is, again, in North America followed by South America and Asia. Use tends to begin at an earlier age with cannabis compared to other illicit drugs, a trend that will likely continue as more jurisdictions move to decriminalize, medicalize, and legalize this psychoactive agent (Peacock et al., 2018; UNODC, 2019).

Approximately one-third of the world's population consumes alcohol—2.4 billion people (1.5 billion men, 0.9 billion women)—with an average daily consumption of just under one standard drink per day for women and just under two for men. Annual estimates are that 6.4 litres of pure alcohol are currently consumed per capita by adults aged 15 and older. Approximately two-fifths of all adults who consume alcohol also report engaging in heavy episodic drinking. Alcohol consumption is generally greater in more affluent nations, which also have fewer gendered differences in the amount consumed. In general, European nations, including Russia, have greater alcohol consumption per capita and a higher percentage of heavy consumption, with North African and Middle Eastern countries recording the lowest global use per capita and the fewest heavy drinkers (Griswold et al., 2018; Peacock et al., 2018).

Rates of addiction to alcohol are calculated at 1.3 percent of the global population, while all other drugs combined equal 0.9 percent. Alcohol use is the seventh leading risk factor for both deaths (2.8 million in 2016) and disability adjusted life years (DALYs), accounting for 2.2 percent of female deaths and 6.8 percent of male deaths globally. The risk of all types of mortality, but cancers specifically, increases as the amount of alcohol consumption increases. Among those aged 15 to 49, alcohol use was the leading risk factor globally, accounting for 3.8 percent of female deaths and 12.2 percent of male deaths. For individuals aged 50 years and older, cancers accounted for a large proportion of total alcohol-attributable deaths in 2016—27.1 percent for women and 18.9 percent for men. The Global Burden of Disease study reports that safe alcohol consumption is zero standard drinks per day. The global rate of premature death from alcohol use has declined from 43 deaths per 100,000 people in 1990 to 35 deaths per 100,000 in 2017, though there were two prominent nations that saw their mortality rates increase during this period: Russia and the United States (Global Burden of Disease Collaborative Network [GBDC], 2017; Griswold et al., 2018). When assessing the harm alcohol produces globally, one extremely important variable that falls outside the Global Burden of Disease Study is injuries and deaths due to impaired driving. Table 3.2 summarizes the percentage of alcohol-related serious road injuries across a range of nations, a statistic where Canada ranks near the top.

Table 3.2: Percentage of Alcohol-Related Serious Road Injuries by Country, 2010

Country	Alcohol-Related Serious Road Injury (%)
Greece	23.0
New Zealand	23.0
Canada	**18.0**
Portugal	17.3
France	15.1
Chile	15.0
Luxembourg	15.0
Denmark	13.0
South Korea	12.9
Switzerland	12.7
Hungary	12.2
Czech Republic	11.1
Belgium	11.0
Poland	9.3
Serbia	9.3
Australia	9.0
Netherlands	8.7
Austria	8.2
Germany	8.0
Russia	6.8
Great Britain	5.0
Iceland	4.4
Israel	2.8
Japan	1.6
Nicaragua	1.0

Source: Data from International Transportation Forum (2018).

While illicit drug use is a substantial global cause of premature mortality and morbidity, and globally, alcohol is used 10 times more than illicit drugs, it is tobacco that contributes to disease burden more than any other psychoactive agent. Eighty percent of the world's 1.1 billion tobacco users live in low- and middle-income nations, with more than half located in Asia, where it is primarily men who use this licit drug. In China, the smoking rate among men is 42 percent, while in Indonesia, a nation of 263 million people, the world's fourth most populous nation, the male smoking rate is 65 percent. More than 8 million people die from tobacco use annually, with nearly 1.2 million deaths being attributed to second-hand smoke. The use of tobacco causes an estimated 71 percent of lung cancer cases, 42 percent of chronic respiratory disease incidents, and almost 10 percent of cardiovascular disease (World Health Organization, 2019c). Smoking ranks behind only high blood pressure as the most preventable cause of death globally (GBDC, 2017). While illicit drug deaths combined account for less than 1 million deaths annually, and the concentration of illicit drug deaths occurs among younger people, tobacco deaths occur primarily among middle-aged and older adults (Degenhardt & Hall, 2012).

DRUG USE IN CANADA

Tobacco and alcohol create the most substance-related problems in Canada, just as they do globally (Konkolÿ Thege et al., 2015b). Health Canada's (2018) national survey reported that 78 percent of Canadians 15 and older consumed alcohol in the past year, with the average age of first drink being 16. Provincial use ranged from a low of 68 percent (85,000) in Prince Edward Island, the last Canadian province to repeal alcohol prohibition, to 84 percent (5.8 million) in Quebec, the first province to repeal alcohol prohibition. In the past 12 months, 21 percent of adult drinkers exceeded the low risk drinking guidelines, of five or more drinks in one sitting, at least once. The rate of alcohol impaired driving was 177 incidents per 100,000 people nationally with alcohol accounting for 13.2 percent of all overdose deaths in Canada (Health Canada, 2018).

Approximately 4.6 million (15 percent) Canadians smoked cigarettes in 2017, slightly more than the 2015 national survey found but still a dramatic decrease from 1965 when nearly half of Canadians did so. Men (17 percent or 2.5 million) were more likely to smoke tobacco than women (13 percent or 2.1 million). Daily smokers averaged 13.7 cigarettes per day while 1 percent reported using chewing tobacco regularly. Interestingly, the same percentage of individuals who reported smoking also indicated they had used an e-cigarette, including 23 percent (460,000) of youth aged 15 to 19, and 29 percent (704,000) of young adults aged 20 to 24. Provincial prevalence ranged from a low of 12 percent in Prince Edward Island to a high of 20 percent in Newfoundland and Labrador. Average cigarettes smoked per day among daily smokers ranged from a low of 12.7 cigarettes in Ontario to a high of 18.6 in Newfoundland and Labrador (Health Canada, 2018).

Illicit drug use remains low among the general Canadian population, though the percentage has increased from 1 percent in the 1990s to 3 percent in 2017, approximately

1 million Canadians. However, this number should not negate the seriousness of opioid misuse that continues to occur across the country. The number of fatal and non-fatal opioid-related toxicity events has risen dramatically over the past decade. Between January 2016 and June 2019, nearly 14,000 opioid-related deaths were recorded in Canada, with one in six being individuals under the age of 25. Canada has averaged 16 opioid-specific hospitalizations each day during this time. During that same time period another 17,000 opioid poisonings lead to formal hospitalizations (Single et al., 1995; Special Advisory Committee on the Epidemic of Opioid Overdoses, 2019).

While opioids have garnered most of the media's attention in Canada the largest increase in illicit drug use was a stimulant, cocaine, and while utilization increased 50 percent in one year it was still only from 2 to 3 percent of adult Canadians. Canadian men continue to report using more illegal drugs than women, with the majority of these users being under the age of 25. The overall pattern of illicit drug use has been consistent across time as less than 1 percent of Canadians reported the use of crystal methamphetamine, or hallucinogens such as LSD and MDMA (ecstasy), in the 1990s, which is similar to the current study's findings (Statistics Canada, 2018).

There has, however, been an increase in the national crime rate relating to psychoactive drugs, specifically MDMA, methamphetamine, and cocaine. There were 7,737 incidents of methamphetamine possession in 2016, 8,996 in 2017, and 13,603 in 2018, the second highest incident rate following only cannabis (which has since become legal). While the rate of methamphetamine possession charges rose 10 percent in 2018, the rate of individuals charged with trafficking, production, and importation or exportation increased 23 percent. Methamphetamine-related offences accounted for 16 percent of all Canadian drug-related crime. A number of police services have indicated that methamphetamine is a growing issue and has been a major factor with regards to increases in both property and violent gun crimes (Graveland, 2018; Huncar, 2018; Wakefield, 2020; Statistics Canada, 2018). Another separate but related issue to consider is drug-impaired driving, with police having recorded 4,423 incidents in 2018, a rate of 12 per 100,000 people. While this is still far less than alcohol-impaired driving charges, it was a 25 percent increase over the 2017 rate (Health Canada, 2018; Moreau, 2019).

Twenty-two (6.5 million) percent of Canadians 15 years of age and older were estimated to have used a prescription psychoactive drug in 2017, with a greater proportion of women than men using these legal drugs. The most commonly prescribed psychoactive drugs were opioids, with 12 percent of the Canadian adult population reporting use of at least one such drug in 2017. In this study, 3 percent, approximately 100,000 people, stated that they had misused a prescribed opioid (Health Canada, 2018).

Regular recreational cannabis use has more than doubled from 1985 (5.6 percent) to 2014 (15.0 percent) among Canadians aged 15 years and older, with use steadily creeping up (Table 3.3). Lifetime use among Canadians is reported as 41.5 percent of the adult population. Cannabis use remains more prevalent among men (19 percent or 2.7 million) than women (11 percent or 1.7 million). Cannabis use ranges from 11 percent (750,000)

Table 3.3: Frequency of Cannabis Use, 15 Years And Over, 2014–2018

Frequency of Use	2014	2015	2016	2017	2018
Total, all frequencies	4,364,163	4,540,920	4,701,240	4,876,544	5,034,949
Once	227,067	232,077	239,289	247,482	255,731
Less than once per month	1,598,718	1,667,111	1,726,717	1,791,548	1,849,851
One to three times per month	770,126	798,179	825,856	856,465	884,165
At least once a week (not daily)	1,147,064	1,195,701	1,238,598	1,285,402	1,327,026
Daily	621,188	647,853	670,780	695,647	718,176

Source: Data from Statistics Canada (2019b).

in Quebec to 23 percent (940,000) in British Columbia (Health Canada, 2018). Another substantive change has been the number of individuals using cannabis for medical purposes: 1.6 million Canadians, over 5 percent of the adult population, in 2018 (Statistics Canada, 2018, 2019b). However, legalization has brought minimal changes in use. In 2019, just over 5 million Canadians (16.8 percent) aged 15 or older reported using cannabis in the three months before a national survey was conducted, an increase of just under 2 percent since legalization. On average, in 2019, 6 percent of Canadians aged 15 or older reported using cannabis daily, approximately the same level as prior to legalization. While those 65 years of age and older were the least likely age group to use cannabis, they were also the age group with the greatest percentage increase since legalization (Roterman, 2020).

Between October 17 and December 31, 2018, the first months of legalized cannabis, police reported 1,454 incidents under the new *Cannabis Act*, which accounted for 4 percent of all cannabis-related offences in 2018. The most common offences reported under the *Cannabis Act* were "importation and exportation of cannabis" (21 percent), possession of illicit or over 30 grams of dried cannabis (or equivalent) by an adult (18 percent), possession of over 5 grams of dried cannabis (or equivalent) by youth (12 percent), and possession of cannabis for the purpose of selling (10 percent) (Statistics Canada, 2018).

The 2018–2019 Canadian Student Tobacco, Alcohol and Drugs Survey sampled 62,580 students in Grades 7 to 12 across Canada. The study extrapolated that 19 percent of students had smoked tobacco with an average age of 13.7 for beginning experimentation. Regular student smokers ranged from a low of 3 percent in British Columbia, Alberta, Manitoba, and Quebec to a high of 8 percent in Saskatchewan. The use of e-cigarettes was estimated to be 20 percent, an increase of 10 percent since the survey was last conducted in 2016–2017. Of those using e-cigarettes, 42 percent indicated they had never smoked an actual cigarette—they were exclusively vapers. As well, while smoking cigarettes on a regular basis was perceived to be a great risk by 66 percent of students, only 14 percent reported that vaping posed a great health risk (Health Canada, 2019).

Alcohol remains the most commonly used psychoactive substance among both Canadian adults and Canadian students in Grades 7 to 12. Forty-four percent of students, approximately 880,000, had used alcohol at least once in the past year with the average age of 13.4 for initial experimentation, 2.5 years sooner than reported in the national adult study. Nearly one-quarter (23 percent, approximately 481,000) of Canadian students had five or more drinks on one occasion, with little difference between males (24 percent) and females (23 percent). The next most commonly used drug, not including caffeine, for this population was cannabis, with 18 percent (approximately 374,000) of young people having used this drug at least once during the study period. The average age of first use of cannabis was 14.3. Other than energy drinks containing caffeine, other drugs were still minimally used by Canadian students:

- energy drinks (caffeine): 29 percent
- synthetic cannabinoids: 4 percent
- stimulants including Ritalin: 4 percent
- hallucinogens: 3 percent
- opioids: 3 percent
- benzodiazepines: 2 percent (Health Canada, 2019)

ECONOMIC IMPLICATIONS OF PSYCHOACTIVE DRUG USE

Global Issues

Alcohol, tobacco, misused prescription, and illicit drug use are major global risk factors for disability and premature loss of life. This burden on national health care and social service systems is accompanied by additional significant economic costs on law enforcement as well as on lost workforce productivity, plus the money actually spent on purchasing these substances. Global illicit drug trafficking is estimated at $320 billion CAD with smuggling of tobacco costing governments an additional $31 billion in lost tax revenue (World Economic Forum, 2015). It is estimated that Americans alone spend over $150 billion dollars on buying illegal drugs annually (Midgette et al., 2019). To that can be added $400 billion, the cost to their economy of addiction issues (Office of the Surgeon General, 2016); the cost of psychoactive drug misuse in the United States is over half a trillion dollars annually. If these sales were to be added to the GDP of the United States, it would add an additional 5 percent to that nation's economic output (Table 3.4).

What is even more important to keep in mind is that the money generated from the sale of psychoactive drugs occurs along a continuum, from primarily developing nations where drugs are grown and the profits go to local farmers, to the profit margin that is made

Table 3.4: Global Income Generated by Psychoactive Drugs (2018)

Substance	Sales ($ billions)
Sedative-hypnotics	509
Alcohol	212
Tobacco	50
Cannabis	45
Mexican drug cartels	29
Opioids (prescriptions)	19

Source: Data from Johnson (2018).

when the drugs are sold in developed nations. For example, the profit margin between what a farmer earns growing opium in Afghanistan compared to the cost of a gram of diluted heroin in North America is 3,745 percent, while the profit margin between what a coca farmer in Colombia earns compared to the cost of a gram of adulterated cocaine in North America is 6,427 percent (London School of Economics, 2014). These profits are what fuel not only organized crime and global criminal enterprises but also insurgent groups such as the Revolutionary Armed Forces of Colombia (FARC) in Colombia and the Islamic State of Iraq and the Levant (ISIL) in the Middle East.

In examining how to respond, Tragler and colleagues (2001) stated that enforcement, while necessary, must be integrated with treatment. They reported that most nations needed to increase spending on enforcement to control drug use, but they added that even more of each nation's drug control budget should be spent on treatment. The other component of crime is the associated violence that comes not with drug use but with drug distribution. In the new millennium, murder rates have increased dramatically in the Caribbean and Latin America. In Jamaica, the murder rate reached 58 per 100,000 inhabitants, while in Mexico over 60,000 individuals have been killed or have gone missing as a result of the drug war since 2006. Drug-related violence is an issue in every inhabited continent in the world. A study in Australia indicated costs of $3 billion CAD a year associated with crime, while the result of fighting between the military and Colombian drug cartels in 1991 led to nearly 1 in 1,000 Colombians being murdered, 10 times the rate of the United States. Systematic evidence-informed reviews suggest that, contrary to the conventional belief that increasing drug law enforcement will reduce violence, drug prohibition actually contributes to drug market violence and higher homicide rates. Well-intentioned policies and law enforcement strategies that aim to control drug markets and their associated violence have often had the opposite effect. Despite all the political and financial investment in repressive policies over the last 50 years, drugs are more available, and more widely used, than they have ever been (International Drug

Policy Consortium, 2012; International Narcotics Control Board [INCB], 2019; Werb, Kerr et al., 2010).

Afghanistan remains the nation responsible for the majority of illicit opium cultivation and production. The 263,000 hectares under known cultivation in Afghanistan in 2018 was seven times that of the second leading nation, Myanmar (37,000 hectares), and nine times that of the third leading nation, Mexico (30,600 hectares). This level of production has actually led to a fall in global prices, in part due to overproduction, and in part due to the competition from synthetic opioids, specifically fentanyl, being produced by Chinese pharmaceutical companies at a much lower cost (UNODC, 2019).

The negative impact of this economic pursuit is most vividly illustrated through the opioid crisis in North America. While the primary media focus has been on deaths due to opioid poisonings, misuse of opioids also puts individuals at risk for HIV, hepatitis, and cirrhosis as well as increasing interpersonal violence and contact with the child welfare system. Despite these facts, what the primary focus has been on is the increasing number of opioid deaths. In the United States between 2002 and 2017, the number of opioid poisoning deaths went from approximately 2,000 to over 49,000 (Roberts, 2019). However, the majority of global opioid use is for legitimate therapeutic use, including pain masking due to injury and surgery, though there is quite a different issue that arises here. In 2016, 80 percent of the world's population consumed just 14 percent of the total amount of prescribed morphine. Thus, there remains a vast difference in the use of opioids for pain masking between developing and developed nations, with one group seemingly over-medicated and the other grossly under-medicated (INCB, 2019) (see also Table 3.1). Of further interest is the finding that in the United States, the top 1 percent of physicians accounted for 49 percent of all opioid doses and 27 percent of all opioid prescriptions. In absolute terms, this small number of doctors prescribed an average of 748,000 morphine milligram equivalents, approximately 1,000 times more than the middle 1 percent (Kiang et al., 2020).

Estimated global illicit manufacture of pure cocaine reached an all-time high of 1,976 tons in 2017, an increase of 25 percent from 2016. This was mainly driven by increases in cocaine manufacture in Colombia, which produced an estimated 70 percent of the world's cocaine. The Colombian government's 2016 peace deal with FARC led to substantive reductions in production in central Colombia, where farmers were controlled by FARC fighters. Unfortunately, other areas have now come under the influence of cartels instead (UNODC, 2019). The illicit drug trade is extremely pivotal to the global economy, with Brazil perhaps providing the best example of this.

In the 1980s, with the expansion of the cocaine trade, Brazil became part of a key drug route, particularly the costal city of Rio de Janeiro with a population of just over 6 million. Young people living in poverty in Rio were recruited to become members of drug gangs during this time, as occurs in many nations. Typically, local gangs provided leisure activities, like sponsoring football (soccer) teams, then provided money for running errands or completing minimally dangerous tasks that would eventually lead to full-time gang membership. As the flow of drugs into Brazil and into Rio increased during the 1990s, so did competition for local dealing and international export. This competition lead to the buying of heavy-calibre weapons, not only to be used against rival gangs but also the police. Due to the increasing revenues, groups from outside Brazil began moving into the country and became successful in taking over territory from local gangs, which instigated an even greater arms race. The situation in the favelas (shanty towns) became so lawless that the police were given bonuses every time they killed a suspected drug trafficker. This escalated arms race between the traffickers and the police directly led to the deaths of 7,542 civilians and 220 police officers, making Rio de Janeiro the leader in deaths from gun violence: 46 per 100,000 inhabitants (International Drug Policy Consortium, 2010). Eventually, the army was brought in to clear the slums in advance of the FIFA World Cup (2014) and the Summer Olympic Games (2016). A similar preparation in Canada for the World's Fair (1986) contributed to Vancouver's Downtown Eastside becoming one of the most impoverished neighbourhoods in Canada, with high rates not only of drug use but also of poverty, sex trade, crime, and violence (Tayler, 2003). This was further exacerbated when Vancouver hosted the Winter Olympics in 2010.

The Brazilian story does not end there. At the height of the global 2008 economic crisis, $3.5 billion CAD from drug cartels in and associated with Brazil was laundered through Brazilian banks to keep global financial markets afloat according to Antonio Maria Costa, head of the United Nations Office on Drugs and Crime (Syal, 2009). In defence of this action, Costa stated that the proceeds of organized crime were the only liquid investment capital available to some banks on the brink of collapse and that only through laundered drug profits was the world's economic crisis averted. The International Monetary Fund estimated that large American and European banks lost more than $1 trillion CAD on toxic assets and bad loans from January 2007 to September 2009, and more than 200 mortgage lenders went bankrupt. During this period, a large portion of inter-bank loans was funded by money that originated from the illegal drug trade in Brazil and elsewhere, as the traditional banking system was essentially paralyzed with fear, with banks unwilling to lend money to one another. Thus, it may have been illicit drug profits that prevented the world from slipping into a global depression, as opposed to prudent central bank and government initiatives (Syal, 2009).

Economists Jeffrey Miron and Katherine Wadlock (2010) completed a cost analysis on government savings from legalizing currently illicit drugs for the United States. They estimated that in 2010 the various levels of government could save $41 billion USD per year in expenditures on the enforcement of current prohibitions, and while there would be different costs associated with increased use with regard to treatment and criminal offences, they would not be as great as the current existing costs. That estimate was redone eight years later with Miron (2018) demonstrating that the cost savings would now be over $100 billion USD ($140 billion CAD). There is no doubt that shifting a focus from enforcement and punishment to revenue generation through taxation, and treatment and health promotion, would be a far better use of government funds. However, there is a caveat: legalizing all psychoactive drugs would require an examination of the economic impact of the existing legal recreational drug trade, for the licit drug market is also a huge component of the world's economy, with some distinct negative implications.

The 26 largest alcoholic beverage companies have a net revenue of $220 billion CAD, with an operating profit of $37 billion CAD. There is, however, significant concentration within the alcohol industry leading to monopoly pricing and extraction of monopoly profits, with alcohol producers from developed countries (e.g., Miller) being among the leading advertisers in developing nations such as South Africa, Ghana, Uganda, Colombia, Ecuador, and Peru (Jernigan, 2009). The breadth of the economic impact of alcohol, both pro and con, is illustrated by examining the case of the United Kingdom. The alcohol industry only accounts for 2.5 percent of the UK's national income, yet there are over three quarters of a million people directly or indirectly employed because of alcohol, the majority working in clubs, pubs, and bars. Unfortunately, most of those positions do not pay well, with an hourly average wage of $12/hour CAD, though the 30,000 individuals working for alcohol producers do earn more, averaging $28/hour. The UK exports more alcoholic beverages than it imports, for a net gain to its economy of $3 billion CAD. The government also brings in $19 billion CAD in tax revenue annually. However, the cost of alcohol misuse due to health, social, work, and criminal justice costs, including premature disability and death, is estimated at $36 billion CAD; England has over 1 million alcohol-related hospital admissions annually. Thus, overall not only is there not a net economic gain provided by the alcohol industry in the United Kingdom, there are also substantive human costs that are not included when only calculating financial savings and losses (Institute of Alcohol Studies, 2017; Public Health England, 2016).

Johnson (2018) states that 100 million people died prematurely from the use of tobacco in the 20th century. At current rates, smoking tobacco will kill a third more people in 2030 than in 2015, rising from 6 to 8 million premature deaths a year. A joint study conducted by the United States National Cancer Institute and the World Health Organization (2016) found that governments around the world received $269 billion USD through taxing tobacco products. However, the total economic cost of smoking from health expenditures and productivity losses totalled $1,436 billion USD in 2012, equivalent to 5.7 percent of global health care spending and 1.8 percent of the world's annual gross domestic product (GDP). Almost 40 percent of this cost occurred in developing countries, highlighting the substantial burden these countries suffer, though tobacco use currently still imposes a heavier economic burden in Europe and North America, where the tobacco epidemic is most advanced (Goodchild et al., 2018). The most dramatic example of the economic consequence of tobacco use can be seen in China, the world's second largest economy. There are over 300 million smokers in China who consume 44 percent of the world's tobacco products annually. If the use of this drug were eliminated, China could add nearly $90 billion CAD to its economy, which is almost half of Canada's annual GDP (World Health Organization, 2017c).

Canada

In 2018 Canadians bought 3,098 million litres of alcohol, equivalent to 507 standard drinks per person over the legal drinking age, though this does not take into consideration alcohol purchased outside of the country by Canadians. Canadian alcohol retailers sold $23.2 billion CAD worth of alcoholic beverages in 2018, bringing in $12.2 billion in net government revenue. Beer was the dominant alcoholic product purchased, with sales of $9.2 billion, followed by wine at $7.5 billion and spirits at $5.5 billion. Whisky (30.2 percent), vodka (24.9 percent), and rum (16.3 percent) were the most popular spirits, accounting for 71.4 percent of total spirit sales (Statistics Canada, 2019a). While cigarette sales in Canada totalled over 27 billion sticks in 2017, this was a decrease from over 42 billion in 2001 (Health Canada, 2018). In contrast, legal cannabis sales have been steadily increasing with new stores and an online presence; legal sales are nearly $1 billion annually, though there are estimates that this only accounts for approximately 14 percent of all cannabis sales in Canada, making the overall Canadian cannabis trade worth around $6 billion annually (Lamars, 2019).

A comprehensive study was completed in 2018 that examined the costs and harms associated with substance use in Canada. The study examined four specific areas: health-care, lost productivity, criminal justice costs, and other direct costs associated with the use of alcohol, tobacco, cannabis, opioids, and other psychoactive agents (Table 3.5).

Table 3.5: Total and Per Capita Costs Due to Substance Use, 2014

	Total Costs ($ millions)	Per Capita Costs
Canada	**38,426**	**1,081**
Newfoundland and Labrador	726	1,373
Prince Edward Island	178	1,222
Nova Scotia	1,204	1,277
New Brunswick	930	1,232
Quebec	NR	NR
Ontario	14,687	1,074
Manitoba	1,401	1,094
Saskatchewan	1,372	1,224
Alberta	5,471	1,332
British Columbia	4,877	1,050
Yukon	71	1,929
Northwest Territories	102	2,329
Nunavut	96	2,652

Source: Data from CSUCHSWG (2018).

Table 3.6: Percentage of Total Costs Due to Substance Use by Cost Category, 2014

	Percentage of Total Costs			
	Healthcare	Lost Productivity	Criminal Justice	Other Direct Costs
Canada	**29**	**41**	**23**	**7**
Newfoundland and Labrador	34	43	17	6
Prince Edward Island	37	35	21	7
Nova Scotia	35	40	20	5
New Brunswick	35	39	20	6
Quebec	NR	NR	NR	NR
Ontario	28	39	26	7
Manitoba	33	40	19	8
Saskatchewan	33	41	19	6
Alberta	30	46	18	6
British Columbia	33	38	22	7
Yukon	37	45	13	5
Northwest Territories	31	53	10	6
Nunavut	39	48	9	4

Source: Data from CSUCHSWG (2018).

Lost productivity due to premature death and disability related to substance use accounted for the greatest costs in all Canadian provinces and territories (Table 3.6), with alcohol or tobacco being responsible for the greatest proportion of costs and harms in each jurisdiction (Table 3.7). However, this should not diminish concerns with illicit drug use: while healthcare costs associated with cocaine decreased 57 percent from $180 billion to $78 billion between 2007 and 2014, costs associated with other central nervous system stimulants, specifically methamphetamine, increased 110 percent from $51 to $107 billion (Canadian Substance Use Costs and Harms Scientific Working Group [CSUCHSWG], 2018).

Likewise, a 2016 study that examined the risk factors accounting for the largest percentage of disability costs found tobacco to be the greatest contributor ahead of factors such as diet, and high blood pressure with alcohol and drug misuse ranked sixth. This pattern has stayed consistent in Canada since 1990 (Alam et al., 2019). In 2017–2018, there were more than 155,000 hospital stays for harm caused by substance use, more than for

Table 3.7: Percentage of Total Costs by Substance, 2014

	Percentage of Total Costs			
	Alcohol	Tobacco	Cannabis	Opioids
Canada	**38**	**31**	**7**	**9**
Newfoundland and Labrador	38	39	5	7
Prince Edward Island	38	34	7	9
Nova Scotia	35	36	7	10
New Brunswick	35	38	7	8
Quebec	NR	NR	NR	NR
Ontario	36	32	8	9
Manitoba	41	31	6	9
Saskatchewan	41	31	5	9
Alberta	44	28	6	10
British Columbia	40	26	8	10
Yukon	57	24	5	6
Northwest Territories	55	28	5	5
Nunavut	45	40	4	4

Source: Data from CSUCHSWG (2018).

all cardiovascular issues including heart attacks and stroke. The median hospital stay was longer than five days, creating a total of 2 million days of hospital stays a year (Canadian Institute for Health Information, 2019a). On average, 10 patients die in hospital every day because of substance use, the vast majority, 77 percent, from health complications related to alcoholism. This is in part because many of those who die prematurely from substance use outside of hospital are using illicit drugs, highlighted by opioid poisonings (Figure 3.1).

Police-reported crime in Canada has increased from 2014 to 2018, though it remains 17 percent lower in 2018 than it was in 2008. There were over 2 million incidents reported in 2018, excluding traffic issues, a rate of 5,488 per 100,000 people. Of these, impaired driving incidents were 190 per 100,000 (177 alcohol related; 13 drug related), though alcohol-related charges dropped 1 percent between 2017 and 2018 while drug-related impairment charges increased 25 percent (3,494 to 4,423). With the legalization of cannabis, cannabis-related criminal offences decreased, but these were replaced by increases for methamphetamine, MDMA (ecstasy), and cocaine-related charges (Moreau, 2019).

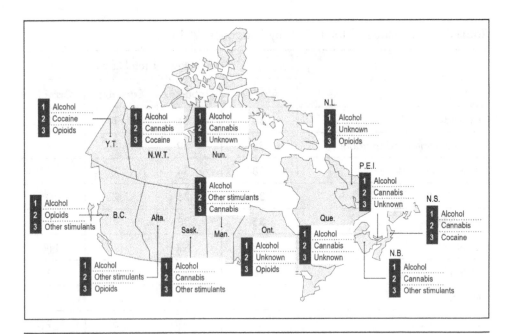

Figure 3.1: Top Three Substances Causing Hospital Stays, by Province & Territory, 2018–2019

Note: "Unknown" refers to unidentified, possibly mixed, substances or a substance that could not be classified in the other categories
Source: Canadian Institute for Health Information (2019b).

Section I Closing Thoughts and Activities

While the focus for most helping professionals is on their own community and the service users that they work with on a regular basis, the global impact of psychoactive drugs and the social and political ramifications cannot be ignored. Neither can the financial aspect of the drug trade, for while there are a multitude of social and health issues that arise due to the use and misuse of psychoactive drugs, the foundation of the drug trade—recreational, pharmaceutical, and illicit—is economics. So before moving forward, do two things. Review the news stories appearing in the media that you regularly read or listen to (see Preface for examples) and consider how many relate directly and indirectly to psychoactive drugs. Next, reflect on a personal incident that underscores your understanding of the social implications of addiction. It may relate to your work or volunteer experience, your travel, or your counselling practice. The intent is for you to fully appreciate how drug use is a global phenomenon that affects us all before moving on to examine the theory of why people use drugs and how we can aid in the prevention and treatment of addiction.

DISCUSSION QUESTIONS

1. Define (a) psychoactive drug, (b) dependency, (c) compulsive behaviour, and (d) addiction.
2. What is the difference between a compulsive behaviour and an addiction? Why is it important for those in the helping professions to understand this?
3. Distinguish between the everyday, popular definition of addiction and the more precise definition provided in Chapter 1. What are the treatment, counselling, and policy implications for these two definitions?
4. What are the reasons a person becomes addicted to a psychoactive drug? How do those reasons align with the ideas from your discussion in Question 1(d)?
5. What distinguishes the different families of psychoactive drugs?
6. What factors contribute to how quickly a person becomes dependent on a psychoactive drug?
7. (a) What are the differences between drug use in Canada and drug use in different nations?
   (b) Was the incidence of drug use greater or lesser than you thought prior to completing the reading?
   (c) Why is North America experiencing a greater rate of addiction than other parts of the world?
8. What are the economic implications of drug use (a) globally and (b) nationally?

SECTION II
THEORIES ON ADDICTION

Why do people use psychoactive drugs? The opening section examined a variety of factors associated with drug use and misuse, but what are the actual reasons that lead to the continued use of drugs by a person? An entire spectrum of theories has been offered to explain the phenomenon of substance use and misuse (Simon & West, 2015; Vogel, 2017). A theory is simply a collection of statements about how the world works. These statements are partially based on assumptions and beliefs combined with an empirical base. However, theory should be more than just a set of interrelated propositions or ideas pertaining to a possible explanation of a phenomenon. Theories should also provide us with a framework within which to further our studies and expand our understanding and be relevant to planning and evaluating social interventions. Good theories organize and explain existing knowledge, are falsifiable and yet simple, providing a framework to allow for future studies that can test outcomes and predictions (Cozby & Rawn, 2012). However, theories, especially in social science, also raise moral questions and entail an examination of our values. In turn, our values shape our standpoint, and determine what we study, what questions we ask, and how we ask them, as well as how we interpret information and what constitutes good evidence.

In studying addiction as a bio-psycho-social phenomenon, a good theory would be one that could explain drug use along five different dimensions, particularly if there was also substantial empirical support for the explanation. The five questions to consider are:

1. Why do people begin taking drugs (commencement)?
2. Why do people maintain their drug-taking behaviours (maintenance)?
3. How or why does drug-taking behaviour intensify (escalation)?
4. Why or how do people stop taking drugs (cessation)?
5. What accounts for the restarting of the drug-taking behaviour or cycle once it has stopped (recommencement or reoccurrence/relapse)?

There is no shortage of theories and perspectives regarding addiction. However, of the dozens of theories that have been postulated to explain substance use and misuse, few can provide adequate responses to all five questions. Most theories also tend to be much easier to disprove than prove, which is one reason that they remain theory rather than becoming fact. However, these imperfect theories give credence to and shape the rise and development of different methods of counselling, treatment, and intervention. If an approach to counselling based on one theoretical model does not work, it indicates that the theory may be in some way flawed. Unfortunately, if the treatment does work, it does not necessarily mean the theory behind it is complete. The following chapters describe several perspectives for you to consider and reflect upon that fall under one of four areas: moral, biological, psychological, and sociological. However, before beginning your reading, complete Table II.1, which provides you with a brief insight into how you view the causes of addiction. Record your scores, and then once you have completed this section, re-do the assessment to determine if your perspective has changed.

Table II.1: Theoretical Orientation Self-Assessment

		Strongly Agree	Agree	Neither Agree nor Disagree	Disagree	Strongly Disagree
1.	Poverty and poor environment are causes of substance misuse.	5	4	3	2	1
2.	The substance misuser is a victim of circumstance.	5	4	3	2	1
3.	If a substance misuser's environment is changed, use of drugs or alcohol will diminish.	5	4	3	2	1
4.	Substance misuse is a symptom of an underlying emotional disturbance.	5	4	3	2	1
5.	The main goal of drug misuse treatment is to gain insight about the reasons a person uses drugs.	5	4	3	2	1
6.	Drug or alcohol misuse results from an inability to cope with life's problems.	5	4	3	2	1
7.	What substance misusers need is advice to quit or cut down their use.	5	4	3	2	1
8.	Substance misuse is a moral issue.	5	4	3	2	1
9.	Jail sentences for possession of drugs are more effective in curbing drug misuse than drug diversion treatment programs.	5	4	3	2	1
10.	A substance misuser has a chronic progressive illness.	5	4	3	2	1
11.	Alcoholism has a biological basis.	5	4	3	2	1
12.	Addiction can't be cured.	5	4	3	2	1

Theoretical Orientation Self-Assessment Scoring

Statement #	Score	Primary Theoretical Orientation
1–3	> 9	Social
4–6	> 9	Psychological
7–9	> 9	Moral
10–12	> 9	Biological

Reminder: After reading this section, re-do the theoretical orientation self-assessment to determine if your perspective has changed.

CHAPTER 4

The Moral Model

FOUNDATIONS OF THE MORAL MODEL

The concepts of morality and addiction have long been entwined (Frank & Nagel, 2017). The moral model is based on the belief that using any drug is unacceptable, wrong, and even sinful. It draws largely upon a social conservative standpoint that drug use arises solely from hedonistic human drives (Vogel, 2017). Proponents of the moral model explain addiction as a consequence of personal choice and desire. Its formal origins can be traced back to the 17th century in Europe when alcohol was debated in religious circles as an example of how men must overcome temptation to exert control over themselves and their destinies (Valverde, 1998). Originally supported by zealous, conservative, religious grass-roots groups in North America during the onset of the Industrial Revolution, the moral model still remains prominent worldwide today, pertaining primarily to illicit drugs but also at times to licit drugs like tobacco. It assumes that users are uniquely responsible for their own behaviour and are capable of making the choice not to use even once fully addicted to a psychoactive agent. Movements, such as the Temperance Unions in Canada, had their underpinnings in this doctrine. It is interesting to note that Temperance Unions were predominantly rural-based and arose as a political movement in part to maintain the status quo and as a battle against urbanization in the 1800s and early 1900s across North America.

It is understandable in an era without medical or social science that lawmakers could only make sense of drug use as a moral problem or being due to a lack of moral fibre or decency, believing that if users had the proper character, they could just stop or at least help themselves (Thombs, 2009). Unfortunately, this moralization of addiction has led us to the wholesale rejection of drug users as people. It views drug users as having deep character flaws, invoking blame and shame while ignoring the complex biological, psychological, and social contexts within which addiction arises. This has also led to the development of language such as drunkard, sot, alcoholic, junkie, and addict, turning people into objects and thus making them far easier to ignore and discard. The moral model has also contributed to use of certain types of psychoactive agents being connected to race. In the United States crack cocaine use became associated with African American users while powdered cocaine (cocaine hydrochloride) use was considered a drug of white users. As the application of the moral model is primarily punishment based, this disparate use of the same drug, only in two different forms, quickly led to differential law enforcement, criminal convictions, and periods of incarceration (Frank & Nagel, 2017). A related bias has been observed in medicine where patients with addiction issues are viewed less favourably or with less compassion by doctors and nurses compared to individuals with other health concerns (Kelly & Westerhoff, 2010; van Boekel et al., 2013).

While the moral model has limited relevance in understanding why people use drugs, it still remains a prominent framework within which vices are judged and policy created. As recently as 1986, the Presbyterian Church in the United States stated that alcohol misuse was a sin because of the harm its use caused in oneself and to others. The Mormon faith, Jainism, and Islam are other examples of religions that have strict rules regarding abstinence from psychoactive substances, while Bahá'ís are forbidden to drink alcohol or to take drugs, except by a doctor's order. Likewise, the Buddha's Noble Eightfold Path encourages refraining from intoxicating substances as they dull the senses and lead to poor decision making. Every month, the day of the full moon, in accordance with the Buddhist calendar, is a national holiday or "Poya day" where alcohol is not served and cannot be purchased (Rahula, 2006).

APPLICATION OF THE MORAL MODEL

Examples of initiatives spawned by the moral model perspective include prohibition, attitudes toward public drunkenness, drunk tanks, anti-smoking lobbies, the criminalization of cannabis, random drug testing in the workplace, and the perpetual "War on Drugs" that is now entering its sixth decade. Since the onset of the most recent War on Drugs, which dates back to the 1970s and President Richard Nixon, the number of individuals incarcerated for drug offences has steadily increased with no corresponding decrease in illicit or licit drug use. However, it was under the Reagan administration that the initiative became firmly entrenched in the United States and was exported globally. During the Reagan administration, the military became engaged in drug law enforcement in the United States and globally, particularly in Central and South America. Drug testing was introduced for federal employees despite the flaws, inaccuracies, and limitations of that procedure (Csiernik, Gorlick et al., 2017). The idea of mandatory minimum sentencing was introduced for drug offences, including the death penalty for "drug kingpins."

The increase of the number of persons incarcerated in the United States ties directly to these two historic events (Figure 4.1). At the beginning of the 21st century, on average an American was being jailed for a cannabis offence every 30 seconds, with a great disproportion being African Americans. While Canada did not reintroduce capital punishment for drug dealers or users, the Harper government did attempt to introduce mandatory

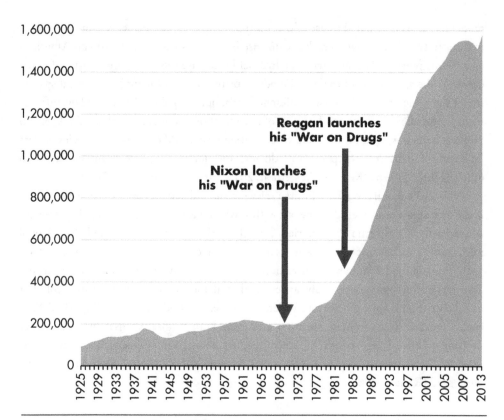

Figure 4.1: US State and Federal Prison Populations, 1925–2013

Source: Adapted from Guerino et al. (2010).

minimum sentencing, though all attempts were struck down by Canadian courts. The War on Drugs has been fought both in the United States and globally along class and racial lines (Brownsberger, 2000; Pettit, 2012). However, it has totally failed to eradicate domestic or global consumption despite creating a vast transnational police apparatus that has propelled mass incarceration in the United States and military intervention abroad (Pembleton, 2018).

The moral model approach has, unfortunately, been taken to even greater extremes in other nations, highlighted by the actions of Philippines President Rodrigo Duterte after he came to power in 2016. Under his term in office the Philippines has withdrawn from the International Criminal Court. This was in direct response to the court's stated intent to finally open an investigation into the 22,983 deaths directly and indirectly linked to Duterte's government sanctioned anti-drug operations that allow military personnel to shoot suspected drug dealers on sight. The anti-drug operations have also led paramilitary groups to not only target drug dealers but drug users, making the Philippines the fourth most dangerous nation to be a civilian in 2019. The United Nations High Commissioner for Human Rights has likewise condemned the government over the extraordinarily high number of deaths and persistent reports of extrajudicial killings relating to drug use (Armed Conflict Location & Event Data Project, 2019).

The moral model perceives dependence on a drug as resulting from a weak moral character. Thus, the problem of addiction, from this perspective, can be remedied simply through building character, through personal will power, by removing oneself from temptation, or through determination alone. This model offers no room for treatment and sees no need for extensive treatment networks, placing the responsibility and the blame solely on the user. Problems with this theory, other than the obvious lack of research support, arise from a lack of consistency in its application. In North America, alcohol is often viewed as distinct from other drugs in this framework, and social class and economic status both significantly impinge on how the moral model is applied. Nevertheless, this view still plays a role in determining how drugs are classified and regulated under the law. An example is that alcohol remains classified as a food in Canada under the existing statutes, while cocaine, a stimulant, is categorized as a narcotic.

The moral model remains a significant block in terms of adequate treatment funding and contributes to the oppression of substance users in North America. It is even a greater issue in many developing nations, where punitive and prohibitionist policies toward drugs are typically justified on both moral and utilitarian grounds. Southeast Asian nations such as Vietnam, Cambodia, and China employ a forced work camp model to "treat" individuals with addiction issues. Vietnam has over 100 rehabilitation camps where individuals with addiction issues can spend two or more years doing forced labour for no wages as their government sponsored "treatment program." In Cambodia, typically poor drug users are taken off the streets and sent to rural camps where, along with working for no wages, some are forced to donate blood, and physical punishment is not an unusual response to unco-operative "clients." In China upwards of 2 million people can be found in residential re-education-through-labour centres operated by the Ministry of Justice, where they can be detained for one to three years. Individuals sent to these centres typically have long drug use histories and have already served short periods of time in jail or a compulsory detox camp. As in Cambodia and Vietnam, the primary function of these centres is "vocational therapy," where residents work 10- to 12-hour days producing goods that are then sold for profit while being paid no wages (Ha & Vaughn, 2017; Human Rights Watch, 2010; Jia et al., 2019; Xiao et al., 2015).

However, the ultimate form of the moral model currently in use is the application of the death penalty for drug use or drug trafficking. Typically, individuals involved in the drug trade are not accused of being guilty of individual, identifiable homicides, but rather as being purveyors of death, whose crimes produce significant national harm. In this manner, the moral model presents drug offenders as threats to the life, values, and health of the state, against whom extraordinary penalties are therefore justified. It is also argued that drug trafficking corrupts a nation's youth, disrupts traditional values, is financed by and profits foreigners, and ultimately funds not only organized crime but terrorist activity both inside and outside the nation (Edwards et al., 2009; Lines, 2007).

The death penalty has been abolished in law or practice in 160 nations. Of the 55 stated retentionist countries that continue to use capital punishment, nearly two-thirds have legislation applying the death penalty for drug-related offences, arguing that such offences fall under the umbrella of the most serious of crimes and thus are equitable to treason and murder. Despite the international trend toward the abolition of capital punishment in the last quarter of the 20th century, the number of countries expanding the application of the death penalty to include drug offences actually increased, from 22 nations in 1985 to 35 by 2020. The death penalty is applied for a wide variety of drug offences, including trafficking, cultivation, manufacturing, importing, exporting, storing, and, even under extraordinary circumstances, simple possession. Though exact numbers of individuals executed annually for drug convictions is difficult to calculate, some data have been collected. In 2019, 122 drug-related executions were confirmed, accounting for 18 percent of total known executions carried out globally with at least 3,000 people convicted of drug offences currently on death row. Five nations regularly use the death penalty for drug related crimes: China, Iran, Saudi Arabia, Singapore, and Vietnam, with the Philippines having an active war on drugs that allows police and military to summarily execute suspected drug dealers in the course of their duties, an action also linked to Brazil. Eight additional nations have capital punishment as an option for drug related crimes but do not regularly execute those convicted of these offences: Bangladesh, Egypt, Iraq, Laos, Pakistan, Palestine (Gaza), Taiwan, and Thailand. An additional 17 nations, including Cuba, India, South Sudan, Sri Lanka, and the United States, have statutes that also allow for capital punishment to be imposed for drug related crimes (Girelli, 2019; Harm Reduction International, 2020).

One final note that, while only indirectly related to capital punishment, still highlights the slippery slope that the application of the moral model brings. Middletown, Ohio, a community of 50,000 between Dayton and Cincinnati, is among the many communities that have been hard hit by the closing of manufacturing plants in the United States. It, like many urban communities, saw a spike in opioid use and poisonings between 2016 and 2018. The strain on the community led to a proposal by an elected city counsellor of a three-strike policy, given the cost of responding to opioid poisonings in the community and the increasing cost of dispensing naloxone, a substance that can reverse an overdose. If emergency services were called a second time to assist or revive an individual due to opioid misuse, the person would have to perform community service for the equivalent amount of money used on the life-saving response. If an emergency call for assistance came in a third time and there was no record of that community service having been completed by the individual in distress, then the dispatcher would not inform first responders of the request for assistance and no response would be provided. This philosophy aligns with another American initiative, Project Prevention (http://www.projectprevention.org), which offers cash incentives to both women and men addicted to drugs, including alcohol, to use long-term or permanent birth control procedures, a euphemism for undergoing a sterilization procedure.

Prior to these human and economic realities arising across North America, Harvard economist Jeffrey Miron (1999, 2005, 2008) was advocating for the elimination of drug prohibition, which is fuelled in large part by the moral model. He has estimated that legalizing drugs in the United States alone would generate over $30 billion USD in revenue if cannabis, cocaine, and heroin were regulated and taxed in the same manner as alcohol and tobacco. To bolster his economic claims, he states that there are more people in the United States using illicit drugs currently than when the War on Drugs began in earnest in the 1980s, and that the primary economic benefactors of prohibition have been drug cartels, along with international organized crime and terrorist groups. Miron's views are supported by data released by the Colorado Department of Revenue (2015) on its first year of legal cannabis sales. The government generated over $50 million in revenue from taxes, licences, and fees, without even considering the additional income tax paid by employees working in this new field. Within five years, Colorado alone had generated $1 billion in cannabis taxes from $6.5 billion in sales, which were used, in part, to fund a range of youth and public health programs including mental health, literacy, and school anti-bullying initiatives (Julig, 2019).

CHAPTER 5

Biological Theories

Biological theories search for a pre-existing or induced chemical, physiological, or structural abnormality as the cause for substance misuse. While developed independently, the biological theories can also be viewed as interdependent, as brain function precedes chemistry and chemistry supports function. Trauma, regardless of the cause, is viewed as an autoimmune response or an environmental event that can initiate the disease process, while trauma experiences can be passed on genetically. As well, stressful experiences early in life can modulate the genetic programming of specific brain circuits underlying emotional and cognitive aspects of behavioural adaptation to stressful experiences later in life. Six specific biological theories will be reviewed in this chapter:

1. Disease (medical) model
2. Neurobiology
3. Genetic theory
4. Brain dysfunction theory
5. Biochemical theories
6. Allergy theory

The Medical Model: Addiction as Disease

Among the most prominent addiction theories is the medical model, which revolves around the concept of substance dependency as a primary, chronic, fatal disease process (Miller, 1999; White & McLellan, 2008). It remains among the most well-known theories informing health and social service professional education, research, policy, and drug treatment. The medical model of addiction was also the centrepiece of policy positions taken by the American National Council on Alcoholism and Drug Dependence and the American Society of Addiction Medicine through the latter half of the 20th century. Addiction, along with other mental health issues, has historically been presented as a disease process in no small part to counter the moral model stance and to increase service use and overcome stigma and oppression (Barnett et al., 2018; Pescosolido et al., 2010).

The initial conceptualization of repeated episodes of drunkenness as an illness rather than a vice first arose in the late 18th century in the United States, when alcohol consumption was exploding, and intemperance was described as a disease that was chronic and progressive. In 1823, Dr. Benjamin Rush published *An Inquiry into the Effects of Ardent Spirits upon the Human Body and Mind: With an Account of the Means of Preventing, and of the Remedies for Curing Them*, in which he vehemently argued that chronic drunkenness is a biological disease. Throughout the 1800s, new labels arose to describe the disease, such as dipsomania, chronic alcoholism, and inebriety, the latter of which acknowledged misuse of other drugs, such as opium, cocaine, and ether, an inhalant, for the first time. Nineteenth-century addiction medical journals consistently characterized alcohol and other drug addiction as a chronic, relapsing disease. The disease concept fell out of favour in the early decades of the 20th century with the rise of the prohibition movement and the re-emergence of the moral model as the dominant addiction standpoint. However, a reformulated disease concept emerged following the repeal of Prohibition. In 1938, the Scientific Committee of the Research Council on Problems of Alcohol stated that an alcoholic should be regarded as a sick person, just as is one who is suffering from tuberculosis, cancer, heart disease, or other serious chronic disorders (White et al., 2002).

Ludwig (1975) stated that sufficient deviation from the normal represents disease; that it is due to known or unknown natural causes; and that elimination of these causes will result in cure or improvement in individual patients. Proponents of the disease theory believe that substance dependency is an involuntary biological trait to which certain people are susceptible, and thus drug users are not responsible for their compulsive drug consumption. Drug use in this theory is thought to be an inherited characteristic that worsens over time with increased consumption, leading to a loss of control over use. In this model the emphasis focuses exclusively on the person, with individuals no longer being scorned or shunned for their illness; rather, they are now considered and labelled sick. Initially, labelling alcoholism as a disease helped remove some of the social disgrace and disapproval of having a problem with alcohol. This change of attitude subsequently resulted in more persons receiving treatment, even while the majority of society still felt that those with an addiction could simply will themselves to stop using drugs without any formal support or treatment.

Under the disease model, while addicted persons are still held responsible for their affliction and uncontrollable cravings, they are now viewed as requiring care, including hospitalization, like any other ill individual (Miller & Gold, 1990). This theory views substance misuse as a progressive disorder that continues to worsen until treated, as illustrated by Glatt's (1958) proposal of the decline of an alcohol-dependent person until they have reached bottom, followed by a slow, staged recovery process (Figure 5.1). Glatt's model was influenced by Jellinek's (1952) seminal work on the increasing progressive stages of dependence on alcohol. Glatt drew on Jellinek's research to create a model with an inverted bell curve: the downward half of the curve describes the nature of alcoholism, and the upward half of the curve, the subsequent potential progression of recovery. Jellinek examined the drinking histories of over 2,000 individuals, though mostly men, and from those devised a four-step progression model. The model begins as a person moves from the pre-alcoholic phase of social or integrated drinking, to the blackout stage with its increasing preoccupation with alcohol, to the stage of loss of control over alcohol consumption, and finally to the chronic phase of prolonged intoxications where drinking takes on its obsessive nature. Jellinek stated that two options arose for an individual at this point: either continue the path of deterioration to death, or find a pathway out of alcoholism through a new understanding of life, which many equate with the Alcoholics Anonymous (AA) stage of experiencing a spiritual awakening (see Chapter 24). Likewise, the low point of Jellinek's model, when the alcohol-dependent person admits being defeated by their use of alcohol, aligns with AA's point of hitting rock bottom. Glatt enhanced Jellinek's idea by adding the ascending component that highlights the process of recovery, beginning with an honest desire for help, followed by steps to stop consuming alcohol and becoming open to a new abstinent way of life, and finally to obtaining a state of grace.

In 1956, the American Medical Association declared that alcoholism was a disease at its annual conference, though it would be another decade until it formally ratified this position. The acceptance of the disease concept by the medical profession led to a paradigm shift for the addiction field, and part of its historical significance is the fact that it was the antecedent event that led to the enormous humanitarian move away from the moral model that transpired throughout the latter half of the 20th century. The disease model allowed drug-dependent persons to receive formal and proper medical care. In Canada, the majority of treatment costs were, and to a large extent remain, directly or indirectly covered under provincial medical plans, through subsidized social service initiatives, or through employer health care benefits. In the United States, many private medical plans provide coverage for those with addiction issues, though with the move to managed care and third-party benefit providers, this is beginning to return to a more moralistic perspective. However, even Jellinek (1960) later stated that alcoholism was labelled as a disease primarily because the medical professional considered it a disease, even if this was not a unanimous belief. This sentiment was subsequently echoed by many others (Berridge & Edwards, 1981; Conrad, 2007; Conrad & Barker, 2010; Fingarette, 1988, 1989; Peele & Brodsky, 1992).

During the 1960s, there were arguments that addiction was a metabolic disease similar to diabetes. Later it was argued that addiction produces changes in brain systems that mediate the experience and anticipation of reward, systems responsible for perception and memory, and higher-order executive systems underlying cognitive control. The disease model states that these changes are directly caused by consumption of psychoactive drugs, and they are difficult if not impossible to reverse (Lewis, 2017). By diseasing drug-using behaviour, this theory allows the medical community to take the lead in the care of those who become dependent upon drugs and to provide ongoing treatment (Morse, 2018). This approach subsequently led to the diseasing of many other behaviours that did not have the same biological basis as does addiction, as witnessed in the Canadian Society of

Addiction Medicine's (2008) definition, which states that addiction is a primary chronic disease characterized by impaired control over psychoactive drugs and also behaviours. The development and expansion of the disease model in Canada and the United States was also in part a response to the large-scale experimentation and drug use in the 1960s and 1970s by white, middle-class youth, along with the lengthy prison sentences imposed for the possession of minor amounts of cannabis for the children and youth of affluent middle-class families during that era (Acker, 2002).

The disease model, like most theories, has its limitations. There is a major dearth of empirical research to substantiate the fact that alcoholism, or any other substance-related problem, is the result of a medical disorder. There is no uniformity of the disease nature of the drug action, nor any standard way to diagnose this disease, nor any reliable or consistent medical method to care for the sick, nor a need for medical care in the majority of the treatment process. The progressive nature of the disorder has been challenged for half a century, and there are many aspects of the disease process that remain deficient. In reality, it has long been recognized that addiction is not an inevitable progression of symptoms and stages, nor a consistent loss of control (Fingarette, 1989; Fisher & Harrison, 1977; Pattison et al., 1977). As well, through labelling alcoholism and drug dependency a disease, some individuals feel just as stigmatized as under the moral model. Empirical reviews have found that despite the fact that addiction in the medical model is described as a chronic, relapsing disease, population-wide surveys suggest that this is not the case. Approximately 80 percent of individuals formerly dependent on an illegal drug, or on a medicine used for non-medical purposes, have been in remission for at least a year. These remission rates are much higher than those for other chronic mental health disorders, with the likelihood of reoccurrence unrelated to the cumulative amount of drugs consumed (Berghmans et al., 2009). As well, simply because drug use produces illness does not alone make it a disease.

Under the disease model, abstinence alone is considered the cure for alcoholism and drug dependency. However, this can be equated to treating a broken leg by amputating it. Neither solves the true problem, though both are remedies. As well, once a person stops drinking alcohol or consuming other psychoactive drugs they are not recovered but in recovery, a state that stays with them until their death. The disease becomes an inescapable component of their persona in perpetuity. The person must become even more vigilant about their recognized disease, entailing a moral obligation to engage in the recovery process (May, 2001). Psychologist Stanton Peele (1983, 1989, 2000, 2016) has claimed that while the disease concept of alcoholism is deeply entrenched in the United States, in many other countries, such as England, it is less of an economic utility as reimbursement for doctors is not dependent on what is defined as a disease. In the United States, however, the reward structure is built on fitting as many things as possible into the doctor's bag. Decades before Peele, Szasz (1967) wrote, "it is quite clear that the fundamental purpose of defining alcoholism as a disease is to bring it under the umbrella of mental illness and so justify the involuntary hospitalization and treatment of the so-called patient" (p. 262).

This has led to quite distinct vested interests between Canada and the United States in labelling drug use a disease (Alexander, 1988; Fingarette, 1988). As well, there are huge economic benefits for pharmaceutical companies that develop lifelong drug treatments for this disease. Many psychoactive drugs, from barbiturates to benzodiazepines, amphetamines, and all the current psychotherapeutic agents, have been developed since the beginning of the 20th century to treat illnesses. Others for which no profitable therapeutic use were initially found, such as LSD and MDMA (ecstasy), became prohibited substances (Singer, 2006).

Despite its shortcomings, the disease model remains extremely popular for several reasons:

- It is a simple solution to a complex problem.
- It was the first theory to challenge the view of the moral model and provide compassionate care.
- It has provided the opportunity for the pharmacological industry to become involved in creating new drugs to reduce drug cravings and ease withdrawal symptoms (see Chapter 16).
- It provides a rationale and the means for individuals to receive ongoing treatment.
- The medical profession, especially in the United States, benefits economically and socially from maintaining ownership of the issue.
- It provides a foundation for the most popular model of addiction recovery, Alcoholics Anonymous.
- Tradition and history create biases that are difficult to change.
- Politically, if drug use is a disease and each individual is personally responsible for their condition, then there is no reason to make social reforms that might prevent the problem.
- There is money to be made in the field and in related adjunct industries.
- It is the most prominent component of the Canadian health care system that allows privatization and thus unregulated health care.

However, outside assisting with detoxification from a few specific drugs, there is limited need for medical practitioners to be directly involved in the treatment of service users with addiction problems.

Alcoholism as a disease has become a great model for treating all kinds of problems as disease. It is self-sustaining, it fits into the American culture, it is economically rewarding, and basically nobody really cares if it has any effect or not: it relieves everybody of guilt. So, calling it a disease essentially means we ignore it as a social condition. (McConnell, 1989, p. 16)

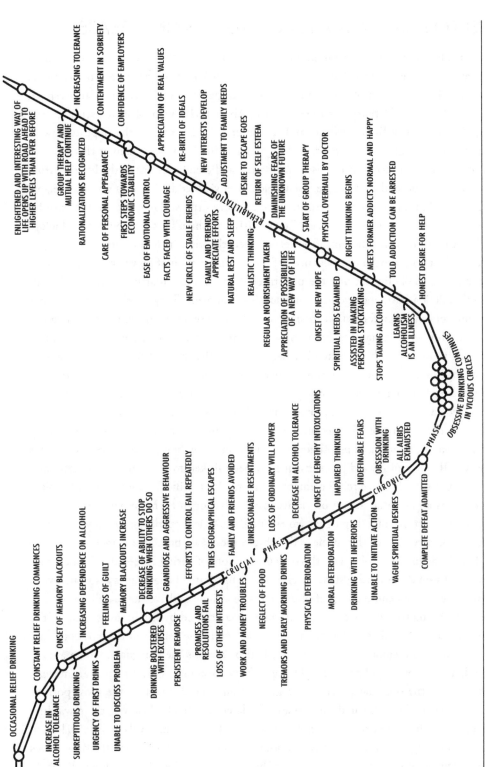

Figure 5.1: Medical Model Process of Alcohol Misuse and Recovery

Source: Glatt (1958).

NEUROBIOLOGY: ADDICTION AS A BRAIN DISEASE

Neurobiological theory is premised on the belief that addiction occurs as a result of an alteration of those brain mechanisms that control human reward systems and motivational states, including systems involved in learning and memory. In 1997, Dr. Alan Leshner, the director of the National Institute on Drug Abuse (NIDA), published a seminal article, "Addiction Is a Brain Disease, and It Matters." Leshner wrote that repeated use of psychoactive drugs rewired and chemically altered the brain in a manner that resulted in compulsive drug seeking and use, making the addicted brain distinctly different from the brain of non-addicted people. Neurobiologists view addiction as a chronic, relapsing brain disease that is characterized by compulsive drug seeking, despite the harmful consequences the drug use produces (Lewis, 2017). Leshner's article would focus biological research initiatives drawing from established theories, including brain dysfunction and biochemical, into a more evidence-informed examination of how psychoactive drugs compromise the brain. During the past three decades, molecular neurobiological studies of addiction have undergone tremendous development. They have yielded enormous amounts of valuable information about neuronal response mechanisms and their adaptive changes through an array of techniques, ranging from in vitro molecular methods to brain imaging procedures. This research has demonstrated that brain structures and functions do change over time due to exposure to psychoactive drugs until they reach a threshold. At this threshold point, the primary symptom of dependence occurs, making it difficult to stop excessive drug use without professional help (Erickson & White, 2009).

Neurobiology theory focuses on the human reward system that is responsible for the perception of physical and emotional sensations and how humans perceive and process reward. The idea of reward has subsequently been linked to how humans perceive and process pleasure. Positive reinforcement is the more scientifically correct term for pleasure and is an essential aspect of motivational behavior in all mammals, providing an incentive to act. Mammals pursue two essential biological purposes: their own survival and the preservation of the species. To achieve these two basic goals, mammals act to address basic instincts—hunger, thirst, reproduction, offspring care—all of which positively activate the reward system. Each stage of motivated behaviour is associated with positive reinforcement, feelings of pleasure that continue to drive the search for reward. Reward and motivation mechanisms are mainly controlled by the limbic system of the brain, a set of cortical and subcortical areas involved in the genesis of the emotions, and in learning and memory. The limbic system also contains the amygdala, which among its other functions regulates the fight-flight-freeze response. Of all neurotransmitters, dopamine is the one that provides the greatest amount of pleasure, the most positive reinforcement when activated, in humans (Scala et al., 2017). However, the rewarding effects of psychoactive drugs that lead to progressively increasing levels of use also lead to a corresponding increase in negative emotional and physical states when the drug leaves the system—withdrawal. These cravings then lead to further drug seeking (Koob & Volkow, 2016).

As with many brain diseases, drug addiction displays both pathological alterations in the transmission of signals within the neural circuitries and the production of defects throughout the brain. In response, the brain continually attempts to keep or return the body to a point of balance or homeostasis, and in so doing, it will adapt to the prolonged or excessive presence of drugs by making changes in brain cells and neural pathways. When people administer a psychoactive drug, it activates the same reinforcement system in the brain that is normally activated by food, water, and sex. While some theories have viewed the role of the limbic system (Nestler, 2005), particularly the amygdala, as crucial to this process (Chambers et al., 2007), others have looked at the effect of reinforcement of dopamine receptors in the mesolimbic system (Koob & LeMoal, 1997; Saal et al., 2003). All of these reinforcers share one physiological effect—increased amounts of dopamine being released in the brain either directly or indirectly through the activation of other neurotransmitters. During this process, prominent physical changes occur in areas of the brain that are critical to judgment, decision making, learning and memory, and behavioural control (Anton, 1999; Chandler, 2003; Naqvi et al., 2007; Wang et al., 2019).

The popular term "the highjacked brain" has underscored neurobiological research in three new areas:

1. drug actions on intracellular signalling systems that mediate cell responses,
2. synaptic plasticity in the course of chronic drug exposure, and
3. the role of dopaminergic and other components of the human reward system,

along with a fourth long-established area:

4. genetic factors that will be examined as a distinct theoretical construct.

Intracelluar Signalling

Psychoactive drugs that produce physical dependency dysregulate the brain by directly or indirectly increasing the amount of dopamine available to produce signals transmitted between neurons or by inhibiting dopamine reuptake, which likewise changes intracellular signalling. Neurons are the dynamic component of the CNS that have the ability to adapt to changes produced by external influences, such as psychoactive drugs. This adaption follows basic physics and occurs in an equal and opposite direction to the initial effect, working to return the body to the initial state of homeostasis. This is the foundation for the development of tolerance. When a person no longer uses the drug, the adaption becomes apparent through the pain of withdrawal. The process occurs through membrane receptors, ion channels, and enzymes, as well as in alterations in cellular metabolism, ion movement, and activation of genes that direct the synthesis of proteins. This process has been demonstrated with CNS depressants, stimulants, and cannabis, and thus chronic exposure to any of these drugs leads to increases or decreases in the cells' internal signalling mechanisms. Thus, excessive dopamine signalling during drug use can affect gene expression, altering synaptic function and brain pathway activity leading over time to negative behaviours in vulnerable individuals (Nestler & Luscher, 2019). However, this adaption is not unique to psychoactive drugs but occurs with a range of sensory stimuli. Thus, signalling pathways are the foundation of all human biological adaption to any environmental stress and not only to psychoactive drugs (Kallant, 2009).

Synaptic Plasticity (Neuralplasticity)

Addiction is a unique brain disease in that it does not arise due to a loss of neurons; rather, neurons are affected when a person consumes a psychoactive agent as chronic drug exposure alters gene expression in the brain. The process of addiction shares many similarities with neural plasticity, which is the biological mechanism through which both learning and memory are shaped. Synapses are specialized structures in the brain where communication between neurons occurs that is dynamic, changing depending on the strength or weakness of the signals that pass through them. Environmental stimuli linked to psychoactive drugs become learned associations, strengthening synaptic pathways with those stimuli and creating sensations that motivate continued drug use. The neurotransmitters dopamine and glutamate are widely distributed throughout the brain, but with greater concentrations in the limbic system and basal ganglia, where they play a key integrative role in motivation, learning, and memory. It is believed that coordinated molecular signalling of dopamine and glutamate systems create stronger synaptic pathways that lead to adaptive changes in gene expression and alter synaptic plasticity, which can reconfigure neural networks and ultimately behaviour increasing drug seeking (Kelly, 2004; Tang & Dani, 2009).

Adaptive responses occur not only within single neurons but also at synapses between neurons. This synaptic adaptive response has two opposite components: long-term potentiation (LTP) and long-term depression (LTD). LTP involves the long-lasting impulse transmission from one neuron to another, where the synapse between them is used repeatedly to convey the chemical message. LTD involves the opposite, a long-lasting decrease in impulse transmission. Both arise due to changes in different neurotransmitter receptors, and as with intracelluar signalling, they are core human adaptive processes triggered by a range of stimuli and not only psychoactive drugs. Thus, when examining addiction, synaptic changes explain how the physical aspect of addiction arises but not, unfortunately, why (Cruz et al., 2014; Kallant, 2009). Related to this is the hypothesis that repeated exposure to psychoactive drugs creates persistent drug-related memories that may be the foundation of chronic reoccurrence. Memories of the drug, drug-related cues, and drug-related contexts are strengthened over time, with repeated drug use reinforcing drug seeking (Slaker et al., 2016).

Another aspect of synaptic plasticity that has been examined in relation to the development of addiction is the role of glucocorticoids (Logrip et al., 2015). Glucocorticoids are natural steroid hormones with potent anti-inflammatory effects that are critical for both short-term and long-term behavioural adaptations to stressful stimuli. Many of these adaptations involve the neurobiological systems responsible for motivated behaviour, and the development of coping behaviours to stressful environmental stimuli. Glucocorticoids contribute to many of the processes through which stress influences both short-term and long-term vulnerability to drug use and have been linked to the establishment of addiction-related neuroplasticity associated with chronic stress, particularly with excessive cocaine use, though much of this work has been limited to animal models (Mantsch & Gasser, 2015).

Dopamine and the Reward System

As previously discussed, dopamine is a crucial neurotransmitter involved in directing and rewarding goal-directed behaviour. Dopamine also enhances the formation of new synapses, along with playing a role in diminishing other reward pathways. Thus, changes in dopamine metabolism bring about structural changes in synaptic networks, changing the way the brain itself is wired (Lewis, 2017). The more a psychoactive drug produces physical dependency, the greater the release of dopamine at the axon terminals of the neurons. This creates the euphoria, or the pleasure response, in the substance user. The core reward circuitry consists of the ventral tegmental area (VTA), nucleus accumbens, and ventral pallidum via the medial forebrain bundle. This system does more than just produce pleasure, however; it is now believed that it is also responsible for more complex cognitive functions, such as attention, reward anticipation, negating reward expectation, and motivation. Drugs that alter endocannabinoids, endorphins, GABA, glutamate, and serotonin indirectly enhance the dopamine reward synaptic function in the nucleus accumbens, as do all psychoactive drugs that directly affect dopamine (Hagele et al., 2014; Volkow & Morales, 2015).

Similarly, the dopamine imbalance model suggests that addiction affects not only the dopamine reward pathways but also pathways affecting motivation, memory, learning-conditioning, habits, inhibitory control, executive function, stress reactivity, and aversion avoidance. These pathways are all dependent upon dopamine transmissions and are also connected with one another through direct and indirect glutamate, GABA, serotonin, and noradrenaline neurotransmitter inputs. This combined interaction, enhanced when many different psychoactive drugs are consumed, broadly impacts behaviour, which aids in explaining the far reaching effects of addiction on mind and body (Bickel et al., 2018).

However, for some substances, tolerance develops with chronic use. When this occurs, users no longer self-administer to feel euphoria but simply to restore a homeostatic level. A greater amount of the drug is now required to be present in the brain for the body to be able to function normally (Gardner, 2011). While different drug groups work through different biological reactions, the outcome is similar—an increase in dopamine activity in the nucleus accumbens and prefrontal cortex. However, what is not yet understood is why only a minority of people become addicted when all psychoactive drugs act the same way in the VTA and the majority of people use some type of psychoactive drug (Kallant, 2009).

Critique

Despite intense research and increasing empirical support, the neurobiological theory still has distinct limits. Its contribution to understanding addiction is the knowledge that almost every cell function appears to be involved. Thus, we are aware that neurons adapt to psychoactive drugs, but they likewise adapt to all types of functional disturbances. In fact, brain changes during the process of becoming physically dependent upon a psychoactive drug are similar to those observed when recurrent, highly motivated goal seeking results in the development of deep habits—in other words Pavlovian learning (see Chapter 6) (Lewis, 2017). This reductionist approach is unable to explain what causes these mechanisms to be brought into play with some individuals, but not others, and why this occurs only through self-administration and not passive exposure (Kallant, 2009). In a scathing critique of the utility of brain imaging, Lilienfeld and Satel (2019) state that the claim that addiction is rooted in brain dysfunction is devoid of scientific content and that this theory has questionable utility and that there is minimal evidence that it leads to any type of effective intervention or that it reduces stigma in any way. As well, those writing in this area continue to call persons with addiction issues *addicts*, adding to the pathologizing of this human condition.

Sociologists in particular have criticized the reductive tendencies of the neurobiological approach that claims a causal link between addiction and physiological processes. It simply cannot fully account for the complexity of human behaviour (Oksanen, 2013). Even more problematic may be the concern that the neurobiological discussion of addiction as a brain disease is simply presenting a revised form of the disease model in an attempt to decrease the oppression faced by those with an addiction and to continue to counter and rebut the still dominant view of addiction as a moral issue. Inherent limits found in the disease model are also present here. While presenting addiction as a neurobiological condition does allow for the same medical care as that for individuals living with other diseases, and while it helps to promote enlightened social and legal policies, such claims may still unintentionally foster the discrimination commonly associated with any pathology. Specifically, the language of neuroscience can reduce blame and responsibility while inadvertently identifying addicted persons as neurobiological "others" and increasing the social isolation of this vulnerable group (Buchman et al., 2010).

Interestingly, the view's first proponent, Alan Leshner (2010), later wrote that he intended his original assertion of addiction as a brain disease to be viewed more as a metaphor and that the initial messaging included a behavioural component that was lost in the rush to produce an empirical understanding of the phenomenon. He also stated that, from his view, a major contribution of conceptualizing addiction as a brain disease was that it further countered the question of why people simply don't stop using through will power alone. He had also hoped that, by championing this approach through the National Institute on Drug Abuse, more biomedical funding for addiction could be obtained to combat the stigma experienced by people who have an addiction, and that criminal approaches that dominate the American response to addiction could be softened.

GENETIC THEORY: ADDICTION AS AN INHERITED DISORDER

Despite the vast numbers of individuals who experiment with various psychoactive drugs, the majority do not become addicted. However, there is a proportion of every human culture who do, and they also tend to differ from the general population in having pre-existing co-morbid traits, including novelty seeking and antisocial behaviour. This has become part of the argument for a genetic basis for the susceptibility to dependence (Hiroi & Agatsuma, 2005). Genetic theory was for a short time out of favour in the 20th century, but it has had a dramatic rebound in prominence with advances in human genome research. Humans have only approximately 20,000 genes, about the same as the nematode worm that grows to only 2.5 mm in length. Human genes must therefore perform multiple tasks, leaving them open to a range of potential coding errors as they produce the range of enzymes, hormones, proteins, neurotransmitters, and all other biological material that allow us to live day to day.

Genetic theory proposes that drug dependency is an inherited disorder. For example, historically, certain Asian groups had a lower mortality from alcoholism than did Europeans. These Asian populations lacked a gene that allows for the efficient processing of alcohol. Thus, when alcohol is consumed, an unpleasant physical response and flushing of the face occurs at much lower dose amounts than for average Europeans. This, in turn, historically led these groups to avoid using large amounts of alcohol, and fewer individuals fell into an alcohol-dependency cycle (Maisto et al., 1995; Stohl, 1988). Genetic studies conducted on different ethnic groups have confirmed that certain genetic allele variations of the enzymes ADH and ALDH are linked either in development of or in protection from alcohol addiction (Moussas et al., 2009), as are enzymes CYP3A4 and CYP1A2 (Zhang et al., 2016). Likewise, some people have a gene that leads to caffeine being metabolized slowly, while others have a gene that allows for far faster metabolism. Those who are fast metabolizers can literally consume coffee after coffee, whereas those who are slow metabolizers are at four times greater risk of having a heart attack by the age of 50 if they drink as little as four cups a day (Cornelis & El-Sohemy, 2007).

Alcoholism has been documented to be strongly familial, running through several generations. The increase in risk for developing alcoholism is from four- to seven-fold among the first-degree relatives of persons with an alcohol dependence compared to the general population, regardless of nationality (Hesselbrock et al., 2013). Inherited personality traits may also influence susceptibility to alcoholism, and neurological disorders that lead to alcohol and substance misuse, such as attention-deficit/hyperactivity disorder, may be transferred from generation to generation. As well, there may be actual cell differences in alcohol-dependent persons that are inherited (Reich, 1988). Fraternal and paternal twin studies, conducted with families where a child was adopted at a young age, have also indicated a genetic component to the development of substance misuse (Bierut, 2011). Approximately one-quarter of the fathers and brothers of those with an alcohol dependency are themselves alcohol-dependent. This compares with an overall rate among men of 3–5 percent while 5 percent of daughters and sisters develop dependency to alcohol (Shuckit, 1999). When adopted offspring of persons with an alcohol dependency were compared to adopted children of biological parents who were not alcohol-dependent, an alcoholism rate three to four times greater for those whose biological parents were dependent was observed (Goodwin et al., 1973). In the Minnesota Twin Family Study, which examined 1,080 twins, there was also evidence for the existence of a highly heritable factor that underlies the association among multiple forms of psychopathology (McGue et al., 2006). Research has also found a degree of heritability to acute adverse and affective responses to opioids (Angst et al., 2012).

Jung (1994) compared brothers who were adopted from families where alcohol dependency was prevalent to those who remained with their natural parents and found rates of misuse to be similar. Heath and colleagues (1989), in one of the first studies to examine female twins, found greater levels of alcohol dependency between identical twins than between fraternal twins, a similar finding to that of Kendler and colleagues (1992). Individuals with a family history of alcohol dependency tend to develop tolerance to alcohol quicker than those without (Morzorati et al., 2002). Van den Bree and colleagues (1998) examined 54 identical and 65 fraternal twins in public and private alcohol and drug treatment programs in Minnesota during the 1980s and found evidence to suggest genetic influences in persons prone to developing an addiction to alcohol.

Good laboratory and field studies exist supporting the genetic theory (Zubieta et al., 2003), with the heritability of drug dependency estimated at 50 percent (Buscemi & Turchi, 2011; Enoch, 2012; National Institute on Alcohol Abuse and Alcoholism, 2000; Sartor et al., 2009). Genome studies have identified 930 genes associated with alcohol dependency, indicating that it is a highly complex trait, on par with human height (Lo et al., 2016). Among these are two specific neurotransmitter genes, that have been shown to be linked to the vulnerability for alcohol dependence (Hesselbrock et al., 2013), as has the alcohol-metabolizing enzyme alcohol dehydrogenase (Kimura & Higuchi, 2011). Genetic variations in the μ-opioid receptor sites in the brain's reward system seem to influence the release of the neurotransmitter dopamine and the degree of pleasure that individuals derive from drinking. Individuals who possess this receptor variant may experience enhanced pleasurable effects from alcohol that could increase their risk for developing alcohol misuse and dependence (Ramchandani et al., 2011) while those with the eNOS or CHRNA2 gene variant are at greater risk for developing physical dependency to cannabis (Demontis et al., 2019; Isir et al., 2016). Similarly, individuals with one of five other variations on their CHRNA2 gene have a slightly greater risk of developing physical dependency to opioids than the general population (Crist et al., 2019).

Distinct genetic influences have been found indicating the likelihood of a person becoming physically dependent on smoking cigarettes (Sharp & Chen, 2018) specifically relating to genes CHRNA5, CHRNA3, and CHRNB4 (Ramoz & Gorwood, 2015), as well as an increased risk of developing lung cancer from doing so (Amos et al., 2010). Likewise, Jackson (2017) identified seven concentrations of genes located on chromosomes

4, 6 (2 clusters), 10, 11, and 19 where variations in alleles placed individuals at greater risk for developing a dependency on alcohol, opioids, or stimulants. Interestingly, some of these clusters placed specific ethnic groups, such as Southeast Asians, at greater risk for alcohol dependency.

Research from animal studies has found several major genetic processes at work in increasing the likelihood of addiction passing from one generation to the next. Psychoactive drugs have been found to have the capacity to:

- change the state of the material that chromosomes are formed from;
- impact gene transcription;
- add methyl molecules to amino acids and DNA; and
- produce noncoding RNA (ribonucleic acid), which is a functional RNA molecule that transcribes from DNA but does not translate into needed proteins (Beayno et al., 2019).

Family, twin, and adoption studies demonstrate clearly that alcohol dependence and alcohol use disorders are inheritable conditions, which in some cases can account for half of the likelihood a person will develop an addiction (Reilly et al., 2017). While an important contributing factor, at this time genetics still cannot explain the majority of cases of substance dependency, nor provide specific treatment interventions. Contemporary thinking considers addiction to be polygenic, which means that there is a critical interaction between genetic and environmental factors that occurs in creating an addiction (Beayno et al., 2019). In a study involving twins from Finland, 76 percent of the total variance in abstinence or choosing to begin to drink alcohol was explained by common environmental effects (Rose et al., 2001). While a subsequent Swedish twin study found that drug misuse is influenced by a diverse set of genetic risks, with a specific liability relating to the neurotransmitter dopamine, vulnerability was also created by environmental factors, especially family instability (Kendler et al., 2012). Environmental factors are also important in determining whether teens experiment with alcohol or other drugs, but it is genetics that is more important than the environment in determining if they will become addicted or not once they do start using (Fowler et al., 2007).

However, heritable should never be confused with unchangeable. Lebowitz and Applebaum (2017) reported that individuals who believed that the genetic theory explained addiction were found to blame those with an addiction issue less than those who did not. These individuals also had an increased confidence in the use of pharmacotherapy as a means to treat addiction and a decreased expectation of the value of psychotherapy. What genetic theory does indicate is that some persons are born with a greater predisposition or inherited risk to develop a substance misuse problem. Thus, genetics can influence the extent of use once an individual has already begun to use. In this regard, genetic factors may be as potent as psychological, physiological, or other biological factors that are necessary for substance misuse to develop and escalate.

BRAIN DYSFUNCTION THEORY: ADDICTION DUE TO A MALFUNCTIONING BRAIN

Chronic drug use can severely damage the nervous system, particularly cognitive functions, cerebral metabolism, and brain morphology (structure). This damage can lead to memory loss, concentration deficits, and increased impulsivity. Under the early biological theory of brain dysfunction, addiction was conceptualized as a chronic relapsing brain disorder that affected circuits that regulate reward, motivation, memory, and decision making—the foundations of neurobiology theory. It is now consistently argued that drug-induced changes in the brain create behaviours that continue despite adverse bio-psycho-social consequences (Cadet et al., 2014). In its definition of addiction, the American National Institute on Drug Abuse (2012) states that it is, in part, a result of prolonged drug use on brain functioning.

That brain damage occurs as a consequence of heavy alcohol intake is a well-established argument found in the alcohol literature of the past 200 years. Jellinek (1960) equated this disorder to what he termed "gamma alcoholism." Brain dysfunction theories postulate that continued consumption of large amounts of alcohol and other drugs leads to damage of brain cells responsible for willpower and judgment. Once a specific level of damage is reached, a single incidence of drug use can paralyze the remaining cells and lead to uncontrolled and excessive drug use as occurs in bingeing. The theory hypothesizes that drug-dependent persons are biologically different, and ongoing research has demonstrated that the brains of dependent and non-dependent individuals are in fact different. Early electroencephalograph (EEG) studies have indicated that there may be a cerebral condition predisposing individuals to alcohol dependency. Regardless, no evidence exists that there are any specific brain cells responsible for willpower or judgment that can be differentially affected by drugs (Chaudron & Wilkinson, 1988).

Brain damage from alcohol due to nutritional deficiencies can partially explain the pathology of alcohol dependency, namely, the permanent loss of control over drinking. It has historically been believed that if a biological problem does arise, it is the result of heavy and/or excessive consumption, not an initial breakdown of a select group of cells. Chronic exposure to drugs does create many modifications to the physiology of the brain, such as impairment of the brain's synapses. By limiting synapse plasticity, new learning can also be impaired. This could allow drug-using behaviour to become more established and lead to even more compulsive use (Ksaanetz et al., 2010). Studies with animals have also shown that heavy alcohol use actually rewires brain circuitry, making it harder to recover psychologically from a traumatic experience. A history of heavy alcohol use could impair a critical mechanism for recovering from trauma, placing people at greater risk for post-traumatic stress disorder (PTSD) (Holmes et al., 2012). While alcohol can produce irreversible neuron death, it also degrades the cerebrospinal fluid, which acts as a buffer for the brain. With abstinence, this can be reversed. Individuals can experience brain volume recovery often within the first two weeks of abstinence, though this varies between brain regions. While motor skills appear to return quickly, higher cognitive functions such as divided attention, which are processed in specific cortical areas, take a longer time to recover (Ejik et al., 2012).

Psychoactive drugs from different families as distinct as cocaine, alcohol, and morphine all affect neurons in the same part of the brain (Saal et al., 2003). Chronic drug use does change brain function, and some of these changes persist after cessation. Wilkinson (1998) contended that addiction is tied to changes in brain structure and function. At its core, addiction is the product of changes in the brain, and thus treatment must focus on reversing or compensating for those brain changes. It has long been argued that the same process that leads excessive alcohol consumption to produce liver damage can create brain damage (Pratt et al., 1990). Li and Wolf (2015) found that cocaine influences brain-derived neurotrophic factor (BDNF) levels in the VTA, along with the amygdala, hippocampus, and frontal cortex. BDNF is a protein that regulates cell growth, survival, and differentiation during central and peripheral nervous system development. Differences in the brains of dependent and non-dependent persons have also been identified, some of which are permanent and others that disappear after cessation of use (Chandler, 2003).

Brain dysfunction theory was among the earliest addiction theories proposed, and much of what was earlier argued, and the ongoing supporting arguments, have now been incorporated into the broader domain of neurobiological theory. However, the ability of many drug-dependent individuals to become and remain abstinent underscores an inherent weakness with brain dysfunction theory. As Frank and Nagel (2017) wrote, people don't simply stop being diabetic by deciding to produce more insulin but individuals can stop being drug dependent by ending their consumption of psychoactive drugs. This act of cessation, while changing the outcome dramatically, does not actually change brain function; rather, it changes brain reaction.

BIOCHEMICAL THEORIES: ADDICTION DUE TO MALFUNCTIONING BIOLOGICAL SYSTEMS

This broad grouping of theories, comprising a variety of related physiological hypotheses, was the precursor to neurobiological theory. Within biochemical theories are discussions of various metabolic disturbances and sensitivities, and vitamin and other dietary deficiencies, such as hypoglycemia, that lead to abnormal cravings, endocrine gland deficiencies, and malfunctioning control centres in the brain. Biochemical theories propose that chemical imbalances exist in the body or are created by the use and then withdrawal process (May, 2001; Rose et al., 2007), or that alcohol is metabolized in some abnormal way that contributes to increased consumption (Fingarette, 1988) or decreased intoxication (Blednov et al., 2007).

For example, one proposed cause of addiction was diet-related, with certain psychoactive drugs providing a "pick up" for a short period after ingestion. Once the food has been processed, the person begins to suffer from withdrawal. In the case of alcohol dependency, individuals may become physically dependent on food elements in alcoholic beverages, such as malt or corn. Alcohol promotes a rapid absorption of these substances, thus increasing their "pick up" effects and helping to relieve withdrawal effects. It has also long been argued that there may be a reciprocal relationship between hypoglycemia and alcoholic tendencies (Tintera, 1966). As well, monoamine oxidase (MAO), a genetically controlled enzyme involved in regulating the neurotransmitters dopamine and norepinephrine, may be a causative factor, as members of families with a history of alcoholism generally have lower MAO levels than do members of families with no such history (Pandey et al., 1988). Researchers at Johns Hopkins University hypothesized that children of an alcohol-dependent parent have altered brain chemistry that makes them most susceptible to becoming alcohol-dependent themselves (Wand et al., 1998). Goldstein (1976) and Snyder (1977) earlier hypothesized that some individuals might have lowered levels of endorphins that leave them unusually sensitive to pain and thus have a far greater reinforcing response to opioids. Similarly, stress hormones have been shown to play a critical role in the development and continuation of alcohol dependence in lab animals. Thus, if this chemical could be blocked, alcohol dependence could be alleviated (Roberto et al., 2010).

Research has also indicated that exposure to the heavy metals, such as lead and cadmium, may also make people more susceptible to alcohol and drug addiction by requiring greater amounts of the drug of choice to be ingested to obtain a significant feeling of euphoria (Nation et al., 1995, 2003; Overstreet et al., 1996). Cadmium, a component of cigarettes, enters the body when a person smokes and can be retained for years. It also crosses the placenta of a smoking mother to the fetus. In experiments in which laboratory rats were exposed to lead, they became supersensitive. Supersensitivity has also been linked with drug use among persons with concurrent disorders. Individuals with existing mental health problems, such as schizophrenia, might be supersensitive due to distinct neurotransmitter interactions. When they consume alcohol, nicotine, or another psychoactive substance, their system reacts much more dramatically or quickly, thus explaining the higher incidence of substance misuse among some groups with other mental health issues. Despite these interesting hypotheses, the actual cause-effect relationships were never fully established. In general, ideas from this theory have been minimized by or incorporated into the broader ideas represented in neurobiological theory.

ALLERGY THEORY: THE INFLUENCE OF SILKWORTH

It has been argued that for some persons, an initial contact with a psychoactive drug leads to an allergic reaction, which produces the subsequent loss of control over consumption. Early support was given to the belief that alcohol dependency was the result of an allergic reaction to the substance. This support was crystallized by the physician who treated founding members of Alcoholics Anonymous, Dr. William Silkworth. Silkworth stated that alcoholism was a physical allergy combined with a mental obsession. At the request of the co-founders of Alcoholics Anonymous, Bill Wilson and Dr. Bob Smith, Silkworth included his views in the book *Alcoholics Anonymous*, which gave great prominence to the view in the early days of the addiction recovery movement. Silkworth compared alcohol dependency to hay fever, in terms of how it progresses over time until it fully emerges as a problematic condition requiring constant treatment. Silkworth wrote:

> We believe, and so suggested a few years ago, that the action of alcohol on these chronic alcoholics is the manifestation of an allergy; that the phenomenon of craving is limited to this class and never occurs in the average temperate drinker. These allergic types can never safely use alcohol in any form at all; and once having formed the habit and found they cannot break it, once having lost their self-confidence, their reliance upon things human, their problems pile up on them and they become astonishing difficult to solve. (Alcoholics Anonymous, 2001, p. xxviii)

Supporters and members of Alcoholics Anonymous and related 12-step groups, such as Narcotics Anonymous (NA), have championed this view and continue to do so, though early references in the AA literature used allergy more as a metaphor rather than an actuality.

Randolph (1956) supported the position that alcoholism was a masked food allergy, and that certain food allergens created a craving for alcohol. However, subsequent research failed to confirm that alcohol stimulated production of any type of anti-alcohol antibody (Jellinek, 1960). As with the disease model, no specific mechanism, pathway, or system has ever been proposed to support this view, nor has an allergic reaction yet to be linked to a single use of any psychoactive drug. While certain individuals may become dependent on a drug after a single usage, the proportion is statistically insignificant and usually better attributable to other factors. Nonetheless, Ohlendorf-Moffat (1993) argued that if food allergies can trigger migraines, why not a dependency to alcohol?

While this theory is largely out of favour, with critiques by Haggard appearing as early as 1944, there may still be some value to examining the allergy link to addiction. Speaking at the 2011 annual meeting of the American Academy of Allergy, Asthma and Immunology, former president Dr. Sami Bahna stated that alcoholic beverages can trigger allergic reactions or exacerbate existing allergies (Rabasseda, 2011). In writing about the opioid crisis, Boyett (2019) stated that "patients in recovery should consider themselves 'allergic' to self-administered controlled substances" (p. 634). While rare, some individuals do have allergies to alcohol itself, while others are allergic to various substances in beer and wine. Symptoms may include red, itchy eyes, nasal congestion, upset stomach, and difficulty breathing. Allergic reactions to an alcoholic beverage can range in severity from a minor rash to a life-threatening asthma attack and anaphylaxis. Researchers have pointed out that alcohol has the capacity to aggravate existing allergies (Dallas, 2011).

CHAPTER 6

Psychological Theories

Psychological theories examine the experience of drug dependency from within the context of an individual's behaviour. They have been advanced as an alternative to the notion that drug dependency is a unitary disease with a specific cause. This standpoint also focuses on observable behaviours of drug use, how the behaviour is learned, modified, and reinforced, and that there may be some psychological component that exists that predisposes an individual to an accelerated pattern of use. Chapter 6 presents overviews of six distinct psychological theories that attempt to explain addiction:

1. Learning theory
2. Personality theory
3. Psychodynamic theory
4. Humanistic theory
5. Attachment theory
6. Rational theory

LEARNING THEORY

Drug addiction can be conceptualized at a basic level as aberrant and maladaptive learning and memory. Among the earliest investigations into why people became addicted were theories that looked at stimuli that give pleasure, relief, or excitement and how reliably and quickly these responses could be produced. Learning is a change in behaviour brought on by a negative or positive experience: reinforcement. If the potential of an action or behaviour reoccurring is increased when another event—the stimulus—occurs, then learning can take place. If the occurrence of the stimulus increases the likelihood of the behaviour, this is positive reinforcement. Negative reinforcement is the process of decreasing the likelihood of a particular action occurring through a process of punishment, which can be physical, such as an electric shock, or psychological, such as a verbal rebuke. Core elements of human learning, conditioning, reinforcement, reward, and motivations are all common concepts involved in the development of an addiction (Luisetto, 2019; Wilson, 1988). Research has also explored how decision-making processes are dysfunctional in those who develop an addiction and that this dysfunction may be fundamental to the commencement and maintenance of drug use (Koffarnus & Kaplan, 2018). The repeated use of drugs in the face of negative consequences suggests dysfunction in the cognitive processes underlying decision making with those who misuse substances, with these individuals valuing risky options more highly when provided different behavioural options. Drug misusers may also have a greater propensity for superficially attractive rewards when making choices and tend to be more efficient in learning from rewards while being less efficient in learning from losses (Verdejo-Garcia et al., 2018).

Classical conditioning is a fundamental learning model, most closely associated with Ivan Pavlov. Pavlovian cues are associated with psychoactive drug use producing lasting influences on behaviour, including the ability to enhance memory consolidation regarding the effect of drug use and withdrawal (Wolter et al., 2019). Pavlovian drug cues have been linked with evoking conditioned autonomic responses, triggering drug craving, activating brain reward circuits, motivating drug seeking, and producing drug use reoccurrence lapse—but also in promoting abstinence (Srey et al., 2015). Drug researchers have identified Pavlovian sign-tracking as a major contributor to the transition from voluntary drug use into poorly controlled drug misuse. Sign-tracking is the conditioning of directed motor action that arises from the pairing of an object with a reward. In Pavlovian sign-tracking procedures, a small object (conditioned stimulus [CS]) is paired with a reward (unconditioned stimulus [US]), producing a conditioned response (CR). The response typically consists of approaching the CS, interacting with it, and eventually consuming it. When sign-tracking behaviour is poorly controlled, it resembles the process of reoccurrence among drug users. Sign-tracking itself resembles psychomotor activation, a behavioural response produced by physical dependency–producing drugs. The effects of sign-tracking on corticosterone levels and dopamine pathways resemble the neurobiological effects of drug use, which supports the classical conditioning explanation for drug misuse (Tomie et al., 2008). Extinction learning, another key aspect of classical conditioning, is the process by which an old negative pattern of learning (in this case, drug use) is replaced by new positive affective associations. A study of cocaine users highlighted that extinction cues were not as powerful as reinforcement cues. This is one reason why extinction training (moving a user toward abstinence) may not be as effective with this population and why classical conditioning remains a valid paradigm to understand the development of addiction (Konova, 2019).

During the 1960s, there was great interest in applying B.F. Skinner's (1953) theories on operant learning to the addiction field. The importance of positive reinforcement, encouraging ongoing drug use and negative reinforcement (withdrawal) that reinforces ongoing drug use, was successfully demonstrated with a range of animals. Operant learning experiments demonstrated that psychoactive drugs acted as behavioural reinforcers just like food, water, or sex, and in some cases were in fact more powerful positive reinforcers. Mammals, other than humans, would voluntarily self-administer psycho-active drugs and would do so when having to choose between the drug and basic rein-forcers (Bickel et al., 2018). The transition from integrated drug use to addiction occurs along a continuum where the psychological mechanisms responsible for drug misuse use evolve from positive reinforcement to negative reinforcement. Misused psychoac-tive agents are initially used at regular intervals in relation to their positive reinforcing properties. This repeated exposure to rewarding substances sets off a chain of secondary reinforcing events, where cues and contexts associated with drug use may themselves become reinforcing, contributing to the continued use and eventual misuse of the drug. As psychoactive drugs tend to be more positively reinforcing than other behaviours, they begin to exceed the value of other social rewards like school, work, friends, and fam-ily, leading to an aberrant narrowing of behavioural actions. In vulnerable individuals, escalation of drug use over time also produces molecular neuroadaptations that further support the development of addiction. When a person becomes physically and psycho-logically dependent, any attempt to stop or even decrease drug use leads to withdrawal and negative emotional states, producing negative reinforcement that further reinforces and thus perpetuates drug use (Edwards, 2016).

Tolerance is also an important process within learning theory and is associated with habituation. Habituation is seen through reduced responses to a drug either because of prior exposure to the substance or because of the presentation of environmental stimuli that in the past have reliably predicted the presence of the drug. Opioid-dependent per-sons, under specific circumstances, have been observed to respond to the mere anticipa-tion of drug effects, to an injection of saline, or to an opioid injected while an antagonist is present, as if they had actually received an opioid drug (Mirin, 1984).

Another key process within the learning theory paradigm is extinction. Extinction is the process where the link between previously established behaviour is weakened until a point is reached when the behaviour no longer has any reinforcing benefit or purpose. This is what the treatment process attempts to accomplish in terminating an individual's mis-use of a substance. Learning theory holds much promise and insight into understanding how drug misuse develops and why drug use continues, and it has been incorporated into both prevention and treatment initiatives.

Social learning theory provides yet another plausible explanation for drug use and misuse (Bandura, 1986). It states that people will repeat any behaviour that brings them some kind of pleasure or reward and will discontinue any behaviour that brings them dis-comfort or punishment. If a drug brings pleasure or relief in a stressful situation, reduces anxiety or fear, or provides status or popularity in an insecure or lonely situation, its use will become a repeated behaviour. Social learning theory also acknowledges the importance of the negative reinforcement role psychoactive drugs play, withdrawal, which further maintains and facilitates usage. If a person lacks alternative coping strategies, if external stressors are too great to deal with, or if there appear to be no apparent avenues of prob-lem resolution, escape through drug use can be a powerful and extremely easily learned behaviour. Many researchers agree that reinforcement is a critical issue in understanding substance dependency (Donegan et al., 1983; Everitt, 2018; Gifford & Humphreys, 2007; Lewis & Lockmuller, 1990; Peralta & Steele, 2010; Woods & Schuster, 1971).

More recently, Lewis (2017) proposed a developmental learning model of addiction. Lewis begins by stating that changes in the brain arise from repeated learning experiences. These settle into brain habits, which links learning to neurobiological theory, which in turn locks in mental habits. Experiences that are repeated the most often and the most consistently become the most compelling behaviours for humans to continue to repeat. This pattern of behaviour is often labelled as desire, and is evolution's premier mechanism for having humans continue to engage in a repeated behaviour. Addiction, then, is an outcome of learning—but learning that has been accelerated through the ongoing pursuit of an attractive goal: the alteration psychoactive drugs produce on the CNS. As we repeat drug seeking and using behaviour, it typically diminishes alternative behaviours, including alternative methods of coping and stress reduction. However, this is more than just a biological pathway, as there is also an emotional component to the desire to use psychoactive drugs and experience their mind-altering effects. This emotional reaction reinforces drug using on a second level, as does the relatively short time period that the drugs produce their physical and emotional impact on the user. Thus, desire to reexperience the positive reinforcement and/or avoid the negative reinforcement reoccurs after only a few hours, bringing with it both physical and psychological reasons to use again, further reinforcing the learning pattern. For Lewis, addiction is a motivated repetition of behaviour that gives rise to deep learning. This pattern accelerates faster than most learned behaviour and becomes more deeply entrenched than other learned patterns of action, due to the intensity of the attraction that motivates us to repeat drug use—especially as the drug produces negative emotional and physical effects during withdrawal.

PERSONALITY THEORY

Personality traits have long been considered risk factors for drug misuse, while at the same time it has been presumed that drug misuse likewise impacts individual personality traits. Traditional personality theory has categorized personality traits into five categories:

1. Extraversion—talkative, lively, impulsive, risk taking, outgoing versus shy, quiet, conforming, passive
2. Agreeableness—sympathetic, kind, warm, co-operative, sincere, compassionate versus harsh, rude, rough, antagonistic, callous, cold
3. Conscientiousness—organized, systemic, efficient, precise, thorough, practical versus careless, sloppy, absent-minded, disorderly, unreliable
4. Emotional stability—relaxed, unemotional, easy-going, unexcitable versus moody, jealous, possessive, anxious, high-strung
5. Openness to experience—intellectual, complex, philosophical, innovative, unconventional versus simple, conventional, uninquisitive, shallow (Hofstee et al., 1992; Saucier & Goldberg, 1996)

Of these five categories, extraversion has been most closely associated with excessive substance use, particularly the attribute of impulsivity. Impulsivity refers to actions that are poorly conceived, risky, or premature and that may result in unfavourable outcomes for the individual. Drug misusers are considered more impulsive than non-misusers (Rodríguez-Cintas et al., 2016; Rømer et al., 2018). Individuals with high trait impulsivity levels have also been shown to be more sensitive to the positive effects of drug intoxication and more likely to return to drug use (van Well et al., 2015). Recent research has also linked those displaying greater degrees of the personality trait of narcissism as being at greater risk of addiction to psychoactive drugs (Bilevicius et al., 2019; Jauk & Dieterich, 2019). However, the idea of an alcoholic personality was extremely popular well before the development of the five personality dimensions and contributed to the rise in popularity of personality tests for those with addiction issues in the mid-20th century (Cox & Klinger, 1988).

The most popular personality theory of substance misuse views the problem as an expression of abnormal personality traits. The characteristics commonly attributed to a drug misuser include:

- highly emotional with a low frustration tolerance
- nonconformity, impulsivity, and reward seeking
- negative affect and low self-esteem
- immature in personal relationships
- inability to express anger adequately
- ambivalence to authority
- excessive anxiety
- perfectionism and compulsiveness
- rigidity
- feelings of isolation
- sex-role confusion (Barnes, 1979; Cox, 1979, 1987; Cox & Klinger, 1988; Dolan et al., 2007; Dom et al., 2006; Linn, 1975)

This broad list supports Miller's (1983a, 1995) point that alcohol-dependent persons have as broad a range of personality characteristics as do those who are not alcohol dependent, and that no consistent personality pattern has yet to be established with one drug, let alone across the range of psychoactive substances.

Bill Wilson, co-founder of Alcoholics Anonymous, observed that many alcohol-dependent persons had a craving for attention and power, just as many ardent prohibitionists of the time did (Alcoholics Anonymous, 2001). Contrarily, persons with alcoholic personalities have also been characterized as passive and dependent, as reflected by their fixation on an external locus of control, the belief that people and agents other than themselves control behaviours and reinforcements. These individuals tend to have low self-worth, be self-derogatory, and are more likely to be depressed, anxious, and impulsive (Cox, 1988).

A difference between alcohol dependent and pre-alcohol dependent personalities is believed to exist, with distinctive personality characteristics predating the drug dependency, though empirical support is difficult to obtain for this assumption. Impulsivity, independence, and rejection of conventional values have characterized the personalities of persons who later in life developed problems with alcohol and other psychoactive drugs. These people impulsively find gratification through drug use, but they have difficulty working toward long-range goals that will bring enduring satisfaction. It is also claimed that the same personality characteristics that existed among pre-alcohol dependent persons are also apparent among those in treatment for alcohol dependency. However, unlike pre-alcohol dependent persons, those assessed as being addicted to alcohol have low self-esteem and show strong negative affect, particularly depression and anxiety. Although the cognitive-perceptual style of those with alcohol dependency is characteristically different from that of those who are not dependent on alcohol, it is unclear whether this distinctive style is a precursor or a consequence of the use of the drug (Cox, 1988). In essence, what came first: the personality issues or the alcohol misuse?

Another view suggests that substance misuse does not constitute a specific entity. Rather it is the symptom of some underlying psychiatric disturbance. Substance misusers do not differ significantly, diagnostically, from other mental health patients, according to proponents of this theory. Albert Ellis (1995), originator of Rational Emotive Behaviour Therapy (REBT) (see Box 24.1), states that most destructive persons with an addiction suffer from one or more severe personality disorders and that there is an underlying biological tendency to easily overreact or underreact to the stresses and strains of living. As well, most persons with a severe personality disorder come from households where their close relatives were also innately highly disruptive, leading them to experience above-average daily life stressors. According to Ellis, extensive therapy is required for these individuals to deal with their underlying behavioural issues.

Another theory relating to personality was postulated by Robert Cloninger (1987), who attempted to establish a relationship between neurotransmitter levels and personality dimensions, thus linking the biological and psychological dimensions of addiction. As dopamine facilitates the perception of pleasure or excitement, Cloninger states that those who exhibit personality traits of exploration, excitability, impulsiveness, extravagance, and disorderliness have active dopamine systems. Those with lower dopamine activity would register lower in novelty-seeking traits. Likewise, those with inactive serotonin systems would exhibit harm-avoidance behaviours in actions that seek to avoid pain and anxiety. Cloninger believed that individuals with inactive norepinephrine systems would develop strong sentimental attachments, as this neurotransmitter inhibits signals associated with reward.

Despite these varied perspectives on personality theory, the literature generally tends to side with the view that personality does not predict illness. Research continues to attempt to determine if those with certain personality characteristics become drug misusers, or if drug use creates a specific type of personality. Thus, the question remains whether the characteristics precede alcoholism and contribute to its development, or whether the traits are a result of alcohol use, and misuse. One study investigating this began by following 12,600 children from birth until the age of 16, though by that time only 4,600 participants remained. Parents were asked about their children's personalities in the first five years of life, after which the researchers interviewed both the children and their parents. The research team found that the personality traits in toddlers most closely associated with teen alcohol use fell into two categories: (1) emotional instability and relatively low sociability, and (2) high sociability, which may lead to sensation-seeking later in adolescence. Childhood temperament prior to age five was a predictor of adolescent alcohol use problems by age 16, after controlling for both socio-demographic factors and parental alcohol problems. Interestingly there still remained heterogeneity, as the researchers found not one high risk group but two. However, in both groups not all of the children were using drugs problematically, with many remaining abstinent through adolescence (Dick et al., 2013). Thus, there are some differences in the psychological profile of those with a greater risk of misusing drugs and those who do not indicate psychological predisposition to drug use (Fehrman et al., 2019; Raketic et al., 2016). It is also worth noting that while some would like to label those with addiction issues as having an addictive personality, we do not label those with diabetes as having a diabetic personality.

PSYCHODYNAMIC THEORY

This perspective arises from Freudian and post-Freudian thought, though Freud himself did not devote much attention to addiction in his extensive writings, despite his own drug dependency on two stimulants: tobacco and cocaine. Freud's work launched the fields of counselling and psychotherapy, yet given the growing interest in neurobiology, it is not without irony to note that Freud himself was trained as a neurologist. He initially turned to hypnosis to aid his patients in talking about their difficult problems before abandoning this option for psychotherapy. Sigmund Freud was the first to provide a systemic explanation of mental health issues, and his views remain influential, if limited by his historic context. In Freud's perspective, there were three potential explanations for all maladaptive behaviour:

1. seeking sensuous satisfaction
2. conflicts among the components of oneself
3. fixation in the infantile past (Kottler & Montgomery, 2010)

Psychoanalysis assumes and accepts the existence of unconscious and dissociated layers in the life of the mind. Freud (1905) did state that alcoholism may be due to the inability to successfully resolve issues among the three components of oneself: (1) the id or instinctual striving for pleasure and/or relief, (2) the superego or conscience, and (3) the ego or coping component of the person. Failure of the ego to resolve issues between conscience and basic instincts can lead to maladaptive coping responses, including use of psychoactive drugs. In Freud's few writings directly pertaining to alcohol misuse, he commented that it could pertain to a fixation at the oral stage of psychosexual development, thus representing the need for the person to obtain immediate oral gratification and pleasure. Early followers of Freud also proposed that all addiction-related behaviours were displacements and re-enactments of early childhood sexual behaviour. This theory evolved to linking addiction to symbolic gratification and oedipal wishes (Bonaparte et al., 1954). Much later in his career, Freud also wrote simply that alcohol was misused by those exhibiting psychopathology to ward off unpleasant feelings (Barry, 1988).

Psychodynamic theory incorporated ideas that were very popular in the mid-20th century, such as denial, justification, rationalization, and intellectualization. This theoretical perspective views the development of addiction as a futile attempt to repair development deficiencies of the self. As a result of these deficiencies, the capacities for regulating tension, for self-soothing, for affect recognition, and for affect consistency are all impaired (Sachs, 2009). Despite the substantive shortcomings of this theory, sensuous satisfaction can apply to any behaviour that brings relief to anxiety, and psychoactive drugs fit very well into this more generalized understanding of sensuality and sexuality. Thus, addiction became generalized with the idea that the voluntary consumption of drugs is initially motivated by the desire for its pleasurable effects. Those who experience unusually strong pleasurable effects from drugs will use them excessively, even to the displacement of normative sexual behaviour, and even when the effects become destructive. The pleasurable effect is usually attributed to relief from anxieties and conflicts or as a substitute for a lack of sexual fulfillment, rather than only direct sensuous satisfaction (Salmon & Salmon, 1977).

Another perspective derived from psychodynamic theory proposes that a block in the emotional development of a child may result in chronic immaturity and a desire to escape from reality, or, alternatively, conflicts among components of the self may lead to substance dependency. This theory emphasizes the importance of parents in shaping an individual's life and meeting a child's needs. If a child's early needs are not met, a deficit may occur that finds resolution later in life through drug use. Psychodynamic theory states that people vulnerable to substance misuse have powerful dependency needs that can be traced to their early years. If an individual's needs are unmet at a young age, they may turn, as they mature, to substances to fulfill them. Although Freud's view is generally centred on sexual fulfillment, it can be applied to addiction as well, as an individual may turn to drugs to fulfill a need that they are unable to do consciously (Barry, 1988). Several studies report that psychodynamic factors create internal conflicts within an individual's psychic structure, which predisposes them to the development, maintenance, and return to drug use (Khantzian, 2003). Studies also assert that psychotherapeutic techniques addressing these internal conflicts can be successful in the cessation of substance use (Woody, 2003).

McClelland and colleagues (1972) countered that addiction could also be viewed as being power based. They interpreted the independence and aggressiveness of many male drinkers as a direct manifestation of a drive for power rather than passivity. They believed that drinking and drug use allowed men to engage in fantasies and feelings of power, and thus it was their sense of powerlessness that led them to misuse drugs. For women, drinking served to reduce rather than enhance fantasies of power, as women who misused substances were more anxious about their femininity (Wilsnack, 1973, 1974). The interconnectedness of sex, aggression, and addiction was also examined by Ahmadi and colleagues (2017) who, not surprisingly, found a relationship between each pairing as well as all three factors in the literature.

Neo-Freudian theorists and practitioners have also argued that the use of drugs allows expression of otherwise repressed tendencies, such as the need for ongoing overt oral gratification or some form of societally suppressed sexuality. The underlying premise remains that drug use relieves unconscious conflicts that individuals cannot deal with at the conscious level. Oral passivity and regression, a lack of security, a replacement for masturbation, internalized conflicts and ego deficits, guilt and unacceptable aggression, leading to desires for self-punishment and sexual denial, have all been proposed by various neo-Freudians to explain drug-dependent behaviour during the first half of the 20th century (Bonaparte et al., 1954; Glover, 1928; Schilder, 1941). However, rather limited empirical research was done then to support these views as the ideas are difficult to conceptualize, and there are ethical implications for studying the concepts, especially as the events that often lead to the misuse of drugs occur many years before the onset of addiction.

Current psychodynamic thinking has returned the core theoretical concept of the pleasure principle. The pleasure principle is viewed as the foundation for understanding human psychological functioning. Contemporary psychodynamic theory states that humans have six instinctual systems: care, lust, play, rage, fear, and panic. Care, lust, and play further the pleasure principle, while rage, fear, and panic generate "unpleasure." Rage, fear, and panic arise in children and youth when parents fail to meet expected obligations. These behaviours include emotional indifference, a lack of emotional availability, emotional abuse, disregard for the safety of the family, inability to financially support the family, and physical aggression and abuse. In families where children are engaged, childhood is excellent and full of pleasure. However, in families where rage, fear, and panic become the dominant instinctual systems, in which unpleasant feelings are constant and inescapable, drugs become a rational mechanism to turn off misery, especially as they also bring pleasure, even if only temporarily. In psychodynamic theory, teenagers are the most difficult addicted population to engage with, as they have just learned how to suffer less and tend to idealize their drug experience and the relief it brings. In psychodynamic theory, individuals who become addicted cannot cope with the constant rage, fear, and panic they feel, and use drugs to turn off these drives. Addiction is viewed as a desperate adaptation to adverse human environments. When one then also considers the economic motivation of the drug industry—recreational, licit, and illicit—the narrative that drug misusers are lying drug abusers, or that getting high is simply a hedonistic activity, is dramatically altered. Instead, drug misusers, who have been using psychoactive drugs since adolescence or even childhood to cut off horrible emotional signals about having been abused, are viewed as acting in a functional if not rational manner. When individuals "get high" it is a behaviour that produces pleasure, but also serves as relief and a temporary escape from traumatic experiences and memories without having to consciously acknowledge unconscious fantasies. Thus, in counselling, the clinician needs to help the service user deal with these drives and to help them in remembering, understanding, and working through past trauma, using words and conscious representations of feelings, memories, and experience to counter the impulse to act addictively (Johnson, 2018).

HUMANISTIC THEORY

Humanistic theory is in part an outgrowth of and response to early Freudian-based theories. This theory, however, examines mental health rather than mental illness. This theoretical perspective, developed by Abraham Maslow (1970), has a much more positive perspective on human motivation and activities. Maslow, who initially trained as an anthropologist, came to believe that all humans strove for critical understanding and empowerment, and a desire for autonomy and independence. His initial model consisted of five distinct stages of human needs that attempt to explain behaviour: physiological, safety, belongingness, self-esteem, and self-actualization. Over the course of his career, he added three additional stages: cognitive needs, aesthetic needs, and transcendence (see Figure 6.1).

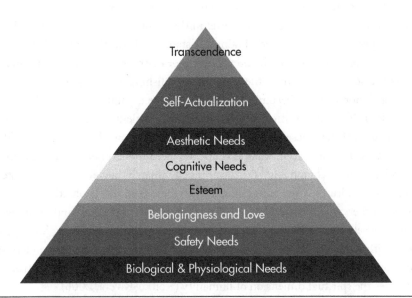

Figure 6.1: Maslow's Enhanced Hierarchy of Needs Model

Sources: Koltko-Rivera (2006); Maslow (1970).

These eight stages can all be directly applied to why drug use begins, is maintained, escalates, stops, and recommences. Stage one in the hierarchy comprises basic human physiological needs, which incorporates all the necessities to maintain life: air, drink, food, sex, and sleep. Physiological needs are the most basic of life's needs, and without the ability to satisfy these core needs, there can be neither personal nor societal advancement. Stage two in the hierarchy includes safety needs, such as the need for health, personal and financial security, as well as the need for familiarity. This second level of need entails the search for a safe, ordered, and secure world with protection from both physical and socially harmful elements. Stage three relates to the need of belonging or, in other words, social and love needs. This includes the need to be able to relate to others, the need for friends and family, and the capacity to develop affectionate, close, personal relationships, including romantic relationships. This category involves not only receiving love but also giving love.

Stage four of Maslow's hierarchy relates to esteem needs, which include the needs required for a stable, positive regard for oneself. This involves not only self-respect, but also respect from others. Esteem needs also consist of the desire for acknowledgment, freedom, importance, independence, prestige, reputation, responsibility, and status. Those searching for esteem needs are seeking feelings of self-confidence and worth. Following this is the first of the additions to the original model, that of cognitive needs. As Maslow applied his original theory, he observed that people also had a need to increase their knowledge. Cognitive needs include the human need to discover, explore, and to learn more about oneself and one's environment. Another addition was that of aesthetic needs, the search for beauty both in nature and in personal artistic expression.

The initial peak of Maslow's final level in the hierarchy was self-actualization; realizing one's personal potential and obtaining a state of self-fulfillment. This was attained through seeking personal growth and achieving peak experiences, though for most people, it is the search rather than the actual accomplishment of this step that is critical. Self-actualization involves becoming what one has the capability of being. It is the need and the desire for self-fulfillment, using one's skills, talents, and experience to maximum benefit both for oneself and others. However, Maslow also added one additional level beyond self-actualization; that of transcendence. The level of self-actualization initially had a spiritual component. With continued research, however, Maslow noted that humans across cultures strove to aid others reach their maximum potential. They reached out to help others in need, thereby securing a larger sense of purpose and meaning. After reaching a level of self-actualization, Maslow states that further striving leads people to connect with a greater whole or a higher truth. This provides a broader understanding of the motivational roots of social progress and human behaviour, such as altruism, and underscores the spiritual dimension of humanity (Koltko-Rivera, 2006).

The humanistic perspective views the primary causes of drug dependency as boredom, frustration, and the inability to reach one's potential because of blockages in Maslow's hierarchy of need fulfillment. When people are denied either access to or the opportunity to meet their next level of need, they turn to drugs to compensate for or escape from their plight. And while drugs can provide an artificial sense of security, in actuality they create greater vulnerability. Humanistic theory also views addiction as a rational protective response to suffering and having one's needs blocked. While biological and other psychological models conceptualize psychoactive drugs as powerful agents that compel individuals to act in self-destructive ways, humanistic theory views addiction as a dysfunctional relationship with substances, developed out of functional, sane attempts to escape a person's suffering. The compulsive use of a psychoactive drug is an attempt to escape pain, blame, shame, and loss rather than being the cause of those affective responses. Humanistic theory considers addiction as a normalized part of the spectrum of human experience and in doing so makes the therapeutic relationship an essential tool in responding to addiction. Individual or group therapy becomes the primary method to remedy drug misuse. Individuals are viewed as much more functional than in psycho-dynamic theory, with greater ability to change and adapt in a positive manner. In the application of this theoretical model, the counsellor focuses on what blocks are impeding a person from realizing their potential. The counsellor's role is to determine what needs are not being met and how drug use satisfies or counterbalances the blockage (Ciovacco & Hughes, 2017).

Humanistic theory has been critiqued for being very weak theoretically, for being overly reductionist, and for not accounting for the origin and nature of the self and human needs. Maslow's original research that examined what makes people successful has been criticized for not being rigorous. Critics also note that Maslow's conclusions did not directly relate to his field of research, resulting in a far too simplistic representation of need. This theory has also been deemed ethnocentric and in-sensitive to cultural differences (Geller, 1982; Hofstede, 1984; Neher, 1991; Smith & Feigenbaum, 2012). Questions have also been raised as to whether a hierarchy exists and if fundamental human needs are truly hierarchical in nature (Cianci & Gambrel, 2003; Wahba & Bridgewell, 1976).

ATTACHMENT THEORY

Attachment has been shown to be an important predictor of relationship quality and well-being. Attachment theory is the study of the universal need for intimate relationships that begins in infancy. From our birth there is an innate motivational-behavioural control system promoting proximity-seeking between infants and caregivers, which in turn provides infants feelings of security. The quality of the attachment relationship arises from the ongoing interactions between the child and the adult (Parolin & Simonelli, 2016). Attachment theory studies the effects of the relationships between people with a focus on long-term emotional bonds, which begin with these early parent-child interactions. Prominent theorists in this area are John Bowlby (1958, 1969), who describes attachment as the lasting psychological connectedness between people, and Mary Ainsworth (1973), who observed what occurred when children ages 12–18 months were separated and then reunited with their mothers. Her work led to the categorization of three major styles of attachment:

1. Secure attachment: When children express distress when separated from their caregivers and joy upon their return. Children with secure attachment know their primary caregivers will provide comfort and reassurance, so they are comfortable seeking them out in times of need. Secure children experience their caregivers' availability, sensitivity, and responsivity.
2. Ambivalent-insecure attachment: When children become extremely and inconsolably distressed when their caregivers leave. This typically occurs in instances where the caregivers are not regularly available, and the child cannot depend upon them to return when the child needs them.
3. Avoidant-insecure attachment: When children avoid the primary caregivers and, when given a choice, do not select the parent over a stranger. This is most commonly the result of neglectful, unpredictable, rejecting, unresponsive, or abusive caregiving that leads to avoidant and anxious behaviour in adulthood (Ainsworth et al., 1978).

To these three stages, Main and Solomon (1986) added a fourth, that of disorganized-insecure attachment. Children who appear disorientated, confused, and even dazed, and who avoid and even resist their caregivers, are placed in this category. This behaviour is typically the result of inconsistent parenting, where caregivers do provide comfort but also invoke fear. This leads the child to display inconsistent attachment patterns, which persist into adulthood and which has been associated with a greater risk of developing an addiction (Cicchetti et al., 1995).

Emotion regulation is a process in which individuals influence the emotions they have, how they are experienced, and how they are expressed. Emotion regulation is another integral part of attachment theory due to the emphasis on adaption to the situation, reduction of distress through seeking an attachment figure, and hyperactivation versus deactivation behaviours that are in response to attachment needs (Bowlby, 1969).

The core idea behind attachment theory is that primary caregivers who are available and responsive to children's needs allow them to develop a sense of security, which some label as love. This then allows the children to explore their environment in a confident manner, knowing they are protected. Children who are securely attached as infants tend to develop stronger self-esteem, and are more sociable and self-reliant as they grow older. They generally become independent and exhibit good school performance. All of these qualities establish a foundation for successful adulthood interactions. Individuals who are more securely attached in childhood tend to have good self-esteem, positive romantic relationships, and the ability to self-disclose to others (Hazan & Shaver, 1987). Failure to form secure attachments early in life can produce a range of mental health issues, including the greater likelihood of turning to psychoactive drugs to achieve a sense of comfort (Ainsworth, 1991; Prior & Glaser, 2006).

Addiction itself has been conceptualized as an attachment disorder, with insecure attachment styles being a major risk factor for the development of addiction. An insecure and unresolved attachment style in adulthood is associated with poor reflective abilities, which can interfere with a parent's ability to consider their child's behaviours and feelings, turning addiction into a generational phenomenon. For parents, and then in turn their children, drugs are used to compensate for an alienated sense of self, to manage fearful and anxious mental states about themselves and others, to regulate emotions and restore comfort, and to find an alternative to attachment functions that should occur through interpersonal relationships (Marshall et al., 2018; Parolin & Simonelli, 2016).

Attachment theory views addiction as an attempt to fill the void resulting from the lack of a secure attachment during childhood, including painful, rejecting, or shaming relationships. As a result, excessive drug use is viewed as an individual's attempt to self-repair psychological deficits and fill the emptiness from childhood. The vulnerability caused by developmental failures and early environmental deprivation leads to an ineffective attachment style as an adolescent and/or adult. Inappropriate attachment behaviours tend to be intensified through the excessive use of psychoactive drugs as observed through problematic regulation of appropriate affect, behaviour, and self-care (Flores, 2001, 2006). A study in India involving 100 female post-secondary students found that women with insecure attachment style were more likely to exhibit distrust and fear and avoid closeness and intimacy in relationships with people around them. This increased risk of alienation put these women at greater risk for developing an addiction themselves (Rathore & Uma, 2019). In another study of attachment, fear of intimacy, and differentiation of self, 158 volunteers, 99 of whom were enrolled in an addiction treatment program, reported higher levels of insecure attachment and fear of intimacy, and lower levels of secure attachment and differentiation of self when compared to a control group (Thorberg & Lyvers, 2006). Similar results were also found in a study of substance-dependent German adolescents (Schindler et al., 2005). A Belgian study of 101 alcohol-dependent in-patients in an addiction treatment facility, who were all parents, displayed abnormal attachment styles and experienced difficulties in securing stable interpersonal relationships (De Rick et al., 2009).

RATIONAL THEORY

The last of the psychological theories to be discussed proposes that some, if not most, people drink alcohol or use other psychoactive drugs without considering or realizing the potential dangers. They are aware of or care only about the positive, short-term effects produced by the substance and generally do not believe they will experience any long-term harm. The theory states that as persons become more knowledgeable and informed about psychoactive drugs, their use of drugs should correspondingly decrease. This theory is based on sound theoretical arguments and empirical outcomes, and the belief that a rational human being will strive toward health and longevity (Allott et al., 1999; Brown, 2001). Health promotion and drug awareness campaigns have been correlated with decreases in drug use. For example, since 1964, smoking rates have dropped by more than half in North America as a direct result of successful education, legislative, and smoking cessation efforts. Education is an essential component in drug use prevention and should be a core component of any treatment practice. School systems now recognize the importance of primary prevention and early intervention, and many school boards now begin their drug education programming in the junior grades (UNODC, 2004). In 2002, Caulkins and colleagues reported that well-developed and delivered school-based substance misuse–prevention programs consistently reduce drug use among adolescents. Likewise, educated health care practitioners can also lead to a decrease in the prescription of psychotherapeutic agents (Ray et al., 1993).

However, the rational model approach does not always work. Health agencies use this approach in developing prevention campaigns with the assumption that being healthy is a driving force among people. However, Järvinen (2012) found that individuals consuming alcohol at higher levels preferred other rationales regarding their use of that drug. Rather than a risk of illness, individuals at higher consumption levels associated alcohol use with socialization, pleasure, and relaxation. A Swedish study found that while short education sessions increased participants' knowledge of alcohol-related risks, it had no impact on their levels of alcohol consumption or binge drinking six and twelve months afterwards (Tinghog, 2014).

In other instances, the rational model can become subverted. In 2011, a warning was issued in Vancouver regarding high-potency heroin and a subsequent increase in fatal overdoses. After the education campaign, semi-structured qualitative interviews were conducted with 18 active heroin injectors to ascertain why, despite being aware of the danger, they did not stop their heroin use. Researchers were surprised to learn that, rather than responding with caution, many users sought out the higher potency heroin. The education campaign was negated by the sales tactics of dealers, the pain and fear of withdrawal, entrenched injecting routines, and the desire for intense intoxication. While the campaign provided accurate information, it did not address the underlying issues pertaining to drug use (Kerr et al., 2013).

Even more concerning is that the rational approach is used by pharmaceutical companies to misinform or at least distract physicians. Pharmaceutical companies covertly influence the publication of research papers (Angell, 2008; Spielmans & Parry, 2010), and many journals now require conflict-of-interest statements from authors along with a disclosure as to who funded their research. Further, it was found that a majority of contributors to past editions of the *Diagnostic and Statistical Manual of Mental Disorders* had consulting contracts with pharmaceutical companies (Cosgrove & Krimsky, 2012; Cosgrove et al., 2006). In addition are the findings of a content analysis of 11 prominent medical journals used by German physicians to keep abreast of new developments in their field. Researchers reviewed 313 journal issues containing drug advertisements, locating 412 articles where specific drug recommendations were made by the authors. Free journals almost exclusively recommended the use of the specified drugs. In contrast, journals financed entirely with subscription fees tended to recommend against the use of the very same drugs. Thus, a distinct bias was found in medical journals that focus on continuing physician education, based on whether the journal was funded by the reader or the advertiser (Becker et al., 2011).

Unfortunately, this is not a new trend. The promotional influence of pharmaceutical manufacturers on the prescribing behaviour of physicians has been noted for nearly half a century. Studies have found that physicians' knowledge of drug properties is more consistent with sales information than with the evidence published in the medical literature. Direct-to-physician promotion of pharmaceuticals has led to the widespread inappropriate use of psychoactive drugs, which in turn has resulted in increased morbidity and mortality for patients. Commercial sources of information for many drugs have consistently overstated their benefits and underestimated their risks, thus demonstrating the utility of the rational model, though not in a positive manner (Kesselheim, 2011). Among the multiple intersecting factors that led to the opioid crisis of the 21st century was the fact that manufacturers were paying some physicians to promote their products in an attempt to induce other physicians to prescribe more of their brand of opioid drugs. Pharmaceutical companies were also marketing patented opioids directly to physicians and this practice was demonstrated by Beilfuss (2019) to have statistically increased the number of opioids prescribed by the targeted physicians.

CHAPTER 7

Sociological Theories

The classification of drugs as licit or illicit is not typically a result of the biological attributes of the substance but rather a social construct. Sociological models not only examine drug use in the context of the entire society, but also how addiction is produced through social practices. Sociological theories hypothesize that larger socio-cultural events influence trends in drug use and that drug misuse does not occur in isolation. Events in the broader environment also need to be considered, such as ceremonies, cultural norms, politics, the political economy, rituals, and the media, as well as the manner in which drugs are regarded and regulated by society. In this chapter we will examine six theoretical explanations for drug use and misuse from a sociological lens:

1. Cultural theories
2. Subcultural theories
3. Deviant behaviour theory
4. Marxist theory
5. Availability-control theory
6. Environmental stress

CULTURAL THEORIES

Perhaps in order to understand Japanese alcohol use from a Japanese perspective, it is important to understand that for many Japanese drinking is their sole hobby, and when asked what their hobby is they will openly say "drinking." At company parties it is custom to keep drinking until your boss stops. Not to drink can be insulting to your colleagues, though I do know some Japanese non-drinkers and I am not sure how they get around the drinking party custom. It doesn't matter what happens while drunk, it is never discussed the next day. Furthermore, drinking alcohol is acceptable in the park, and even on the train. (Heather Dorion, personal communication, 2007)

Culture is a set of thoughts shared by members of a social unit that include common understandings, patterns of beliefs, and expectations. Cultural guidelines are generally unwritten rules of conduct and direction for acceptable behaviour and actions reflecting the morals and values of a specific group. Cultural theory begins with this premise in attempting to describe and explain the process of drug use in relation to societal norms. This perspective moves significantly beyond the simpler disease and related biological models and its predecessor, the moral model, in understanding the process of addiction. Regardless of how potent a psychoactive substance may be, its effects are moderated by the practices, norms, and environmental context of the user (Waldorf et al., 1991).

The use of psychoactive substances and how their use is interpreted is affected by culture. Common patterns that emerge across cultures are drug use for healing or medical care (e.g., morphine for surgery), customary regular use (e.g., coffee during work breaks), intermittent special occasion use (e.g., wine at weddings), and excessive use (e.g., addiction to recreational, prescribed, and illicit drugs). Cultural norms both encourage and discourage use and misuse, with these norms defining what is or is not considered problematic drug consumption within a group. Cultural factors also shape responses to substance use, including the social handling of problematic situations and persons. Drinking and other drug use are so culturally prominent that they serve as markers that distinguish one culture from another (Room, 2015).

Socio-cultural theorists support the demystification of substance use and the study of drugs within an integrated life model. As early as 1943, Horton asserted that the primary function of alcohol in a culture was to reduce anxiety. Thus, substance misuse would be more prevalent in societies where anxiety abounded and where few alternatives to drinking alcohol and using other psychoactive drugs as tension-releasers existed. These societies would also exhibit the highest rates of intoxication. Bales (1943) built and expanded on Horton's premise using cultural and cross-cultural studies. He stated that cultures influence alcohol use in three distinct ways:

1. by the degree to which they operate to bring about acute needs for adjustment of inner tensions such as guilt, suppression, aggression, conflict, and sexual tension in their members;
2. by the attitudes toward drinking that they produce in the members, seen in the information exchange, including advertising; and
3. by the degree to which the culture provides substitute means of satisfaction beyond substance use in the form of positive alternative lifestyle options.

Four distinct cultural patterns of drug use have been identified (Schutten & Eijnden, 2003). The first are abstinent cultures, where the overall attitude toward drugs, including alcohol, is negative and all alcoholic beverages are forbidden. Middle Eastern nations, such as Saudi Arabia, typify this pattern. The second are ambivalent cultures, where the attitude toward alcohol use is positive in social settings but negative in others. The African nation of Morocco is an example of this cultural pattern. Morocco is a democratic Islamic nation that has a Parliament, but where the hereditary king's decisions supersede Parliament. Islam forbids the drinking of alcohol, but it is widely available throughout the nation. Along with the availability of alcohol in hotels and upscale restaurants in the larger urban centres, wine and beer can be bought from liquor stores and supermarkets and even in small communities in the Atlas Mountains. Likewise, while marijuana is an illicit drug, it is openly cultivated and is a major economic vehicle in the north of the nation, where other cash crops are difficult to grow.

Permissive cultures are ones where the use of alcoholic beverages and other intoxicants (e.g., cannabis) is acceptable, though a negative attitude toward public impairment remains, such as Canada. Finally, ultra-permissive cultures are those where the attitude is permissive toward both drinking and alcohol-related problems. This last model is most likely to be observed in a culture that is experiencing a rapid social change, especially where there is a heavy economic interest in alcohol production and distribution. The most recent example of this is what has occurred in Russia since its attempted transition to a free market economy and its retrenchment under the protracted leadership of Putin.

Cultures tend to have lower rates of alcohol problems when the rules governing the use of substances are clear, uniform, and prohibitive with specific social sanctions associated with use; when members of the culture are exposed to alcohol at an early stage and observe adults using alcohol in moderate amounts in settings that discourage the use of the drug as an intoxicant, such as at meals or during religious ceremonies; and when the excessive use of alcohol, including drunkenness, is uniformly discouraged and proscribed (Whitehead & Harvey, 1974). Examples of this pattern of drug use are the traditional Chinese and Jewish communities.

Boyd (1983) contrasted the difficulties Chinese policy makers of the early 20th century had in attempting to curb opium use with those of a neighbouring nation, India, which had far fewer problems with opium despite an even longer history of use. The difference according to Boyd was that in India, opium had been employed for centuries for medicinal and ceremonial purposes, while in China, it did not have the same historic or cultural uses and had first been used as a recreational substance. The use of opium had become so well integrated into Indian society that it was not seen as a social problem and rarely caused a debilitating dependency, a situation that continues today despite the enormous population of that nation. Similar to China, North American society experiences problems with most psychoactive drugs because there is no clear cultural consensus on use. Contemporary North American culture allows and even encourages the ingestion of psychoactive drugs for personal use and for the attainment of quick physical and emotional pain relief. The use of drugs is poorly integrated, with attitudes toward drug use being ambivalent and inconsistent. People tend to drink one way with members of the family, another way when with business associates, and yet a different way at a party with friends and strangers.

Cultural theory also considers the role of media in the development of drug use, misuse, and addiction. Marketing cues may influence the path that individuals take both toward becoming addicted as well as moving away from maladaptive consumption and addiction. Beginning in the 1930s, the tobacco industry paid prominent movie stars, such as Gary Cooper, Joan Crawford, Clark Gable, Carole Lombard, Barbara Stanwyck, and Spencer Tracy, $10,000 per year to promote their product (Lum et al., 2008). A 2005 study of 6,500 children reported that of the 10 percent who were smokers, nearly 40 percent stated they tried smoking as a result of the way it was portrayed in the movies (Sargent et al., 2005). As well, both tobacco and alcohol consumption rates have been linked to advertising tactics and specific product exposure in videos and movies, which, despite policy changes, continue to target adolescents (Barker et al., 2018; de Bruijn et al., 2016; Davis et al., 2019; Hafez & Ling, 2005; Ota et al., 2008; Snyder et al., 2006; White et al., 2017; Wilkinson et al., 2009).

All verbal and visual alcohol references were recorded in an examination of 46 hours of televised British professional football (soccer) matches. An average of 111 visual references per hour or about two per minute were detected, typically through sponsorship signs in the stadium, on uniforms, and through actual verbal references to alcohol during the broadcast (Graham & Adams, 2013). The average annual number of alcohol ads seen by youth watching television in the United States increased from 217 in 2001 to 366 in 2009, approximately one alcohol ad per day. During the same time period, youth were 22 times more likely to see an alcohol product ad than an alcohol company-sponsored "responsibility" promotion warning against underage drinking and/or alcohol-impaired driving. Exposure to alcohol advertising influences underage drinking and the development of alcohol-related problems (Center on Alcohol Marketing and Youth, 2012). Another American study found that the overall exposure to brand-specific alcohol advertising was a significant predictor of underage youth alcohol brand consumption, with youth ages 13 to 20 more than five times more likely to consume brands that advertise on national television and 36 percent more likely to consume brands that advertise in national magazines compared to brands that don't advertise in these media. Likewise, correlation between exposure to cannabis in popular music and early cannabis use among urban American adolescents has been found (Primack et al. 2009).

SUBCULTURAL THEORIES

Subcultural theories take a slightly different approach to explaining psychoactive drug use than do cultural models, though they also view the environment as playing a large role in determining whether a person will drink or take drugs. However, this model places greater emphasis on the significance of a variety of specific psychosociological variables in determining the extent of the drug use within a specific population. For example, to become a problem drinker, a culture must permit drinking, and heavy drinking at least occasionally, before the individual is in a position to become a problem drinker. Consumers of alcohol often become conditioned at an early age to expect that alcohol or other psychoactive drugs can do great things for them. Fisher and Harrison (1997) indicated that Irish-Americans were a classic example of this pattern.

Lawson and colleagues (1983) reported that 30 percent of children with parents who were alcohol-dependent themselves developed alcoholism, compared with 5 percent of children with parents who used alcohol moderately and 10 percent of children whose parents abstained. While this is also a potential argument for a genetic model, the fact that those children whose parents did drink but in a non-problematic manner had lower rates of alcoholism than abstainers better supports a subcultural orientation. Lawson (1992) reported that disengaged, rigid families who are conflict-orientated and repressed, along with moralistic families, were the most likely to produce children who later developed an addiction to alcohol.

A distinct subculture that silently emerged in the 20th century with an above-average consumption of drugs involves post-secondary students. Throughout North America, as well as in Western Europe, high volumes of alcohol consumption and risky single-occasion drinking occur among college and university students. This consumption is associated with considerable harm to both those who consume the alcohol and their fellow students. Male students in particular tend to consume alcohol more often and in higher quantities. Consumption typically occurs during social gatherings for social enhancement, social camaraderie, and tension reduction. Students without family obligations and those living alone, with roommates, or in areas with a high density of students are more likely to consume alcohol in higher quantities and to engage in higher risk behaviour, as are those of greater socio-economic status. Students who consume excessive amounts of alcohol also tend to overestimate the extent of their fellow students' alcohol consumption (LaBrie et al., 2007; Wechsler et al., 2000; Wicki et al., 2010).

In a study examining young American adults, seven distinct subcultures were identified, three of which were associated with specific music genres. Young adults who did not fall into a music categorization—homebody, young professional, or religious—had the lowest probability of being regular substance users. Those who were part of the generic social/partier subculture were more likely to use alcohol, marijuana, tobacco, and e-cigarettes compared to the other subcultures. Those who identified as alternative were more likely to be current users of marijuana and illicit drugs, while those who belonged to the country group were the most likely to be users of cigarettes and smokeless tobacco. Those belonging to the hip-hop subculture were more likely to be current users of marijuana and e-cigarettes (Moran et al., 2019).

Atkinson and Sumnall (2016) examined young women in the United Kingdom who participated in a subculture of intoxication, and the way they pursued pleasure and friendship was quite distinct from young male drinking culture. Women's drug use behaviour remains more scrutinized and stigmatized than male use, and that is something that has not changed over time. However, the emergence of social media has allowed for different forms of self-expression than have been available to past generations. The intersection of social media, drug use, contemporary ideals of femininity, and displays of hyper-sexuality has led to the practice of uploading drinking photographs to demonstrate popularity, enhance social standing, and develop a sense of belongingness. The women in Atkinson and Sumnall's study invested large amounts of time and energy in developing and monitoring displays of their drinking behaviour on social media sites, illustrating intoxication and hyper-sexual appearances that challenged traditional presentations of femininity.

A second subcultural theory proposes that there are people who feel alienated from their own particular society and have no sense of belonging. This alienation prohibits them from feeling bound by society's rules governing drug use, and they therefore have a higher risk of developing a dependence on drugs (Rankin, 1978). Supporting this are animal studies that found that leaders of groups are less likely to take drugs than are their subordinates (Kuhar, 2002). Both cultural and subcultural theories view the remedy for drug misuse as a unification of cultural norms and societal expectations. Research in this field continually points to an increase in drug use when cultural norms and expectations begin to break down.

There have been a few studies that empirically support this theory. One examined enlisted members of the American navy and found that they had a far greater use of alcohol than did either civilian members or the general population. Several issues specific to the navy were found to contribute to problem drinking, according to the study, including the young age of recruits, alternating periods of exertion and boredom within the role, and a culture that emphasizes drinking as a mechanism for bonding, recreation, and stress relief (Ames et al., 2009). Similarly, the California Department of Health Services (2005) found that smoking overall had decreased over the years in the state except among some very specific subcultures, including Korean men, members of the lesbian, gay, bisexual, and transgender community, and members of the armed forces. Immigrants from India and China were found less likely to smoke, though their children born in the United States had a rate of use closer to the mean.

A third variant of subcultural theory arises from the ongoing criminalization of drug use in response to the "War on Drugs" and the complex manner in which social, political, and environmental factors interact in creating culture. By criminalizing large segments of specific subgroups because of their use of drugs, criminal activity within these subcultures becomes not only normalized but also creates a sense of social cohesion. Thus, naturalizing illegal activity within these groups and the violation of society's rule of law in this one area erodes adherence to society's rules in general. Further, in groups where production or distribution of illegal drugs has become a primary means of economic survival, social cohesion is created along with ties of loyalty and reciprocity to the group and its behaviours, including violence, rather than to the larger society's rules of conduct. This is further solidified if the subculture is socially vulnerable due to structural and oppressive factors that support drug use within the community. These factors include less education, less access to employment, and greater risk of violence in the community, which is of course linked to the greater use and distribution of illegal drugs. Thus, drug issues need to be addressed by policies that deal with social exclusion, such as not being part of the broader public discussions, the lack of access to existing services, the lack of income to satisfy basic needs, and the lack of employment options other than from participating in the underground economy (Briones et al., 2013).

DEVIANT BEHAVIOUR THEORY

A third theoretical explanation that some sociologists have proposed to explain drug use is through deviant behaviour or delinquency. Becker (1963) argued that deviant behaviour is defined as the failure to obey group rules. This orientation emphasizes the fact that many users are individuals who are rejected and separated from the mainstream of society. A person may originally attract attention through some unusual or rebellious act, such as minor crime, public mischief, or illicit drug use, which can also include underage drinking or the use of tobacco. If this behaviour meets with a significant negative reaction from the surrounding society, the individual can be forced into an isolated lifestyle, and drug dependency may result or be maintained and escalate (Topalli, 2005). What is critical to understand is why some behaviour is socially constructed as deviant and who benefits from this definition, as nothing in society has an inherent meaning; rather, it is given meaning. This theory underscores the fact that a diagnosis of alcoholism or drug addiction is a label and a negative subjective judgment made in relation to societal standards of normality. This judgment is contingent on factors that diverge from culture to culture, and the classification of addicted persons can depend on a range of factors, including but not limited to age, ethnicity, geographic location, leisure pursuits, sex, sexual orientation, social status, or even the drug of choice. Thus, the notion of deviance is a social construct, not a quality of the act a person commits but rather a consequence of how the dominant group interprets the act and sanctions the persons engaged in the action (Becker, 1963).

The social construction of labels in society occurs mainly through the mass media, which shapes our individual and collective consciousness by organizing and circulating the discrete knowledge individuals have, and the contexts, of their everyday lives (Adoni & Mane, 1984; Goode & Ben-Yehuda, 1994). The media can create a panic by leading citizens to believe that the behaviour of deviants, in this case drug users, poses a substantial threat to society, such as through a crack cocaine, crystal meth, or OxyContin epidemic, depending on the era and the context. The larger society then persecutes such drug users, treating them with neglect or hostility—often both. This increases the negative labelling and misrepresentation of the deviant group in the media, as evidenced by the use of the slang term "hillbilly heroin" to refer to OxyContin. Rather than seeing the person who uses drugs as a colleague, friend, or parent, society comes to see the person as an object, an addict. This is how such persons then begin to view themselves, which allows them to engage in additional behaviours labelled as deviant.

The use of marijuana in Jamaican culture, in contrast to its historic use in continental North America, is an example of differential drug use by culture. Khat is a licit drug in Africa and Arabia and yet was prohibited in Canada with no parliamentary debate. Similarly, coca leaves have been used for thousands of years in South America and can be purchased in markets, much like caffeine in North America. Yet with its refinement and introduction to developed nations, a major drug misuse problem emerged, often appearing to overwhelm other psychoactive drug issues that in absolute numbers are still a much greater social and health problem.

The idea of deviant behaviour has long been associated with specific geographic environments, particularly neighbourhoods in urban areas that have experienced deprivation. Social capital is a concept that examines the relationships among people who live and interact in a society, as well as in smaller designated spaces, that allow them to function effectively together. Social capital views social relations as vital resources that lead to the development of human capital (e.g., education, knowledge, ability, skills, creativity of an individual). The greater the social capital of a neighbourhood, the greater its human capital. Social capital is associated with the ideas of democracy, trust in political institutions, economic wealth, physical and mental health, and violent crime. A national Swedish cohort study examined the relationship between drug misuse and social capital and reported that the lower the level of social capital in a neighbourhood, the greater the risk of drug misuse among its residents (Sundqist et al., 2016). As social capital decreases, the more likely a community or neighbourhood is to be labelled and characterized as deviating from social norms, especially when there is visible drug use. The classic Canadian example of this is the Downtown Eastside of Vancouver, particularly East Hastings, which has become synonymous with the opioid crisis.

MARXIST THEORY

As with Freudian-based psychodynamic theory, Marxist models have been applied to almost every social problem. Marxism has as its central focus the relationship between human labour and capital, the means of production, and the class struggle that Marx examined from slavery to the age of feudalism to the establishment of guilds—the predecessors of the union movement of the late 19th and 20th centuries. For Marx, oppression applied to gender, race, religion, but most importantly, to class. It entailed not just exploitation, but also marginalization. In Marxist philosophy individuals' problems cannot be separated from their environment, or their class status. A Marxist discussing substance misuse would claim that human problems are the direct result of the economic and sociological structure of a culture. Specifically, any society that denies equal opportunities to all citizens or allows one powerful group to exploit less powerful or powerless groups will witness the development of many social problems. These will be most evident in, but not the exclusive domain of, those most greatly disenfranchised. These social problems are the direct result of the stresses and anxieties of an unjust society that does not permit all citizens the right, ability, or opportunity to flourish (Marx, 2004).

Social problems can take many forms: aggression, crime, mental illness, or drug dependency and addiction. The specific problems that a given individual has depend on the environmental circumstances that are prevailing at the time or which exerted a major influence in the past. Thus, personal predisposition can be a factor in determining whether a person develops schizophrenia, an addiction, or becomes physically abusive. The intent of this theory is to take the blame and responsibility that has historically exclusively focused only on the failings of an individual and focus it on those external environmental factors that created the context for the development of drug use or other social issues. This has particular relevance in North America, where an underlying factor in the permitting or prohibiting of drugs was the association of the drug with a threatening foreign culture and/or unruly members of the working class, particularly those who opposed capitalist interests through labour unrest and unionization (Stevens, 2010).

For many critics, the one common concern is how Marxism works on an individual level in addressing the substance use and misuse of the affluent. For Marx, the one true human need was to work, to labour. He claimed that what differentiates humans from animals is our human spirit, our ability to imagine and create our work and to use our intelligence to devise and understand our purpose. Those who did not have any reason or need to contribute to the means of production turned to drugs in their boredom, in a search for some type of meaning in their lives (Marx, 2004). A variety of studies in the United States have indicated that more affluent adolescents were actually more likely to use alcohol and other drugs than were peers from lower socio-economic communities. Disposable income, disconnected families, and pressure to succeed all contributed to drug use among affluent young people, as did the simple ability to buy fake identification and the drugs themselves (Wested, 2007). It is also critical to recognize that wealth alone does not insulate people from unjust societal conditions. Marxism is a philosophy, not merely a political idea. Marxists believe that a systems change is required to address problems such as drug misuse. Despite a tendency to be classified and dismissed as a theory of rhetoric, Marxist views do have some validity and a role in providing a global perspective on substance dependency, as well as in critiquing other theoretical perspectives.

The other value in Marxist thought in terms of addiction theory is that it forces us to consider not only demand-side issues but also supply-side issues. Addiction became a moral issue in North America with the intersection of Protestantism and early capitalism. From this arose the notion of renouncing drinking in favour of piety, workplace productivity, and economic gain (Reinarman, 2005). Alcohol consumption was labelled problematic as it was associated with organized labour and its challenge to the status quo of early capitalist enterprises. Dry zones were created around work sites, and company towns outlawed taverns and alcohol (May, 1997; Petersen, 1987).

Historically, drugs have played a prominent role in world economics, as discussed in Chapter 3. Alcohol and tobacco fueled economic growth in the United States, the Caribbean, and parts of South America during the 1700s, with high profit because slaves provided the vast majority of labour. With increased wealth, plantation owners from Virginia to Brazil were able to buy even more slaves to further increase their profits and further drive the slave trade (Crane, 1980; Curto, 2011; McCusker, 1970). In the 20th and 21st centuries, the drug trade has been a consistent means to obtain money for weapons in armed conflicts against economically superior aggressors, be it in Southeast Asia, Central and South America, or the Middle East (McCoy, 2003; Otis, 2014). This is not only a historic issue, however, but one whose practice continues to the present day.

Poverty is a complex and pervasive issue worldwide. More than half of the developing world lives in poverty, with over 1 billion people worldwide living on approximately $1 CAD a day with another billion earning between $1 and $2 dollars. Thus, when there is a chance to become more economically independent or provide for oneself and one's family, it is hardly surprising many in developing nations take that opportunity. Nations with lower gross domestic products (GDP), such as Afghanistan, Colombia, and Yemen, tend to be illicit drug exporters whereas affluent nations like Canada, the United States, and those in Western Europe tend to be illicit drug importers. Countries in the middle of the list, such as Brazil and India, which are also importers, also tend to be nations with greater economic disparities between rich and poor with a small middle class (Keefer et al., 2008; United States Department of State, 2019). Thus, Marxist theory directs us to examine the roles that poverty, social exclusion, and the lack of meaning in one's labour play in increasing the risk of addiction, on both the demand and supply side of the drug equation.

AVAILABILITY-CONTROL THEORY

As with many of the previous models discussed, the availability-control or consumption model was initially built around alcohol use. However, like the others, it can also be equally applied to the range of psychoactive substances. In most contemporary societies where alcohol is consumed, some type of control is exercised over its use. However, most governments have moved beyond the informal rules that underlie the cultural and subcultural theories and introduced formal substance-control laws.

The most basic law of economics links price to demand. Thus, logically, as the price of alcohol or any other drug increases, consumption should decrease, particularly among those with the least amount of disposable income, which includes teens and young adults. A series of international studies conducted during the 1970s found similar results in the consumption pattern of alcohol across numerous different cultures (Bruun et al., 1975). The availability theory of alcohol-related problems asserts that the greater the availability of alcohol in a society, the greater the prevalence and severity of alcohol-related problems in that society. This research confirmed the earlier pioneering work of French demographer Sully Ledermann (1956), who postulated that a change in the average consumption of alcohol in a population is likely to be accompanied by a change in the same direction in the proportion of heavy consumers (Figure 7.1). Since heavy use of alcohol generally increases the probability of physical and social damage, the average consumption should be closely related to the prevalence of such damage in any population. Any measures that

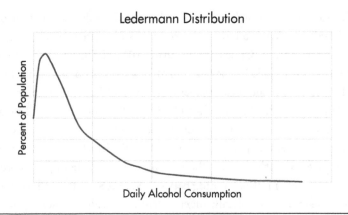

Ledermann Distribution

Figure 7.1: Ledermann Alcohol Consumption Distribution

Source: Adapted from Ledermann (1956).

may be expected to affect overall consumption, such as those regulating the availability of alcohol, are also likely to affect the prevalence of alcohol problems, and hence should be a central consideration in any prevention programming (Boniface et al., 2017; Schmidt & Popham, 1978; Skog, 1980).

In the Ledermann distribution equation, while the absolute number of drinkers changes and the proportion of those who actually drink varies, the pattern remains consistent across the different populations studied. Changes in the proportion of the drinking population who are at risk or who may be defined as problem drinkers are directly related to changes in the average alcohol consumption. The higher the average consumption, the greater the proportion of drinkers who develop an alcohol dependency. If the attitudes to alcohol use and intoxication are liberal, then the average consumption is largely dependent on availability. If there are no limits on supply and distribution, the theory states that the main social factor effecting changes in average alcohol consumption will be changes in the relative cost of alcoholic beverages. For example, in Finland, the impact of alcohol tax cuts in March 2004 was significant, resulting in an estimated eight additional alcohol-positive deaths per week, a 17 percent increase compared with the weekly average of 2003 (Koski et al., 2007), along with an increase in head injuries and deaths from head injuries (Vaaramo et al., 2012). In Norway, a one-hour extension of bar closing hours led to an increase of an average 20 violent incidents on weekend nights per 100,000 people per year (Rossow & Norström, 2012). In contrast, when five local councils (municipalities) in England brought in restrictions regarding the licensing of alcohol establishments, they reported an average reduction in alcohol-related hospital admissions (6 percent), violent crimes (4 percent), and sexual crimes (5 percent) (de Vocht et al., 2017).

Likewise, when British Columbia allowed the privatization of liquor stores in 2003, there was a rapid increase in the total number of liquor stores per 1,000 residents. The increase in the number of outlets was followed by an increase of alcohol-related deaths of 3.25 percent for each 20 percent increase in private store density (Stockwell et al., 2011). A follow-up study found that a 10 percent increase in the average minimum price for all alcoholic beverages was associated with a 31.7 percent reduction in alcohol attributed deaths, with the pattern holding for two to three years after the price increases. Further, a 10 percent increase in the number of private liquor stores in British Colombia was associated with a 2.5 percent increase in acute deaths attributed to alcohol, and a 2 percent increase in total alcohol-attributed mortality (Zhao et al., 2013). A similar trend was reported in Ontario after it eased restrictions on where alcohol could be purchased and found the number of emergency room visits increased to 4.4 times more than the rate of overall visits between 2003 and 2016, with the greatest increase among those aged 25–29 and women (Spithoff, 2019). This supports existing research that had found that the greater alcohol outlet density, the greater alcohol consumption and related harms, including health, injury, crime, and violence (Campbell et al., 2009; Connor et al., 2010). In contrast, alcohol-related disease mortality declined by 7.0 percent after a 1990 tax increase for spirits and beer in New York State (Delcher et al., 2012). It has been estimated that doubling the tax on alcohol in the United States would reduce alcohol-related mortality by an average of 35 percent, traffic crash deaths by 11 percent, sexually transmitted disease by 6 percent, violence by 2 percent, and crime by 1.4 percent per year (Wagenaar et al., 2010).

To reduce alcohol-related problems, the average consumption of a group must be changed. Availability-control theory recommends raising the price of alcoholic beverages relative to disposable personal income to reduce the rate of alcohol-related health problems so that those who drink within recommended limits are hardly affected, while heavy drinkers, who cause the most alcohol-related harm, pay the most. Minimum unit pricing and discount bans could save hundreds of millions every year in health care costs, crime, and employment costs. Policies that lead to increases in the prices of cheaper drinks available in bars, clubs, and supermarkets promise the greatest impact in terms of crime and accident prevention, primarily by reducing the consumption of 18- to 24-year-old binge drinkers (Delcher et al., 2012; Meier, 2008). Other methods of reducing consumption include:

- raising the drinking age
- controlling the number of outlets distributing alcohol
- reducing hours of sales
- limiting advertising
- sobriety checkpoints
- lowered legal blood alcohol content (BAC) levels for driving
- administrative licence suspension for those close to the legal BAC limit
- graduated licensing for novice drivers
- screening and brief interventions for risky drinkers (Babor et al., 2003; Chaloupka et al., 2002; Kypri et al., 2006; National Alcohol Strategy Advisory Committee, 2015; Patra et al., 2012; Wagenaar et al., 2009)

The decrease in Canadian smoking rates, prior to vaping, have also been directly cor-related with the country's high cigarette taxes and restrictions on access in terms of strictly enforcing age of purchase. This includes a program urging retailers to ask for identifica-tion of anyone looking less than 25 years of age even though it remains legal to purchase tobacco products at age 19. Similarly, when Utah increased its tobacco tax in 2010 from $0.695 per pack to $1.70 USD, cigarette sales dropped by nearly 10 million packages, or 15 percent of total consumption. It was predicted that approximately 13,000 people would quit smoking after the tax was raised, but actual figures indicate that closer to 19,000 one-pack-a-day smokers had quit. Calls to the state-run tobacco quit line increased by more than 150 percent in the first year the tax increase was instituted (Gehrke, 2011). Similarly, in New York City, when taxes were increased along with prohibiting smok-ing indoors, tobacco use fell 19 percent, while in Oregon a combination of taxation and increased education led to a decrease of 11 percent in tobacco purchasing (Centers for Disease Control and Prevention, 1999, 2007).

Sanctioning the sale of drugs to reduce addiction problems is not a new idea. Even before the great alcohol prohibition experiment, Great Britain attempted to keep her North American colonists in line by restricting activities such as gambling, which was associ-ated with public drinking, and requiring taverns to also provide food and lodging. When extending the model to illicit drug use, society tends to see increases in drug use and drug problems with increases in the availability and distribution network of drugs. The rise in prominence of cocaine can be partially explained by this theory. After Colorado legalized the recreational use of cannabis, it moved from seventh (10.4 percent) to second (12.7 per-cent) in per capita use in the United States, a 22 percent increase in those acknowledging use of the drug in the month prior to the survey (United States Department of Health and Human Services, 2014). The opioid crisis in the United States has been linked in part to physicians who received direct payment from pharmaceutical companies for prescribing these drugs. Doctors who received opioid-specific payments prescribed 8,784 more opioid daily doses (oxycodone, hydrocodone, and fentanyl) per year than did their peers who received no such reimbursement (Nguyen et al., 2019). The availability-control theory not only provides a good model of how and why alcohol and other drug-related problems arise, but also provides a series of solutions for dealing with this social issue. However, not only supply but also demand must be decreased if one is to fully respond to both local and global issues of addiction.

ENVIRONMENTAL STRESS

The impact of stressful life events has been widely acknowledged to be associated with drug misuse (McCabe et al., 2016). However, it is not just individual stressors that have this effect, but the entire context within which individuals live. Environmental stress and deprivation increase vulnerability to substance misuse in humans and promote drug-seeking behaviour in animal models (Boivin et al., 2015). Even neurobiologists have begun to concede that the environmental context combines with and even shapes genetic factors in influencing the development of drinking behaviours and drug use disorders (Enoch, 2011, 2012; Young-Wolff et al., 2011). The studies discussed in Chapter 1 involving soldiers returning from Vietnam speak directly to the role of the environment in inducing drug use and addiction (Robins et al., 2010; Roffman, 1976).

In the 1960s a device was created at the University of Michigan that allowed rats and other test animals to self-inject heroin. A needle, which was connected to a pump via a tube running through the ceiling of a modified Skinner box (see Figure 7.2), was implanted in the veins of rats, allowing them to inject themselves with the drug simply by pressing a lever. By the end of the 1970s, hundreds of experiments using similar apparatus had indicated that rats, mice, monkeys, and other captive mammals would willingly self-inject large amounts of various psychoactive drugs, including amphetamines, cocaine, and heroin (Woods, 1978).

However, when one examines a Skinner box, it is easy to observe that it is a cramped, minimalist environment with few behavioural options available for a caged animal, especially ones with implanted needles tethered to a self-injection apparatus. As well, most animals are social creatures, especially rats, and in these experiments, they were isolated and removed from direct contact with other members of their species. The question was posed as to whether the animals would self-inject drugs at the same rate in a more natural environment (Goldstein, 1979).

In responding to this question, Canadian psychologist Bruce Alexander truly brought to light the role of stressful social environments in creating addiction. Alexander and his colleagues examined the role of social isolation and stress on drug use in an extensive study undertaken at Simon Fraser University during the 1970s and 1980s. These became known as the "Rat Park" experiments and even served as the subject of a comic book (www.stuartmcmillen.com/comics_en/rat-park). Each Rat Park was approximately

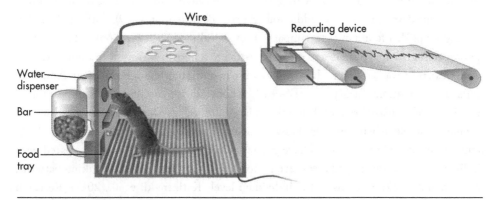

Figure 7.2: Skinner Box

Source: Lilienfield et al. (2011, p. 244).

200 times larger than a typical Skinner box and featured a peaceful forest scene painted on its plywood walls. Empty tins, wood scraps, wheels, balls, bedding of cedar shavings, and even private spaces that allowed for mating and other social interactions were spread throughout the environment (Alexander et al., 1981). The space housed between 16 to 20 rats of both sexes at one time, thus providing companionship without the severe distress caused by overcrowding.

In Rat Park, the rodents had the option of drinking from two water dispensers placed at the end of a tunnel. One contained a morphine solution and the other had no psychoactive substance added. A series of different experiments were designed, including force-feeding heroin to the rats before letting them choose from which dispenser to drink. Regardless of the circumstances, the rats in the open space of Rat Park always consumed less heroin than those in the Skinner box, sometimes up to 20 times less. Some even went through voluntary withdrawal by drinking only the unlaced water. Not all Rat Park inhabitants remained abstinent, but those in the less stressful environment always, without exception, used less. No experimental outcome produced as strong an addiction response in rats living in the natural environment compared to a cage (Alexander, 1985, 1988; Alexander et al., 1981). Alexander concluded that when the stressful social environment was altered, drug use diminished, findings that were subsequently replicated by several other scientists (Bozarth et al., 1989; Schenk et al., 1987a, 1987b; Shaham et al., 1992). Extrapolating his findings to humans, Alexander stated that people can ignore drugs and avoid addiction even when drugs are plentiful if their environment has limited additional stressors. Much of the research with animals on the creation of addiction and its attribution to biological and psychological processes has involved the forced consumption of substances by animals in isolation. This weakens the foundation of many evidence-informed theories because they fail to acknowledge the importance of the social dimension of addiction.

Since the Rat Park study and the findings on soldiers returning from Vietnam, other research has further supported the importance of the environment as a major contributing factor to the development of an addiction (Ruisoto & Contador, 2019). Fothergill and her colleagues (2015) found that the impact of low childhood socio-economic status (SES), poor maternal mental health, and issues adjusting to school in early grades among African American boys was a direct pathway to drug use in mid-adulthood. For African American girls, a combination of early low SES, early school adjustment, and a lack of peers were predictors of increased risk of drug misuse in adulthood. A Danish study linked serious economic problems with increased risk of alcohol misuse (Just-Østergaard et al., 2018), and disadvantaged social groups have greater alcohol-attributable harms compared with individuals from advantaged areas, even after accounting for different drinking patterns, obesity, and smoking status at the individual level (Katikireddi et al., 2017). Research has also found significant connections between negative urban living variables and increasing supply and demand for licit and illicit drugs. These include inadequate urban infrastructure, changes in social and cultural norms, slum environments, and homeless-ness (Morgan & Mall, 2019).

People do not use psychoactive drugs only because they are available, or allowed by society, but also because drugs affect both the mind and the body. Psychoactive drugs alter realities, change perception, and impact one's behaviour, both positively and negatively. However, they ultimately produce extremely rigid modes of behaviour. Thus, addiction is a process, not just an event. It is more than a behaviour and far more than a mere illness, which means that the temporal and spatial elements of addiction must always be con-sidered. Addiction arises at a particular time and in a particular space and is constantly transforming and developing. Even when we know how a drug operates in the brain, we still need to examine the effect on the social environment of that specific brain function (Oksanen, 2013).

Section II Closing Thoughts and Activities

Some of the theories discussed in Section II were able to answer the five questions that define a strong theory, presented at the beginning of this section, better than others. Some that continue to garner support are actually quite poor in terms of their rationale and their empirical support. However, no single perspective discussed in this section provides a definitive explanation of why people become addicted to psychoactive drugs. Even neurobiologists now recognize the importance of the environment and social factors, while no one can deny genetics and brain chemistry have a significant impact on how one person reacts to one drug versus another. This knowledge then forces us to view addiction through a holistic lens, and to acknowledge that addiction truly is a bio-psycho-social phenomenon with various dimensions intersecting to produce this condition. The holistic model that arises from this section encapsulates the various theories and acknowledges the interconnectedness of the bio, the psycho, and the social. This model can be represented in the following manner:

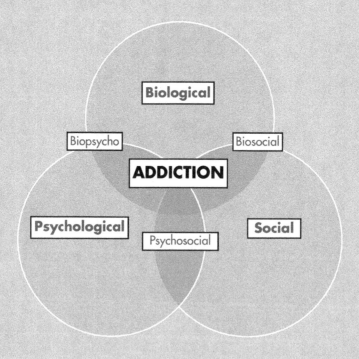

DISCUSSION QUESTIONS

1. Now that you have finished reading Section II, go back and complete Table II.1 again. Was there a change in your scores? Why or why not?

2. Rank the following in order from the most useful to the least useful in terms of explaining drug use: (a) biological theories, (b) psychological theories, and (c) sociological theories. What factors did you consider in creating your three lists?

3. Consider your pre and post scores from Table II.1. How do your values and beliefs influence the way you rank the various theories?

4. Using all the theories presented in Section II, draw your own theoretical model illustrating why people use drugs. Be creative and briefly explain your model.

5. What overarching ideas guided your creation of this model?

SECTION III

PSYCHOACTIVE DRUGS

Psychoactive drugs can be classified in a variety of different ways, one of which is along pharmacologically related groups or families.

1. Depressants (Chapter 8)

    Depressants slow the body's metabolism and the functioning of both the central and peripheral nervous systems. Mood enhancement occurs because of the disinhibition properties of this drug group. While central nervous system depressants slow brain activity, they do not necessarily depress a person's mood. The following drugs are included in this group:
    - barbiturates
    - non-barbiturate sedative-hypnotics
    - benzodiazepines, including Z-drugs
    - inhalants, including solvents, aerosols, and anaesthetics
    - antihistamines
    - alcohol

2. Opioids (Chapter 9)

    Opioids can also be classified as depressants, as they too slow brain and central nervous system activity. In addition to their sedative action, opioids also mask pain and can act as cough suppressants. Opioids are a naturally occurring substance (codeine) but there are also semi-synthetic (heroin) and synthetic (fentanyl) opioids available. This grouping of drugs has been prominent across North America due to the risk of unintended drug poisonings leading to drug overdose deaths.

3. Stimulants (Chapter 10)

    These substances produce a general increase in central nervous system activity, including mood elevation, increased vigilance, and postponement of fatigue. The following drugs are considered stimulants:
    - cocaine
    - amphetamines
    - Ritalin and related drugs to treat attention-deficit/hyperactivity disorder (ADHD)
    - anorexiants
    - decongestants
    - khat

- bath salts (methylendioxypyrovalerone and mephedrone)
- betel
- nicotine
- caffeine

4. Hallucinogens (Chapter 11)

Hallucinogens produce generalized disruption in many parts of the brain, with especially profound effects on perception, cognition, mood, and behaviour. Hallucinogens can be placed into five categories:

- LSD-like
- phenylethylamines: mescaline-like psychoactive agents
- dissociative anaesthetics (PCP and ketamine)
- novel psychoactive substances
- cannabis

5. Psychotherapeutic Agents (Chapter 12)

These drugs are used to treat persons with specific mental health issues. Rather than increasing, decreasing, or disrupting central nervous system activity as other psychoactive agents do, the primary function of psychotherapeutic agents is to return a user to a homeostatic level. There are three categories of psychotherapeutic agents:

- antidepressants
- antipsychotics
- mood stabilizers

The effect of a drug will depend on the amount taken at one time; the past drug experience of the user; the circumstances in which the drug is taken; the place, feelings, and activities of the user; the presence of other people; the simultaneous use of other drugs; and the manner in which the drug is taken. Short-term effects are those that appear rapidly after a single dose and disappear within a few hours or days. Long-term effects are those that appear following repeated use over a longer period of time.

Figure III.1 provides an illustration of the increasing effect of CNS depressants and CNS stimulants as larger amounts are consumed. A person who has not previously used a psychoactive drug begins at a level of homeostasis, or balance. Once a CNS stimulant or depressant is administered, the first step is euphoria, a major reason any psychoactive drug is administered. A distinct pattern then follows for each. For CNS depressants, including opioids, after euphoria a user will experience relaxation, followed by sedation, drowsiness, stupor, unconsciousness, and potentially a coma state and death if sufficient amounts of the drug are taken. With a CNS stimulant, after euphoria, a user would expect to feel excitation, followed by a state of agitation, irritability, and even violence, physical spasms, convulsions, and, if sufficient amounts of the drug are taken or if the substance is administered for a long enough period of time, coma, and potentially death. Hallucinogens are not illustrated in Figure III.1 as their primary effect is not the production of euphoria but rather a disconnect between the physical world and the user's perception of it. However, many hallucinogens do have secondary depressant and stimulant effects, and these would follow the same pattern as illustrated in Figure III.1. Finally, the purpose of psychotherapeutic agents is to bring a user back to a homeostatic or neutral state when they are feeling overly agitated, clinically depressed, or are exhibiting psychotic behaviours. Table III.2, found at the conclusion of this section, presents a summary of the lethal dose levels of several of the drugs from the different groups that will be discussed in the following chapters.

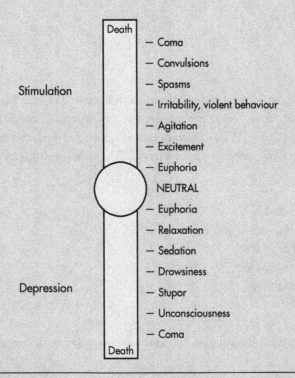

Figure III.1: Effects of Central Nervous System Depressants and Stimulants

CHAPTER 8

Depressants

Depressants slow the body's metabolism and the functioning of both the central and peripheral nervous systems. Mood enhancement occurs because of the disinhibition properties of this drug group. While central nervous system depressants slow brain activity, they do not necessarily depress a person's mood. The following drugs are included in this group:

- Barbiturates*
- Non-barbiturate sedative-hypnotics*
- Benzodiazepines*
- Inhalants/solvents
- Antihistamines
- Alcohol

*These drugs constitute the sedative-hypnotic sub-group within the larger family of CNS depressants.

BARBITURATES

slang: *general:* abbots, barbs, barbies, downers, goofballs, idiot pills, sleepers, stumblers
       amobarbital (Amytal): blues, blue angels, blue clouds, blue devils
       amobarbital (Tuinal): Christmas trees, double trouble, rainbows
       pentobarbital (Nembutal): nebbies, yellows, yellow dolls, yellow jackets
       secobarbital (Seconal): reds, red birds, red bullets, red devils, seccy

Barbiturates are potent central nervous system depressants that are classified as sedative-hypnotics. Sedatives are used to relieve anxiety and to produce a sense of calm, while hypnotics induce sleep and are used to treat insomnia or produce surgical anaesthesia. Initially developed in the late 19th century, diethyl-barbituric acid was first marketed by Bayer in Germany, giving rise to profound changes in the pharmacological approach to treating psychiatric and neurological disorders at the turn of the 20th century. Within the first decade of that millennium, barbiturates became widely used to therapeutically treat individuals with serious neuroses and psychoses, which are now treated with psychotherapeutic agents. Patients would receive intravenous injections, and through the heavy sedation produced, they would be more likely to respond to the suggestions offered through the directive psychotherapy of that era. Those with more severe conditions, such as schizophrenia, were given larger doses to induce calmness and sleep. One barbiturate used for this purpose was sodium pentothal, which would become better known as "truth serum." It was used to sedate prisoners during World War II and have them reveal military facts during the stage of stupor the drug produced. Barbiturates were also used in treating sleep disorders of the general population and for surgical anaesthesia, as well as being the first effective pharmacological tool for the management of epileptic seizures. Over 2,500 barbiturates have been synthesized, with 50 being effective and safe enough to be used clinically. These include amobarbital (Amytal, Tuinal), pentobarbital (Nembutal), and secobarbital (Seconal) (Table 8.1). In small doses, barbiturates relieve anxiety, tension, convulsions, and high blood pressure by producing calmness and muscular relaxation through their effects on the neurotransmitter gamma-aminobutyric acid (GABA).

Table 8.1: Barbiturates Sold in Canada

Generic Name	Brand Name	Medical Use
Allobarbital	Dialog	insomnia
Amobarbital	Amytal Tuinal	insomnia, sedation, seizures
Barbital	Malonal Veronal	insomnia
Butalbital	Fiorinal Lanorinal	tension headaches
Butobarbital	Soneryl	insomnia, sedation
Methylphenobarbital	Prominal	epilepsy, daytime sedation
Pentobarbital	Nembutal	insomnia, sedation, seizures
Phenobarbital	Luminal Gardenal	epilepsy
Secobarbital	Quinalbarbitone Seconal Tuinal	insomnia, sedation, seizures

Source: Data from European Monitoring Centre for Drugs and Drug Addiction (2015).

Barbiturates can also be used to place persons who have suffered severe physical trauma into a coma-like state to aid in their recovery (López-Muñoz et al., 2005).

However, soon after barbiturates were being widely prescribed, many users discovered that these drugs also provided them with a pleasurable intoxicating effect. Larger doses led to impaired judgment, loss of coordination, delayed reaction time, slurred speech, decreased respiration, and impaired short-term memory. These effects made it dangerous to drive a car or perform other complex tasks while consuming these drugs. As well, use of barbiturates during pregnancy has been linked to birth defects and behavioural abnormalities in babies. Despite their widespread use during the first half of the 20th century, no barbiturate succeeded in eliminating the main drawbacks: the development of dependence, and death by overdose and through unmanaged withdrawal. The lethality of barbiturates led to them becoming a common method of suicide attempts and part of the lethal mixture employed in some American states that retain capital punishment for the execution of convicted criminals. Currently, the most common licit use of these psychoactive agents is to prevent and mitigate epileptic seizures, but they remain used to lesser degrees for treating severe headaches, migraines, and other types of related pain, as well as for some gastrointestinal and asthmatic disorders. Phenobarbital is also used in cases of withdrawal syndromes from other sedative-hypnotics with shorter half-lives (López-Muñoz et al., 2005). Barbiturates are so potent that they are used as one component of drug cocktails to aid in medically assisted deaths in Canada, which has led some to label them as death with dignity drugs.

It is also important to know that this class of sedative-hypnotics does not produce completely normal sleep as it disrupts the dream cycle. Users may feel tired and irritable even though a sleeping state occurs. Accumulation of barbiturates in body tissue can often occur because of their long half-life and long-term, frequent administration. The resulting chronic intoxication is characterized by impaired central nervous system function, reflected by deficits in attention, memory, judgment, cognitive ability, fine and gross psychomotor skills, and emotional disorders such as mood swings, depression, and hostility. Physical signs of barbiturate use include glazed eyes, dry skin, rapid breathing, rapid pulse, high blood pressure, cramps, nausea, tremors, and possibly mild to severe convulsions. Mood depression is common with prolonged use, as is aversion to light and noise, insomnia, and some hallucinations. With regular use, tolerance to the effects of barbiturates develops, though more slowly to the harmful effects than to the sleep-inducing or intoxicating effects. Typical overdose for a healthy 77 kg male would be as little as 11 100 mg pills (see also Table III.2). As well, with continued heavy use, the difference between an effective dose and a fatal dose narrows, and the risk of fatal overdose increases.

Physical and psychological dependence is common with this family of psychoactive agents. Physical dependence on barbiturates can be one of the most life-threatening of all the drug dependencies because of the symptoms that appear shortly after abrupt cessation.

Withdrawal starts four to six hours after the last dose and can last for up to two weeks. Abrupt withdrawal leads to progressive restlessness, anxiety, and possible delirium, delusions, grand mal seizures, and potentially death. Temporary sleep disturbances may lead a user to incorrectly decide that more of the drug is required. There is a high cross-tolerance with other depressants, particularly alcohol. Some alcohol-dependent persons use barbiturates as a substitute for, or in addition to, alcohol. Barbiturates can be legally purchased with a prescription and come in four durations of action: long-acting, intermediate-acting, short-acting, and ultra-short-acting. Usually only the short- and intermediate-acting drugs such as Seconal and Amytal typically appeal to street users (Levinthal, 2012).

NON-BARBITURATE SEDATIVE-HYPNOTICS

slang: *general:* knockout drops
chloral hydrate mixed with alcohol: Mickey Finn
Doriden: doors
Quaaludes: Joe Fridays, lemons, lewds, lovers, Q, Quads, Vitamin Q, soapers, wallbangers

The non-barbiturate sedative-hypnotics are a group of drugs with actions that are very similar to those of the barbiturates. They were first introduced in 1954 as a "safe, non-addictive" alternative to barbiturates, and various types were available as over-the-counter medications for nearly 20 years. However, physical dependence was soon discovered to be a serious problem, and their use became more restricted. Drugs in this group that are controlled substances in Canada are chloral hydrate (Noctec) and paraldehyde, Schedule F (controlled medicine, available by prescription); methaqualone (Dormutil, Mandrax, Parest, Quaalude, Somnafac), Schedule III (restricted but still available on a limited basis by prescription); and meprobmate (Equanil, Miltown, Solacen), Schedule I (narcotic). Other members of this family that may not be legally sold in Canada are ethchlorvynol (Placidyl), glutethimide (Doriden), methyprylon (Noludar), and the most well-known member of this group, methaqualone (Quaalude, Mandrax).

Methaqualone was originally produced as a therapeutic agent as it is an effective anti-malarial, but it was soon discovered that it also possessed a very powerful euphoria and sleep-producing effect. By 1972, it was the sixth most frequently prescribed drug in the United States (Falco, 1976). However, one disturbing side effect was, like barbiturates, its disruption of rapid eye movement (REM) sleep. Typically, adults have four REM cycles per night. While Quaalude and other non-barbiturate sedative-hypnotics allow a person to obtain the physical rest required while asleep, they can suppress REM sleep. If REM sleep is suppressed for as little as two to three weeks, a person's ability to function begins to deteriorate and the person can begin to exhibit psychotic-like behaviour. As well, tolerance is quick to develop, and sleep, initially produced by 300 mg of the drug, can require up to 2000 mg. For a typical 54 kg woman, the lethal range begins at 5400–5500 mg (Csiernik, 2019).

While North American production was discontinued in 1983, Quaalude remains an available street drug. Case studies have suggested that methaqualone may possess a misuse potential exceeding that of any of the barbiturates. Quaalude is not manufactured or distributed in Canada but continues to be smuggled in and can be used alone or also to offset a cocaine, amphetamine, or crystal methamphetamine high. At low doses, glutethimide and methaqualone are likely to produce calmness, sedation, drowsiness, relaxation, and lethargy, but they are just as likely to cause anorexia, nausea, and gastrointestinal discomforts. Large doses of these drugs produce a barbiturate-like intoxication. Non-barbiturate sedative-hypnotics are associated with rapid deterioration of vital signs during overdose. However, at high doses, respiratory depression is less marked than with the barbiturates, so the risk of accidental overdose is somewhat lessened. Respiratory depression can be intensified by the simultaneous administration of codeine or any other related CNS depressant. Cardiovascular complications and seizures with these psychoactive agents can be quite severe, with cardiovascular collapse and coma resulting from misuse of these substances. Other common effects include dizziness, lethargy, exacerbation of existing pain, and the above-mentioned reduction of REM sleep, resulting in less dreaming. Effects of long-term use are primarily a continuation of short-term effects because of a buildup of the drug in the body. Even after discontinuation of drug use, a lack of motor coordination, unsteadiness, muscle weakness, visual difficulties, thinking and memory impairment, slurring of speech, as well as tremors, irritability, and apathy may remain (Seymour & Smith, 2011).

Development of tolerance to the sleep-inducing effects and to the euphoric and sedative effects is rapid, as it is with barbiturates. If the user wishes to maintain the original intensity of any of these desired effects, the size of the daily dose must be increased. A high degree of cross-tolerance occurs between these drugs and both alcohol and barbiturates. As well, both physical and psychological dependence can occur quickly. Withdrawal, while not as severe as with barbiturates, may also be life-threatening and must be medically monitored. Early withdrawal symptoms tend to occur within 24 hours after the last dose and may include sweating and fever, alternating with chills, nausea and vomiting, abdominal cramps, abnormally rapid heart rate, headache, tremors, muscle twitches and spasms, agitation and hyperactivity, insomnia, or brief periods of agitated sleep accompanied by nightmares, uncontrollable facial grimaces, psychosis-like syndromes characterized by disorientation, delirium, hallucinations and paranoid delusions, and grand mal seizures. Some of these symptoms, including grand mal seizures, have abruptly occurred in regular users without their abstaining from the drug. The caution necessary in using barbiturates applies also to the use of all non-barbiturate sedative-hypnotics (Seymour & Smith, 2011).

BENZODIAZEPINES

slang: *general:* benzos, downers, sleep away, tranqs, Zs
Librium: libbys
Rohypnol: forget-me, Mexican valium, roachies, roofies
Valium: foofoo, howards, mother's little helpers, V's, vals, vallies, yellows
Xanax: dogbones, footballs, four bars, X-box, xanny, zanis, zanibars

Benzodiazepines are also referred to as minor tranquillizers, anti-anxiety agents, and anxiolytics-sedatives. All benzodiazepines act by enhancing the actions of a natural brain chemical, gamma-aminobutyric acid (GABA). However, they do not increase the organic synthesis of GABA in any way. The natural action of GABA is augmented by benzodiazepines, which exert an extra, often excessive, inhibitory influence on neurons. However, extended use of benzodiazepines can actually decrease the synthesis of GABA in certain areas of the brain, further contributing to the dependency cycle.

Benzodiazepines were introduced to replace barbiturates and non-barbiturate sedative-hypnotics in the treatment of anxiety and insomnia, as well as to serve as anti-convulsive agents. These drugs are much safer than previously synthesized sedative-hypnotics as they rarely cause a fatal overdose. The typical lethal range for a 77 kg male is anywhere from approximately 1000–7000 5 mg tablets, though it can take fewer for other members of this drug family, such as Serax, to produce an overdose (see Table III.2). While benzodiazepines are much less likely to produce an overdose compared to either barbiturates or non-barbiturate sedative-hypnotics, overdose is still possible, particularly when benzodiazepines are mixed with another CNS depressant such as alcohol. These drugs are also a major contributor to the accidental poisoning of children and prescription drug–related emergency room visits for adults (Substance Abuse and Mental Health Services Administration, 2013). Table 8.2 summarizes the benzodiazepines currently available in Canada, their equivalent strengths, and their primary therapeutic purpose.

Short-term effects from benzodiazepines are variable, depending on the dose, personality of the user, and the user's physical health and anxiety level. They include the following:

- calming hyperactivity tension and agitation
- relaxing muscles and relieving anxiety
- combatting withdrawal effects of other depressant drugs, primarily alcohol
- impairing muscle coordination
- producing dizziness, low blood pressure, and/or fainting
- inhibiting short-term memory

Table 8.2: Benzodiazepines and Z-Drugs

Drug	Half-Life Hours	Equivalent Strength (mg)	Therapeutic Purpose
Alprazolam (Xanax, Xanor, Tafil)	6–12	0.5	S
Bromazepam (Lexotan, Lexomil)	10–20	5–6	S
Chlordiazepoxide (Librium)	5–30	25	S
Clobazam (Frisium)	12–60	20	AC, S
Clonazepam (Klonopin, Rivotril)	18–50	0.5	AC, S
Clorazepate (Tranxene)	36–200	15	S
Diazepam (Valium)	20–100	10	S
Estazolam (ProSom, Nuctalon)	10–24	1–2	H
Flunitrazepam (Rohypnol)	18–26	1	H
Flurazepam (Dalmane)	40–250	15–30	H
Halazepam (Paxipam)	30–100	20	S
Ketazolam (Anxon)	30–100	15–30	S
Loprazolam (Dormonoct)	6–12	1–2	H
Lorazepam (Ativan, Temesta, Tavor)	10–20	1	S
Lormetazepam (Noctamid)	10–12	1–2	H
Medazepam (Nobrium)	36–200	10	S
Nitrazepam (Mogadon)	15–38	10	H

Table 8.2: Continued

Drug	Half-Life Hours	Equivalent Strength (mg)	Therapeutic Purpose
Nordazepam (Nordaz, Calmday)	36–200	10	S
Oxazepam (Serax, Serenid, Serepax, Seresta)	4–15	20	S
Prazepam (Centrax, Lysanxia)	36–200	10–20	S
Quazepam (Doral)	25–100	20	H
Temazepam (Restoril, Normison, Euhypnos)	8–22	20	H
Triazolam (Halcion)	2	0.5	H
Z-Drugs: Second-Generation Benzodiazepines			
Zaleplon (Sonata)	2	20	H
Zolpidem (Ambien, Stilnoct, Stilnox)	2	20	H
Zopiclone (Zimovane, Imovane)	5–6	15	H
Eszopiclone (Lunesta)	6 (9 in elderly)	3	H

Note: AC = anticonvulsant; H = hypnotic (induces sleep); S = sedative (eases agitation and anxiety)
Source: Ashton (2002).

While a normal therapeutic dose produces relaxation and a feeling of well-being, higher doses may produce a state similar to that of intoxication by alcohol or barbiturates. Excessive use results in drowsiness, lethargy, disorientation, confusion, memory impairment, trance-like episodes, double vision, personality alterations, and other symptoms resembling drunkenness. Benzodiazepines can also sometimes produce unexpected paradoxical effects, such as agitation, insomnia, aggression, rage, and hostility—the very symptoms for which they have been prescribed (Ashton, 2013).

Chronic use of benzodiazepines leads to both physical and psychological dependence. Withdrawal from minor tranquillizers is similar to that from other sedative-hypnotics.

Commonly observed effects include tremors, sweating, hypersensitivity to sensory stimuli, blurred vision, tingling sensations, tinnitus (ringing of the ears), insomnia, headache, difficulties in concentration, anorexia, increased lethargy, indifference to one's surroundings, memory, cognitive, and psychomotor impairment, irritability and emotional flatness, disorientation and confusion, sleep disturbances, gastrointestinal upsets, along with sexual dysfunction and menstrual irregularities.

The withdrawal syndrome ranges in intensity from progressive anxiety, restlessness, insomnia, and irritability in mild cases to delirium and convulsions in severe cases. As with other psychoactive drugs, the intensity of the reaction depends on the dose level, duration of use, and individual user differences. Benzodiazepines can be obtained legally with a prescription. Despite the issue that misuse creates, these drugs do have legitimate therapeutic value and are relatively safe if used for a specific purpose and on a short-term basis, generally not exceeding four weeks. After four weeks of use, physical dependency to the drug is likely to occur, though there have been some reports of physical dependency beginning in as little as two weeks of regular use (Ashton, 2005).

Halcion, introduced in 1983 for insomnia, is typical of the debate surrounding the risks and benefits of this family of drugs. Halcion has a very brief onset time and thus is quite effective in producing sleep for those suffering from insomnia. Its effectiveness led to its legalization in over 90 nations worldwide within a decade. However, in 1989, a user who claimed that she became involuntarily intoxicated while taking the drug and unknowingly killed her mother brought a multimillion-dollar lawsuit against the drug's manufacturer, Upjohn Pharmaceutical. The suit never went to trial, though the plaintiff did receive an undisclosed settlement from Upjohn. A minority of other users also reported adverse reactions from the drug, such as increased anxiety, memory loss, hostility, hallucinations, and paranoia, so that warning labels were added to every prescription (Dyer, 1994). Interestingly, during the 1991 Gulf War, both United States President George Bush and Secretary of State James Baker were prescribed and were consuming Halcion. Benzodiazepines were also at the centre of the largest pharmaceutical lawsuit in the United Kingdom in the 20th century. Involving over 14,000 individuals, nearly 2,000 law firms sued benzodiazepine manufacturers claiming the pharmaceutical companies knew of the dependence potential but intentionally withheld this information from physicians (Peart, 1999). This would be a harbinger of the opioid crisis that would engulf Canada and the United States two decades later. Despite this, benzodiazepines continue to be widely prescribed (Lembke et al., 2018; Maust et al., 2018).

With the greater acknowledgement of the sexual violence perpetrated against women in Canada, there has been a parallel concern with the use of Rohypnol or "roofies." Referred to in the media as the date-rape drug, Rohypnol, while not a legal drug for sale in Canada, is legally manufactured and distributed in Mexico and Latin America for severe sleeping disorders and as a pre-anaesthetic medication. Rohypnol has no taste, colour, or odour, and when it is dropped into an alcoholic beverage, its consumption can cause dizziness, confusion, memory loss, impaired judgment, and prolonged periods of blackout. The formal name for this state is anterograde amnesia (United States Department of Justice, 2003a).

Studies have found that more than one-third of older Canadians have a prescription for at least one benzodiazepine. As licit substances, these drugs are covered by provincial drug insurance plans. The use of benzodiazepines in the older adult population has been associated with an increased risk of falls, fractures, and accidents, as well as contributing to the erroneous diagnosis of Alzheimer's or other forms of dementia. This is in part due to decreasing liver functioning in seniors, which lengthens the time it takes for the body to metabolize the drug. Thus, greater amounts are present in the bodies of older adults for longer periods of time. Older persons following a prescription can easily and unintentionally intoxicate themselves and do so on an ongoing basis. Criteria for benzodiazepine use among seniors is that all long-acting versions with a half-life greater than 24 hours, including diazepam, flurazepam, chlordiazepoxide, and clonazepam, should be avoided. Prescriptions for short- and intermediate-acting benzodiazepines, those with a half-life of less than 24 hours, should not exceed the following dosages: alprazolam (Xanax), 2 mg; lorazepam (Ativan), 3 mg; oxazepam (Serax), 60 mg; temazepam (Restoril), 15 mg; and triazolam (Halcion), 0.25 mg (Dionne et al., 2013).

In this century, benzodiazepine use has increased in many nations worldwide. Easy access via the internet has also increased the use of these drugs without medical supervision. Unfortunately, many physicians are not well versed in benzodiazepine management, with little expertise in withdrawal in long-term users. Detoxification centres also tend to withdraw patients too rapidly, apply rigid rules and "contract" methods, and provide inadequate support or follow-up without addressing the underlying psychological component that accompanies addiction to these drugs (Ashton, 2013).

In the late 1980s, a new group of non-benzodiazepine sedative-hypnotics were introduced to treat insomnia that were intended to produce less physical and psychological dependency: cyclopyrrolones. They quickly became known as Z-drugs and include zaleplon (Andante, Sonata, Starnoc), zolpidem (Ambien, Edluar, Intermezzo, Zolpimist), zopiclone (Dopareel, Imovane, Zimovane), and eszopiclone (Lunesta). This subgroup of sedative-hypnotics has a quick onset and short duration of action due to having shorter half-lives than traditional benzodiazepines (Ciraulo & Oldham, 2014). The most prominent feature of Z-drugs is that they decrease the length of time it takes a person to fall asleep while increasing the typical length of time the user sleeps. However, as in the past when other new types of sedative-hypnotics were first synthesized and were promised to be non-addictive, it was quickly learned that cyclopyrrolones produce both physical and psychological dependency, which meant that when a person stopped using them all at once, even after short periods of use, withdrawal symptoms were produced. While withdrawal was not as severe as first-generation benzodiazepines, people still experienced restlessness, anxiety, and increased insomnia (Pottie et al., 2018).

INHALANTS/SOLVENTS

slang: *general:* air blast, huff, oz, spray

amyl nitrate: aimes, Amsterdam special, boppers, poppers, rush

gammahydroxybutyrate (GHB) and/or gamma butyrolactone (GBL): cherry meth, easy lay, G, Gamma-O, grievous bodily harm, goop, growth hormone booster, jib, liquid ecstasy, liquid E, oxy-sleep, salty water

isobutyl nitrate: quicksilver, rush snappers, whiteout

nitrous oxide: buzz bomb, hippy crack, laughing gas, nox, whippets, whip-its

rubber cement ball that is burned and inhaled: snotball

Inhalants include volatile gases, substances that exist in a gaseous form at body temperature, refrigerants, solvents, general anaesthetics, and propellants (see Table 8.3). Except for nitrous oxide, more commonly referred to as "laughing gas," and related aliphatic nitrates, all inhalants are hydrocarbons. These substances not only have depressant effects but can also produce minor hallucinogenic effects on the central nervous system. Misuse of volatile hydrocarbons and anaesthetics is not new. Getting high by inhaling ether or nitrous oxide was common in Europe and North America during the 1800s. Sir Humphry Davy introduced the idea of using "laughing gas" as an anaesthetic before surgery, as well as recreationally. Today this drug can be purchased for recreational use in the form of poppers (amyl or butyl nitrate) or whip-its (nitrous oxide). These highly flammable yellowish liquids are usually sold in small glass screw-top bottles and have gained popularity as the drug can relax muscles and enhance sexual excitement. The contents are released by crushing or popping the container and inhaling. During this process, oxygen is partially cut off to the brain. In combination with the drug, this produces a relaxed, warm state within 10 seconds that lasts for several minutes.

Widespread acknowledged sniffing of solvents contained in plastic model glues and nail polish removers began during the 1960s and has since been labelled as volatile substance abuse (VSA). The short-term effects of inhalants are dose-related and similar to those of the other central nervous system depressants. The initial effect of inhalation is a feeling of mood enhancement or euphoria, characterized by light-headedness, pleasant exhilaration, vivid fantasies, and excitation. Nausea, increased salivation, sneezing and coughing, loss of coordination, depressed reflexes, and sensitivity to light may also occur. In some users, feelings of invincibility may lead to reckless, dangerous, violent, or bizarre behaviour. Physical effects include pallor, thirst, weight loss, nosebleeds, bloodshot eyes, and sores on the nose and mouth (Hancock & McKim, 2018).

Some solvents, such as benzene, can cause reduction in the formation of blood cells in the bone marrow. Others may impair the functioning of the liver while still others may impair the functioning of the liver and kidneys. Contrarily, amyl nitrate and butyl nitrate dilate blood vessels. Deep inhalation or sniffing repeatedly over a short period of time may result in disorientation and loss of self-control, unconsciousness, seizures, or

Table 8.3: Inhalants and Solvents

Class	Examples	Found In
aliphatic/ aromatic hydrocarbons	Benzene	detergent, glue, furniture wax, lacquer thinner, paint
	Butane	fuel
	Gasoline	fuel
	Hexane	cleaning fluids
	propane	fuel
	Toluene	model cement, paint stripper, ink
	Xylene	lighter fluid, ink
aliphatic nitrates	amyl nitrate	room odorants
	butyl nitrate	industrial solvents
esters	amyl acetate	plastic cements
	ethyl acetate	lacquer thinner
ethers	diethylether	anesthetic, GHB
gases	nitrous oxide	anesthetic, propellant in canned whipping cream
halogenated hydrocarbons	chloroform	anesthetics
	Freons	aerosol propellant
	halothane	cleaning fluids
	perchlorenthylene	aerosol propellants
	trichlorethylene	Industrial solvent, anesthetic gas
ketones	Acetone	nail polish remover
	methyisobutyl ketone	household cements
	methylethyl ketone	model cement

Source: Data from National Institute on Drug Abuse (2020).

hallucinations, both auditory and visual. There have been some links between the use of these two nitrogen-based inhalants and Kaposi's sarcoma, a rare form of cancer affecting the immune system. Long-term exposure in industrial settings to solvents has also been linked to the development of cancer (de Vocht et al., 2009).

Gamma hydroxybutyrate (GHB) and gamma butyrolactone (GBL) are two solvents that gained attention as they have been identified as potential date-rape drugs. GHB was originally marketed as a surgical anaesthetic and used in Europe for the treatment of insomnia and narcolepsy and as a pharmacological aid for alcoholism. In the United States, it was sold without prescription as a health food and body-building supplement. GBL is a chemical used in a range of industrial cleaners. GBL, when consumed, is actually converted by the body during metabolism into GHB. Adverse effects when consumed in large quantities include hypothermia, dizziness, nausea, vomiting, weakness, loss of peripheral vision, confusion, agitation, and hallucinations. However, when these liquids are added to an alcoholic beverage, they can produce memory loss and unconsciousness. Within 5 to 20 minutes, the person who has consumed GHB and alcohol can suffer amnesia, confusion, and seizure-like activity. Ingesting too much GHB can lead to respiratory difficulties and a coma-like state or even death (Brennan & Van Hout, 2014; United States Department of Justice, 2003b).

Acute physical health effects of solvent use can include abdominal pains, amnesia, mood depression, diarrhea, fatigue/sleepiness, headache/hangover, inattentiveness, irritability, incoordination, loss of appetite, nausea/vomiting, and rapid or irregular heartbeat. Long-term effects include the development of both physical and psychological dependence. Peripheral nerve, liver, and kidney damage, and infertility among male sniffers, have all been documented, as has anxiety, excitability, irritability, restlessness, bone marrow damage, chronic nosebleeds, short-term memory loss, and issues with sleep. Neurological damage also occurs, affecting balance, gait, reasoning, and sensory perceptions such as taste and smell, with the solvent toluene actually destroying the brain tissue of chronic misusers, leading to permanent, irreversible brain damage. Solvent misuse has also been reported to cause death through suffocation and by sudden sniffing death (SSD). As a result of inhaling solvents, the cardiac muscle of a user becomes sensitive to the adrenal hormone epinephrine. If a user is suddenly startled and flees, suffers a panic attack, or engages in some other form of vigorous activity, epinephrine is secreted, and a catastrophic cardiac arrhythmia can occur. The user can die of a heart attack, regardless of age or physical condition. Case studies of sudden sniffing death have also been reported with butane and propane. As solvents are frequently sniffed from a plastic bag, it is also possible for a user to be rendered unconscious by the drug and accidentally suffocate if the bag is not removed from the face (Chenier, 2001; S. Cruz, 2011).

Regular use of inhalants induces tolerance, making increased doses necessary to produce the same effects. After one year, a glue sniffer may be using several tubes of plastic cement to maintain the effect for the same length of time as was originally achieved with a single tube. Since the body develops a tolerance to the drug, users must increase their dosage if they wish to obtain the same effects, thereby increasing the risk of hazardous health effects. Regular users often become emotionally depressed, lose interest in their surroundings, experience diminished motivation, and may develop serious and often irreversible neurological damage. Withdrawal symptoms such as chills, hallucinations, headaches, abdominal pains, muscular cramps, and delirium tremens (DTs) have been reported, though the latter is not commonly observed. The constant sniffing of solvents can also lead to vapours remaining within the body or saturating the skin or clothing of the user. If a match is lighted to smoke a cigarette or joint, users can set themselves on fire (Hancock & McKim, 2018).

Volatile substance misuse is most often associated with young males, but women of childbearing age are also known to misuse solvents. When used during pregnancy, inhalants pass from the mother across the placenta into the bloodstream of the developing fetus. Chronic solvent use can prematurely terminate a pregnancy in the initial 20 weeks of development. It can also produce fetal solvent syndrome, which is similar to fetal alcohol spectrum disorder (FASD). Solvents can significantly reduce the amount of oxygen available for transfer to a developing fetus, producing brain damage that affects learning, memory, higher-level judgment, and decision-making abilities throughout the life cycle. Fetal solvent syndrome is evident in low birth weight, low levels of muscle tone, congenital facial abnormalities, a head size too small for a newborn's body size, and blunted fingers. Chromosome damage is also possible (Bowen, 2011).

A major reason solvents are so problematic is because of their accessibility and availability. Solvents can be legally purchased by anyone, and a variety of different inhalants can be found in every household. As well, there is no restriction on possession, and only retail merchants can truly control access by limiting the purchase of a solvent. The second major concern is age of use. The majority of users range in age from 8 to 16, with an average age of 12 to 13, although there are adult sniffers. Inhalants provide a cheap, widely available means of achieving intoxication. In addition to enhancing mood, these substances tend to decrease the intensity of negative feelings such as anxiety, depression, inferiority, or boredom. Solvents tend to be an early experimental drug, though young, poor, adolescent males, and young members of isolated Indigenous communities across Canada tend to use solvents to a greater extent than do members of other populations. However, solvents are an even greater problem outside North America, particularly in developing nations (Mohan et al., 2018; Sah et al., 2020)

ANTIHISTAMINES

slang: tripelennamine mixed with pentazocine (Talwin): T's and blues

Antihistamines, first used in the 1940s, have many therapeutic uses. Over 40 different types are available that are:

- effective in combatting the symptoms associated with certain types of allergic reactions, such as hay fever (phenyltoloxamine [Sinutab]; tripelennamine [Ro-Hist]; pheniramine [Triaminic]), though they have no value in fighting the common cold virus;
- used as anti-nauseants in the treatment of ailments such as motion sickness (Gravol);

- used in sleeping aids (diphenhydramine [Benadryl, Nytol, Sominex]);
- valuable as anti-spasmodics (diphenhydramine [Valdrene]); and
- useful in treating persons with excessive stomach acid (cimetidine [Tagamet]).

The extent of the usefulness of these psychoactive drugs is typically not realized, but in the adult Canadian population, the prevalence of rhinosinusitis alone is 5.7 percent of women and 3.4 percent of men (Chen et al., 2003). Globally, allergic diseases are a significant cause of morbidity and a substantive burden on the health care system of both developed and emerging economies. Allergies affect at least 30 percent of the world's population, impacting nearly 80 percent of all families to varying degrees (Sánchez-Borges et al., 2018).

At therapeutic doses, common effects of the antihistamines include drowsiness, dizziness, and mild impairment of CNS function, perception, concentration, and psychomotor abilities that is further enhanced by the use of alcohol or other sedative-hypnotics. Other effects include lethargy, mood enhancement, gastrointestinal discomfort, and appetite suppression. Higher doses can further enhance mood or cause minor hallucinatory effects, especially when mixed with alcohol or other CNS-depressant drugs. When antihistamines are used regularly at therapeutic dose levels, adverse effects are generally mild and tend to be similar to short-term low-dose effects. With chronic regular use, however, the effectiveness of the drugs appears to diminish. Regular topical application of certain antihistamines can cause allergic skin rashes, impaired coordination, confusion, disorientation, muscle twitching, and tremors (Hancock & McKim, 2018). Among older individuals, extended ongoing use can lead to the diminishment of natural histamine in the CNS. This can lead to dementia-like symptoms, though these lessen once the antihistamine is no longer being administered (Tannenbaum et al., 2012).

Tolerance to the sedative effects of the antihistamines develops with regular use as the liver increases its ability to metabolize the drug. If an antihistamine is regularly used for its psychoactive effects, users may become physically and psychologically dependent. Antihistamines produce little euphoria, and what is produced rapidly decreases with regular use. As with other psychoactive drugs, children can be more easily accidentally poisoned, with as few as 87 tablets of Nytol being lethal for a 54 kg person. However, the use of antihistamines by women to combat morning sickness has not produced any issues during pregnancy or developmentally. Likewise, all antihistamines are considered safe to use while breastfeeding, as minimal amounts are excreted in the breast milk and do not cause any adverse effects to the infant (Seto et al., 1997; So et al., 2010).

ALCOHOL

slang: 2-4, 26 ouncer, booze, brewski, browns, brown pop, fire water, forty pounder, hooch, grog, kegger, mickey, shots, snort, suds, vino

The most commonly misused psychoactive drug worldwide is ethyl alcohol: ethanol. It is the waste product formed when yeast utilizes sugar as an energy source during fermentation, and it has been associated as a contributing factor in more than 230 diseases. As alcohol production has been possible for thousands of years, well before even the simplest of human technologies, alcohol must occasionally have been available to prehuman primates and prehistoric humans. It is unlikely that enough occurred naturally to be incorporated into religious and social custom, and probably no widespread use developed until fruits and grains came under cultivation, leading anthropologists to believe this was one factor that led to the development of agrarian society. This would have occurred approximately 10,000 years ago, and there are many indications that the early growth of agriculture owes much to the effects of alcohol.

Alcohol indirectly stimulates dopamine release in the ventral striatum of the brain, which is a key component of the central nervous system's reward system. The neurobiology of alcohol involves several neurotransmitters, though the importance of GABA and glutamate, another neurotransmitter, has been increasingly emphasized. Alcohol may inhibit both GABA and glutamate terminals in the ventral tegmental area (VTA) of the brain, which in turn amplifies the release of dopamine (Paul, 2006; Ticku, 1990). As little as two standard drinks (Figure 8.1) diminishes the prefrontal cortex of the brain, the area involved in tempering a person's level of aggression. This may explain, in part, why the use of this CNS depressant is associated with so many violent acts (Denson, 2011).

Alcohol content varies from product to product, as illustrated in Table 8.4. Nevertheless, a drink is a drink is a drink: 1.5 oz. of liquor, a 12 oz. bottle of beer (5 percent alcohol), a 5 oz. glass of table wine (12 percent alcohol), and a 4 oz. glass of fortified wine all contain the same amount of ethanol (Figure 8.1). They affect human physiology

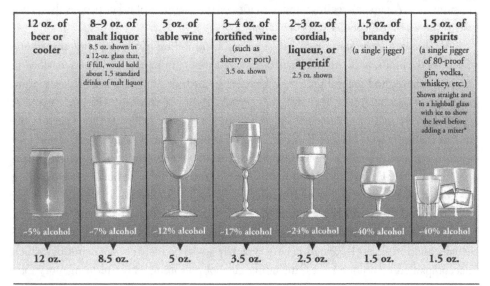

Figure 8.1: Standard Drink Chart

Note: *It can be difficult to estimate the number of standard drinks in a single mixed drink made with distilled spirits. Depending on factors such as the type of spirits and the recipe, a mixed drink can contain from one to three or more standard drinks.

Source: National Institute on Alcohol Abuse and Alcoholism (2005, p. 24).

Table 8.4: Alcohol Content of Various Forms of Beverage Ethanol

Beverage	Concentration of Alcohol (Percent by Volume)
"light" beer	2.5–4.5
regular beer	5
malt liquors	6.5
table wine	8–14
fortified wines (sherry/port/vermouth)	16–20
ciders	5–12
sake	14–16
spirits (gin, vodka, whiskies, rum, cognac)	40
liqueurs, regular	16–56
liqueurs, cream and egg-based	16–18

in a consistent manner as measured by blood alcohol content (BAC), though there are distinct differences between men and women (Table 8.5). Differences in effects from person to person produced by beverage alcohol do not generally result from the type of drink consumed, but rather from the person's size, previous drinking experiences, and rate of consumption. A person's feelings and activities or the presence of other people also play a role in the way the alcohol affects behaviour.

Alcohol is a depressant drug that produces disinhibition in the user and anaesthetic effects on the brain. Short-term effects include relaxation, impaired coordination, slowing down of reflexes and mental processes, changes in attitude, and increased risk taking to the point of bad judgment, including dangerous driving or working with machinery. A significant minority of pedestrians killed by motor vehicles are legally intoxicated at the time of the collision (Dultz & Frangos, 2013). Drinking heavily over a short period may produce a poisoning effect commonly referred to as a hangover, which includes headache, nausea, shakiness, and possibly vomiting beginning 8 to 12 hours after drinking has ceased. A hangover is the body's reaction to too much alcohol. In part it is related to withdrawal from alcohol and dehydration. The poisoning is a result of the by-products that arise when the liver metabolizes ethanol that include acetaldehyde, formaldehyde, and formic acid. Hangovers are typically associated with binge drinking, which is accompanied by unique issues, including alcohol poisoning, short-term memory loss, unplanned sexual activity, suicidal ideation, and injury and death from engaging in high-risk behaviour (King et al., 2011).

Binge drinking and alcohol misuse also regularly result in physical and emotional injury, assaults, and various forms of trauma, with Canada leading all developed nations for the rate of road fatalities due to alcohol impairment at 33.6 percent (Coyle, 2016).

Table 8.5: Blood Alcohol Content by Sex

FEMALE											
Lean Body Weight		**Number of Drinks**									
POUNDS	KILOS	1	2	3	4	5	6	7	8	9	10
100	45.4	.05	.09	.14	.18	.23	.27	.32	.36	.41	.45
120	54.4	.04	.08	.11	.15	.19	.23	.27	.30	.34	.38
140	63.5	.03	.07	.10	.13	.16	.19	.23	.26	.29	.32
160	72.6	.03	.06	.09	.11	.14	.17	.20	.23	.26	.28
180	81.6	.03	.05	.08	.10	.13	.15	.18	.20	.23	.25
200	90.7	.02	.05	.07	.09	.11	.14	.16	.18	.20	.23
220	99.8	.02	.04	.06	.08	.10	.12	.14	.17	.19	.21
240	108.8	.02	.04	.06	.08	.09	.11	.13	.15	.17	.19
MALE											
Lean Body Weight		**Number of Drinks**									
POUNDS	KILOS	1	2	3	4	5	6	7	8	9	10
100	45.4	.04	.08	.11	.15	.19	.23	.26	.30	.34	.38
120	54.4	.03	.06	.09	.12	.16	.19	.22	.25	.28	.31
140	63.5	.03	.05	.08	.11	.13	.16	.19	.21	.24	.27
160	72.6	.02	.05	.07	.09	.12	.14	.16	.19	.21	.23
180	81.6	.02	.04	.06	.08	.11	.13	.15	.17	.19	.21
200	90.7	.02	.04	.06	.08	.09	.11	.13	.15	.17	.19
220	99.8	.02	.03	.05	.07	.09	.10	.12	.14	.15	.17
240	108.8	.02	.03	.05	.06	.08	.09	.11	.13	.14	.16

Note: Milligrams of alcohol in mL of blood; rate of elimination 15 mg per hour.

Source: Alberta Liquor and Gaming Commission (2018).

While there has been a documented benefit against coronary heart disease from moderate alcohol consumption, it does not apply equally to the entire population, but only to those with a specific cholesteryl protein (Mukamal, 2012; O'Neill et al., 2017), nor does it mitigate the other body systems that are negatively affected (Box 8.1) nor the fact that even low doses impact cognitive and emotional processing (De Pirro, 2019). Chronic alcohol use is a substantive contributor to premature mortality (Roerecke & Rehm, 2013).

Box 8.1: Damage to the Body Produced by Chronic Alcohol Consumption

Risks increase along with the amount of daily alcohol consumption, including the following:

- Blood: anemia, increased bruising and bleeding
- Bones: reduced bone mass and absorption of calcium, increased risk of osteoporosis
- Brain: decreased executive function (high-order cognitive capacities that include planning, reasoning, flexibility, decision making, and goal-oriented behaviour), loss of balance, seizures, damage to peripheral nerves, loss of supportive connective tissue, impaired learning and memory capacity, increased risk of all forms of dementia highlighted by Wernicke-Korsakoff syndrome
- Cancer: breast, bowel, colon, esophagus, gastric, larynx, liver, mouth, pancreatic, pharynx, prostate, rectal, throat, and testicular
- Cardiovascular System: increased cholesterol levels, blood pressure, risk of stroke, heart failures, cardiac arrest, intracerebral hemorrhages, arrythmias (including atrial fibrillation, decreased ability of the heart to pump blood)
- Endocrine System: infertility, impotence, and decreased sperm production
- Liver: fatty liver disease, alcoholic hepatitis, fibrosis, cirrhosis
- Lungs: increased risk of pneumonia and tuberculosis
- Muscles: increased inflammation, swelling, tenderness, and weakness
- Pancreas: pancreatitis
- Stomach: chronic heartburn, gastritis, ulcers

Sources: Azodi et al. (2011); Babor et al. (2001); Beier et al. (2011); Bell et al. (2017); Day & Rudd (2019); Ferrari et al. (2007); Heinen et al. (2009); Lachenmeier et al. (2009); Malik et al. (2008); Maurel et al. (2011); Spas & Weyandt (2015); Schwarzinger et al. (2018); Van Skike et al. (2019); White et al. (2002); Zhang et al. (2007); Zhao et al. (2016).

As well, there is the irreversible damage that occurs as a result of a woman's drinking during the course of her pregnancy, that of fetal alcohol spectrum disorder. FASD is a collective term rather than a diagnostic category, including Fetal Alcohol Syndrome (FAS), Alcohol Related Neurodevelopmental Disorder (ARND), and partial FAS (pFAS). FASD is the leading cause of developmental disability, affecting 9 out of every 1,000 Canadian infants. Estimates of the annual cost of fetal alcohol spectrum disorder in Canada is in the $2 billion CAD range. FASD, along with prenatal alcohol exposure (PAE), impacts each child differently, though there are commonalities within different diagnostic categories. As alcohol freely crosses the placenta from mother to child, the risks for the unborn child increase the more a pregnant woman drinks, though at this time, no safe level of drinking has been established. Primary disabilities from FASD include impairments in attention, verbal learning, and executive functioning as the direct result of damage to the brain caused by prenatal alcohol exposure. It has also been linked to increased risk of childhood leukemia. Secondary disabilities are deficits not evident at birth but that arise from primary disabilities and interaction with the environment, such as mental health and addiction issues, conflict with the law, and difficulties with education, employment, and family relationships. Drinking alcohol during pregnancy may lead to cognitive impairment; heart, face, joint, and limb abnormalities; lower birth weight; hyperactivity with shorter attention spans; poor self-concept; depression; and aggression. The disabilities created by FASD are not minimized with time and continue to create difficulties and marginalize individuals throughout their adult lives (Burnside & Fuchs, 2013; Denys et al., 2011; Kully-Martens et al., 2013; Latino-Martel et al., 2010; Popova et al., 2015; Rutman & Van Bibber, 2010).

Chronic alcohol consumption blunts the biological clock's ability to synchronize daily activities to light and disrupts natural activity patterns. It continues to affect the body's clock, or circadian rhythm, even days after the drinking ends. Other than regulating sleeping and waking, the circadian rhythm also affects physiological functions, such as hormonal secretions, appetite, digestion, activity levels, and body temperature. Ongoing disruption of the body's natural clock increases the risk of developing cancer, heart disease, and depression. Regular use of alcohol also induces tolerance, making increased doses necessary to produce the same effects (Hasler et al., 2012). When tolerance develops, alcohol-dependent people may drink steadily throughout the day without appearing to be intoxicated. As these persons may continue to work reasonably well, their condition may go unrecognized by others until severe physical damage develops or until they are hospitalized for other reasons and experience alcohol withdrawal symptoms. Tolerance is lost if the drinker abstains but is quickly regained once alcohol consumption resumes. A person tolerant to the effects of alcohol is also tolerant to the effects of many other CNS-depressant drugs. Physical and psychological dependence are common among alcohol misusers.

When an alcohol-dependent person stops drinking, the individual will experience withdrawal symptoms ranging from mild to severe. Withdrawal may consist of shakes or tremulousness (nearly always over the first two days after cessation of drinking), anxiety and agitation, flushing of the skin, sweating, sleeplessness, and restlessness. Seizures may occur during the first 48 hours, with a peak frequency between 13 to 18 hours, and may continue up to five days after alcohol consumption ends. This can be followed by hallucinations, intense psychomotor agitation, and acute anxiety. Delirium tremens (DTs) can start suddenly and usually peak three days after the last drink. Paranoia and disorientation to time, place, and person are also common, as is intense restlessness, fever, and profuse sweating (Hancock & McKim, 2018).

Combining alcohol with cannabis or any other CNS depressant can intensify the combined effects to a potentially lethal level. Although extremely large doses of alcohol can kill by suppressing the brain's autonomic nervous system's control over breathing, this rarely happens as a drinker typically passes out before a lethal dose can be taken or vomits before all of the ingested alcohol can be absorbed. The lethal blood alcohol level (BAL) for humans is approximately 0.5 percent, although heavy drinkers with an enhanced tolerance to the drug have been known to survive considerably higher levels. The phases of an alcohol overdose consist of confused thinking, poor judgment, mood swings, poor concentration, marked muscle coordination problems, slurred speech, nausea and vomiting, anaesthesia (sleepiness), memory lapses, and finally respiratory failure, coma, and, as with excessive amounts of any CNS depressant, possibly death.

CHAPTER 9

Opioids

Opioids are also referred to as narcotics, opiates (opium derivatives), narcotic analgesics, and opioid analgesics, though "opioids" is the most inclusive term. Opioids are found in nature and occur in both synthetic and semi-synthetic forms. They mimic endogenous endorphins neurotransmitters, which occur naturally in the body. The use of opium is described in the writings of the Sumerians as early as 4000 BCE. The ancient Greeks knew about the uses of poppy juice, or opion, and described the occurrence of tolerance and dependence. During the Middle Ages, the plant was used by Arab physicians for sedation, analgesia, and relief of dysentery, and Arab traders are thought to have introduced this psychoactive drug to the Far East at that time. The majority of opium currently harvested for licit use by Canadians comes from Afghanistan, Tasmania, and Turkey. These poppy fields are owned by international pharmaceutical corporations and are under strict government control.

Opium from the Asian poppy *Papaver somniferum* is eaten or smoked. While many opioids are injected intravenously, the popular perception of the way to administer this substance, they may also be smoked, taken orally, or across mucous membrane. Opioid analgesics can be classified with CNS depressants, as both slow CNS functioning. However, along with their disinhibiting characteristics, opioids also remove the emotional reaction to pain. They do not eliminate pain; rather, they mask it and assist people in dealing with its psychological component (Zhao et al., 2007). Opioids also slow down the gastrointestinal tract and act as a cough suppressant, as one of their primary effects is depression of the medulla oblongata, which is responsible for controlling cardiac, respiratory, and vasomotor centres. Opioids, like all psychoactive agents, are metabolized mainly in the liver. Excretion occurs largely via the kidneys, although some metabolites are excreted in the feces. Elimination is usually complete in a few hours, although a few members of this family of drugs, notably methadone and buprenorphine, are metabolized and excreted much more slowly.

Opioids are used medically to relieve acute pain as a result of disease, surgery, or injury; in the treatment of some forms of acute heart failure; and in the control of diarrhea.

They are also of great value in the control of chronic pain in the later stages of terminal illnesses, such as cancer, where dependence and dose levels are no longer an issue. Opium customarily produces an exaggerated feeling of well-being and a temporary release from anxiety. Despite their media portrayal, opioids are relatively benign in comparison with other psychoactive agents. The most harmful long-term implication of opioid use is often the lifestyle users maintain, which is primarily a result of the global prohibition against heroin. Perhaps because of this, the non-medical use of prescribed opioids has increased dramatically in Canada over the past decade. Doctors grapple with balancing the pain-masking benefits of opioids with the risk of creating dependency if they are overused or misused (Nosyk et al., 2012). With illicit use, particularly injection drug use, abscesses, bacterial heart infections, cellulitis, liver disease, HIV, hepatitis C, and possible brain damage may result from infections associated with unsterile injection techniques. Pulmonary complications, including various types of pneumonia, may also result from an unhealthy lifestyle, as well as the depressant effect of opioids on respiration. Emboli— small, undissolved particles or air bubbles—may block small blood vessels in the lungs, brain, heart, or other organs. With chronic use, weight loss, reduction in testosterone, and suppression of the immune system are common. As well, the greater the daily dose level of opioid, the greater the risk for road trauma (Goodman, 2013; Levinthal, 2012).

Tolerance to the many effects of opioids, including respiratory depression, analgesia, sedation, nausea, and enhancement of mood, develops within days of continuous use, though overdose remains a concern. If administration is intermittent, little change in drug sensitivity is observed. However, regular users become both psychologically and physically dependent on opioids. Chronic opioid use is defined as a person who has filled 10 or more prescriptions or has received more than 120 continual days' supply of an opioid in the first year after an incident, including but not limited to a surgical procedure. If a person has undergone surgery, the first 90 days are not included. This is in part because individuals with chronic, non-cancer pain prescribed opioids for as little as 90 days have triple the incidence of drug dependency compared to those who receive other medications. However, this rate increases dramatically the more potent the opioid and if the prescription extends beyond 90 days (Perkins et al., 2019). The consensus that is building is that there is great value in using opioids for acute pain, for post-surgery pain, and for individuals who are palliative, but not for those with chronic pain conditions (Busse et al., 2017; Schembri, 2019).

Opioids cross the placenta, as do all other psychoactive drugs, and thus withdrawal has the same physical effects on the fetus as it does on the drug-using mother. During pregnancy, withdrawal from opioids has been associated with placental abruption, which could be life-threatening for the woman. When an infant is born to a mother who is dependent on opioids, there is a recognizable withdrawal syndrome, known as Neonatal Abstinence Syndrome (NAS). NAS consists of central nervous system irritability including tremors, increased muscle tone, high-pitched crying, seizures, gastrointestinal tract dysfunction highlighted by feeding difficulties, and temperature instability. If not addressed at birth

NAS can be fatal, though it is readily treatable and specific protocols have been developed. Fortunately, no long-term cognitive effects have been observed arising from NAS, unlike with alcohol or solvent use during pregnancy (Jansson & Velez, 2012).

Opioids affect endorphins in the brain, the body's natural pain maskers, along with GABA and dopamine. The binding of opioid drugs to endorphin receptors reduces the excitability of neurons, which is likely the source of the euphoric effect and reduction of the sensation of pain. This is a key issue in that opioids do not kill pain, rather they mask it. Once the opioid is metabolized by the body the pain returns, leading to repeated and eventually increased use of the drug if the underlying reason for the pain is not resolved. The euphoric effect produced by all opioids appears to involve the GABA-inhibitory inter-neurons, which reduce the amount of GABA released. This in turn reduces the amount of dopamine released. By inhibiting this inhibitor, opioids increase the amount of dopamine produced and the amount of pleasure felt. However, a complicated relationship exists between the opioid receptor system and the dopamine system, with blockage of one or the other interfering with but not completely removing the reinforcing effects of opioids on the brain. This is partially responsible for some of the odd physiological effects observed, such as when tolerance to euphoria develops, but there is no equivalent tolerance to respiratory depression. Altering endorphin levels in the brain creates respiratory depression, along with euphoria, sedation, decreased gastrointestinal motility, spinal analgesia, sedation, dyspnea (shortness of breath), tolerance, withdrawal, dysphoria during withdrawal, and ultimately dependency. Changes in brain biochemistry resulting from the use of opioids are not temporary. Both chronic and, in some cases, limited use of drugs can produce long-lasting changes in brain neurochemistry, as well as in cell development and structure (Trescot et al., 2008).

Patterns of purposeful drug-seeking behaviour associated with opioids are difficult to break, and the return to drug-using rate is significant. Withdrawal from opioids, which may begin as early as a few hours after the last administration, produces uneasiness, chills, nausea and vomiting, stomach cramps and diarrhea, insomnia, fever, irritability, restlessness, excessive sweating, and crawling skin sensations known as parasthesia (Gevirtz et al., 2011). These symptoms are accompanied by a substantive craving for the drug. Withdrawal symptoms typically start from 8 to 16 hours after the last administration of the opioid, and the shorter the half-life of the drug, the quicker the onset of symptoms. The worst symptoms peak in intensity between 36 to 72 hours after cessation of drug use. The primary withdrawal syndrome typically lasts from five to eight days, though a much longer period with milder symptoms is not unusual. Some bodily functions may not return to normal levels for as long as six months, depending on how long the drug was administered. Sudden withdrawal by heavily dependent users who are in poor health has occasionally been fatal. However, withdrawal is much less dangerous to life than are alcohol, barbiturate, and non-barbiturate sedative-hypnotic-induced withdrawal syndromes, though ironically far more painful. Overall, the symptoms are similar to an extremely severe, exceedingly aching, long-lasting case of the flu. With opioids, overdose is of much greater concern than withdrawal. An overdose of opioids is indicated by the combination of pinpoint pupils, depressed respiration, and ultimately coma. Death almost always results from respiratory depression within a few hours of administration, although late complications such as pneumonia, pulmonary edema, or shock can also be fatal.

Opioids can be categorized into the following groups:

- *Natural opioids or opioid alkaloids*: derived directly from opium or dried poppy juice, including codeine (methylmorphine), morphine, and opium
- *Semi-synthetic opioids*: chemically modified versions of opioid alkaloids like codeine or morphine, which are typically more potent than the natural form of the drug, including heroin, hydromorphone (Dilaudid), and oxycodone (Perocet and Percodan)
- *Synthetic opioids*: produced to mimic the effects of natural opioids with only minimal structural similarities to opium, including fentanyl, hydrocodone (Novahistex DH), meperidine (Demerol), methadone, and propoxyphene (Darvon)

As well, there is a subgroup of non-psychoactive drugs known as *opioid antagonists*, which, when administered, counteract the effects of opioids, primarily respiratory depression, though they have also been used for other therapeutic purposes. These include naloxone (Narcan), naltrexone (Revia), and pentazocine (Talwin).

NATURAL OPIOIDS

Codeine (methylmorphine)

slang: AC/DC, Captain Cody, cody, coties, dreamer, fours, nods, school boy, syrup, sizzurp (codeine, antihistamine, Sprite, and dissolved Jolly Rancher candy)

Codeine is derived from the opium poppy. It is a drug of comparatively low potency used in cough syrups and in preparations containing non-opioid pain suppressants such as aspirin. In Canada, low doses can be bought without a prescription in some jurisdictions. Discovered in 1832, codeine is often used by opioid-dependent persons when more potent drugs are unavailable as it is metabolized into morphine by the liver. It is also partially subject to non-medical use because of its ready availability. Dependence, tolerance, and withdrawal are similar to that experienced by a morphine misuser, though much less intense. Due to potential negative effects, codeine is no longer recommended for use in Canada by children under the age of 12 or by breastfeeding mothers, who metabolize the drug quickly. As with other, more potent opioids, a toxic reaction to codeine includes dizziness, confusion, extreme drowsiness, and shortness of breath or difficulty breathing, and if the dose is high enough, seizures (Health Canada, 2013).

Morphine

slang: dreamer, first line, God's drug, M, Miss Emma, Mr. Blue, monkey, morph, mud,
         Murphy, white stuff

Like codeine, morphine is a natural substance derived from the opium poppy. It is used clinically for pain management, especially continuous dull pain, and is a standard treatment for many forms of extreme pain. Discovered in 1803, it has the second-greatest dependency liability after heroin. Morphine inhibits GABA neurons via the opioid receptors, resulting in an increase in dopamine input and enhancing a sense of euphoria. Most commonly injected, it can also be smoked, inhaled, or swallowed. As morphine is not as lipid soluble as heroin, codeine, or methadone, onset of action is not as prompt. Drowsiness and mental clouding occur at doses higher than those required for pain relief. Lethargy and impaired concentration and cognition are also common with the use of this psychoactive agent (Hancock and McKim, 2018).

Opium

slang: A-bomb (when mixed with cannabis), aunti, Aunti Emma, big O, black pill,
         Chinese molasses, Chinese tobacco, dream stick, dreams, God's medicine, joy
         plant, midnight oil, O

Opium is a crude resinous preparation obtained from the unripened seed pods of the opium poppy. It has an unpleasant odour and bitter taste that frequently produce nausea when it is consumed. Morphine comprises approximately 6–12 percent of the bulk of crude opium, with codeine comprising 0.5–1.5 percent. Opium is smoked because of its euphoric properties, while clinically it can be used to treat diarrhea and dysentery. However, it has been largely replaced as an analgesic by other naturally occurring, semi-synthetic, and wholly synthetic substitutes, such as morphine, hydromorphone, and meperidine. Nonetheless, a highly purified form of opium marketed as Pantopan is still occasionally used when a person cannot tolerate morphine. Dependence and tolerance are much lower and less marked with opium than with morphine.

"Doda" is the term used for ground dried poppy pods or poppy heads. These grounds are either eaten or more often added to water or tea for their therapeutic effects, primarily among members of the Southeast Asian community. In the past, it could be purchased as a spice in East Indian markets across Canada. Known as "the poor man's heroin," these leftovers of opium production induce relaxation and calm rather than the euphoric effect of most other members of this family of psychoactive substances. The drug does not enter Canada in its powder form, but as legally imported dried flowers for flower arrangements. The tea version is often so mild that it is not classified as a narcotic. However, despite its low levels of opium, it is still possible to become physically and psychologically dependent on doda.

SEMI-SYNTHETIC OPIOIDS

Buprenorphine

slang: bupe, orange guys, subs, subbies

Buprenorphine is a partial opioid agonist that produces less sedation than methadone and morphine, which are full opioid agonists, while decreasing cravings for other opioids and preventing opioid withdrawal. The effects of buprenorphine peak one to four hours after the initial dose. Adverse effects are similar to those of other opioids, and include nausea, vomiting, and constipation. Buprenorphine is well tolerated and comparatively safe to use during pregnancy compared with other opioids. However, Neonatal Abstinence Syndrome can still occur, as with all opioids (Srivastava & Kahan, 2006).

The primary use for buprenorphine is as an alternative to methadone in the maintenance and treatment of opioid dependence. It has also been found to significantly decrease NAS when provided sublingually, resulting in a shorter duration of treatment and hospital stay for infants compared to treatment with other opioids such as morphine (Kraft et al., 2017). Buprenorphine is typically used in combination with naloxone (see below) to create Suboxone, which, if taken sublingually, will safely stave off the withdrawal effects of opioids. If taken intravenously, however, Suboxone will trigger an immediate withdrawal reaction as it bypasses the liver and proceeds directly through the blood-brain barrier to the CNS. Buprenorphine has a much lower risk of overdose than methadone and is also more effective in tapering as it has less severe withdrawal effects. While buprenorphine is safer for use than methadone for individuals at risk for respiratory depression, such as elderly patients and those taking benzodiazepines, it is far more expensive. The therapeutic dose range is 8–16 mg daily (Kahan et al., 2011).

Heroin (diacetylmorphine or diamorphine)

slang: Aunt Hazel, Bart Simpson, big H, big Harry, black tar, blue velvet, bobby brown, brown crystal, dust, girl, H, hardball (mixed with cocaine), horse, junk, Mexican Mud, nickel deck, scag, smack, speedball (mixed with cocaine), red chicken, spider

Heroin, derived from the German *heroisch*, meaning "powerful," was initially synthesized in 1874 in England from morphine but was not marketed until 1898 by Bayer in Germany. Heroin is a powerful semi-synthetic opioid analgesic, much more potent than morphine in its psychoactive effects. Like so many other drugs, it was initially marketed as presenting no addiction risk. This, of course, was later demonstrated to be grossly incorrect, but not until it was in wide use as a cough syrup and to decrease chest pain from pneumonia and tuberculosis (Levinthal, 2012).

Through its ability to widen blood vessels, heroin provides a feeling of warmth. The euphoria it produces has been regularly described as an orgasmic-like high, along with a feeling of detachment from life. Although it has only ever been used by a very small percentage of persons and regularly ranks among the drugs least used by Canadians, it remains widely publicized due to the lucrative drug trade and the continuing controversy over its medical use. Heroin is a highly effective pain masker. It has been approved on a limited basis for managing the severe pain associated with terminal illness and for limited use when methadone is not effective. Physical effects may include restlessness, vomiting, nausea, fatigue, dry mouth, and a warm, heavy feeling throughout the body. Other physical effects are constipation, increased urination, contraction of the pupils, itchy skin, and slowed breathing. With larger doses, pupils contract to pinpoints, the skin becomes cold, moist, and bluish, and breathing becomes slowed or even stops, thereby causing death. Long-term effects can include pulmonary complications, constipation, menstrual irregularities in women, and reduction in reproductive hormone levels for both men and women (Trescot et al., 2008).

Tolerance to heroin develops rapidly with regular use, and both physical and psychological dependence occurs. Overdose is generally due to users injecting pure or minimally cut heroin rather than the typical dose, which tends to be diluted with substances such as sugar, baking soda, or baby powder. Withdrawal symptoms usually appear four to five hours after the last dose and can be quite severe. They often last 7 to 10 days and include severe anxiety, insomnia, increased perspiration, chills, shivering, and tremors. The pain of withdrawal has been said to be more like that of bone cancer than of severe flu. However, as previously stated, while highly unpleasant and physically painful, withdrawal is much less life-threatening than that from heavy use of alcohol, barbiturates, or non-barbiturate sedative-hypnotics. Heroin is used primarily by intravenous injection, though it can also be smoked, inhaled, swallowed, and administered by skin-popping. Due to its extremely high dependence liability, it is one of the few drugs that is globally prohibited (Sproule, 2004).

Hydromorphone (Dilaudid)

slang: D's, delats, dillies, hospital heroin, hydro, juice, M2s

Synthesized in 1936, hydromorphone is also a morphine derivative. It is a potent analgesic used to mask severe pain and to suppress the cough reflex. It can be administered both orally and intravenously, though the latter tends to produce pain and tissue irritation when the drug is used chronically. Dilaudid produces less nausea, vomiting, and drowsiness than does morphine but more intense respiratory depression. This drug has a pain-masking potential that is seven to eight times that of morphine. Tolerance and physical dependence develop, with withdrawal symptoms also similar to that of a severe, long-lasting, painful flu. Psychological features of withdrawal are depression, anxiety, insomnia, and loss of appetite, combined with periods of agitation. As well, a smaller amount of hydromorphone is required to produce an overdose when compared with other opioids (Table 9.1). Its pharmacodynamic profile, including onset of action and time to peak levels, is similar to heroin, and in double-blind experiments, situations when neither

Table 9.1: Opioid Potency Comparison

Potency*	Drug	Trade Names
100	Fentanyl	
40	Buprenorphine	Suboxone
10*	Heroin	*depending upon purity
10	Methadone	
8	Levorphanol	
7	Oxymorphone	Numorphan
5	Hydromorphone	Dilaudid
3	Desomorphine	Permonid
1.5	Oxycodone	Percocet, OxyContin
1.2	Hydrocodone	Vicodin
1	Morphine	
0.5	Tramadol	Ultram, Conzip
0.5	Tapentadol	Tapal, Nucynta, Palexia
0.4	Meperidine	Demerol
0.2	Dihydrocodeine	Panlor
0.1	Codeine	Tylenol 3
0.07	Propoxyphrene	Davron

Note: *The opioid potency scale is based on morphine = 1, and the relevant potency of all other opioids is in comparison to morphine.
Sources: Pereira et al. (2001); Vieweg et al. (2005).

user nor experimenter are aware of what substance is being administered, the effects of hydromorphone could not be distinguished from heroin (Fulton et al., 2012).

An extended-release form of hydromorphone hydrolcholoride, manufactured by Purdue Pharma (2004), is also available. Marketed as Palladone, it too is a controlled substance and is available in 12 mg, 16 mg, 24 mg, and 32 mg capsules. It is intended only for adults with long-term constant, chronic pain. However, as with any extended- or gradual-release drug, if it is chewed or crushed, the drug is released much faster than intended. A significant euphoric reaction can then be obtained, and a risk of overdose occurs.

Oxycodone (Percodan)/OxyContin (oxycodone HCl controlled-release)

slang: blue, cotton, hillybilly heroin, kicker, killers, O's, OC, Ox, Oxy, Oxycoffin, Oxycotton, Percs

Oxycodone, first produced in 1938, is created by modifying codeine. It is a white, odourless crystalline powder used to treat moderate to severe pain. It has powerful mood-enhancing, analgesic, and sedative effects. It is available alone or in combination with non-opioid analgesics, such as acetylsalicylic acid (Percodan) or acetaminophen (Percocet). Administration is intended to be exclusively oral. Oxycodone has the potential to produce powerful physical dependence in users because of its potent effects, especially if not administered orally.

OxyContin was developed in 1995 by Purdue Pharma. It was made available in Canada in 1996 as a time-release version of oxycodone for use in the management of moderate to severe pain when a continuous, around-the-clock analgesic is needed for an extended period of time. OxyContin was originally intended for use with individuals who had already developed a level of opioid dependency for chronic pain, and thus it has the potential to lead to death through respiratory depression among non-tolerant individuals, even if used properly. However, it soon became a drug of choice by prescribing general practitioners not only for its analgesic effects, but also because it was initially marketed as being non-addictive. OxyContin, however, has a potency 16 times greater than a single Percocet. Issues also arose with this opioid when, rather than being administered as intended, when its use is not much more problematic than other opioids, it was instead crushed and injected or simply chewed and then swallowed, leading to a rapid release of the opioid properties that were intended to be gradually released, producing a potent psychoactive effect. This altered method of administration has led to issues with diversion and increased reports of overdose and death and was the foundation for the current opioid crisis. Over a five-year period, of the people coming to the medical withdrawal service of the Centre for Addiction and Mental Health in Toronto, Ontario, for the treatment of opioid dependence, those having a problem with OxyContin increased steadily from fewer than 4 percent to 55 percent (Sproule et al., 2009). To mitigate public concern,

OxyContin was replaced by its manufacturer with OxyNeo, which provides similar pain management but when crushed turns into a gooey gel making it more difficult, though not impossible, to alter and administer in an unintended manner. The rate of OxyContin overdoses after the introduction of OxyNeo fell substantively, however, there was a corresponding increase in heroin use that was soon followed with fentanyl being introduced into the drug supply (see Box 9.1).

A major component of the OxyContin controversy was its marketing. Heavily promoted by Purdue Pharma as being a safe opioid, it became one of the top-selling prescription drugs in North America. Sales in Canada increased from $3 million in 1998 to $243 million CAD in 2010, at the height of the controversy regarding its safety and misuse. At the University of Toronto, the textbook *Pain Management*, paid for and copyrighted to Purdue, was distributed free to students. Early versions of the book claimed that continuous-release opioids like OxyContin had low misuse potential, and a later edition stated that physicians had an ethical duty to consider opioids for non-cancer patients, contradicting best practice guidelines of the time. Purdue's financial ties to the Canadian medical community are extensive. Of 49 experts on a panel that produced new practice guidelines on using opioids to treat non-cancer patients, 12 were receiving speaking or consulting fees of more than $5,000 a year from Purdue or other pharmaceutical companies. Western University's Dr. Morley-Forster reported that her pain clinic in London received $200,000 from Purdue in one year (Blackwell, 2011).

SYNTHETIC OPIOIDS

Carfentanil

slang: drop dead, grey death, serial killer

The most well-known, legal variant of fentanyl is carfentanil. Carfentanil has a potency 100 times greater than fentanyl, which makes it 10,000 times as potent as morphine for an equivalent dose. Like fentanyl, carfentanil was first synthesized by a team of chemists at Janssen Pharmaceutica. It is intended to anaesthetize large animals and to be used in veterinary medicine and was never meant for human consumption. When mixed into heroin or other street drugs the risk of overdose is heightened even more than with fentanyl, due to carfentanil's far greater potency and lethality (European Monitoring Centre for Drugs and Drug Addiction, 2017).

Fentanyl

slang: Apache, China girl, Chinatown, dance fever, friend, goodfella, great bear, jackpot, king ivory, murder 8, Tango and Cash, TNT

First developed in 1959 for use as a general anaesthetic, fentanyl is a synthetic drug primarily prescribed to provide physical and emotional relief from acute pain, principally for palliative care patients or those with long-term chronic pain who experience breakthrough pain when using other opioids. It has rapid onset and short duration of action. It is thus primarily administered transdermally to make its use more convenient for those who are severely ill, with each patch designed to slowly release the potent substance over 72 hours. However, a sublingual spray and lollipop version that transfers the pain-masking properties via mucous membrane are also available for cancer patients. Fentanyl is quickly metabolized through the liver and has no active metabolites. Within 72 hours, approximately 75 percent of fentanyl is excreted, primarily through the urine as metabolites. Fentanyl is approximately 80–100 times more potent than morphine (Grape et al., 2010), with such a potential for lethality it is used as the chemical means for capital punishment in states such as Nebraska. A noticeable increase in illict use of fentanyl coincided with the prohibition of OxyContin in jurisdictions across North America (see Box 9.1).

Box 9.1: The Opioid Crisis

Oxycodone in the form of Perocet and Percodan became a well-established mechanism to mask minor to major pain, leading it to be regularly prescribed and used. As with many opioids there was some misuse leading to addiction, but not an extraordinary amount. An attribute of these substances that did lead to excessive misuse is that oxycodone has a relatively short half-life and needs to be taken every four hours to maintain its effect. However, this was also burdensome to many, as it required taking the drug upwards of six times per day. OxyContin was a resolution to this issue. It has the same pharmacology of oxycodone with one major exception—it is a time-released version and only needed to be taken orally once every 12 hours. This intended administration method, versus subsequent methods, became one of the contributing factors to the opioid epidemic that has gripped North America. Individuals quickly learned that rather than swallowing the pill, OxyContin could be crushed and administered via mucous membrane (sniffed through the nose), producing a far greater impact in a far shorter period of time, including a euphoric effect in minutes with a drug that was intended to provide pain relief for up to half a day. However, that was only part of the issue. Through the latter half of the 20th century and into the early 21st century, there was a belief within the medical community that there was a low risk of addiction with OxyContin, even when used for extended periods of time, if the presenting issue was chronic pain. However, what was even more problematic was the active marketing campaign that drug companies were about to start, led by Purdue Pharma but including others such as Abbott Laboratories.

There have been increases in opioid use globally throughout the 21st century from developed nations as geographically disparate as England and France in Europe to Australia and New Zealand in the Pacific Rim. However, increasing opioid use in those nations was not nearly as substantive as that in Canada and the United States. This has been directly attributed to differences in both the prescribing practices and the characteristics of the health services in these countries. Canadians are the second-highest users per capita of opioids in the world, only behind Americans. In North America, there was not only lucrative compensation for sales staff but also, in the United States, financial payments to physicians who prescribed large amounts of OxyContin when it was first introduced. This encouraged sales staff to be creative in minimizing the potential risks of OxyContin when speaking to physicians, and in some cases promoting OxyContin as a non-addictive opioid agent. These were not simply errors by those not trained in the pharmacology of the drug, but outright lies: OxyContin has the same chemical composition as oxycodone, a drug long known to produce physical and psychological dependency. These tactics contributed to OxyContin sales rising from $64 million CAD in its first full year of sales in North America to over $2.1 billion by 2002. By the time Purdue Pharma filed for bankruptcy protection in 2019, estimates of total OxyContin sales were $40 billion CAD for North America, making the family who privately owned the company among the richest in the United States. This, however, was only the foundation for the opioid crisis. After a decade of these practices the increase in opioid use became evident to public health officials and addiction counsellors. A proper response would have been to increase treatment, both pharmacological and psychosocial, but the actual response precipitated the drug crisis: limiting access to and outright prohibition of the drug with no enhanced counselling supports.

When you compare the potency of various opioids (Table 9.1) you will note that OxyContin is more potent than morphine by one-half. When an individual is dependent on a drug and that drug is taken away, it is rare that the person goes down the potency scale, as the drug will not provide the same level of euphoria nor will it be as effective in mitigating withdrawal effects. The functional response is to seek out opioids further up the potency scale. Addiction specialists predicted that with the restrictions placed upon OxyContin there would be a surge in heroin use, which is exactly what occurred. What caught nearly the entire field by surprise, however, was the introduction of fentanyl into the drug supply. From an economic perspective, it was a brilliant move by drug dealers.

Heroin is expensive, not to cultivate or harvest, but because it is an illicit drug. The cost to smuggle and sell the drug increases its price over 3,000 percent compared to the cost of other licit opioids, all of which are derived from the same pharmacological source. Fentanyl is a licit opioid. It has been used for decades with a small population of individuals undergoing short-term but serious surgical procedures, those with long-term chronic pain who have become tolerant to less potent opioids, and those who were terminally ill and for whom issues of addiction were no longer a pressing issue. By mixing small quantities of fentanyl with heroin, drug dealers were able to produce a far more potent mixture at a far lower cost. However, as this process is haphazard and inconsistent, often there are "hot spots" in the mixture. Hot spots are doses where there is a greater concentration of fentanyl and less heroin, making the drug potentially lethal, even to long-term opioid users. When we add globalization to the mix, and large pharmaceutical companies in China finding new export markets in North America, the crisis scenario was almost complete.

Three other unexpected outcomes further fueled the crisis. First, because of cost factors, fentanyl was being added to cocaine and even cannabis before it was legalized in Canada, leading to unintended drug poisonings. Historically, drug dealers were careful not to poison their customers, but this practice in some areas fell away. Second, after experiencing the potency of fentanyl and not overdosing, individuals began to seek out fentanyl-laced heroin to inject. The third and final factor creating the Canadian opioid crisis rests with politics in Canada. As the crisis was just beginning, the ruling government of the time, the Harper Conservatives, led by Minister of Health Rona Ambrose, fought against public health initiatives to open supervised injection sites. They litigated against them at every level in the British Columbia legal system, and when the Supreme Court of British Columbia ruled in favour of supervised injection sites as a public health right, they took the case to the Supreme Court of Canada. After the highest court in the country ruled that supervised injection sites were a health practice and a right of citizenship for Canadians, the Harper government enacted new legislation. The new law allowed the opening of supervised injection sites but only in areas where not one complaint was received, making it virtually impossible to open any new facility. This law was changed by the Liberal government, led by Justin Trudeau, but not until thousands of potentially preventable deaths had occurred across Canada and fentanyl-laced illicit drugs had become part of the drug chain.

Between 2016 and 2018, 11,577 premature deaths of Canadians have been attributed to opioids, with the rate rising from 8.4 to 12.0 deaths per 100,000 Canadians. Three quarters of those dying are men, with the percentage attributed to fentanyl poisoning rising from 50 percent in 2016 to 70 percent in 2018. Only premature death from tobacco and alcohol exceeds this rate, though those tend to occur, on average, at a greater age than individuals dying from opioids. Not surprisingly, it is individuals from lower-income neighbourhoods who are at a far greater risk from being harmed using opioids.

Sources: Barry et al. (2016); Cairncross et al. (2018); Canadian Institute for Health Information (2016); Canadian Public Health Association (2016); Government of Canada (2019a); Leung et al. (2017); Standing Committee on Health (2016).

Hydrocodone (Novahistex DH)

slang: vikings

Hydrocodone, synthesized in 1955, is more potent than codeine and is the psychoactive component of Vicodin. It was initially intended for use as a cough suppressant: an antitussive. However, it was quickly discovered upon wider clinical distribution that high doses can produce euphoria and sedation, and it quickly became used as a pain-masking agent despite its substantive misuse potential. Dependence to hydrocodone is greater than that to codeine, with tolerance also occurring much more rapidly. The severity of the withdrawal reaction ranges between that produced by codeine and that by morphine (Walsh et al., 2008).

Meperidine (Demerol)

slang: peth

One of the earliest synthesized opioids, meperidine was first made available in Germany in 1939, just prior to World War II. It is effective as a short-acting oral analgesic. It can also produce central nervous system excitement at high doses, manifested by muscle twitches, tremor, and agitation. It remains widely used in clinical settings, though with chronic administration metabolites can accumulate and give rise to toxic reactions. Meperidine produces both physical and psychological dependence similar to that of morphine, though tolerance is slower in developing. Withdrawal begins in three hours, peaks in eight to twelve hours, and ends in four to five days. There is little nausea, vomiting, and diarrhea, but muscle twitching, restlessness, and anxiety are much worse than with morphine (Hancock & McKim, 2018).

Methadone

slang: dollies, done, fizzies, juice, meth, my drink, the drink

Methadone is a white crystalline powder or colourless crystals. While available in tablet form, it is administered in a liquid form in its current primary global use in harm reduction. Methadone is a long-acting analgesic with properties similar to those of morphine. Its synthesis began prior to World War II in the laboratories of the German pharmaceutical company IG Farben as an alternative to opium-based analgesics. It is unlike morphine in that it is highly effective when administered orally. As it is excreted slowly, it is effective for up to 24 hours. Methadone is currently used primarily as substitution therapy for opioid-dependent individuals as it produces morphine-like actions and cross-tolerance but does not produce euphoria for opioid users when given orally. However, tolerance and withdrawal do occur in methadone users, as does a degree of sedation initially, though development is much slower than with other opioids. Without other forms of intervention, chronic users become both psychologically and physically dependent on methadone just as they were to the drug that has been substituted. Ternes and O'Brien (1990) claimed that a street heroin user can be placed on methadone and then weaned off within 10 days, yet there are Canadians who have been receiving methadone for more than 20 years with no intention to move to cessation. Methadone is no longer used exclusively with those moving away from heroin use. Its use has been expanded to replace opioids in general, including less potent opioids. While methadone is very effective, it requires careful adherence to dosing guidelines and close monitoring because its long half-life increases the risk of overdose. Methadone provides a helpful tool for reducing some components of craving and drug use reoccurrence, with its use directly responsible for decreased risk of mortality among individuals who had been misusing other opioids (Cousins et al., 2016).

Methadone's side effects include weight gain (due to lowered metabolism), dental issues (due to decreased salivation), constipation, numbness in extremities, sedation, and, for some, hallucinations. Long-term use will also create sexual dysfunction due to decreased testosterone levels in males, as occurs with chronic use of any opioid. Those in methadone maintenance programs may thus require testosterone supplements as treatment adjuncts (Samaan, 2014). An interesting unintended side effect is methadone's ability to kill leukemia cells, which anti-cancer drugs commonly used in conventional therapies failed to kill (Friesen et al. 2008).

Propoxyphene (Davron)

slang: none known

Propoxyphene is a mild analgesic used to relieve mild to moderate pain as an alternative to codeine. Synthesized in 1955, dependency on, tolerance to, and withdrawal from Davron are similar to that produced by codeine. Davron has one-half to two-thirds the potency of codeine when administered orally. It is sold alone or in combination with acetylsalicylic acid (ASA) and was regularly among the top 10 most-prescribed substances in North America in the latter half of the 20th century. Misuse is minimal as high doses produce dizziness, skin rashes, skin irritation, and, if injected, the risk of toxic psychosis.

ANTAGONISTS

Naloxone (Narcan)

slang: no street use

Naloxone is a pure antagonist, with no pain relief or psychoactive properties. Naloxone's primary therapeutic use is to reverse the opioid-induced respiratory depression that is commonly observed in cases of overdose. However, this drug will not reverse the respiratory depression caused by high doses of other psychoactive drugs. Naloxone begins working within 30 seconds of injection and even quicker when inhaled. It can also be used in the control of seizures induced by meperidine or propoxyphene. Naloxone kits have become a core, cost-effective harm reduction response to the North American opioid crisis (Coffin & Sullivan, 2013; McDonald & Strang, 2016). When Naloxone is administered to an opioid-free individual, there is little or no discernible effect other than occasional mild dysphoria. When orally administered, naloxone can also improve symptoms of opioid associated constipation, which is common in those using opioids to address issues of chronic pain (Meissner et al., 2000). Suboxone, a safer though more expensive alternative to methadone, is a combination of four parts buprenorphine to one-part naloxone.

Naltrexone (Revia)

slang: no street use

Naltrexone is an antagonist with properties similar to those of naloxone, but with a much longer duration of action. As with naloxone, even after prolonged use its discontinuation does not produce any withdrawal effects, respiratory depression, gross behavioural effects, or euphoria. Naltrexone is very efficient at suppressing the effects of heroin. This allows it to be used as a protective drug with heroin users as Antabuse and Temposil once were with alcohol-dependent persons. Clinical trials have demonstrated that those using extended-release naltrexone are more likely to remain abstinent than when only counselling is provided, with return to opioid use increasing when naltrexone is no longer provided (Krystal et al., 2001; Lee et al., 2018). As well, at doses of 50 mg, naltrexone can work to reduce cravings for alcohol and it has also been touted for use with persons who have impulse control disorders, such as gambling and kleptomania (Kirchmayer et al., 2003; Litten & Allen, 1998). More recently, at lower doses of 2–12 mg, naltrexone has been demonstrated to have anti-inflammatory properties that mitigate symptoms of chronic fatigue syndrome, Crohn's disease, and fibromyalgia (Bolton et al., 2020; Polo et al., 2019).

Pentazocine (Talwin)

slang: tall, T's and Blues (mixed with antihistamines), kibbles and bits, one and ones, poor man's heroin, ritz & T's, T's & R's (mixed with Ritalin)

Pentazocine, synthesized in 1962, is a weak opioid antagonist with moderate analgesic properties, though it is more accurately classified as an agonist-antagonist rather than a pure antagonist. Pentazocine was created to relieve pain without producing a dependence or leading to misuse, as does use of other narcotic analgesics. Tolerance can develop, though it is slower than with most opioids. Talwin has no cross-tolerance with any other opioid. Withdrawal effects include abdominal cramps, chills, hypothermia, vomiting, and both a physical and psychological craving for the drug. Unfortunately, when combined with the antihistamine tripelennamine hydrochloride, such as Benzoxal, and injected, a heroin-like effect is produced. This combination is referred to as "T's and Blues." Combining Talwin with Ritalin produces a similar effect. Attempts have been made to prevent this mixing by adding naloxone (see above) to create Talwin Nx, but this has not completely stopped the practice.

CHAPTER 10

Stimulants

Stimulants are psychoactive agents that increase not only the activity of the central nervous system but also the autonomic nervous system. Mood enhancement occurs because of these drugs effects, as do mild-to-substantive physiological changes. Upon initial ingestion of a stimulant euphoria is typically produced, followed by excitement and then agitation among the more potent members of this family of drugs. Higher doses produce irritability, violent behaviour, spasms, convulsions, and, in infrequent extreme cases, death, which is even possible with excessive caffeine use. More common and frequent short-term effects include enhanced concentration, increased vigilance, increased blood pressure, increased strength, reduced fatigue, reduced appetite, and feelings of power. While all stimulants increase alertness, as a family, they exhibit considerable differences in the nature of their effects and in their relative potencies.

Central nervous system stimulants include:

- Cocaine
- Amphetamines
- Methamphetamine
- Methylphenidate (drugs to treat attention-deficit/hyperactivity disorder)
- Anorexiants
- Decongestants
- Khat
- Bath salts (methylendioxypyrovalerone and mephedrone)
- Betel
- Nicotine
- Caffeine

COCAINE

slang: Angie, base (crack), baseball (crack), bazooka (mixed with cannabis), beam me
up Scotty (mixed with PCP), Bernie's Flakes, big C, blow, boy, C, bonecrusher
(crack), coke, crack, flake, hardball (mixed with heroin), hunter, jelly, king's habit,
line, nose candy, nose powder, Peruvian lady, snow, snowflake, speedball (mixed
with heroin), stardust, white horse, Yale

At the close of the 19th century, cocaine hydrochloride was the world's newest wonder
drug, touted as a cure for everything from morphine addiction to tuberculosis. It was a
component of wine approved by the Vatican and a variety of patent medicines, including
cough drops for children, and, of course, a soft drink to counter the evils of consuming
alcohol. Cocaine is a mixture of a local anaesthetic and a central and sympathetic nervous
system stimulant. It produces its psychoactive effect by directly inhibiting the reuptake
of dopamine in the CNS. This increases the availability of dopamine in the synapse and
increases dopamine's action on postsynaptic neurons, producing enhanced mood along
with euphoria. Cocaine has a short half-life, prompting users to repeatedly administer
cocaine to re-experience its intense subjective effects. With continued use of cocaine, the
body relies upon this drug to maintain rewarding feelings. The person is no longer able to
feel the positive reinforcement or pleasurable feelings of other basic rewards such as food,
water, or sex. It has also been discovered that the brain's dopamine system is related to
mental health issues and that any negative changes that occur during adolescence due to
drug use may not be reversible later in life, including alterations that lead to lifelong cravings for psychoactive drugs (Euopean Monitoring Centre for Drugs and Drug Addiction,
2009a; Siciliano et al., 2016).

There are 250 different coca plants, though cocaine hydrochloride, the powder form
of the drug, is extracted primarily from the leaves of the *Erythroxylon coca* bush. This particular coca plant grows on the eastern slopes of the Andes, mainly in Peru and Bolivia,
though two other varieties are also used for cocaine production, one from the Amazonian
basin and the other from Colombia. Traditionally, inhabitants of the Andes mixed coca
with ash or lime and placed it in the mouth like chewing tobacco. The juice was allowed
to trickle into the stomach and served as a mild stimulant to facilitate heavy labour at
high altitudes. Its cultivation for medicinal purposes, such as stomach upset, colic, nausea,
diarrhea, headache, dizziness, toothache, ulcers, asthma, and fatigue, dates to the begin-
nings of recorded history in South America. Coca leaves are also a source of vitamin B
and vitamin C. Cocaine was also used extensively as an anaesthetic for eye operations,
dentistry, and facial surgery and remained a preferred local anaesthetic in a few circumstances in Canada until the beginning of the 21st century. Currently some coca is still
legally grown in Peru and Bolivia for processing into de-cocalized flavouring agents that
are sold to international manufacturers of soft drinks. Coca is widely available throughout
public markets and stores throughout Andes nations, with no restrictions on the sale of

coca tea, leaves, or mints (Csiernik, 2019; European Monitoring Centre for Drugs and Drug Addiction, 2008).

The extraction process to produce illicit cocaine powder is a very toxic one. It entails mixing coca leaves with a host of toxic chemicals, including kerosene, gasoline, acetone, potassium permanganate or potassium hydroxide, and/or toluene, and then placing the mixture into a press and crushing it to obtain a thick paste. The mixture is then treated with hydrochloride or sulphuric acid to remove further impurities, resulting in crystalline cocaine powder: cocaine hydrochloride. The few legal importers of cocaine, particularly those using it for medical purposes, do not use such a harsh refinement process. Cocaine may be smoked, sniffed (snorted), or injected directly into the veins or rubbed along the gums. To obtain crack from cocaine powder (cocaine hydrochloride), all one needs to do is to add a weak base, such as a combination of baking soda and water. Crack and cocaine are the same substance, only in different forms. Crack is cocaine that can be smoked, while cocaine hydrochloride is not heat-soluble except with significant modification. The absorption of crack is so rapid that a user can experience the drug effect within eight seconds. This rapid delivery to the brain and equally efficient excretion is a major cause of crack cocaine misuse.

Short-term effects of cocaine are similar to those produced by the body's own adrenaline. A naive or infrequent user of cocaine will feel and exhibit a variety of effects, such as enhanced mood, self-confidence and self-esteem, increased energy, increased sex drive, decreased appetite, increased concentration, garrulousness (talkativeness), increased alertness, increased motor activity, anxiety, and rapid respiration. Cocaine also increases body temperature and heart rate, and is a vasoconstrictor, leading to a rise in blood pressure and consequently increasing the risk of stroke among chronic users. High doses can cause cardiac arrhythmia, hypothermia, seizures, and, unlike any other stimulant, respiratory depression. Vomiting also brings its own risk of death by aspiration. With larger doses the person will experience stronger and more frequent "highs," exhibit bizarre, erratic, and sometime violent behaviour, and even paranoid psychosis during periods of sustained administration (coke run). Symptoms subside when administration is discontinued, but periods of severe depression may persist. The risk of convulsions increases with larger doses and sometimes a sensation of something crawling under the skin is perceived. With long-term use, cocaine, when snorted, can cause tissue damage in the nasal passages due to its irritating properties. When smoked over the long-term, cocaine can also cause damage to the lungs and to the pleasure-perceiving portions of the brain. Chronic cocaine use has also been linked to such diverse problems as memory loss and renal failure. Death from overdose can occur either from cocaine alone or in combination with other substances that affect the respiratory control centre in the brain. As cocaine has anaesthetic properties, it is quite dangerous when combined with CNS depressants such as alcohol, barbiturates, or heroin, as it has the increased potential to produce death through respiratory arrest. Anorexia and weight loss, gastrointestinal disturbances, and impotence have also been observed in chronic users, as well as stiffer arteries, higher blood pressure, thicker heart muscles, increased risk of aneurysms, strokes, seizures, and hemorrhaging in tissues surrounding the brain. Cocaine-dependent individuals appear aged compared to their peers, and their mortality rates are up to eight times higher than in the healthy population of equivalent age. Psychological and physiological changes typically associated with old age, such as cognitive decline, brain atrophy, glaucoma, and immunodeficiency, occur in middle-aged cocaine-dependent individuals, with the annual rate of grey matter volume loss in cocaine-dependent individuals almost twice that of healthy non-users (Ersche et al., 2013; Kozor et al., 2014; Sproule, 2004).

Over the course of a single binge, cocaine users become less sensitive to the mood-enhancing effects of the drug and consequently tend to increase the dose in an attempt to compensate for the decreased effect. This acute tolerance has been demonstrated in laboratory situations as well. Their sensitivity to the drug can, however, be restored with a period of abstinence. The powerfully reinforcing effects of cocaine, both as a euphoriant and as a treatment of post-drug craving, are overwhelming for many users. Experiments with laboratory animals suggest that cocaine has among the strongest behaviourally reinforcing qualities of all psychoactive drugs. Rats, given the choice, have selected cocaine over food, water, and access to a sexual partner. Cocaine dependence can have devastating effects on the life of individuals, not only because of the pharmacological effects of the drug, but also due to its cost. Upon abrupt discontinuation of drug administration, abstinence symptoms similar to those associated with amphetamine withdrawal are observed. Symptoms, including fatigue, severe mood depression, lethargy, and irritability, are commonly referred to as the "crash," which can also include abdominal and muscle cramps, dehydration, and a general apathy. As well, information about the risks associated with cocaine use and pregnancy have been widely publicized. Cocaine, like most psychoactive drugs, is transferred across the placenta, and its use may cause placental abruption, the premature detachment of the placenta from the uterus. This can cause bleeding, pre-term birth, and, in severe cases, fetal and maternal death. Women who use cocaine have a significantly greater chance of giving birth prematurely, with the fetus suffering withdrawal symptoms. However, unlike with alcohol and solvents, there is no fetal cocaine syndrome other than the issues arising from the withdrawal process (Lewis et al., 2007; Ross et al., 2015).

Between 450 and 600 kg of coca leaf are required to produce 1 kg of cocaine hydrochloride paste. Historically, a typical Colombian farmer receives on average from $2 to $3 CAD per kilo of coca leaf, while the actual cost of a kilo of cocaine paste is between $800 and $1,300 CAD. By the time the drug has been transported to port to be smuggled out of the country, the price can range from $6,500 to $13,000 CAD, with a markup of 50 percent by the time the drug reaches Central America, and another 50 percent on its reaching the Mexico-US border. A typical kilo that has been successfully smuggled into the United States retailed for approximately $40,000 CAD in 2010, with a gram of refined kilo having an average market price of $220, though there is great variance across the country. However, as the kilo of paste has also undergone chemical alteration that decreases its purity while increasing its weight, a kilo that initially cost as little as $800 at source can now have a street value of over $400,000, or a 500-fold increase in value along the network. The majority of profit is made at the end of the process. Thus, approximately 1 percent of profit is seen at the source, 10 percent in transit, and 66 percent at the point of final distribution (Briones et al., 2013). The trade in cocaine has contributed to hundreds of thousands of deaths across South and Central America. Mexico alone has recorded 275,000 drug related deaths since 2006 with an average of 95 murders per day in 2019, as gangs and cartels fight for control of the lucrative trade and civilians continue to be caught in the crossfire.

AMPHETAMINES

slang: amp, beans, bennies, black and white, black beauty, black cadillacs, black mollies, brain pills, bumblebees, crank, dexies, lid poppers, pep pills, splash, truckers, uppers, wake-ups

Amphetamines are a group of drugs whose action on the body resembles that of adrenaline. They are chemically related to the naturally occurring catecholamine neurotransmitter substances norepinephrine and dopamine. Amphetamines are used to raise energy levels, and reduce appetite and the need for sleep, while providing feelings of clear-headedness and power. Amphetamines initially attracted favourable clinical attention by their reported ability to elevate the mood of clinically depressed persons and to reduce the appetite of the obese. One form of amphetamines, benzedrine inhalers, became popular for the relief of nasal congestion. Amphetamine effects on non-mental state and mood are in many respects similar to those of cocaine: first, relief from fatigue, increased ability to concentrate, and improved physical performance, then euphoria, followed later by depression and fatigue during the withdrawal phase. Amphetamines have been given to combat pilots regularly since World War II, and it is estimated that 200 million amphetamine tablets were distributed to military personnel during that conflict to fight battle fatigue. It had previously been believed that the dependence liability of amphetamines was low, and therefore they have historically been sold widely without prescription as decongestants and, in the United States, as appetite suppressants and legal stimulants (Hancock & McKim, 2018).

Although the first synthesis of amphetamines occurred in 1887, the physiological effects of these compounds were not fully appreciated until the late 1920s. At that time, it was reported that these compounds could constrict blood vessels, increase blood pressure, and dilate the bronchial tubes. Between 1935 and 1945, the mood-altering and stimulant properties of amphetamines were recognized, and they were subsequently used to treat overeating, depression, narcolepsy, Parkinson's disease, hyperactivity in children, and the sedation caused by some anti-epileptic drugs (Sproule, 2004).

Regular use of amphetamines induces tolerance to some effects, making increased doses necessary to produce them. Tolerance does not develop for all effects at the same rate; however, it does develop rapidly for the mood-enhancing effects, necessitating an increase in dosage. While a therapeutic dose averages 30 mg, doses of up to 1 g have been given to tolerant users without them demonstrating any exaggerated effects. Cross-tolerance between amphetamines and other amphetamine-like CNS stimulants has been clinically observed, though there does not appear to be cross-tolerance with cocaine due to their disparate chemistries. Both physical and psychological dependence occur with chronic amphetamine use. Animals made dependent on amphetamines and then withdrawn from them will work very hard to get more of the drug and will keep trying approximately twice as long as similar animals made dependent on heroin. The most common symptoms of withdrawal among heavy users are fatigue, long but disturbed sleep due to disrupted REM cycles, irritability, strong hunger, abdominal and muscle cramps, apathy, and moderate to severe depression, which may lead to suicidal behaviour. Fits of violence have also been frequently observed. These disturbances can be temporarily reversed if the drug is taken again, with the withdrawal itself usually subsiding after several days of abstinence (Levinthal, 2012).

METHAMPHETAMINE

slang: blade, chalk, chrissy, crank, crystal, crystal meth, dust, glass, go, ice, ice cream, quartz, Scooby Snax, tina, weak, whiz, yaba, yellow barn

Methamphetamine enjoyed popularity in Canada in the 1970s, but the harsh toll it took on the body made it a relatively short-lived phenomenon. However, it re-emerged during the rave era of the late 1990s, becoming known as "the poor man's cocaine." The fact that it could be created from chemicals available locally gave it a greater breadth of manufacturing potential than cocaine, which has to be imported. Methamphetamine, like all amphetamines, is a white, odourless, bitter-tasting crystalline powder that can lead to memory loss, aggressive behaviour, violence, and paranoid and psychotic behaviour if misused. Part of this behaviour is because its use allows an individual to remain awake for extended periods of time, not needing to sleep. The prolonged lack of REM sleep and subsequent lack of dreaming are associated with paranoid and psychotic behaviour (NIDA, 2019).

Crystal meth is a synthesized from of methamphetamine that can be smoked, thus creating a fast, intense stimulant response similar to that of crack cocaine, with a much longer duration of 6 to 12 hours. Among the reasons for its popularity is that users initially experience an increased and intensified sex drive, along with feelings of enhanced sexual pleasure. This is because the use of this drug can release up to 12 times as much dopamine in the CNS as eating one's favourite food or engaging in non-drug-enhanced sex. This effect dissipates, though, with as little as six months of regular use. There is no known behaviour that humans engage in that releases even close to the amount of dopamine that is released through the use of this psychoactive substance (United States Department of Justice, 2003c).

Long-term physical effects include damage to the heart and cardiovascular system, liver, kidney, and lungs; memory impairment; mood swings; malnutrition; a decrease in the body's ability to produce sufficient levels of dopamine for normal functioning; and possible premature death through prolonged use. The toxic ingredients used to synthesize the drug also lead to severe tooth decay, labelled "meth mouth." Teeth become blackened and rot to the point where they fall out or need to be pulled because of damage to the gums and roots (Canadian Centre on Substance Abuse [CCSA], 2005; Li et al., 2014; Werb, Rowell et al., 2010; Westover & Nakonezny, 2010). The psychological effects of long-term methamphetamine use include increased risk of anxiety, depression, and paranoia; insomnia; reduced concentration and poor memory; psychosis or psychotic behavior; violence; and homicidal or suicidal thoughts. Regular use of methamphetamine also leads to both physical and psychological dependence (NIDA, 2019).

Methamphetamine has become an increasingly important public health concern in Canada, even if it has not received the same media attention as the opioid crisis or cannabis legalization. Crystal meth in particular is the source of significant health, social, and economic harms for users of the drug and their communities (Fairbairn et al., 2007). High rates of methamphetamine use in Canada among certain groups, particularly street youth, gay and bisexual youth, men who have sex with men (Scheim, 2017), and rave attendees (Palamar et al., 2015), indicate the widespread and increasing use of the drug (Fairbairn et al., 2007).

METHYLPHENIDATE: DRUGS TO TREAT ATTENTION-DEFICIT/HYPERACTIVITY DISORDER

slang: Diet Coke, kiddie cocaine, kiddie speed, r-ball, silver bullet, smarties, vitamin R, west coast, kibble and bits, one and ones, poor man's heroin, ritz & T's, T's & R's (mixed with Talwin)

The Ciba-Geigy company synthesized methylphenidate (Ritalin) during the 1940s to break a patent by a rival pharmaceutical manufacturer of stimulants. Ritalin was initially marketed to treat chronic fatigue, depression, and narcolepsy, and to offset the sedating effects of other medications, including barbiturate overdose (Alexander & Stockton, 2000). Presently, Ritalin, Concerta, methylpehidate extended release (Biphetin), atomoxetine (Strattera), and dextroamphetamine (Adderall) are commonly used to treat attention-deficit/hyperactivity disorder (ADHD) in children and adults. ADHD is a congenital condition that can be misdiagnosed in children as a behavioural or conduct disorder leading to improper prescription of psychoactive medication. ADHD has historically been described as a pattern of inattention and/or hyperactivity, impulsivity, and behavioural symptoms that lasts for at least six months to a degree that interferes with a child's development. It entails disruptions in more than one environment, so not only school but also home or peer interactions must be impacted. It is a serious condition; in Canada, incident rates of ADHD in the correctional population are 5 times greater than what we see in the community and 10 times greater for youth (Scott et al., 2016). Recent neuroimaging research has led a consortium of doctors to argue that the brain structure of children with attention-deficit/hyperactivity disorder differs from that of normally developing children and it is a difference that can be detected through an MRI, meaning ADHD is a neurological disorder (Hoogman et al., 2017).

Drugs such as Ritalin and Concerta have the capacity to increase the attention span of both children and adults with and without ADHD. This has led some to label medicine for this condition as "sit down and shut up" drugs. However, increases in academic performance have been repeatedly documented once this drug is taken as prescribed (Grizenko et al., 2013). In contrast to amphetamines, ADHD drugs are not taken up into the dopamine terminal. Rather, they block the transport mechanism and prevent the reuptake of dopamine from the sending neuron, thus allowing more dopamine to flow across the synaptic cleft to activate surrounding neurons. This increased flow of dopamine allows the brain to carry on its executive functions as would a normally functioning brain, counteracting the effects of ADHD. The question of what effect ADHD drugs have on a misdiagnosed child or adult whose executive brain functions are working properly has not been fully addressed. The label of ADHD can easily be applied to children who do not fit other medical criteria, including highly intelligent children who are restless and bored in a school system developed to teach the average child. However, critics contend that there is just as great a chance of underdiagnosing as overdiagnosing ADHD, thereby failing to assist a child who could benefit from the drug. Those with untreated ADHD have a greater chance of underachieving academically, increased drug use in adulthood, and becoming involved with the criminal justice system (European Monitoring Centre for Drugs and Drug Addiction, 2009a; Fusar-Poli et al., 2012; Lee et al., 2011).

An American study found that providing methylphenidate to youth, primarily boys, diagnosed with ADHD reduced the likelihood of contracting a sexually transmitted disease 3.6 percent, having a substance misuse disorder by 7.3 percent, and physical injury by 2.3 percent per year compared to those diagnosed with ADHD but not medicated. While these annual percentages are low, they add up quickly over a lifetime, especially given 1 in 10 North American children are given this diagnosis (Chorniy & Kitashima, 2016). Another study following 579 children found that the medication led to suppression of adult height but not long-term symptom reduction (Swanson et al., 2017).

There is no question that Ritalin, Concerta, and related medications are effective, as they not only aid those with ADHD but also those who suffer from seizures (Santos et al., 2013). Brain imaging indicates long-term use of Ritalin can increase white matter (responsible for connecting different parts of the CNS) in the brains of youth, but not adults (Bouziane et al., 2019). The controversy is not only with the drug, but with whom it should be used and how widely. The Ontario Ministry of Health and Long-Term Care (2010) states that 5–12 percent of school-aged children (8–10 percent of boys and 3–4 percent of girls under 18) have ADHD. Over two-thirds continue to meet the diagnostic criteria into adolescence and 60 percent into adulthood. However, some have questioned whether some children diagnosed with ADHD actually have fetal alcohol spectrum disorder. There is also a trend now to treat adults who are unable to focus or concentrate. Post-secondary students are also unintended users in this group of CNS stimulants—they attempt to obtain a competitive academic edge by using these drugs to decrease fatigue and enhance focus during exam periods.

ADHD is the most commonly diagnosed children's mental health disorder globally. From 1990 to 1997 in Canada, there was more than a 500 percent increase in the number of Ritalin prescriptions written, with a greater likelihood of a prescription being obtained when some type of family disruption occurred, such as a divorce (Strohschein, 2007). In the United States, use in children jumped 46 percent from 2002 to 2010 (Chai et al., 2012), likewise rising in Canada from 1994 to 2007 (Brault & Lacourse, 2012). During the same period, advertising by drug companies for this drug also rose. In the United States, the Food and Drug Administration has cited every manufacturer of a major ADHD drug, including Adderall, Concerta, Focalin, Vyvanse, Intuniv, and Strattera, for false and misleading advertising since 2000 (Schwarz, 2013).

As with any psychoactive agent, the use of ADHD drugs has a range of negative side effects, such as loss of appetite, nervousness, tics, Tourette's syndrome, cardiac arrhythmia, increased blood pressure, rash, dry mouth, and abdominal pain (Sumnall et al., 2008). The use of Ritalin and related stimulants has also been shown to delay physical growth (height and/or weight) and development in children (Faraone et al., 2008). More troubling, however, is the work of Breeding and Baughman (2003), who have linked 160 cardiovascular deaths between 1990 and 1997 to the use of Ritalin, and the fact that in 2004, Eli Lilly attached a suicide ideation warning when it released Strattera. In 2015, Health Canada issued a safety review for methylphenidate. According to its review, these drugs may contribute to suicide ideation and/or suicide action. These drugs should also never be taken by preschool-aged children, especially as clinical trials of many ADHD drugs have not been designed to assess for either rare adverse events or long-term safety and efficacy (Bourgeois et al., 2014).

ANOREXIANTS

slang: preludes, slims

Diethylpropion and fenfluramine are examples of lesser amphetamines that have been regularly prescribed over short periods of time to assist with weight reduction and treat clinical obesity, replacing the more potent amphetamines that were used as anorexiants prior to the early 1970s. Fenfluramine in particular does not produce nearly as much CNS stimulation as the rest of the amphetamines, and, in fact, causes drowsiness in some users. However, its excessive use has become associated with cardiovascular problems, especially when used in combination with phentermine. However, in general, anorexiants are not drugs of choice among illicit users, but large doses may be consumed as a last resort if more potent stimulants are unavailable. Examples of anorexiants include phentermine (Ionamin), diethylpropion (Tenuate), fenfluramine (Ponderal), and phenmetrazine (Preludin).

DECONGESTANTS

slang: pseudococaine, robo-tripping

Phenylpropanolamine (PPA), propylhexedrine (PDE), and pseudoephedrine (PSE) are the most prominent decongestants. They all have chemical structures similar to that of amphetamine, though with a much lower dependency liability. Each has been available as an over-the-counter (OTC) medication, though as a group they have come under increasing legal scrutiny since 2000 due to direct health risks, athletic performance–enhancing capabilities, and their use as a precursor in the production of methamphetamine, all of which has led to dramatic modifications in their OTC status. Like other CNS stimulants, decongestants constrict blood vessels, and through this process relieve nasal and sinus congestion. They also became widely used as anorexiants due to their accessibility. Decongestants have historically been found in many cold and allergy medications, often in combination with an antihistamine. Decongestants primarily produce their therapeutic action by activating receptors found on blood vessels of the mucous membrane that lines the nasal passage (Sproule, 2004).

Common side effects of decongestants include sleeplessness, anxiety, dizziness, excitability, and nervousness. As decongestants are CNS stimulants when used for extended periods of time, they produce health risks associated with all stimulants: increased blood pressure, risk of heart attacks, strokes, seizures, and kidney failure. Anxiety, restlessness, and insomnia can also occur. However, when decongestants are administered at recommended therapeutic doses for the management of nasal or sinus congestion, hypertension is unlikely to be a problem except in the most sensitive of individuals. Unfortunately, when they are self-administered as stimulants, high doses are often taken because of their relatively weak central nervous system effects (Cantu et al., 2003).

KHAT

slang: Abyssinian tea, African salad, Arabian tea, Bushman's tea, cat, Catha, chat, Flower of Paradise, oat, Somalia tea

Khat/qat leaves were chewed by warriors in Western Africa and the Arabian Peninsula to fight fatigue, and even Alexander the Great instructed his soldiers to use khat prior to engaging in battle. While a relatively new drug of misuse in North America, its use dates back to ancient Egypt where it was used alongside alcohol. Khat is a fundamental part of social and cultural traditions in parts of Yemen and East Africa, with use by 85 percent of adult males in some of these communities. Worldwide, this small shrub, whose formal name is *Catha edulis*, is the most popular stimulant from the monoamine group. It is native to East Africa, and widely cultivated in Yemen, Somalia, Kenya, and Ethiopia. Khat leaves contain cathine and cathinone, which are chemically similar to amphetamine. Among many Islamic nations, its use is considered much more acceptable than other drugs, including alcohol, with as many as 5 million daily users throughout the Horn of Africa (Khatib et al., 2013; Spinella, 2001).

Khat has crimson-brown leaves that turn yellow-green and leathery with age. Its use in Canada increased with the influx of Somali refugees and immigrants since the end of the 20th century. In Eastern Africa and Southern Arabia, where it is most commonly used, it is a social drug, consumed by chewing the leaves or brewing them in tea, though it can also be smoked. Like all stimulants, khat use temporarily dispels perceptions of hunger, fatigue, and depression while enhancing concentration and motor activity. Users report that khat provides energy and a euphoric feeling, with short-term stimulant effects similar to those of several cups of coffee. There have been some health concerns, though, about khat's ability to suppress appetite, prevent sleep, increase respiration, and lead to hyperactive behaviour, followed by withdrawal effects featuring a general malaise (Nasrulla, 2000). As well, along with short-term effects such as constipation, dizziness, insomnia, loss of appetite, migraine headaches, and stomach upset, long-term effects such as liver, kidney, lung, and cardiovascular damage have been reported among chronic users. Ongoing use of this natural CNS stimulant can also produce negative cardiovascular and gastrointestinal effects, anxiety, insomnia, disorientation, tremors, aggression, paranoia, hallucinations (visual as well as auditory), and delusions. Withdrawal is typically accompanied by depression. Some chronic khat users have been reported to suffer permanent brain alteration, including symptoms similar to those associated with Parkinson's disease and, in severe cases, paranoid psychosis. While recreational use is not associated with significant impairment, physical and psychological dependency to the substance is possible (Carvalho, 2003; Khatib et al., 2013; Spinella, 2001).

Khat is a legal substance in much of Europe and in the regions where it is grown, accounting for more than one-third of Yemen's economic output. It was also a legal commodity in Canada until 1997. However, on May 14, 1997, it became criminalized and was removed from the Food and Drug Act to the Controlled Substances Act, making possession and importation of this substance illegal. In the first two months of criminalization, the RCMP made over two dozen seizures totalling approximately 750 kg of the drug. Ironically, when the traffickers boarded their planes, they were importers who generally had declared their possession of khat as it was a legal substance. However, as they flew across the Atlantic, their property suddenly became illegal. In 1997, when it was still a licit substance, it typically cost $40–60 CAD a bundle. When it became an illicit drug, the price quickly doubled (Dubey, 1997).

BATH SALTS (METHYLENDIOXYPYROVALERONE AND MEPHEDRONE)

slang/brand names: Arctic blast, blue silk, charge, cloud 10, gold rush, hurricane Charlie, ivory snow, ivory wave, kamikaze, lunar wave, meow meow mystic, ocean burst, plant fertilizer, pure ivory, purple wave, red dove, scarface, snow leopard, stardust, vanilla sky, white knight, white lightening, wicked X, zoom

Bath salts are not intended as a relaxing additive for washing but rather are one of several designer drugs or legal highs that have emerged in the 21st century, primarily in an attempt to avoid legislation prohibiting other potent stimulants and hallucinogens. Bath salts have been placed into a broader classification of new psychoactive substances (NPS), which are not regulated by the 1961 United Nations Single Convention on Narcotic Drugs or the 1971 United Nations Convention on Psychotropic Substances. The substances include both synthetic compounds, such as synthetic cannabinoids, synthetic cathinones, and piperazines, and traditional plant-based psychoactive substances, such as khat (*Catha edulis*), kratom (*Mitragyna speciosa*), and *Salvia divinorum* (Briones et al., 2013).

Bath salts are pharmacologically most closely related to khat. Their psychoactive property is derived from the same source, cathinone, though the synthetic version is much more potent. While cathinone was synthesized by pharmaceutical companies in the late 20th century, its derivatives did not become broadly used within the drug trade until the beginning of this century. It also shares some pharmacological similarity with methylenedioxymethamphetamine (MDMA/ecstasy) but with less hallucinogenic and more stimulant properties closer to the effects of methamphetamine. In a study of the rewarding and reinforcing effects of methylendioxypyrovalerone (MDPV), rats showed self-administration patterns and escalation of drug intake nearly identical to methamphetamine (Cameron et al., 2013a, 2013b; Kyle et al., 2011).

Bath salts are typically sold in 50–500 mg packets. The price ranges from $25 to $50 per 50 mg packet, though as little as 5–10 mg can produce a psychoactive effect. This drug can be administered orally, across mucous membrane, via inhalation, or injection. The energizing and often agitating effects occur because of increased levels of dopamine, which also increase a user's heart rate and blood pressure. This surge in dopamine creates feelings of euphoria, increased physical activity, heightened sexual interest, a lack of hunger and thirst, muscle spasms, sleeplessness, and, when sleep does occur, disrupted dream cycles. Behavioural effects include erratic behaviour, teeth grinding, lack of recall of how much of the substance has been consumed, panic attacks, anxiety, agitation, severe paranoia, hallucinations, psychosis, self-mutilation, and behaviour that can be aggressive, violent, and, in extreme cases, move beyond suicidal ideation to suicidal action. Overdose is possible due to heart and blood vessel problems. This drug lacks any type of regulation, leading to inconsistency in the amount of the psychoactive ingredient between brands.

In 2012 the government of Canada made it illegal to possess, traffic, import, or export methylendioxypyrovalerone unless authorized by regulation (Antnowicz et al., 2011; Ross et al., 2012; Wieland et al., 2012).

BETEL

slang: none known

The betel plant is an evergreen and perennial creeper, with glossy heart-shaped leaves and a white flower cluster. It belongs to the *Piperaceae* family, which includes pepper and kava, and acts as a mild stimulant when administered orally. Betel quid is a combination of betel leaf, areca nut, and slaked lime, though in some cultures, spices are also added for additional flavour. Tobacco is also commonly added, and this product, known as *gutka*, can be readily purchased in foil packets/sachets and tins. It is consumed by placing a pinch of the mixture in the mouth between the gum and cheek, and gently sucking and chewing. The excess saliva produced by chewing may be swallowed or spit out as with chewing tobacco. Betel quid, while uncommon in North America, is regularly used by over half a billion people, mostly throughout Southeast Asia and the Indian subcontinent, making it the fourth most commonly used psychoactive drug after caffeine, alcohol, and tobacco. It is used as a mouth freshener and a taste enhancer, for impotence and gynecological problems, for parasitic intestinal infection, and for indigestion and prevention of morning sickness. It remains most commonly employed, however, as a mild stimulant euphoric because of the amount of psychoactive alkaloids it contains. Chewing betel quid increases the capacity to work, causes a hot sensation in the body, and heightens alertness. It is most commonly used among lower socio-economic groups to avoid boredom and to suppress hunger. Long-term use has been linked to increases in precancerous lesions on the outside and inner lining of the mouth, esophagus, oral cancer of the lip, mouth, and tongue, and pharynx (Floraa et al., 2012; Gupta & Ray, 2004; Lin et al., 2011; Nair et al., 2004).

NICOTINE

slang: butts, cigs, coffin sticks, smokes

Nicotine, in combination with its agent of delivery, tobacco, is the leading cause of premature death of any psychoactive agent in Canada and throughout the world, directly responsible for 7 million deaths globally each year. Tobacco use, heart disease, and violence are the leading causes of human death and disability, with tobacco use responsible for approximately 10 percent of all mortality, half of which occurs in four nations: China, India, Russia, and the United States (World Health Organization, 2017a). Tobacco continues to be marketed globally, with a specific focus on youth, specifically young women (American Cancer Society, 2009), with an increasing emphasis on e-cigarettes and vaping (see Box 10.1). Ironically, while in developed nations there is growing concern around e-cigarette use and the associated health dangers of vaping among youth, in developing nations the concern is the millions of children cultivating tobacco rather than attending school (Southeast Asian Tobacco Control Alliance, 2013). Nicotine is such a toxic substance that a few pure drops placed on the tongue has the ability to quickly kill a healthy adult, while there are sufficient toxic remnants in the filter of a typical cigarette to make a child ill if consumed. A lethal dose of nicotine for adults is approximately 60 mg, but very small amounts, as low as 4 mg, can produce severe illness. Tobacco smoke consists of some 500 compounds, including tar, ammonia, acetaldehyde, acetone, benzene, toluene, benzoapyrene, dimethylnitrosamine, methylethylnitrosamine, naphthalene, carbon monoxide, and carbon dioxide. Furthermore, upwards of 4.5 trillion cigarette butts are littered worldwide each year. The most common form of human-made litter, cigarette butts are 98 percent plastic and can linger for 10 years before they degrade, contributing to global environmental pollution (Euromonitor International, 2014).

Nicotine is the psychoactive agent found in tobacco that makes its use a compulsive behaviour, and it occurs naturally in only three species of tobacco plants: *Nicotiana tabacum*, *Nicotiana rustica*, and *Nicotiana persica*. This psychoactive agent is produced by these plants so that insects do not eat their leaves, thus acting as a natural insecticide. All three species contain between 0.6 and 0.9 percent nicotine, though tobacco manufacturers manipulate nicotine content, and the greater the concentration the greater the dependency liability (see Figure 10.1). Traditional cigarettes contained 16 mg of nicotine, with e-cigarettes ranging from 0 to 36 mg equivalents (Land et al., 2014).

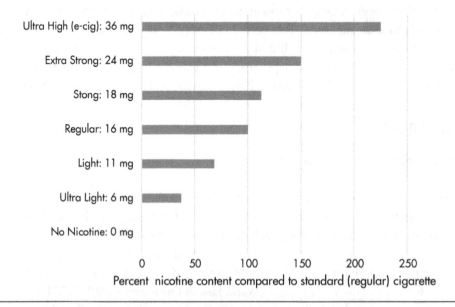

Figure 10.1: Comparing Nicotine Content

Source: Adapted from Stanton and Hatsukami (2019).

Tobacco originated in the Ecuadorean and Peruvian Andes mountain range, where it had been growing for at least 5,000 years before the Incas began to use it. By about the 1st century CE, tobacco was widely used in culturally specific ways throughout North and South America. Tobacco was one of the first plants Europeans brought back to Europe, where it quickly became popular among the elite classes. They began to inhale the smoke and demand an increased supply from the Americas. Europeans taught the Ottomans how to cultivate and cure tobacco, though over time, the Turks perfected their own approach to growing, curing, and smoking tobacco through a hookah. The distinct flavour and intensity of Turkish tobacco led to a billion-dollar business, which in turn has led to significant health and social costs (Gately, 2001).

Nicotine stimulates the release of dopamine in the nucleus, a major part of the brain's reward system. Habitual smokers continually stimulate the nucleus accumbens, thereby causing dependence due to the complex activation of the core and shell of the nucleus (Balfour, 2004). Research indicates that opioid receptors, GABA B, cannabinoid C_1, and dopamine D_2, are all involved in the creation of nicotine dependence (Berrettini & Lerman, 2005). Nicotine is a mild stimulant that in cigarette smoke is delivered, along with the tar, in the form of tiny particles suspended in the gaseous phase. The drug is absorbed rapidly from the lungs and can reach the brain within eight seconds. As cigarette smoke acidifies the saliva, the drug is not efficiently absorbed orally. Smokers do not absorb much nicotine unless they inhale the smoke, though nicotine can be effectively absorbed across the oral or nasal mucosa if the drug is administered in the form of chewing tobacco or snuff. The elimination half-life of nicotine, among the shortest of all psychoactive drugs, is approximately 30–60 minutes. Frequent smokers often light their next cigarette before all of the nicotine from the previous one is cleared from the body. When they do, the drug can accumulate in the tissues over the course of a day's regular use (Hancock & McKim, 2018).

Nicotine is a central nervous system stimulant that increases heart rate and blood pressure; depresses the spinal reflex; reduces muscle tone; decreases skin temperature; increases acid in the stomach; reduces urine formation; precipitates a loss of appetite; increases adrenaline production, and stimulates, then reduces, brain and nervous system activity. In non-smokers, small doses, even less than one cigarette, may produce an unpleasant reaction that includes coughing, nausea, vomiting, dizziness, abdominal discomfort, weakness, and flushing.

For both men and women, regular smoking reduces life expectancy by five to ten years (Woloshin et al., 2008). Long-term effects of smoking and nicotine ingestion include narrowing or hardening of blood vessels in the heart and brain, leading to an increased risk of heart attack or stroke in all age groups; shortness of breath; more respiratory infections, such as colds and pneumonia; chronic bronchitis; oxygen deprivation of all body tissues; and a risk of 16 distinct forms of cancer: lung, mouth, larynx, esophagus, skin, bladder, kidney, pancreas, stomach, gastric system, breast, bowel, blood, head, neck, and cervix, in part due to the mutations it produces in DNA. Smoking tobacco has also been associated with stomach ulcers, impotence, increased risk of brain hemorrhages and brain

Table 10.1: Outcomes of Smoking*

Roll of Two Dice	Outcome Probability	Disease Outcome
2	1/36	No Disease
3	2/36	Cancer of the Lips
4	3/36	Cancer of the Mouth
5	4/36	Stroke
6	5/36	Emphysema
7	6/36	Lung Cancer
8	5/36	Bronchitis
9	4/36	Heart Disease
10	3/36	Ulcers
11	2/36	Wrinkles
12	1/36	Cancer of the Tongue

Note: *This table highlights the health risks of smoking. When smokers begin regularly using tobacco, they have no idea what the health impacts will be as they are individual and random. By rolling two die, you can replicate the likelihood of the disease you would develop if you became a regular smoker.

Source: Hall & Vander Bilt (2000).

damage, cognitive decline and memory loss, increased risk of developing chronic obstructive pulmonary disease (COPD), emphysema, progression of multiple sclerosis symptoms, and risk of thrombosis in users of birth control pills (Alexandrov et al., 2016; Boffetta & Straif, 2009; Borchers et al., 2009; Freedman et al., 2007; Healy et al., 2009; Hunt et al., 2005; Richards et al., 2003). Table 10.1 provides examples of possible outcomes from the risk of chronic tobacco use based upon probability theory and the roll of two die.

Nicotine crosses the placenta, and women who smoke during pregnancy tend to have smaller babies and are more likely to give birth prematurely. They also have a greater number of stillbirths, and deaths among their newborn babies—sudden infant death syndrome (SIDS)—are also more common than in non-smokers, as is the risk of having a child who develops ADHD (Thapar et al., 2003). In 1997, Dr. Michael Moffat of the University of Manitoba found that Indigenous infants were three times as likely to die from sudden infant death syndrome and that exposure to cigarette smoke was a major contributing factor. Infants living in the homes of smokers are more prone to respiratory infections and problems. Swedish researchers Montgomery and Ekbom (2002) found that children of women who smoked during pregnancy were more likely to develop diabetes later in life than were children of non-smoking mothers. There is also a greater risk of birth defects among children born to smoking versus non-smoking mothers, including cardiovascular/heart defects, musculoskeletal defects, limb reduction, missing/extra digits, clubfoot, facial defects, eye defects, orofacial clefts, gastrointestinal defects, and undescended testes (Hackshaw et al., 2011).

Tolerance to nicotine does develop and is most clearly reflected in the many short-term symptoms that are either not present or greatly reduced while the chronic user is smoking. Regular smokers quickly become less sensitive to the effects of nicotine, as well as to those of carbon monoxide and the constituents of tar. Tolerance develops particularly rapidly to the nausea and dizziness experienced by the first-time smoker. Smokers generally report that the first cigarette of the day produces the most intense effects. This phenomenon suggests the rapid development of tolerance during the day, and its equally rapid loss at night.

A significant long-term effect of smoking is physical and psychological dependence upon tobacco. Both are commonly observed when daily use exceeds 10 cigarettes. Particular emotional states and environmental events, even after some months or years of abstinence, can precipitate craving for a cigarette. Nicotine, in the first-time smoker, produces primarily aversive effects. The initiation of a smoking habit, therefore, is highly dependent on psychosocial factors, although biological factors may also play a role. Signs of tobacco dependence include a history of several unsuccessful attempts to reduce consumption even though a serious tobacco-related physical disorder is present, and the appearance of withdrawal symptoms while abstaining. The feeling of relaxation that regular smokers often report when smoking is also partially due to the body's dependence on nicotine and the staving off of withdrawal effects. Physical dependence on nicotine leads to a variety of withdrawal symptoms when a smoker attempts to stop. A person in the early stages of withdrawal may experience anxiety, irritability, increased appetite, mild confusion, emotional depression, difficulty concentrating, anger, sleeping problems, and changes in blood pressure and pulse rate (Levinthal, 2012).

Those who use smokeless tobacco may avoid the problems associated with inhalation but are far from risk-free. Not only is there an enhanced risk of oral cancer, but even in casual users, there is a loss of sensitivity to salty, sweet, and bitter foods. Along with a discolouration of teeth comes the risk of damage to both teeth and gums, leading to gum disease and loss of teeth. As well, the nicotine in either chewing tobacco or snuff leads to an increased chance of heart attacks and stroke (Rodu & Jansson, 2004).

In a study of people using multiple psychoactive drugs, it was discovered that a majority found cigarettes more difficult to quit than their primary drug of choice (Kozlowski et al., 1989). Approximately 1,000 people seeking alcohol or drug treatment at the Ontario Addiction Research Foundation's Clinical Institute during the 1980s were asked to compare quitting smoking with the difficulty of quitting their alcohol or other drug dependency, the strength of their strongest urges, and the pleasure they derived from use. The researchers found that

- 74 percent of respondents indicated that cigarettes would be at least as hard to give up as alcohol or the other drugs that they were in treatment for;

- 57 percent said cigarettes would be harder to give up;
- heavy smokers, who smoked within 10 minutes of waking or more than 20 cigarettes per day, were much more likely to find quitting cigarettes at least as difficult as avoiding alcohol or drugs;
- 28 percent of the cocaine users said that cigarette urges were stronger;
- smoking was consistently rated as less pleasurable than alcohol or other drugs;
- almost 60 percent of the alcohol users found cigarettes less pleasurable;
- 96 percent of cocaine users derived more pleasure from cocaine; and
- approximately 95 percent of all smokers in the study who had stopped returned to using at least once.

Second-hand smoke (SHS) is primarily composed of side stream smoke emitted from the smouldering tip of a cigarette and partially from exhaled mainstream smoke. It contains a complex mixture of approximately 4,000 chemical compounds in the form of gases and particulate matter and has been classified as a human carcinogen and an indoor air pollutant. Hirayama's (1981) ground-breaking research examined the effects of second-hand smoke on non-smokers. He studied 265,000 Japanese persons over 14 years and found a statistically significant relationship between the mortality rates of non-smoking wives of heavily smoking husbands. Non-smoking women married to smoking husbands were twice as likely to die from lung cancer than those married to non-smoking spouses. This relationship has since been observed in 11 different studies (Douville, 1990; Doyle, 1987). A meta-analysis reported that pregnant women exposed to second-hand smoke are 23 percent more likely to experience stillbirth and 13 percent more likely to give birth to a child with a congenital malformation. However, it is still unclear if there are times during a woman's pregnancy when she is more vulnerable. It is thus strongly recommended to prevent second-hand smoke exposure in women both before and during pregnancy (Leonardi-Bee et al., 2011). Second-hand smoke also increases the risk of coronary heart disease by approximately 30 percent (Barnoya & Glantz, 2005); exacerbates the asthma of non-smokers (Eisner et al., 2005), especially among children (Tabuchi et al., 2015); and increases the risk of dementia and breast cancer (Llewelyn et al., 2009). A Canadian study, based in Montreal, found that the greater the amount of second-hand smoke a child inhaled the greater the chance that they would exhibit signs and symptoms of depression, though parental depression was not taken into consideration in the sampling (Wellman et al., 2018). Worldwide, over 1 million deaths annually are attributed to second-hand smoke (World Health Organization, 2019b).

There is now also concern about third-hand smoke (THS), which consists of tobacco smoke pollutants found in SHS that have settled on the surfaces of an indoor space and are later re-emitted into the air. THS includes particulate matter that has accumulated on surfaces and in dust, or has become trapped in carpets, upholstery, fabrics, and other porous materials commonly found in indoor environments. THS consists of nicotine, 3-ethenylpyridine (3-EP), phenol, cresols, naphthalene, formaldehyde, and tobacco-specific nitrosamines, and can persist months after smokers have left the environment. Given the persistence of high levels of nicotine on indoor surfaces, including clothing and human skin, THS is an unappreciated health hazard whose implications are not yet fully understood (Matt et al., 2011).

Despite nicotine being the most lethal of all psychoactive drugs, it does have some potential uses other than for killing insects. Research that began at Duke University, in Durham, North Carolina, the heart of the American tobacco belt, as well as subsequent work at the University of Vermont Medical College of Medicine, has found that nicotine may be beneficial in combatting Alzheimer's and other memory-degrading diseases. Nicotine has also been shown to alleviate some symptoms of Tourette's syndrome, Parkinson's disease, and arthritis, calm hyperactive children, and relieve some anxiety disorders (American Association for the Advancement of Science, 2000; Chen et al., 2010; Finckh et al., 2007; Ritz et al., 2007; Thacker et al., 2007). Recent research has also found that a steady supply of nicotine can alleviate symptoms of schizophrenia (Koukouli et al., 2017). As well, Indigenous peoples throughout the Americas have historically used tobacco for specific cultural and religious purposes. Smoke from ceremonial tobacco is used in traditional healing ceremonies, as smoke represents and accompanies prayers as they ascend toward the Creator.

The positive news for those who have smoked for extended periods of time is that on cessation of tobacco use, the body begins to recover almost immediately. Within the first day, carbon monoxide levels drop in the body and the oxygen level in the blood returns to normal. Only one week after quitting, lung capacity begins to increase, bronchial tube inflammation and heart attack risk both decrease, while the senses of both taste and smell begin to recover. By the three-month mark, lung functioning typically improves by one-third, while within six months, coughing, sinus congestion, and feelings of tiredness all improve. One year after quitting, risk of smoking-related heart attack decreases by 50 percent, with cardiovascular disease risks such as stroke decreasing within five years, though still greater than never smokers. After a decade, the risk of premature death due to lung cancer is halved, and after 15 years, the risk of death from smoking-related heart attack is the same as a non-smoker (World Health Organization, 2019c). However, those who stop smoking do gain weight. Nicotine suppresses leptin, a hormone in the brain that controls appetite, just as cocaine and amphetamines do. Once nicotine ingestion is ended, leptin is more readily released, increasing one's appetite. Increased eating will result in weight gain unless activity levels increase correspondingly. As nicotine artificially suppresses appetite, it is not surprising that on cessation an average increase of 4.5 kg in body weight after 12 months of abstinence persists, most of which occurs within the first three months after quitting. While more than 10 percent of those who quit will put on as much as 9 kg, 16 percent of quitters actually lost weight (Aubin et al., 2012).

Box 10.1: Friend or Foe—E-Cigarettes and Vaping

The addiction field is fascinating for many reasons, in part due to the never-ending number of controversies that emerge. First, there is no drug that is safe to inhale into your lungs: the lungs were never intended to process any type of particulate matter, be it tobacco, cocaine, crystal meth, or cannabis. Secondly, as has been stated previously, nicotine, in combination with tobacco, leads to more premature deaths than any other psychoactive drug. For this reason, e-cigarettes, or electronic nicotine delivery systems (ENDS), were promoted as a harm reduction approach. E-cigarettes are battery-powered tubes that heat liquid nicotine, flavours, and other chemicals into a vapour that can be inhaled, though they are also used to inhale cannabis, cocaine, and crystal meth. Although a patent was given in 1965 for a smokeless, non-tobacco cigarette, the current version, e-cigarettes, did not become mass produced until earlier in the 21st century, gaining a foothold first in China, where a revised patent led to mass production (United States Department of Health and Human Services [USDHH], 2016b).

Manufacturers proposed that e-cigarettes, by not requiring the burning of tobacco but only the vaporizing of nicotine, would reduce cancer-related harms. This process is what led to the term "vaping" rather than smoking. Rather than inhaling hot fumes, which also damage lung tissue, cool vapour would be drawn into the lungs, which would be safer, though not entirely safe. All of this was speculation; when e-cigarettes were introduced, there were no empirical studies on either their short- or long-term effects, and all health-related claims were being made by e-cigarette producers, who were directly and significantly profiting from sales. These included established multinational tobacco companies that had witnessed their profits dropping as tobacco smoking steadily decreased across North America with the increased awareness of the dangers of smoking. The introduction of products such as JUUL, Suorin Air, Envii FITT, and MYLÉ—high-tech e-cigarettes capable of delivering nicotine at levels comparable to cigarettes, and just as efficiently—has quickly reversed the progress made in reducing societal smoking rates by marketing to younger, often underage, individuals. Further, these products not only contain flavourings that make them even more attractive to younger smokers, but also a range of additives whose long-term effects are unknown.

An empirical literature examining the effects of e-cigarettes on users has now begun to emerge. There is evidence that, for those already smoking tobacco, e-cigarettes are a mechanism to reduce use and move toward abstinence, as they do contain fewer numbers and lower levels of most tobacco-related toxins (Manzoli et al., 2017) and produce lower levels of physical dependency (Liu et al., 2017). Some studies have found smokers who used e-cigarettes who have attempted to stop either with or without formal treatment were more likely to report continued abstinence than those who used a traditional pharmacotherapy product (see Chapter 16) or used no smoking cessation aid (Brown et al., 2014; Hajek et al., 2019). However, a meta-analysis of 38 studies reported that the odds of completely quitting the use of cigarettes were 28 percent lower among individuals who used e-cigarettes compared with those who used other approaches (Kalkhoran & Glantz, 2016). Another study found that those decreasing the amount of nicotine in the vapes they purchased over time did not actually decrease the amount of nicotine consumed, as they tended to puff more intensely (Soar, 2019). This is identical to outcomes discovered among many regular cigarette smokers who switched to light cigarettes but simply ended up smoking greater quantities or inhaling more deeply, so that there was no actual change in the amount of nicotine inhaled; due to increased inhalation, carbon monoxide and tar intake levels actually increased (Strasser et al., 2007).

While there remains uncertainty as to the extent to which vaping tobacco contributes to smoking cessation, e-cigarettes have been shown to assist individuals in decreasing the absolute number of tobacco products consumed by up to three-quarters (McKeganey et al., 2019). Statistical analysis also predicts that if one individual were to smoke cigarettes and a second were to vape the same amount, the person vaping would have a longer life expectancy, though still shorter compared to a non-smoker or non-vaper (Levy et al., 2018).

The principal constituents most commonly found in e-liquids are propylene glycol, vegetable glycerin, nicotine, ethanol, acetol, and propylene oxide. Nicotine is a psychoactive substance and its use is a health risk, especially to younger consumers, pregnant women, and fetuses. The aerosol propellants in e-cigarettes are harmful, as are the by-products when other psychoactive agents, particularly cannabis but also cocaine or crystal meth, are vaporized. One of the harm reduction arguments for vaping has been the decrease in cancer causing agents, but the vapour produced by e-cigarettes that contains propylene glycol and vegetable glycerin produces formaldehyde, while propylene oxide and nitrosamines are respiratory irritants and potential carcinogens (Sleiman et al., 2016; USDHH, 2016b). Vaping still releases particulate matter into the air that any person may inhale—not only those vaping. There are short-term changes to cardiovascular functioning when a person vapes, but there is insufficient evidence to determine if this is a temporary or permanent change. Likewise, heavy metals are also released by vaping, though in initial studies there are far lower levels of cadmium associated with vaping as compared to smoking. Vaping still produces lung irritation and damage, the extent to which is unknown, though now that vaping has been around for a while, substantive lung damage and deaths attributed exclusively to vaping have begun to be reported (Stratton et al., 2018). In 2019, the Centers for Disease Control and Prevention (CDC) announced that there were hundreds of confirmed cases of lung disease and several confirmed deaths directly attributable to vaping. This is not surprising, as preliminary research has indicated that vaping alters lung cells in a way that would lead to both bronchitis and emphysema (Ghosh et al., 2019). However, the health issues being reported in the media appear, in some cases, to be an outcome of oil-based by-products, such as vitamin E acetate, coating lung tissue and impairing breathing capability. Preliminary research in animal studies has indicated that there is a link between vaping and both cancer and DNA damage (Canistro et al., 2017; Kadimisetty et al., 2017). As well, there have been multiple reports of e-cigarette devices exploding or catching fire, creating other unintended negative health and physical outcomes and leading to lawsuits against the manufacturers (Llamas, 2019). Finally, e-cigarette users report a greater incidence of sleep issues than do non-users (Brett et al., 2019).

CAFFEINE

slang: coffee: cup of joe, cup of tar, java, joe, mud

While alcohol is the most commonly misused psychoactive drug in the world, caffeine is the world's most used psychoactive drug, with estimates of 120,000 tonnes consumed globally each year. Over 80 percent of Canadians consume caffeine on a regular basis, with an estimated 15 billion cups of coffee alone sold annually in Canada. Historically, there is evidence that tea was known to the Chinese about 3000 BCE, and well-documented reports exist of its use in the first few centuries CE. Coffee plants evolved in Ethiopia and it was well established in the Arab world by the 7th century, though it did not gain popularity in Europe until nearly 1,000 years later (Weinberg & Bealer, 2001).

Caffeine, in its pure form, was first isolated from coffee in 1820. Presently, caffeine-containing beverages and food constitute such a large portion of a normal diet that the psychoactive substance is wrongly thought of more as a nutrient than as a drug by some. The active ingredient in caffeine is methylxanthine, and it is derived from any of several plants:

- seeds of *Coffea arabica* and related species (coffee)
- leaves of *Thea sinensis* (tea)
- seeds of *Theobroma cacao* (cocoa, chocolate)
- leaves of the South American mate plant *Ilex paraguariensis* (yerba mate)
- kola nuts from the tree *Cola acuminata* (cola drinks)

Caffeine taken in beverage form begins to reach all tissues of the body within five minutes. Peak blood levels are reached in approximately 30 minutes. Half of a given dose of caffeine is metabolized in about four hours, more rapidly in smokers and less rapidly in newborn infants, women in late pregnancy, and sufferers of liver disease. Normally, almost all ingested caffeine is metabolized. Less than 3 percent appears unchanged in urine, and there is no day-to-day accumulation of the drug in the body.

Due to its tendency to constrict cerebral blood vessels, caffeine is used in combination with other drugs to combat migraine and other cerebrovascular headaches associated with high blood pressure. However, contrary to popular belief, caffeine is not effective in ameliorating headaches due to other causes, and in some cases, it may even exacerbate pain. In other medical uses, caffeine is employed to counteract certain symptoms, such as respiratory depression associated with CNS-depressant poisoning and also as:

- a respiratory stimulant in babies who have had apnea episodes (periods when spontaneous breathing ceases);
- an emergency bronchodilator in asthmatic children;
- a substitute for methylphenidate for children with attention-deficit/hyperactivity disorder;
- an anti-fungal agent in the treatment of skin disorders;
- an aid in fertility because of its ability to enhance sperm mobility; and
- a mild stimulant for an assortment of medical problems.

Much of the caffeine that is taken out of coffee, approximately 2 million pounds a year, is bought by the soft drink industry and added to soft drinks and energy drinks. Agents used to remove caffeine include methylene chloride, ethyl acetate, and effervescence plus water. Generally, ginger ales, club sodas, tonic waters, root beers, and most fruit-flavoured drinks contain no natural or added caffeine. If caffeine is added, it must be listed on the label. Pepper beverages, such as colas, commonly contain caffeine.

When taken even in moderate amounts, such as one or two cups of brewed or percolated coffee, caffeine can produce stimulant effects on the central nervous system similar to those of small doses of amphetamines. This can include producing mild mood elevation, feelings of enhanced energy, increased alertness, reduced performance deficit due to boredom or fatigue, postponement of feelings of fatigue and the need for sleep, and a decrease in hand steadiness, suggesting impaired fine motor performance. Small doses of caffeine can also increase motor activity, alter sleep patterns (including delaying the onset of sleep), diminish sleep time and reduce the depth of sleep (including altering REM patterns), while also increasing respiration, blood pressure, and metabolism (Hancock & McKim, 2018).

Like steroids, caffeine is stored in intracellular sites in the body. While low to moderate daily doses of caffeine do not appear to produce harmful effects in healthy adults, higher daily consumption of approximately 1000 mg of caffeine for a healthy 80 kg male 20–40 years of age—less for women, older persons, lighter persons, and especially children—can result in caffeinism. This is characterized by irritability, anxiety, restlessness and agitation, headache, light-headedness, rapid breathing, tremor, muscle twitches, increased sensitivity to sensory stimuli, light flashes, tinnitus, gastrointestinal upset, abnormally rapid and irregular heartbeat, and disrupted sleep. Chronic long-term caffeine misuse has been linked with ulcers, persistent anxiety, raised cholesterol levels, and depression. It can also decrease potassium levels in the body, which, if prolonged, can negatively affect nerve and muscle cells. Three or more cups of coffee per day or its caffeine equivalent has also been recently linked to bone loss in older women. Caffeine also crosses the placenta, and high levels of consumption have been linked with fetal arrhythmia as the fetus does not yet possess the enzymes necessary to metabolize caffeine. Caffeine effects appear with decreasing doses as a person becomes older; intake should thus decrease with age. The marketing of energy drinks and energy pills has seen a subsequent rise in the number of emergency room admissions and hospitalizations due to caffeine overdoses, which were rare until this century (Gupta & Gupta, 1999; Jabbar & Hanly, 2013; Kerrigan & Lindsey, 2005; McCarth et al., 2006). The consumption of caffeinated alcoholic beverages has also become a health and safety concern because of the increasing number of incidents of automobile collisions and physical and sexual violence arising from the use of this hybrid substance (Brache & Stockwell, 2011; Price et al., 2010; Weldy, 2010). Substantially lower doses can prove problematic to children, for, like nicotine, caffeine can also be used as an insecticide, though it is less potent (Thomson et al., 2015).

Tolerance develops to most of caffeine's effects, with clinical experiments demonstrating that tolerance to the cardiovascular effects of caffeine can develop within four days. Consumption of 350–600 mg of caffeine on a regular basis causes physical dependence. There is also evidence that users may develop a mild psychological dependence on caffeine, as manifested by the well-recognized morning coffee habit. Clearly, factors such as taste and aroma are important as reinforcers, since coffee drinkers cannot always be persuaded to switch to tea and vice versa.

Interruption of the regular use of caffeine produces a characteristic withdrawal syndrome, particularly an often-severe headache that can be temporarily relieved by ingesting caffeine. Absence of caffeine also makes regular users feel irritable, lethargic, anxious, and fatigued. Withdrawal can begin between 3 and 48 hours after the last administration of caffeine. Relief from these withdrawal effects is often given as a reason for ongoing use of caffeine.

CHAPTER 11

Hallucinogens

The term "hallucinogen" is applied to any psychoactive substance that is administered to produce radical changes in a person's mental state, an effect that entails distortions of reality, including, but not limited to, sensory hallucinations. Many hallucinogens are synthetic creations manufactured in laboratories, but there are also approximately 100 species of plants that can produce hallucinogenic effects along with the secretions of a variety of amphibians. Biological substances that can create hallucinations include seeds, mushrooms, fungi, and flowers, plus certain forms of toad slime and venom. Hallucinogens can be placed into five categories:

- LSD-Like Hallucinogens
- Phenylethylamines: Mescaline-Like Hallucinogens
- Dissociative Anaesthetics
- Novel Psychoactive Substances
- Cannabis

While central nervous system depressants and stimulants initially produce euphoria with ingestion, hallucinogens cause a distortion in the way the brain perceives stimuli and thus how the user relates to the physical environment. The neurotransmitter serotonin is most closely identified with hallucinogens. Cannabis, though, is linked with anandamide, which is one explanation for why cannabis works in a distinct manner on the CNS compared to other hallucinogens (González-Maeso et al., 2007).

Hallucinogens may be administered orally, inhaled, injected, and, in the case of LSD, absorbed transdermally. Drugs categorized under this heading produce sensations of separation from self and reality, as well as unusual changes in thoughts, feelings, and perceptions, including delusions and illusions, but without typically creating delirium. Illusions and delusions may include a loss or confusion of body image, altered perceptions of colours, distance, and shape, and an apparent distortion, blending, or synthesis of senses whereby one sees sounds and smells colours. These agents can also produce severe anxiety and panic, "a bad trip." Physical effects for one grouping of hallucinogens, phenylethylamines, are similar to those produced by amphetamines: rapid pulse, dilated pupils, arousal, excitation, impaired motor coordination, and muscle weakness. Contrarily, two categories, dissociative anaesthetics and cannabis, have secondary effects much more closely related to central nervous system depressants. Occasionally hallucinogens can also produce convulsions. In low doses, hallucinogens produce a spectrum of effects according to the properties of the particular drug and the individual user's sensitivity to them. Users may experience dissimilar reactions to the same drug on different occasions, finding the effects sometimes pleasant and at other times disturbing and threatening. Flashbacks, or Hallucinogen Persisting Perception Disorder (HPPD), usually visual in nature, have been reported to occur months or even years after even a single experience with a hallucinogen. They are generally quite disturbing and can be potentially dangerous, depending on what the person is doing when they occur. They may even precipitate or intensify already existing anxieties or psychoses in some users, though HPPD is discussed more than it is documented (Hancock & McKim, 2018).

For the majority of hallucinogens, with the exception of cannabis, long-term effects are purely psychological. Hallucinogens interfere with the chemicals in the body involved in processing cognitions and emotions. Tolerance develops within days, so even if users take the drug regularly, after three to four days, no effects are felt. As a result, physical dependence does not develop. As there is no physical dependence, there are no withdrawal reactions, even with long-time users. Thus, these are not fully addictive agents, again with the exception of cannabis. Chronic users may become psychologically dependent, however, with all the associated problems of that state (Levinthal, 2012).

From the late 1950s to the early 1970s, researchers explored the use of several different hallucinogens to treat the existential anxiety, despair, and isolation associated with advanced-stage cancer, but also with addiction, primarily alcoholism. Those studies described critically ill individuals undergoing psychospiritual revelations, as had early shamans, often with powerful and sustained improvement in mood and decreased anxiety, as well as a diminished need for pain medication. Despite promising initial results, inconsistent outcome and the spectre of these being illicit substances precluded ongoing research (Grob et al., 2011; Smart et al., 1967). This century has seen a resurgence of interest in using different hallucinogens, such as ibogaine, psilocybin, ketamine, LSD, and MDMA, in attempts to treat anxiety, depression, and PTSD, as well as addiction (Jerome et al., 2013; Krebs & Johansen, 2012; Parrott, 2014).

LSD-LIKE HALLUCINOGENS

Known as indolealkylamines, this family bears similarity to serotonin, 5-hydroxytryptamine, one of the transmitter substances that occurs naturally in the brain.

d-Lysergic Acid Diethylamide (LSD)

slang: acid, aeon flux, barrels, Bevis & Butthead, big D, black star, black sunshine, black tabs, blotter, blue vials, California sunshine, chocolate chips, fields, golden dragon, heavenly blue, instant zen, lens, Lucy in the Sky, microdots, Might Quinn, pink panther, purple hearts, royal blues, sunshine, Syd, tabs, twenty-five, wedding bells, windowpane, yellow sunshine, zen

LSD is a colourless, tasteless, odourless, semi-synthetic drug derived from a fungus that grows on rye and other grains that has a profound effect even in small doses on the neurotransmitter serotonin. It was discovered in 1938, though its effects were not truly appreciated until 1943 when research scientist Dr. Albert Hoffman, a future Nobel committee member working for the Sandoz pharmaceutical company, accidentally ingested a small quantity (250 mcg) while attempting to create a new heart stimulant drug. This small amount was five times the amount required to produce hallucinations, and the effects produced were quite surprising.

LSD is the most powerful of all known hallucinogens. A dose as small as 0.05 mg (50 mcg) may produce changes in perception, mood, and thought. The initial effects of this drug are felt in less than an hour, generally last from 8 to 12 hours, and then gradually taper off. Shortly after ingestion, LSD can produce a variety of physical symptoms, which include increased heart rate and blood pressure, elevated body temperature, reduced appetite, nausea, vomiting, abdominal discomfort, rapid reflexes, motor incoordination, relaxed bronchial muscles, and pupillary dilation (Smart et al., 1967). However, it is among the hallucinogens that is being examined for potential therapeutic uses for cluster headaches and anxiety, and as a cure for addiction, though in lower doses than recreational users administer (Krebs & Johansen, 2012; Sewell et al., 2006).

LSD greatly increases blood flow to the visual cortex expanding primary visual cortex functional connectivity, which produces insights into why users often see visual hallucinations. LSD also diminishes the user's capacity to differentiate the boundaries of one object from another and of the self from the environment. For some, this is a pleasant sensation, but for others, the feeling of loss of control may result in a panic reaction. In rare instances, a long-term psychotic reaction has resulted from a single episode of use, although a predisposition for psychosis or schizophrenia existed prior to drug use in these cases. A user may experience several different emotions at the same time or swing rapidly from one mood to another. Hearing may likewise be intensified or merged with visual perception, and a user's sense of time may also be affected. Impairment of short-term memory often occurs (Carhart-Harris et al., 2016). Microdosing has become a popular way to use this drug. Microdosing entails ingesting small amounts of the drug, less than 20 percent of a typical dose, so that the person is not overwhelmed by the drug's effect but the administration is large enough so that there is a perception of increased creativity and energy. However, even at these low dose levels, tolerance will build after a few days of regular use.

Another potential after-effect of LSD use is Hallucinogen Persisting Perception Disorder, more commonly referred to as a flashback, a spontaneous reoccurrence of the sensations that occurred during a prior drug experience. A flashback can be experienced days, weeks, or even years after the last ingestion of LSD, though the likelihood of reoccurrence diminishes with time. The effects range from pleasant to severely anxiety-producing. Chronic LSD use has also been associated with amotivational syndrome, apathy, disinterest in the environment and with social contacts, and also with a general passive attitude toward life, though it does not appear to produce chromosomal damage. While there are no known deaths directly attributable to the pharmacological effects of LSD in humans, there have been many reports of deaths due to LSD-associated accidents and self-inflicted harm.

One of the most famous and enduring urban drug legends involves LSD. A warning flyer is directed toward parents concerning *blue star tattoos*. The warning appeals to parents to be aware of a small piece of paper containing a blue star about the size of a pencil eraser. This paper is supposedly soaked with LSD, and it can be absorbed through the skin. On the paper there may be other brightly coloured tattoos of cartoon characters, such as Superman, Bart Simpson, Mickey Mouse, Donald Duck, or an assortment of other Disney characters. The message goes on to say that young lives have already been taken and to forward the message on to other concerned parents and professionals. However, there has yet to be one verified case anywhere of blue star tattoos, even though the warning has been circulating for over 40 years (https://www.snopes.com/fact-check/blue-star-acid).

Psilocybin

slang: Alice, boomers, fungus, magic mushrooms, Mexican mushrooms, shrooms, Simple Simon

Psilocybin is the active ingredient in the *Psilocybe mexicana* mushroom and some of the other psilocybe and conocybe species. It was historically used in religious ceremonies in southern Mexico by Indigenous peoples, including the Hopi, and continues to be used by the Yaqui People as part of their seeing ceremony. Psilocybin and the related drug psilocin are derivatives of tryptamine and are chemically related to both LSD and DMT (dimethyltryptamine), though roughly 100 times less potent and with a shorter duration of effects. The threshold level to create a psychoactive response is 250 mg. In pure form, psilocybin is a white crystalline material, but it may also be distributed in crude mushroom preparations, intact dried brown mushrooms, or as a capsule containing a powdered material of any colour. It is usually taken orally but may also be injected. Doses of the pure compound generally vary from 4–10 mg, although amounts up to 60 mg are not unusual (Levinthal, 2012).

The initial effects of this drug are felt approximately 30 minutes after ingestion and usually last several hours, with the peak occurring two to four hours after oral administration. The short-term effects of psilocybin include an increase in blood pressure, heart rate, and body temperature. Initially, the user experiences nausea, vomiting, and intestinal cramping. Later, distortions of visual stimuli and pseudo-hallucinations are likely to occur. They are accompanied by further distortions of time, space, and body image; heightened sensory awareness; synesthesia, the perception of the melding of the senses; and a loss of boundaries between oneself and the environment. While users claim to gain insight into themselves and experience a greater sense of creativity, use of this drug impairs concentration, attention, cognition, and memory. As well, past events may be vividly recalled.

A self-reported online study of 1,993 respondents, primarily men, report the effects of their psilocybin use. Over 80 percent of respondents indicated that their experience using the drug was positive, but there were associated risks with using even though psilocybin is the least likely substance to produce a drug poisoning (Table III.2). Even some respondents who overall rated their experience as positive experienced psychologically difficult or challenging experiences—a "bad trip"—after using psilocybin. Thirty-nine percent of respondents stated it was among their top five most challenging lifetime experiences. Due to becoming disassociated from their environment, 11 percent stated that they put themselves or others at risk of physical harm, though less than 3 percent reported behaving in a physically aggressive or violent manner. Of the 1,993 respondents, 151 sought treatment for ongoing psychological symptoms related to using the drug, though only three individuals indicated that use led to the onset of psychotic symptoms. The greater the dose level the more likely an individual was to have a negative experience with the drug. Thus, while bad trips do occur, no deaths due directly to a psilocybin overdose have been documented. Psilocybin has negligible misuse potential, and there is a low risk of physical dependence; however, individuals with mental health issues should avoid this drug, as it can exacerbate existing conditions as well as heighten feelings of fear and confusion (Carbonaro et al., 2016).

Like LSD, psilocybin is one of several hallucinogens being touted as an option to treat anxiety, cluster headaches, depression, post-traumatic stress disorder, and addiction and is also being microdosed to enhance creativity (Carhart-Harris et al., 2018; Grob et al., 2011; Sewell et al., 2006). As part of a randomized controlled study, individuals with life-threatening cancer diagnoses were given single doses of medical-grade psilocybin in conjunction with psychotherapy. The addition of psilocybin to the counselling produced rapid, robust, and enduring anti-anxiety and anti-depressant effects for those experiencing cancer-related psychological distress (Ross et al., 2016).

Dimetheyltryptamine (DMT)

slang: businessman's special, businessman's trip, Dimitri, snakes

DMT, similar to psilocybin in its effects, was historically used by the Santo Daime and the União do Vegetal, South American Indigenous Peoples who lived along the Amazon basin prior to the arrival of Europeans. It was ingested in a brewed form known as *aya-huasca*, or *yage*, meaning either "vine of the dead" or "vine of the souls." DMT is also naturally excreted by the human pineal gland and is believed to play a role in dreaming and possibly near-death experiences and other mystical states. When used recreationally in North America, DMT is often administered in combination with cannabis, which is soaked in a solution of DMT and then dried and smoked in a pipe or cigarette. DMT can also be made into a tea and consumed orally—this is the ayahusasca version that has become increasing popular outside South America (dos Santos, 2013).

Acute administration of DMT has limited physical risk associated with it; the most common response in both new and experienced users is nausea and vomiting. However, even in low doses DMT can produce significant perceptual, cognitive, and affective mod-ifications, highlighted by hallucinations, and the greater the dose the greater the reac-tion. The experience of using ayahuasca is typically pleasant, although not physically easy, highlighted by changes in visual perception, synaesthesia between the auditory and visual senses, feelings of deep introspection, and enhanced mood that can last four to six hours. There is also an association with heightened introspection and creativity with the use of DMT. This may be in part because DMT affects the frontal and paralimbic brain regions as well as the amygdala and parahippocampal gyrus, which affect emotional arousal. New ayahuasca users have described their first use as producing a significant reduction in the intensity of minor psychiatric symptoms (Cakic et al., 2010; dos Santos, 2013; Riba et al., 2011). There has been no documentation of individuals becoming physically dependent on ayahuasca or any other source of DMT (Gable, 2006).

With DMT, the sensory and perceptual effects tend to be more immediate and intense than those of other hallucinogens, which speaks to the lipid solubility of the substance. As a result, anxiety reactions and panic states are more frequently associated with DMT than with other hallucinogens within this family, partially because of the unexpectedly rapid onset of its effects. These symptoms can be substantively exacerbated if a person has a seri-ous mental health issue such as schizophrenia or bipolar disorder (dos Santos et al., 2017). Likewise, the effects of DMT disappear much more rapidly than those of other members of this family, typically within 30 to 60 minutes after administration. DMT also acts as a monoamine oxidase inhibitor (MAOI) (see Chapter 12). MAOIs are antidepressants that can interact with a variety of drugs and foods, such as red wine and old cheese, and these combinations can produce hazardous and potentially fatal results (dos Santos, 2013).

Morning Glory Seeds

slang: flying saucers, heavenly blues, pearly gates

The predominant active ingredient in morning glory seeds, lysergic acid amide (LSA), is a natural alkaloid that is chemically related to LSD but is approximately one-tenth as potent. The seeds, if eaten whole, usually pass through the digestive tract with little effect upon the user. When seeds are chewed, effects begin after approximately 30–90 minutes and again are similar to those of LSD. Depending on the variety of seeds, an estimated 300 would produce effects equivalent to those of a 0.02–0.03 mg dose of LSD. However, LSA can be extracted and injected to produce a faster and more intense experience (Schiff, 2006). Morning glory seeds are packaged commercially and sold legally throughout North America. Many varieties have been treated with insecticides, fungicides, or other chemicals that are poisonous, with some varieties specially treated to induce nausea if eaten. As with all members of this subgroup of hallucinogens, no known deaths have occurred as a direct result of the psychoactive properties of LSA.

PHENYLETHYLAMINES: MESCALINE-LIKE HALLUCINOGENS

Most phenylethylamines, while sharing the psychoactive effects produced by the LSD family of hallucinogens, are actually more closely related to the neurotransmitter norepinephrine than serotonin. Though considerably weaker than LSD, in equal doses they produce similar sensory and psychological effects. However, phenylethylamines cannot be used to prolong the hallucinogenic effects of LSD once the maximum effects are reached and tolerance occurs.

Phenylethylamines also bear a structural relationship to amphetamines. At high doses, these drugs can produce agitation and marked stimulation of the peripheral nervous system, manifested in both an abnormally accelerated heart rate and high blood pressure. Like most members of the LSD family, the majority of drugs in the mescaline family are produced only for the street user in illicit laboratories. Their simple molecular structure has made it easy to produce large numbers of derivatives. However, unlike most members of the LSD-like hallucinogens group of psychoactive agents, use of some members of this family of drugs has led directly to deaths through hypertensive crisis, including increases in blood pressure leading to a stroke.

Mescaline

slang: big chick, blue caps, britton, buttons, cactus, cactus head, half moon, mesc, mescal, moon, topi

Mescaline is the only entirely natural alkaloid in this drug family, though it too can be synthesized. Mescaline is prepared from the Mexican peyote cactus and the San Pedro cactus found in Ecuador and Peru. It has historically been used in religious ceremonies of Indigenous Peoples from South America through Mexico to the Southwestern United States. It is currently recognized as the legal sacrament of the Native American Church (NAC) of North America and is used in the church's formal ceremonies. The NAC expanded throughout the United States and into Canada in the early part of the 20th century, bringing peyote with it. Even though peyote was not an illegal substance, RCMP and local police engaged in extensive surveillance of Canadian reserves to determine if peyote was being used. Their concern was not with the use or misuse of peyote, but with its power to unite First Nations in response to the oppression and subjugation they endure under the reserve system (Dyck & Bradford, 2012).

In using the drug psychoactively, the heads or buttons of the cactus are dried and then sliced, chopped, or ground and sometimes placed into capsules. Peyote can also be smoked, and occasionally users inject it. It is considerably less potent than LSD but can be much more powerful than cannabis. At low doses, from three to six peyote buttons or 300–500 mg of mescaline, effects appear slowly and last from 10 to 18 hours. Physical effects include dilation of pupils, an increase in body temperature, some muscular relaxation, nausea, and vomiting. The common psychological effects include euphoria, heightened sensory perception, visual hallucinations (which users generally realize are imaginary), perceived alterations of one's body image, and difficulty in thinking. Accounts of mystical or religious experiences have been regularly reported with use of this psychoactive substance and have been highlighted in both television and movies. Higher doses can produce headache, hypotension (low blood pressure), cardiac depression, and slowing of the respiratory rate, despite its secondary stimulant properties. Hallucinations typically begin one to two hours after administration. There have not yet been any reports of harmful dependence or withdrawal reactions among those who, like the NAC, use peyote on a regular basis in a formal, culturally specific process and where use is neither indiscriminate nor irresponsible (Halpern et al., 2005).

Methylenedioxyamphetamine (MDA)

slang: love drug, love trip

MDA is a serotonin-releasing chemical related both to mescaline and to the amphetamines. It produces both LSD-like hallucinogenic effects and stimulant effects. It is customarily swallowed but may also be sniffed or injected. When MDA is taken orally, the effects are first perceived after approximately half an hour and may last up to eight hours. It can be found as a white to light-brown powder and sometimes as an amber liquid. For many users, low doses of MDA, from 60–150 mg, are reported to artificially produce a sense of peacefulness and emotional closeness to others. For this reason, it has been labelled as the "love drug." Users generally report a sense of well-being along with heightened tactile sensations, intensification of feelings, a heightened level of consciousness, and increased self-insight. Physical effects, which become more pronounced as dosage increases, include dilation of pupils, increased blood pressure, increased body temperature, profuse sweating, and dryness of the nose and throat. Doses of 300–500 mg all produce significant amphetamine-like effects, including hyperactive reflexes, hyperresponsivity to sensory stimuli, hypothermia, and agitation. Hallucinations, seizures, and respiratory insufficiency due to spasms of chest muscles can also potentially occur. These serious physical reactions require immediate medical treatment as MDA-associated deaths and near-deaths have been regularly reported (Hancock & McKim, 2018).

The long-term effects and dependence-liability of MDA are largely unknown, with no evidence yet reported of physical dependence occurring. Most problems arise with MDA as a result of a substitute and less desirous drug such as phencyclidine (PCP), para-methoxyamphetamine (PMA), or paramethoxymethamphetamine (PMMA) being sold as MDA. Use and distribution of MDA has waned with the emergence and increased popularity of MDMA. In studies with animals, long-term use of MDA created damage through serotonin depletion. It also caused damage to axons and nerve terminals, which can have protracted effects on behaviour. This suggests that even moderate doses of the drug may pose risks (Bauman et al., 2007; Harkin et al., 2001).

3,4-Methylenedioxymethamphetamine (MDMA)

slang: Adam, b-bombs, Bermuda triangle, bickie, blue kisses, blue lips, blue nile, California sunrise, clarity, E, ecstasy, elephants, euphoria, Eve, love pill, M & M's, molly, rolling, running, Scooby Snax, snowball, speed for lovers, swans, thizz, X, XTC, yuppie psychedelic

MDMA is more commonly referred to as ecstasy and was first manufactured in 1912 by the German pharmaceutical company Merck. There is a belief that "Molly," a popular slang term for the drug, is a pure form of MDMA. However, given the illicit nature of this substance, purity remains an issue. Overdoses occur not because of its enhanced purity, but rather because "Molly" often consists of a harsher substance, typically PMA or PMMA.

MDMA is a derivative of oil of sassafras and oil of nutmeg and was synthesized by chemists looking for amphetamine-like drugs to help suppress appetite. In the mid-20th century there was experimental use of the drug by some psychiatrists to facilitate psychotherapy. It was even briefly called "the penicillin of the soul" when it was claimed to assist in overcoming neuroses, increase self-confidence, and induce feelings of euphoria. Through the release of serotonin, it decreases activity in the amygdala, a region of the brain associated with the fear response, and increases activity in the prefrontal cortex, where higher level brain processing occurs. This allows it to be used to help individuals remove the fear that often accompanies painful memory recall. Users report feelings of warmth, closeness, diminished anxiety, empathy, peacefulness, increased energy level, and a positive "vibe" for several minutes to several hours, with peak effects occurring two to four hours after ingestion (Bershad et al., 2019; Kuypers, et al., 2017). However, with President Nixon's commencement of the War on Drugs in 1970, a virtual prohibition was placed on clinical trials for nearly 40 years. With increasing appreciation for the pharmacology of the drug, more contemporary clinical trials have demonstrated that in low doses MDMA has therapeutic utility in treating PTSD in conjunction with psychotherapy (Feduccia & Mithoefer, 2018; Mithoefer et al., 2018; Ot'alora et al., 2018) and potentially alcohol misuse (Sessa, 2018).

However, no psychoactive drug is free of risk, and psychotherapy patients in clinical trials have reported a variety of negative physical side effects, including sweating, blurred vision, fluctuations in blood pressure, loss of appetite, and joint stiffness. Chronic illicit ecstasy use produces a range of side effects in doses as small as 30 mg, though a typical tablet contains 75–125 mg. These effects range from teeth grinding, dehydration, anxiety, insomnia, fever, and loss of appetite to more substantive issues including hyperthermia, uncontrollable seizures, high blood pressure, anxiety, paranoia, and depression caused by a sudden drop in serotonin levels in the days following use, which has led acute withdrawal symptoms to be called Blue Tuesdays, Serotonin Tuesdays, and Suicide Tuesdays. Recreational MDMA use has also been shown to interfere with memory formation, with regular users achieving lower academic outcomes than nonusers, but also lower scores than users of only alcohol or cannabis. Serotonin levels may not return to pre-use levels for up to two years among those who chronically use this drug. Ongoing use has also been demonstrated to cause long-lasting damage to brain areas critical for thought, as excessive amounts of MDMA can damage nerve cells that use serotonin to communicate in areas of the brain where conscious thought occurs. As well, ecstasy use has been associated with reduced white matter integrity in the brain, which can enhance symptoms of depression and anxiety. Reported fatalities have been attributed to the pressure the drug can produce on the heart and respiratory system, though absolute numbers remain very low and are often a result of hyperthermia and dehydration. Persons most vulnerable to the negative effects of MDMA are those with pre-existing heart disease, epilepsy, diabetes, or mental health issues (Bolla et al., 1998; Martins & Alexandre, 2009; Papaseit et al., 2018; Rogers et al., 2009; Zakzanis & Young, 2001).

The global nature and environmental destructiveness of the psychoactive drug trade is well illustrated in the production of MDMA. Currently, the production of sassafras oil, the source of MDMA, has been linked to the devastation of old growth forests in southwest Cambodia. Sassafras oil from the Cardamom mountain area of Cambodia is more than 90 percent pure, and the desire to access this limited resource has resulted in the mass harvesting of trees, which severely damaged the local ecosystem. Illicit factories throughout the region, and the influx of workers into the camps, led to a depletion of wildlife in the area as well as the pollution of the rivers from chemical runoff from the distilled oil. These rivers flow into the rest of Cambodia through the Mekong and Tonlé Sap rivers. Thus, not only was the flora and fauna from the immediate area being killed off, but the entire nation's water system became more polluted (United Nations Office for the Coordination of Humanitarian Affairs, 2008).

Paramethoxyamphetamine (PMA) and Paramethoxymethamphetamine (PMMA)

Slang: chicken powder, chicken yellow, death, double-stacked, Dr. Death, green rolex, killer, mitsubishi, mitsubishi double-stack, red death, red mitsubishi, white mitsubishi

PMA and PMMA are hallucinogenic stimulants with effects similar to those of mescaline and ecstasy (MDMA). Once absorbed into the system, PMMA is metabolized to PMA. PMA both increases the release and decreases the reuptake of serotonin, and can inhibit monoamine oxidase. The physical effects usually include greatly increased pulse rate and heart rate, high blood pressure, increased and laboured respiration, highly elevated body temperature, erratic eye movements, muscle spasms, nausea and vomiting, tachycardia, and hallucinations. At the same dose as MDA, PMA can be fatal because of the way it interferes with blood pressure, body temperature, and pulse rate, leading to renal failure, convulsions, coma, and death far more frequently than other hallucinogens. Only a slight chemical modification is required to alter the safer MDA to the more toxic PMA. This can lead to increased profits for dealers as it is cheaper to produce PMA than MDMA. Fatalities are most often reported from MDA or MDMA use when PMA has mistakenly and inadvertently been taken, as there is no way to discern between the two without a chemical test. This increase in fatalities is in part because, while the amphetamine component of PMMA and PMA is much more potent and longer lasting than that of MDMA, there is a delayed onset of effects. Individuals who believe they have taken MDMA may double dose when the initial onset of effect is slow, further increasing the risk of overdose (Lurie et al., 2012).

2,5-Dimethoxy-4-methylamphetamine (DOM)

slang: STP-serenity, tranquillity and peace, super terrific psychedelic

DOM, known as "STP" on the streets, is chemically related to mescaline and amphetamines. It was originally synthesized in an effort to find a treatment for schizophrenia in 1964. Typically administered orally, it is considerably more potent than mescaline, but less potent than LSD at equivalent dose levels. Physical effects can include sleeplessness, dry mouth, nausea, blurred vision, sweating, flushed skin, and shaking, while at low doses it also acts as an amphetamine. Exhaustion, confusion, excitement, delirium, and convulsions may also occur in large doses. Severe adverse reactions, the "bad trip," are frequent, and the effects of the drug may last from 16 to 24 hours. Although there have been no official reports of deaths directly attributable to STP, users who have already experienced psychological disturbances may suffer a prolonged psychotic reaction. Tolerance to DOM develops within three days, and thus there have been no reports of physical dependence on this hallucinogen. It is produced in laboratories specifically for the illicit drug market as there are no current medical uses for this substance (Hans, 2010).

Trimethoxyamphetamine (TMA)

slang: Christmas trees, true mon amis, tutor marked assessment

TMA is an infrequently encountered hallucinogen that also has stimulant effects. TMA is more potent than mescaline and may be taken orally or injected. After approximately two hours, the user experiences intensified auditory and tactile sensations and mescaline-like hallucinations. TMA also produces some unusual effects as the size of the dose is increased. However, the amount required to produce an effect is very close to the toxic level. The mescaline-like effects observed at lower doses of TMA tend to be replaced at higher doses by such behaviour as unprovoked anger and aggression. TMA is prohibited in most nations, making its production subject to clandestine synthesis and producing a drug with varying quality and thus inconsistent effects (Freeman & Alder, 2002).

Nutmeg

slang: none known

The known active ingredient in nutmeg, myristicin, is chemically related to TMA. To obtain a psychoactive effect, nutmeg kernels may be eaten, ground, or powdered, with the powder form typically snorted. Nutmeg may produce feelings of depersonalization and unreality. Low doses may also produce mild, brief euphoria, light-headedness, and CNS stimulation. At higher doses, there may be rapid heartbeat, excessive thirst, agitation, anxiety, acute panic, vomiting, and hallucinations. The effects begin slowly, last several hours, and are most often followed by excessive drowsiness. Recovery from nutmeg intoxication is slow and involves an extremely physically unpleasant hangover effect. Although nutmeg is readily available, it is generally only used when other hallucinogens are not obtainable and by groups who are unable to obtain other types of psychoactive drugs. Despite its innocuous association with Christmas, nutmeg misuse is possible and there have even been reported cases of fatal poisoning (Hancock & McKim, 2018; Stein et al., 2001).

Ibogaine

slang: Ibo, Indra

Ibogaine is a naturally occurring psychoactive alkaloid found in the root of the shrub *Tabernanthe iboga*, which grows in the rainforest of western Central Africa. As it can produce visual hallucinations during a waking dream-like state, it has been historically used at moderate doses as a shamanic drug. At high doses, it can mimic a near-death experience and has therefore become an integral part of coming-of-age rituals to help young men prepare for the responsibilities of adulthood. At low doses, it is purported to have aphrodisiac properties. Ibogaine is prohibited in some countries as its use has been linked to cardiac arrest and seizure even several days after its last use. While ibogaine is legal to possess in Canada—Ibogaine Hydrochlorid (Ibo HCl) has been assessed for its utility in the treatment of addiction, particularly to opioids—the sale of health products containing ibogaine is no longer permitted (Alper et al., 2008; Maas & Strubelt, 2006).

Ibogaine is a white powder and is typically administered in capsule form, with effects beginning within 40–60 minutes after ingestion. At doses of 3–5 mg per kg of body weight, ibogaine has a mild stimulant effect. At greater doses, those of 10 mg per kg of body weight or more, users are more likely to experience visual hallucinations, enhanced mood, and a sense of calm and euphoria. The peak experience lasts approximately two hours, producing a dream-like state. However, ibogaine use can also induce anxiety, apprehension, mental confusion, and neurotoxicity, commonly witnessed in the form of ataxia, which consists of dizziness and muscle incoordination. Nausea and vomiting are also common responses to high doses, as both ibogaine and its primary metabolite noribogaine are toxic. Its use is not recommended for those with an existing mental health condition as ibogaine works not only as a moderate opioid receptor agonist, which is why it may aid in opioid withdrawal, but also as a serotonin reuptake inhibitor, which explains its hallucinatory effects (Alper et al., 1999; Floresta et al., 2019; Kubiliene et al., 2008).

Jimson Weed

slang: devil's apple, devil's weed, locoweed, stink weed

Jimson weed (*Datura stramonium*) was again in the headlines at the beginning of the 21st century in Central Canada because of misuse. Jimson weed, which is native to South America, was introduced to North America sometime during the 1800s and now grows wild throughout the continent. The psychoactive components of jimson weed are atropine and hyoscyamine, members of the alkaloid family, which are also active ingredients in belladonna, another poisonous plant. The large, jagged, bitter-tasting leaves produce vivid hallucinations if dried and smoked. Non-psychoactive effects include dilated pupils, flushed skin, confusion, blurred vision, increased heartbeat, and anxiety. In the fall, the plant produces thorny fruit pods that, if eaten, can lead to bizarre and violent behaviour. This behaviour may necessitate hospitalization until the effects subside. As little as a teaspoon of seeds can produce an overdose that results in circulatory collapse, coma, and, in severe cases, even death (Hancock & McKim, 2018).

DISSOCIATIVE ANAESTHETICS

These hallucinogens belong to the arylcycloalkylamine family and possess depressant properties along with their hallucinatory effects. They produce a wide spectrum of responses, making it difficult to predict experiences from one usage to the next. The term "dissociative anaesthetic" refers to the state in which a person is aware of physical sensations such as touch, pressure, and pain, but the brain does not interpret the messages.

Phencyclidine (PCP)

slang: amoeba, angel dust, animal tranquilizer, beam me up Scotty (mixed with coaine), black dust, busy bee, crystal, DOA (dead on arrival), hog, elephant tranquillizer, embalming fluid, mint leaf, mint weed, monkey tranquillizer, orange crystal, rocket fuel, soma, snorts, tic tac, wack

The pharmaceutical company Parke-Davis originally developed PCP in the 1950s as an experimental general intravenous anaesthetic. It was called Sernyl to reflect the idea of the serenity it was hoped the drug would create. The company was preparing to market PCP for human use when it discovered, at the clinical experimentation stage, that the undesirable possible side effects included convulsions during surgery, delirium, confusion, visual disorientation, and hallucinations as the drug wore off. Not to experience a total economic loss, Parke-Davis re-labelled PCP as Sernylan and marketed it as an anaesthetic for primates. A decade later, PCP was available to street drug users in San Francisco, and during the 1970s, use became widespread throughout North America, primarily because the drug was extremely inexpensive and relatively easy to produce.

PCP is not chemically related to either LSD or mescaline. It produces its hallucinogenic effects by blocking a specific neurochemical receptor site, the NDMA subtype of glutamate, which plays a part in pain perception, learning, memory, and emotion. PCP is a difficult drug to classify accurately. Different doses produce different effects as it interacts with most neurotransmitter systems because it is an arylcyclohexylamine compound. This gives it not only hallucinogenic and CNS-depressant effects, but also weak stimulant properties. It is also known to control dopamine in the brain, causing a person to experience elation, not typical in the majority of hallucinogens. In various users, the effects of PCP may resemble the action of a mild stimulant, an analgesic, an anaesthetic, or a hallucinogen, and in some users a combination or some or all of these effects (Hancock & McKim, 2018).

PCP at low doses will most often produce a feeling of euphoria, relaxation, and sedation. Perceptual distortions of time, space, body image, and visual or auditory stimuli are fairly common. There is often a feeling of dissociation from the environment so that the user feels totally isolated. Impairment of a number of higher brain functions, such as attention, concentration, judgment, motor coordination, and speech, can also occur. Physiological effects include constriction of the pupils, blurred vision, an increase in body temperature, and mild stimulation of the cardiovascular system. Higher doses of PCP, which can be as little as 10 mg in a non-tolerant user, can induce an acute toxic psychosis, including paranoia, confusion, disorientation, restlessness, hallucinations, anxiety, agitation, personal alienation, delusions, and bizarre and sometimes violent behaviour.

Muscular rigidity and spasm, twitching, or absent reflexes may appear at high doses. When given in large amounts, PCP also has an analgesic effect that prevents users from experiencing pain resulting from injuries. This factor tends to increase the severity of injuries, because the user fails to take any type of protective action. Other physiological effects experienced at high doses include irregularities in heartbeat, fluctuations in blood pressure, abnormally high body temperature, respiratory depression, severe nausea and vomiting, and hypersalivation. At very high doses (150–200 mg), seizures, coma, and respiratory arrest may result in death. Hypertensive crises, stroke, and renal failure have also been reported, as has stupor, catatonic rigidity, and accidental and/or violent death (Csiernik, 2019).

Long-term effects of PCP include the possibility of flashbacks, prolonged anxiety, social withdrawal and isolation, severe depression, impairment of memory, and the inability to think abstractly. Impairment of thought, along with unpredictable and violent behaviour, has also been observed in chronic PCP users. These symptoms may take several months to abate once the user has stopped ingesting the substance. A toxic psychosis has also been observed in chronic users of PCP with no history of psychiatric disorder to drug use, though the exact role of PCP in the etiology of these symptoms is unclear. Tolerance does appear to develop to PCP use. Withdrawal symptoms have been reported in animals, but the development of physical dependence has yet to be confirmed in humans. Psychological dependence appears to occur in some users, but the prevalence is still undetermined (Domino & Luby, 2012).

Ketamine

slang: big K, breakfast, cat killer, cat tranquilizer, cat valium, donkey, horsey, jet, K, ket, kitkat, kitty, special K, super acid, vitamin K

Ketamine is a white, powdery, short-acting synthetic dissociative anaesthetic developed in 1962 at the Parke-Davis laboratories in Michigan and first used medicinally during the Vietnam War. Despite its hallucinogenic properties, it is still used in short surgical procedures where a patient needs to be unconscious only for 10–15 minutes as it does not suppress the respiratory system and after-effects last only one to three hours. Ketamine can be used in settings where modern anaesthesia machines and equipment are rare or non-existent. It is inexpensive and easily available, and unlike modern techniques such as inhaled anaesthesia, it requires minimal equipment and training. Ketamine's high level of safety makes it a primary surgical drug in low- and middle-income countries, disaster situations, and conflict zones, where anaesthesiologists are scarce, and where running water, electricity, and oxygen are unreliable. It has been on the World Health Organization's (2014) list of essential medicines since 1985 and the WHO has constantly argued against nations that have attempted to prohibit use of this drug for the above reasons. However, in developed nations such as Canada where there are other less problematic drugs available for surgery, ketamine is primarily used as an animal tranquillizer for a wide range of mammals, including elephants, camels, gorillas, horses, pigs, sheep, goats, dogs, cats, rabbits, snakes, guinea pigs, birds, gerbils, and mice (Jansen, 2000).

Ketamine produces feelings of serenity, changes in perception, and dissociation between mind and body, termed the "K-hole" effect. However, when too much is consumed, feelings of confusion and loss of short-term memory occur, and, in severe cases, stupor or unconsciousness, which some have equated to an out-of-body or near-death experience. While ketamine produces anaesthesia quickly, it also raises the heart rate, and even low doses can produce delusions and mental confusion that can progress to hallucinations and degrees of dissociation bordering on a schizophrenic-like state. Violent dreams and flashbacks have been associated with both clinical and non-medical use of the drug. Ketamine was one of a number of drugs that gained popularity at raves and all-night dance clubs, and it has been associated with spiked drinks and used as a date-rape drug. Physical effects can include a loss of motor control, leading to difficulties in walking, standing, and talking, cardiovascular issues, temporary memory loss, numbness, nausea, loss of sensory perception, and respiratory depression. It is possible to overdose on ketamine, and deaths have been reported from its misuse. Chronic use may produce kidney damage, shrink the bladder irreversibly, impair memory and cognitive functions, and produce delusional, dissociative, and schizophrenia-like symptoms (Curran & Morgan, 2000; Morgan et al., 2008).

Ketamine has been found to produce positive affective responses in individuals with a diagnosis of treatment-resistant depression, including major depressive disorder, bipolar depression, pain disorders, and co-morbid depression and pain disorders. Ketamine has also been demonstrated to have anti-anxiety and anti–suicidal ideation properties (Allen & Ivester, 2017; Canuso et al., 2018; Iadarola et al., 2015; Price et al., 2009; Singh, Fedgchin et al., 2016). There have also been some preliminary studies indicating that ketamine can be of value as a pharmacological component for treating substance use disorders (Ettensohn et al., 2018).

NOVEL PSYCHOACTIVE SUBSTANCES (NPS)

Novel psychoactive drugs have also been called legal highs, in that these synthetic substances were created not only to produce a psychoactive effect but also to possess a chemical structure that, at least initially, made them legal. NPS are defined by the United Nations Office on Drugs and Crime as drugs (either in a pure form or part of a preparation) that are not controlled by the 1961 Single Convention on Narcotic Drugs or the 1971 Convention on Psychotropic Substances, but that pose a threat to public health. Over 700 NPS have been documented, with new ones developed on an ongoing basis (UNODC, 2017). While the majority of these substances fall within the hallucinogen family, others have primarily stimulant or opioid properties. Those with hallucinogenic properties follow the chemical structure of the subgroups discussed earlier in the chapter:

1. Phenethylamines such as 4-bromo-2,5-dimethoxyphenethylamine (2C-B-Fly), 4-Methylampheamine (4-MA), and methiopropamine (MPA) are more potent and produce more arousal than previous phenethylamines, as they have stronger amphetamine-like characteristics than mescaline. Typical effects are sensory-enhanced hallucinations, particularly visual hallucinations, stimulant-like euphoria, and heightened erotic sensations. The side effects are also quite potent, including insomnia and sweating and cold extremities, followed by fluctuations in body temperature, agitation, vasoconstriction, chest pain, painful urination, headache, nausea, tachycardia, anorexia, anxiety, and negative affect (Society for the Study of Addiction [SSA], 2016; UNODC, 2013).

2. Piperazines such as 1-Benzylpiperazine (BZP) and ethylphenidate have a chemical structure similar to MDMA, meaning they have both hallucinogenic and stimulant properties. Piperazines release and inhibit the reuptake of dopamine, serotonin, and norepinephrine, producing euphoria, intensify sensory experience, and enhance mood, though they remain less potent than amphetamines and produce fewer hallucinogenic effects than either MDA or MDMA. Negative physical side effects include agitation, excessive sweating, hypertension, tachycardia, seizures and vomiting, and risk of damaging the heart muscle (SSA, 2016; UNODC, 2013).

3. Substituted tryptamines such as alpha-methyltyrptamine (AMT), 5-methoxy-N, N-dimethyltryptamine (5-MeO-DMT), and 5-methoxy-N, N-diisopropyltryptamine (5-MeO-DIPT) are similar to LSD, producing primarily hallucinogenic effects, though unlike LSD-like hallucinogens they also produce minor secondary stimulant effects, even at low doses. Documented side effects include agitation, restlessness, confusion, lethargy, vomiting, pupil dilation, jaw clenching, and increased blood pressure, temperature, and respiration (SSA, 2016; UNODC, 2013).

4. Phencyclidine-type substances such as 3-methoxy-PCP, 4-methoxy-PCP, 3-methoxy-PCE, and methoxetamine (MXE, Mexxy) are the smallest subgroup of NPS, and all are derivatives of either PCP or ketamine. Intoxication can produce effects from mild neurological and physiological reactions, euphoria, and dissociation from the physical body, to stupor or a light coma state (Roth et al., 2013).

5. Synthetic cannabis (synthetic cannabinoid receptor agonists, or SCRAs) is the largest group of NPS, which produces effects similar to delta-9-tetrahydrocannabinol (THC) while having an array of chemical structures. SCRAs bind to the same cannabinoid receptors in the brain and other organs as anandamide, though far more efficiently than cannabis. There are also no cannabinoids in synthetic cannabis, and thus these substances have none of the therapeutic qualities of natural cannabis products (see Box 11.1). The most common versions, Spice and K2, contain a mixture of plant material and chemical-grade

synthetic cannabinoids. The effects of smoking these synthetic drugs are reported as cannabis-like; however, the drugs tend to be 2 to 50 times more potent than cannabis and have more toxic side effects. Along with producing a positive psychoactive effect, synthetic cannabinoids increase energy and decrease inhibitions. Similar to natural cannabis, synthetic cannabis can create a sense of hunger and drowsiness in users, impacting concentration and coordination. Negative side effects can include tachycardia, hypertension, muscle jerking, vomiting, seizures, and psychotic behaviour, including engaging in acts of violence. Chronic use has been linked to kidney damage and fatal heart attacks, with acute use having the potential to produce severe agitation, anxiety, panic, irritability, confusion, memory loss, and temporary psychosis in a small number of instances. There have been regular reports of overdoses and deaths due to the use of synthetic cannabinoids (European Monitoring Centre for Drugs and Drug Addiction, 2009b; Hermanns-Clausen et al., 2013; Lauritsen & Rosenberg, 2016; Malyshevskaya et al., 2017).

CANNABIS

slang: A-bomb (mixed with heroin or opium), Acapulco gold, Acapulco red, ace, bazooka (mixed with cocaine), BC Bud, bhang, blunt, boom, B.T., chronic, Columbian, doobie, dope, gangster, ganja, grass, hemp, herb, home grown, jay, kiff, Mary Jane, Maui Wowie, Northern lights, pot, purple haze, ragweed, reefer, sinse, skunk, smoke, spliff, tea, Thai stick, weed

Cannabis is classified as a hallucinogen because of its ability to alter perception at low doses and produce hallucinations at high doses. However, it affects a totally different neurotransmitter than all other hallucinogens, anandamide, which interacts with endocannabinoid receptor sites in the brain and the gut. The use of cannabis is widespread because the hemp plant is remarkably hardy and can grow easily and quickly in almost every climate zone. Cannabis preparations are obtained primarily from the female flowers of the plant *Cannabis sativa* and, to a smaller extent, from the leaves and shoots. Like opium, it is a biological product with many components. While the plant contains numerous cannabinoids, the constituent of cannabis mainly responsible for its psychoactive effects is delta-9-tetrahydrocannabinol (THC), which was first identified in 1965. The potency of a given preparation is largely determined by its concentration of THC, although the presence of other cannabinoids, notably cannabidiol (CBD) and, to a lesser extent, cannabinol (CBN), may influence the effects to a small extent. In total, there are over 100 distinct cannabinoids (Grof, 2018).

Cannabis varies in colour from greyish-green to greenish-brown. Hashish is the dried caked resin produced from the tops and leaves of the female plant and is sold in solid pieces. A cigarette is typically dipped into cannabis oil, a liquid, before lighting. Cannabis oil typically has the greatest average potency, though levels of cannabis potency have increased substantially with the development of hydroponics and the subsequent legalization of the drug in Canada. Cannabis was first criminalized in Canada in 1923, in part because of the publication of activist Emily Murphy's (1922) book *The Black Candle*, which described cannabis as a drug menace. Cannabis was thus included, along with heroin and cocaine, as an illicit drug when Canada implemented its first drug laws. This was finally overturned in 2018 though this did not diminish the underground market in cannabis sales in Canada. As well, the term *cannabis* is now used rather than *marijuana*, as the historic roots of the latter term evolved from the slang term for brothel and also as a derogatory term for Latinos in an attempt to further stigmatize users during the early part of the 20th century (Booth, 2005).

When a person smokes cannabis, the active ingredient, THC, travels quickly to the brain. THC binds to THC receptors, anandamines, which are concentrated in the limbic system, areas within the reward system of the brain. Other parts of the brain with large amounts of anandamide receptors include those regulating the integration of sensory experiences with emotions, as well as those controlling functions of learning, motor coordination, and some autonomic nervous system functions. This explains why the administration of THC disrupts executive function, attention, hormone secretion, motor initiation and movement, decision making, and mood. The action of THC in the hippocampus explains its ability to interfere with memory, and the action of THC in the cerebellum is responsible for its ability to produce a loss of balance. However, while THC quickly penetrates the CNS, the proportion of a dose that crosses the blood-brain barrier is low because of the high proportion of THC that binds to plasma proteins. This means that after smoking, peak CNS levels occur within 10 minutes (European Monitoring Centre for Drugs and Drug Addiction, 2009a; Huestis & Smith, 2016).

Edible cannabis provides an alternative method of consumption to smoking or vaping. Some individuals perceive the euphoria that occurs after consuming edible cannabis as more intense than when cannabis is inhaled. It is recommended that individuals who are new to using edible cannabis start with products containing no more than 2.5 mg of THC, as it can take up to four hours to feel the full effects of edibles. Thus, consuming more within a short timeframe can result in over-intoxication, including severe anxiety and panic, nausea and vomiting, and in extreme cases paranoia. The recommendation is that individuals gradually consume edible cannabis products and, after an initial dose, wait at least four hours before consuming more. The intoxicating effects of edibles can last up to 12 hours, with some residual effects lasting up to 24 hours (CCSA, 2019).

First cultivated in prehistoric Asia, virtually every part of the cannabis plant is usable, though it is only the leaves and flowers that have psychoactive properties. There has been increasing recognition and acceptance of cannabis's therapeutic qualities, though the therapeutic potential of the cannabinoids does not diminish the risks associated with excessive recreational use. Chronic use can produce side effects, and tolerance can develop to some of the beneficial effects (see Box 11.1).

At low to moderate doses, the effects of cannabis products are somewhat similar to those of alcohol: relaxation, disinhibition, euphoria, and the tendency to talk and laugh more than usual, though it can also cause unpleasant effects in some users. However, these seem to occur less frequently and generally with less intensity than with other hallucinogens. Using cannabis can increase the heart rate, as well as heighten appetite, while reddening the eyes and producing a quite reflective sleepy state in the user. Cannabis also impairs short-term memory, logical thinking, and the ability to drive or operate machinery because it impairs judgment and motor control. It also produces changes in the perception of time, distance, touch, sight, and hearing, and can affect balance. Risk of automobile collision begins at low levels of use and escalates with the dose, increasing even more so when alcohol is also consumed. After alcohol, cannabis is the second most common cause of impairment leading to traffic collisions for males in the 18–30 age range (Asbridge et al. 2012; Santamarina-Rubio et al., 2009). An examination of fatally injured drivers in Canada between 2000 and 2006 revealed that 14.9 percent of those tested were positive for cannabis. Since then, cannabis use across the country has increased (Beirness & Beasley, 2009), with the reported cost of impaired driving due to cannabis costing of over $1 billion annually in Canada when premature death, injuries resulting from the collisions, and property damaged are totalled (Wettlaufer et al., 2017).

At very large doses, the effects of cannabis are similar to those of LSD and other hallucinogenic substances. The user may experience anxiety, confusion, restlessness, depersonalization, excitement, anxiety reactions, and even acute psychosis. Panic reactions are occasionally produced by smaller doses in inexperienced users. Flashbacks have also been reported occasionally in cannabis users. These are defined as recurrences of cannabis-induced symptoms that appear spontaneously days to weeks after the acute drug effects have worn off. The underlying mechanism is not clear, but it is likely that the drug experience has triggered some change in thought patterns that can be evoked by environmental stimuli.

There is a strong association between cannabis use and a broad range of primary mental illness, particularly bipolar disorder and anti-social, dependent, and histrionic personality disorders. Cannabis can enhance or trigger a psychotic episode in persons with family histories of this type of mental health problem, manifesting earlier than with the disease alone (González-Pinto et al., 2008). Cannabis use has been confirmed to have a definitive adverse effect on mental health, with frequent current use having a larger effect than infrequent current use or past use. Factors that make individuals more susceptible to cannabis use also make them more susceptible to mental illness (van Ours & Williams, 2009). However, cannabis use has still to be shown to cause schizophrenia, yet for those who are genetically predisposed to schizophrenia, there seems to be a correlation between cannabis use and onset of psychotic symptoms. Children with a mother with schizophrenia are at a five times greater risk of developing schizophrenia and a two and a half times greater risk of developing cannabis-induced psychosis. Thus, while it may not be psychologically dangerous for most people to use this drug, there is a distinct risk among a small proportion of the population (Arendt et al., 2008). People with first-episode psychosis tend to have smoked higher potency cannabis, for a longer time and with greater frequency, than healthy controls. Among individuals with anxiety disorders, regular cannabis users report mental health–related functional problems more often than non-users. Regular cannabis users also report accomplishing less due to emotional problems and more commonly having emotional problems interfere with social activities than do non-using controls (Lev-Rana et al., 2012, 2013).

Cannabis is not water soluble, and thus it is retained in a user's body fat. Cannabinoids from one joint may be retained in the body for up to a week. Once a chronic user stops using cannabis, they could still test positive 45 days after the last administration. Long-term effects of cannabis include impaired cognitive function on several levels, from basic motor coordination to executive functioning, including the ability to plan, organize, solve problems, make decisions, remember, think abstractly, and control emotions and behaviour. Additional effects include emotional lability (flatness), apathy, learning deficits, decreased energy, increased risk of mood depression, increased risk of stroke, decreased ability to fight infections, greater risk of head, neck, and throat cancers than non-users, increased endocrine system difficulties, decreased testosterone production and sperm count, inhibition of ovulation, and decreased fertility, depending on the quantity, frequency, age of onset, and duration of cannabis use (Aldington et al., 2007; Crean et al., 2011; Daling et al., 2009; Messinis et al., 2006).

Cannabinoids cross the placental barrier and may affect the expression of key genes. Though there is no evidence to suggest an association of cannabis use during pregnancy with an increased risk of premature birth, miscarriage, or major physical abnormalities, reduced birth weight and body length among heavy cannabis smokers has been noted. However, greater impacts arise as children grow into adulthood. By age four, deficits in memory, verbal and perceptual skills, and verbal and visual reasoning can be noted. Impaired performance in verbal and quantitative reasoning and short-term memory has also been found in a study of six year olds whose mothers reported smoking one or more joints per day while pregnant. Testing of children in Grade 3 has found that prenatal cannabis exposure can impair abstract reasoning and reading and spelling achievement. Children of maternal cannabis users expressed significantly more depressive and anxious symptoms at age 10 compared to children of non-users, and increased risk of ADHD and other learning disabilities. Brain imaging studies of young adults ages 18–22 indicate that in utero cannabis exposure negatively impacts the neural circuitry involved in aspects of executive functioning, including working memory. There is clear evidence that while there is no fetal cannabis syndrome, prenatal exposure to cannabis has subtle adverse effects that are greater the more cannabis a mother smoked while pregnant (Porath-Waller, 2016; Psychoyos & Vinod, 2013).

Smoking a single joint has the same impact on breathing capacity as up to five cigarettes. Cannabis smokers had lighter symptoms, such as wheezing, coughing, chest tightness and phlegm, compared with tobacco smokers. Cannabis smokers suffer more fine damage to their lungs, impacting the ability to bring in oxygen and take away waste gases. As a result, lungs have to work harder. As well, smoking cannabis can cause changes in lung tissue that may promote cancer. Cannabis can harm the lungs' airways more than tobacco as its smoke contains twice the level of carcinogens, such as polyaromatic hydrocarbons, compared with cigarettes. Additional health risks arise as joints are typically smoked without a proper filter and almost to the very tip, which increases the amount of smoke inhaled. Cannabis smokers also tend to inhale more deeply and for a longer time, facilitating the deposit of carcinogens in the airways, than do tobacco smokers. This can mean that cannabis smokers end up with five times more carbon monoxide in their bloodstream compared to tobacco smokers (Aldington et al., 2007, 2008). Vaping cannabis has not alleviated these risks, and another issue has arisen as vitamin E oil and other additives are believed to produce lung damage much more quickly than traditional inhaling of the drug (see Box 10.1). Cannabis condensates have been found to be more toxic than those of tobacco, though tobacco condensates appeared to induce genetic damage in a concentration-dependent manner, whereas the matched cannabis condensates do not (Maertens et al., 2009). Other problems associated with tobacco smoking, such as constriction of airways and development of emphysema, also appear to be more of an issue with cannabis smoke, as the intake of tar and other carcinogens is greater with cannabis than with tobacco smoke. Studies that examined lung cancer risk factors or premalignant changes in the lung found an association of cannabis smoking with increased tar exposure, decreased immune response, increased risk of tumours, increased oxidative stress, and bronchial abnormalities compared with tobacco smokers and with non-smokers (Mehra et al., 2006).

Considerable tolerance can develop within a week to most of the acute effects of cannabis if the drug is administered several times per day. Less frequent smokers report a loss of sensitivity to the desired effects of the drug over the course of several months of regular administration. Despite earlier beliefs to the contrary, both psychological and physical dependence to cannabis do occur. Physical dependence can occur with as little as two joints per day. Withdrawal symptoms occur four to eight hours after abrupt termination of drug administration and can last three to four weeks. They can include anger, irritability, aggression, insomnia, anxiety, and sleep disturbances accompanied by vivid dreaming (Copeland et al., 2009). Users have also been reported to "green out," which is when a person feels particularly unwell after smoking cannabis. This unpleasant experience can make the user turn pale green and feel sweaty, dizzy, and nauseous. It is similar to an overdose, with some people even passing out. Combining cannabis with alcohol appears to increase the likelihood of a user "greening out" (Vandrey et al., 2008). Increasing cannabis use in late adolescence and early adulthood is also associated with a range of adverse outcomes later in life, including poorer educational outcome, lower income, greater dependency on social assistance, unemployment, and lower relationship and life satisfaction (Ferguson & Boden, 2008).

Box 11.1: Risks and Benefits of THC and CBD

There is an active debate regarding the risks and benefits of cannabis. Cannabis is composed of many constituent elements: the psychoactive component is delta-9-tetrahydrocannabinol (THC), but there are also dozens of cannabinoids, many of which have been claimed to produce therapeutic benefits. While more research is required, and is ongoing, the following is the current list of both risks and benefits associated with the use of cannabis. The majority of risks are associated with the use of delta-9-tetrahydrocannabinol through smoking or vaping. The majority of the benefits arise from using cannabinoids, which themselves are not psychoactive. However, cannabinoids, like any foreign substance, need to be taken in a regulated, controlled manner or they too can produce negative side effects.

Documented Therapeutic Uses for Cannabis: The Benefits of CBD
Reduces symptoms of:

- acute anxiety
- acute depression
- acute stress
- antibiotic-resistant infections
- diabetes
- epilepsy
- fibromyalgia
- inflammatory bowel disease
- multiple sclerosis
- Parkinson's disease
- post-traumatic stress disorder
- psychosis symptoms
- rheumatoid arthritis
- social anxiety disorder
- spasticity
- Tourette's syndrome

Provides:

- nausea relief
- pain relief
- increased sleep

Documented Risks Associated with Cannabis Use

- Amotivational syndrome: Apathy and diminished ability to concentrate.
- Anxiety: Chronic cannabis use can enhance this psychological state.
- Bone mineral density: Extensive cannabis use can decrease bone density, leading to an increased risk of fractures.
- Brain development: Heavy cannabis use can negatively impact the hippocampus and amygdala, also decreasing grey matter density.
- Cannabinoid hyperemesis syndrome (CHS): Chronic, heavy cannabis use can produce nausea and vomiting along with abdominal pain.
- Cardiovascular system: Chronic cannabis use can accelerate cardiovascular age and increase the risk of death from hypertension.
- Cognitive deficits: Chronic exposure to THC alters short-term object-recognition memory, episodic memory, and working memory.
- Crohn's disease: The use of cannabis for more than six months at any time for individuals with inflammatory bowel disease symptoms increases the need for surgery.
- Dental: Chronic cannabis use is associated with tooth decay.
- Dependency: Ongoing cannabis use produces both physical and psychological dependency, including withdrawal symptoms upon cessation.
- Depression: Chronic cannabis use can increase symptoms of depression over time.
- Education: Regular cannabis use in adolescence approximately doubles the risks of early school-leaving, while persistent cannabis use during adolescence has been associated with a decline in IQ scores.
- Mental health: Regular cannabis use increases the risk of developing bipolar disorder, as well as enhancing symptoms of mania and hypomania in individuals diagnosed with bipolar disorders. Increased incidence of suicidal ideation, suicide attempts, and death by suicide have been reported among heavier cannabis users compared with non-users.
- Motor vehicle collisions: Cannabis use is a contributing factor to an increased risk of motor vehicle collisions and fatalities.
- Periodontal disease: Cannabis use increases the risk of gum disease, contributing to swollen and bleeding gums.
- Poisoning: There is a risk of children accidentally consuming cannabis edibles intended for adults and being poisoned.
- Pregnancy: Birth weights for babies of women using cannabis at least once per week before and throughout pregnancy were lighter than the offspring of non-users. Newborns exposed to cannabis exhibit sleep disturbances, an issue that can last for a few months up to three years. As with any smoked substance, there

is a greater risk of sudden infant death syndrome in homes where cannabis is smoked compared to homes where there are no smoked substances.

- Psychosis and schizophrenia: Cannabis use can produce psychosis-like effects, including delusions and delirium, among those with a pre-disposition for psychosis. Chronic cannabis use is associated with changes in resting-state brain function with a meta-analysis finding that the age at onset of psychosis for cannabis users was 2.7 years younger than for non-users.
- Respiratory disease: Individuals who smoke or vape cannabis have more issues with coughing, wheezing, shortness of breath after exercise, nocturnal chest tightness, and mucus development. Cannabis smoking aggravates both asthma and bronchitis symptoms.
- Sperm mobility: Preliminary findings suggest that chronic cannabis has a negative impact on male reproductive health.

Source: Csiernik (2019).

CHAPTER 12

Psychotherapeutic Drugs

In general, depressants and opioids slow down the ANS and CNS, stimulants speed them up, and hallucinogens disrupt the way the brain processes sensory input. The function of all these drugs is to move the user away from a homeostatic balance point, whereas the function of psychotherapeutic agents is the opposite. The purpose of antipsychotics, mood stabilizers, and antidepressants is to move the user back to homeostasis, back to their natural balance point. Mental health has become a much more discussed issue in our society, and the function of these psychoactive agents is to assist in addressing psychosis, bipolar disorder, and depression.

MENTAL HEALTH ISSUES

Psychosis

Psychosis is a condition where an individual is not connected to the reality of their physical surrounds and environment. The person is unable to determine what is physically real and if what they perceive is real or not. It is characterized by delusions and hallucinations, and behaviour that is inappropriate to the person's context. Individuals experiencing a psychosis also have difficulty in making decisions and caring for themselves. While schizophrenia—a lifelong condition involving changes in behaviour, delusions, and hallucinations lasting longer than six months that disrupts social functions, school, or work—is the most well-known example of psychosis, other types include:

- schizoaffective disorder, when a person has both a mood disorder like depression or mania and schizophrenia;
- schizophreniform disorder, when symptoms last less than six months;
- brief psychotic disorder, when a person has only short, sudden episodes of psychotic behaviour lasting less than a month that is typically a response to a stressful situation;

- delusional disorder, when the person has false beliefs relating to actual real-life situations that could be true but are not;
- substance-induced psychotic disorder, which occurs during the withdrawal period from drugs, as pharmacologically distinct as alcohol and methamphetamine;
- psychotic disorder due to a medical condition, when symptoms arise due to an illness affecting the brain such as a tumor; and,
- paraphrenia, schizophrenia that occurs due to aging disrupting brain functioning (American Psychiatric Association, 2013).

The symptoms of psychosis have been divided into four categories: positive symptoms, negative symptoms, cognitive deficits, and mood symptoms. Positive symptoms consist of delusions, hallucinations, and thought disorders. Delusions are fixed, false beliefs that a person comes to believe are true and that often become central organizing principles of their lives. They can be associated with feelings of persecution or of constantly being observed. Hallucinations and disorganized thinking are false sensory perceptions that have no basis in corresponding external sensory stimuli. Auditory hallucinations are the most common sensory disturbance, but hallucinations pertaining to sight, touch, smell, and taste also occur. Negative symptoms consist of a loss of affective responsiveness, including apathy, social withdrawal, impaired affect, or anhedonia (the lack of feeling pleasure). Cognitive deficits include issues with attention, memory, executive function, and behaviour, including the ability to initiate and stop actions, monitor and change behaviour as needed, and engage in future planning. Mood symptoms are highlighted by dysphoria, a state of anxiety and restlessness, and depression (M. Cruz, 2011; Sue et al., 2011).

Bipolar Disorder

Bipolar disorder was first called *manic-depressive*, and was described as a person's mood fluctuating, often quickly, between melancholia and mania. This state is now called bipolar disorder, a condition where a person moves from feelings of depression, often expressed by feelings of hopelessness, to those of exaggerated well-being or excessive, euphoric views of themselves, their status, and/or their success. These swings in mood are typically followed by a return to homeostasis, which is called *euthymia*. Mania occurs when a person's mood is continually elevated, and often also irritable, requiring a decreased need for sleep. Behaviour is highlighted by excessive talkativeness, racing thoughts, easy distractibility, and often grandiosity, an unrealistic sense of importance and superiority. Periods of depression are the more common and longer lasting state (Noll, 2007).

Bipolar disorder is diagnosed when individuals have experienced at least one episode of mania, with a typical first episode occurring at age 18, though it can arise anytime during adulthood. Bipolar II is diagnosed in those who have had at least one episode of depression and one episode of hypomania, but have never experienced an episode of full mania. (Hypomania has the same features as mania, but the episode is less severe and does not cause the same degree of impairment, and the person can be quite creative and productive, though the nature or pace of the behaviour is out of character for the person.) Cyclothymic disorder, on the other hand, entails numerous hypomanic episodes and numerous depressive episodes over a two-year period, none of which meet full criteria for either mania or depression. Rapid cycling occurs when a person has had four or more mood episodes that can be major depression, mania, or hypomania within one year. A mixed episode is when the individual experiences mania and depression during the same period, for a week or more. In a mixed episode, a person could report feeling sad or hopeless with suicidal thoughts, while still feeling highly energized. Outwardly they may appear agitated, with disturbed sleep patterns and a major change in appetite (American Psychiatric Association, 2013).

Depression

Depression is a mental health condition beyond sadness or grief and is clinically labelled major depressive disorder (MDD). It is a chronic, recurring, and debilitating mental illness that is prevalent globally and that substantively impairs social functioning—and can be life threatening. Its cause is a combination and interaction of genetics, biochemistry, personality, and the environment, and thus like addiction is a bio-psycho-social condition. Individuals can also experience a major depressive episode (MDE), which is a period of two weeks or longer when the person experiences intense feelings of major depression such as feelings of sadness and hopelessness, fatigue, weight gain or loss, changes in sleeping patterns, loss of interest in activities, and, in extreme cases, thoughts of suicide. Multiple MDEs are more common than a single episode. In contrast, a state of depression can occur in response to a single event as well as being a more chronic condition (World Health Organization, 2017b). Depression consists of various symptoms, including but not limited to:

- persistent sadness;
- a lack of interest in previously enjoyed activities;
- thoughts of death or suicide;
- difficulty sleeping;
- feelings of worthlessness;
- feelings of guilt;
- difficulty concentrating;
- change in appetite;
- agitation;
- irritability; and
- feeling tired and worn out (American Psychiatric Association, 2013).

There is one additional form of depression called dysthymia. It differs from the other forms in that it is a more chronic, low-grade, persistent state of mood disruption. It does not completely impair functioning, but it does impede an individual's ability to carry out necessary daily functions. Dysthymia is defined as a chronic sadness that lasts more than two years (Cuijper et al., 2010). The greatest fear with all forms of depression, however, is that it may escalate to self-harming behaviour if not properly addressed.

ANTIPSYCHOTICS

Antipsychotics are psychoactive drugs used to treat not the illness but the underlying symptoms of various psychoses by reducing behavioural and physiological responses to stimuli and producing drowsiness and emotional quieting. Antipsychotics work on positive symptoms but unfortunately have minimal impact on negative symptoms or cognitive deficits. Antipsychotics are not effective in decreasing emotional lability (flatness) or social withdrawal or increasing interpersonal communication. They are also referred to as neuroleptics, as they have the ability to produce psychomotor slowing, emotional quieting, and emotional indifference. Antipsychotics produce no euphoria, unlike CNS depressants and stimulants, but rather act to return users to a more homeostatic state. Neither physical nor psychological dependency has been documented even when these drugs are taken for years. Regrettably, as many as one-third of those diagnosed with a psychotic condition are not positively affected by these drugs (Rampino et al., 2019).

A major concern with the use of antipsychotics is the range of negative adverse effects, as they work primarily by blocking dopamine throughout the entire CNS. Resulting side effects can include insomnia, vivid dreaming, nightmares and disrupted sleep patterns, confusion, disorientation, disruptions in concentration, headaches, spasms and shaking, and sedation or fatigue (Inaba & Cohen, 2011). Additionally, members of this family of psychoactive drugs produce extrapyramidal side effects, which include impairment or loss of voluntary movement, involuntary movement of the face and jaw, tremors, feelings of restlessness leading to constant motion such as rocking, muscle rigidity, and Parkinson's-like symptoms (Raman-Wilms, 2014).

Antipsychotic drugs are grouped into first generation antipsychotics (FGAs), also referred to as typical or classic antipsychotics, and second generation antipsychotics (SGAs) (Table 12.1). SGAs became available on the Canadian market in the 1990s. Their introduction, and the fact that they were viewed as safer, if more expensive, options than FGAs, led to a marked increase in antipsychotic medication prescribing for children and youths. In particular, aripiprazole (Abilify) and risperidone (Risperdal) have been demonstrated to reduce ADHD symptoms, including irritability, aggression, self-injury, tantrums, and mood swings, particularly in children with autism spectrum disorder. However, as with all psychoactive drugs, there are negative side effects—in this case weight gain and an increased risk of developing high cholesterol and Type 2 diabetes

(Lamberti et al., 2016; Loy et al., 2012). While FGA use has declined with the emergence of SGAs, they continue to be prescribed as they are far less expensive (Alessi-Severini et al., 2008).

SGAs are also regularly prescribed to institutionalized seniors exhibiting dangerous agitation or psychosis where there is a risk of harm to themselves, other residents, or staff. The use of SGAs with seniors has been reported to reduce distress, improve quality of life, and reduce caregiver burden, with aripiprazole and risperidone demonstrating the best results. SGAs also are less likely to produce extrapyramidal symptoms. However, the use of either SGAs or FGAs with this population comes with increased risk of stroke, mortality, weight gain, and acute cardiovascular effects (Reus et al., 2016). In 2015, Health Canada conducted a safety review of aripiprazole (Abilify) and reported that there was a link between ongoing use of this SGA and a heightened risk of two impulse control disorders, problem gambling and hypersexuality. A minority of long-term Abilify users, who had no prior history of impulse control disorders, experienced uncontrollable urges after they began taking the drug. Further, within days to weeks of reducing the dose level or totally discontinuing aripiprazole, the urges stopped (Health Canada, 2015).

A great deal of off-label use of SGAs is now occurring. Other than being used to treat psychosis, SGAs are now routinely administered, often by general practitioners, to treat obsessive-compulsive disorder, Tourette's syndrome, autism spectrum disorder, disruptive behaviour disorders, depression, eating disorders, general anxiety syndrome, insomnia, and bipolar disorder, which historically was treated with an entirely different subgroup of psychotherapeutic agents. However, controversy remains about the overall effectiveness of these drugs. Early experiments on FGAs found those with an agreed-upon diagnosis of schizophrenia who received a placebo were less likely to be hospitalized than those who were prescribed chlorpromazine, thioridazine, or trifluoperazine (Schooler et al., 1967). This raised the question of whether these drugs, while effective in the short term, made individuals more vulnerable to psychosis in the long term (Whitaker, 2005).

Between 1996 and 2011 in British Columbia, there was an overall fourfold increase in the prescription of antipsychotic drugs. However, SGAs surged 18-fold, from 0.3 to 6.0 per 1,000 people. The groups with the greatest increases were males aged 13 to 18, males aged 6 to 12, and females aged 13 to 18; in other words, children and adolescents (Ronsley et al., 2013). In Canada, SGA prescriptions for children grew 114 percent between 2004 and 2009, compared to 36 percent for ADHD drugs and 44 percent for selective serotonin reuptake inhibitor (SSRI) antidepressants. While some SGAs were prescribed to treat psychosis in children, the majority were prescribed for off-label mental health disorders, including aggression in ADHD, oppositional defiant disorder, and conduct disorder, irritability related to autism spectrum disorder, and other related mood disorders. The most commonly prescribed drug, Risperdal (risperidone), was used on average for 90 days in children aged 1 to 6, 180 days in children aged 7 to 12, and 200 days in children aged 13 to 18, despite concerns regarding metabolic side effects and the lack of formal sanction on their use with children by Health Canada. A similar trend has been reported both in the

Table 12.1: Antipsychotic Psychoactive Agents

Type	Drug	Brand Name
First Generation		
butyrophenones	haloperidol	Haldol
phenothiazines	chlorpromazine perphenazine thioridazine trifluoperazine	Largactil, Thorazine Trilafon Mellaril Stelazine
rauwolfia alkaloids	reserpine	Serpasil
thioxanthenes	chlorprothixene fluphenazine flupenthixol thiothixene zuclopenthixol	Tarasan Prolixin Depixol, Fluanxol Navane Acuphase, Clopixol
Second Generation		
	amisulpride aripiprazole asenapine brexpiprazole cariprazine clozapine iloperidone loxapine lurasidone olanzapine paliperidone quetiapine risperidone ziprasidone zotepine	Solian Abilify Saphris Rexulti Vraylar Clozaril Fanapta Loxitane Latuda Zyprexa Invega Seroquel Risperdal Zeldox Lodopin

Source: Adapted from Procyshyn et al. (2017).

United Kingdom and the United States, raising the question of whether mental health assessment has truly improved, or if more children are simply being medicated as a means of social control (Pringsheim et al., 2011).

Among 139 individuals who participated in a 20-year study based in Chicago, 70 were diagnosed with schizophrenia. Participants were assessed with standardized instruments for major symptoms, psychosocial functioning, personality, attitudinal variables, neurocognition, and treatment. Beginning at the 4.5-year follow-up period, those who had not taken antipsychotic medication for prolonged periods were less likely to have experienced episodes of psychosis and had longer periods of time with no symptoms, compared to those who had taken antipsychotic medication for the entire duration of the study. Though still experiencing reoccurrences, the limited use group did so less frequently than those regularly taking antipsychotic drugs. Those self-selecting not to constantly use drugs developed better coping skills and were assessed as being more resilient, having lower anxiety scores, and having superior neurocognitive skills (Harrow et al., 2012). Amato and colleagues (2018) found that while initially both FGAs and SGAs blocked the synaptic release of dopamine, over time they stopped doing so, and rather than blocking release began to enhance the release of dopamine. This offers another possible explanation as to why individuals in placebo groups returned to drug use less than those in treatment groups.

MOOD STABILIZING PSYCHOACTIVE DRUGS

Though only approximately 1 percent of the Canadian population is affected with bipolar disorder, there are a variety of forms of this condition that have resulted in a range of treatment protocols. While there are several pharmacological options to treat mania there are fewer for the maintenance of homeostasis and for the depression stage. Lithium carbonate, valproate (valproic acid), and carbamazepine have been the traditional pharmacological responses to bipolar disorder (Table 12.2); however, there is an increasing number of SGAs (Table 12.1) being used to address the manic aspect of the disorder (Muralidharan et al., 2013). Interestingly, given the discussion of off-label use above, SGAs are now often recommended when an individual first presents with a manic episode, with valproate being an alternative treatment as it has less risk of adverse motor reactions, followed by carbamazepine. However, neither valproate nor carbamazepine is recommended for women of child-bearing age because of the risks these drugs pose to a fetus (Etemad et al., 2012), and in those instances, lithium is always prescribed—though recently there has been evidence that it too can contribute to birth defects (Munk-Olsen et al., 2018). If the person's mania is still not controlled, it is recommended that benzodiazepines be used along with SGAs. Likewise, if a person has been prescribed an SGA but the mania is not controlled, then the use of valproate or lithium is recommended. If a person presents with depression and is prescribed only antidepressants, there is a risk that they can shift into a period of instability or even mania. In these situations, antidepressants are discontinued and replaced with the traditional bipolar medications, with lithium being the first choice. Likewise, if a person's depression does not lift, then the use of lithium, valproate, or carbamazepine is the next step in the treatment plan (Goodwin et al., 2016).

Lithium carbonate is a naturally occurring salt with perceivable effects occurring as soon as one week after first administration. It is used primarily for long-term treatment of bipolar disorder with the goal of preventing further manic and depressive episodes. It is distinct from other mood stabilizers as it also reduces the risk of suicide. Lithium works at multiple levels, beginning with clinical changes to mood by counteracting mania and depression and diminishing suicidality (Malhi et al., 2013; Schloesser et al., 2007).

However, lithium, like lead, is a heavy metal, and is the same chemical from which batteries are made. Side effects of lithium can be unpleasant and include fatigue, headaches, dysphoria, vertigo, nausea, dry mouth (often with a metallic taste), fine motor tremors, slurred speech, and weight gain. Monitoring is essential, as chronic users can have the substance accumulate in their bodies. The effects of lithium intoxication include drowsiness, anorexia, muscle twitching, and vomiting, and at higher levels, convulsions, coma, and potentially death. Thus, levels of the drug in the body must be regularly monitored through blood tests (Alda, 2015; Beaulieu et al., 2008).

Valproate was first synthesized in the late 1880s, though it was not implemented as a treatment option for those with bipolar conditions until the 1960s. It is included on the World Health Organization's 2014 list of essential medicines. Valproate is used to maintain stability and has been found to be most useful for persons experiencing rapid cycling and mixed states. It works by stabilizing electrical activity in the brain. However, there is no such thing as a totally safe psychoactive drug. Side effects of valproate may include nausea, vomiting, abdominal cramps, anorexia, diarrhea, indigestion, increased appetite leading to weight gain, sedation, tremors, and decreased liver functioning (Reinares et al., 2013; Salloum et al., 2005).

The third psychoactive agent commonly prescribed to those with bipolar conditions is carbamazepine. Carbamazepine is also prescribed to persons with epilepsy, schizophrenia, and fibromyalgia. It has similar effectiveness to lithium for those experiencing an acute manic episode. While the exact mechanism of action of carbamazepine is still unknown, its effect is to inhibit the generation of rapid action potentials in the brain, which reduces overall electrical activity in the CNS. The most common side effects of carbamazepine include dizziness, drowsiness, nausea, and vomiting. Other side effects include skin rash, dry mouth, diarrhea, anorexia, constipation, abdominal pain, drowsiness, blurred vision, and ataxia. This is a drug that also needs to be closely monitored when prescribed, as its use is associated with an increased risk for suicidal thoughts and behaviour compared to other mood stabilizers, and levels in the blood above 24 grams can be toxic (Maan & Saadabadi, 2018).

Table 12.2: Mood Stabilizing Psychoactive Agents

Drug	Brand Name
lithium carbonate	Eskalith, Lithane, Lithobid
lithium citrate	Cibalith
carbamazepine	Tegretol
Valproate (valproic acid)	Depakene, Epilim

Source: Adapted from Procyshyn et al. (2017).

ANTIDEPRESSANTS

Canadians take dozens of different types of antidepressants (Table 12.3), the majority of which work by increasing the brain's concentration of neurotransmitters. These are considered to be typical antidepressants and, as with antipsychotics, there is both a first and a second generation. The two types of first-generation typical antidepressants are monoamine oxidase inhibitors (MAOIs) and tricyclic antidepressants (TCAs). Monoamine oxidase inhibitors work by preventing the release of monoamine oxidase, leading to more of this neurotransmitter in the synaptic cleft. Blocking monoamine oxidation also produces sedation and, along with this, lowered vigilance and significantly decreased reaction time, making operating machinery or motor vehicles more hazardous. Weight gain is also a common side effect of MAOI use (Hancock & McKim, 2018; Raman-Wilms, 2014). Another risk factor involves eating foods containing high amounts of tyramine, such as cheese or dairy products, which when combined with MAOIs create cardiovascular problems including increased heart rate and hypertension (Hillhouse & Porter, 2015). MAOI withdrawal can lead to a worsening of depressive episodes, acute confusion, anxiety, and in severe cases catatonia (Warner et al., 2006).

The second group of first-generation typical antidepressants, TCAs, bring neurons back to homeostatic levels by prolonging the exposure of the receptors in the brain to the neurotransmitters in the synaptic cleft over several weeks. TCAs do not produce sufficient immediate stimulation to create a significant shift in mood, with initial effects not usually felt for 10 to 14 days. For some users it takes as long as two months before the full effects are perceived. However, side effects including dizziness, memory impairments, and drowsiness can begin upon commencement of use. TCAs produce a number of other side effects, mainly due to their interference with the autonomic nervous system, including decreased saliva production leading to poor dental health, blurred vision, low blood pressure, and suppressed REM sleep (Hancock & McKim, 2018; Raman-Wilms, 2014).

Negative side effects, and the slow response time, of first-generation typical antidepressants were key factors that led to the development of the second generation, which includes selective serotonin reuptake inhibitors (SSRIs), selective serotonin-norepinephrine reuptake inhibitors (SSNRIs), and norepinephrine-dopamine reuptake inhibitors (NDRIs). As indicated by their names, these antidepressants work by blocking the reuptake of specific neurotransmitters in the synaptic cleft, be it serotonin (Celexa, Lexapro, Paxil, Prozac, Zoloft), serotonin and norepinephrine (Cymbalta, Effexor, Savella), or norepinephrine and dopamine (Wellbutrin, Zyban).

The most common side effects produced by SSRIs are nausea, headaches, insomnia, weight gain, and sexual dysfunction, with a slight risk of seizure if the user suddenly stops taking the drug (Turner et al., 2008). However, as use in the general population escalated, reports of SSRI-triggered mania and psychosis rose from 10 to 20 percent of users (Whitaker, 2005). Side effects of SSNRIs include both sedation and insomnia, sleep cycle disruption, decreased REM sleep, increased sleep awakenings, production of vivid nightmares, and headaches. As tolerance builds, upwards of one-third of users can experience breakthrough depression after several months, and as with other antidepressants there is substantive reporting of weight gain and sexual dysfunction (Hillhouse & Porter, 2015). Despite different neurotransmitters being affected, NDRI treatment outcomes for major depressive disorder are equal to that of both SSRIs and SSNRIs. However, NDRIs also

Table 12.3: Antidepressants by Pharmacological Category

Type	Drug	Brand Name
First-Generation Typical Antidepressants		
monoamine oxidase inhibitors	isocarboxazid moclobemide phenelzine seleqiline tranylcypromine	Marplan Manerix Nardil Emsam Parnate
tricyclic antidepressants	amitriptyline amoxapine clomipramine desipramine doxepin imipramine nortriptyline	Elavil Asendin Anafranil Norpramin, Pertoframe Adapin, Sinequan Tofranil Allegron, Aventyl, Noritren, Nortrilen, and Pamelor
Second-Generation Typical Antidepressants		
selected serotonin reuptake inhibitors (SSRIs)	citalopram fluoxetine fluvoxamine nefazodone paroxetine sertraline trazodone vortioxetine	Celexa Prozac Luvox Serzone Paxil Zoloft Desryel Trintellix, Brintellix
selective serotonin-norepinephrine re-uptake inhibitors (SNRIs)	duloxetine milnacipran venlafaxine	Cymbalta Savella Effexor
Norepinephrine-dopamine reuptake inhibitors (NDRIs)	bupropion	Wellbutrin Zyban
Atypical Antidepressants		
	agomelatine mianserin mirtazapine nefazodone opipramol tianepetine trazodone	Melitor, Thymanax Tolvon Remeron Dutonin, Serzone Insidon Stablon, Coaxil Trazorel

Source: Adapted from Procyshyn et al. (2017).

produce negative side effects, such as chronic dry mouth, nausea, restlessness, tremors, and insomnia, though less sexual dysfunction and seizure risk upon withdrawal is reported compared to other second-generation antidepressants. However, there remains a similar rate of tachyphylaxis in one in five to one in ten regular users (Procyshyn et al., 2017).

As suggested by their name, atypical antidepressants do not work by blocking the reuptake of neurotransmitters to the sending neuron (axon terminal), but rather by changing neurotransmitter levels through other mechanisms—though in every case neurotransmitter levels are altered to bring the user back to a more homeostatic level. The primary effects of atypical and typical antidepressants, besides mood elevation, are improved appetite, increased physical activity, improved thinking and memory, and lessened feelings of guilt, helplessness, and inadequacy. However, as indicated above, all antidepressants produce side effects as their impact on neurotransmitters affects all parts of the ANS and CNS. In general, antidepressants can initially cause restlessness and agitation before they begin to alleviate the symptoms of depression, and this agitation can be severe enough to lead to hostility, either expressed outwardly against others or inwardly toward the user. There is a distinct risk of suicide as these drugs begin to work but have not yet become fully functional, particularly among children and young adults who receive higher-than-recommended therapeutic doses at the onset of treatment (Miller et al., 2014). If a person abruptly stops taking antidepressants, discontinuation syndrome occurs, which is in essence withdrawal. Like opioid withdrawal, this has been likened to having the flu, though the pain is not as severe. Withdrawal symptoms from antidepressants can be grouped into six categories: sensory (feelings of tingling and/or numbness), disequilibrium (dizziness, vertigo), somatic (lethargy, headaches, anorexia), affective (anxiety, sadness, irritability), gastrointestinal (nausea, vomiting, diarrhea), and sleep disturbances (Warner et al., 2006).

Finally, there is an ongoing debate regarding whether antidepressants serve much use, beyond a placebo effect, for dysthymia as well as for major depressive disorder. Many users indicate that they feel better using antidepressants, especially second-generation typicals and atypicals, yet historically there is limited empirical support for these claims.

Section III Closing Thoughts and Activities

The various positive and negative effects of different psychoactive drugs have been discussed throughout this section. However, the substance comprises only one-third of the equation in determining the actual effect an individual experiences when using a drug. Not surprisingly, the other two components are the environment and the user. Factors associated with these other two components of the equation are presented in Table III.1.

Table III.2 provides a summary of the lethal dose level for drugs from the different families discussed in this section, allowing for a comparative examination of the relative biological risk associated with various psychoactive agents. There is one additional factor to consider whenever discussing psychoactive drug consumption, and that is quality control. Even licit, highly regulated production of psychoactive agents leads to a range of unwanted side effects, even when physical and psychological dependency are not produced. With illicit drugs, many poisonings and overdoses are not a result of the drug administered but rather a result of the contaminants in the substance. Some are added purposefully to decrease cost of production or to add an enhanced psychoactive effect, though often they also result from the inexperience of the drug producer or an unintended chemical reaction (Cole et al., 2011).

Table III.1: Factors Influencing Addiction

Individual Factors: Short-Term	Individual Factors: Long-Term	Environmental Factors
Expectations	Emotional stability	Where you are
Build and Weight	Self-esteem	Who you are with
Sex	Confidence	Comfort level
Fatigue	Role models	Cost
Acute illness	Coping skills	Availability
Medication	Other resources	Social acceptance
Other drug use	Leisure skills	Legality of the drug
	Predisposition	
	Chronic illness/pain	
	Trauma	

Table III.2: Psychoactive Drug Lethality

Drug	Dose Level	Lethal Range for a 54 kg/120 lb. Person	Lethal Range for a 77 kg/170 lb. Person
Acetone (nail polish remover—inhalant)	liquid	1–6 oz.	1–8 oz.
Alcohol (depressant)	Standard drink	9	17
Amobarbital (barbiturate)	65 mg capsule	18	25
Amoxapine (antidepressant)	100 mg tablet	27–270	39–390
Benadryl (antihistamine)	25 mg capsule	44–88	62–124
Caffeine: Diet Coke (stimulant)	liquid	180 cans	260 cans
Caffeine: Nodoz (stimulant)	100 mg capsule	100–136	141–193
Cannabis (hallucinogen)	10% THC/ joint	150	200
Dexedrine (amphetamine)	10 mg capsule	10–20	10–20
Doriden (non-barbiturate sedative-hypnotic)	250 mg tablet	22–109	31–155
Dramamine (antihistamine)	50 mg tablet	27–270	39–390
Elavil (antidepressant)	100 mg tablet	19–27	27–39
Haloperidol (antipsychotic)	5 mg tablet	164–1,640	232–2,320
Fiorinal (opioid and barbiturate)	300 mg tablet	23–31	33–44
Lithium (bipolar medication)	300 mg tablet	15–20	15–20
Methadone (opioid)	5 mg tablet	16	22
Methyl alcohol (depressant)	liquid	2–6 oz.	2–9 oz.
Miltown (pre-benzodizaepine depressant)	200 mg tablet	27–136	39–193
Nembutal (barbiturate)	50 mg capsule	16	22

Drug	Dose Level	Lethal Range for a 54 kg/120 lb. Person	Lethal Range for a 77 kg/170 lb. Person
Oxazepam (benzodiazepine)	10 mg capsule	273–2,730	387–3,870
Oxycodone (opioid)	4.5 mg tablet	78	110
Phenobarbital (barbiturate)	30 mg tablet	39	55
Placidyl (non-barbiturate sedative-hypnotic)	200 mg capsule	27–136	39–193
Psilocybin (hallucinogen)	100 mg capsule	1,700	2,400
Quaalude (non-barbiturate sedative-hypnotic)	150 mg tablet	37–183	52–260
Ritalin (stimulant)	10 mg tablet	16	22
Seconal (barbiturate)	50 mg capsule	31	44
Sudafed (decongestant)	30 mg tablet	26	36
Talwin (opioid)	50 mg tablet	5	7
Thioridazine (antipsychotic)	25 mg tablet	33–330	46–460
Toluene (in nail polish—inhalant)	liquid	.16–1 oz.	.25–1.25 oz.
Trilafon (antipsychotic)	2– 25 mg tablet	76–100	108–142
Valium (benzodiazepine)	5 mg tablet	545–5,450	773–7,730
Valproic Acid (antipsychotic)	250 mg capsule	11–110	15–150
Xanax (benzodiazepine)	1 mg capsule	6,229	8,834

DISCUSSION QUESTIONS

1. Discuss the implications of long-term alcohol use. How did your understanding of addiction influence your discussion?

2. (a) Which drug is more problematic in terms of short-term use and long-term use: nicotine or cannabis?
    (b) After you have listed your points, reflect on how many of them are based on facts, how much on your beliefs, and how much on the media and what your peers think.
    (c) Which of the two has more therapeutic utility?

3. Opioids are more hazardous than depressants. Do you agree or disagree with this statement? Discuss why.

4. Rank the CNS stimulants from most to least problematic. What factors do you need to consider in creating your ranking?

5. Are the potential therapeutic benefits of hallucinogens, other than cannabis, enough to begin to legalize these substances? What facts would you raise in making your arguments for legalization?

6. In what context would you recommend the use of psychotherapeutic drugs? What are the ethical implications of recommending the use, or not, of these drugs?

7. What constitutes safe psychoactive drug use?

8. A new group of people has been discovered on a desert island. They have never been exposed to any psychoactive drugs. You are minister of the Drug Secretariat and must decide which psychoactive drugs (discussed in Section III) you would allow to be brought to the island and which you would ban. Create two lists and explain your rationale.

SECTION IV

PREVENTION

School-based drug education remains the great hope for preventing psychoactive substance misuse, for the longer drug use can be delayed, the less likely it is to become a lifelong issue (Christensen & Kohlmeier, 2014; Jit et al., 2010; Norström & Pape, 2012; Odjers et al., 2008). Prevention initiatives offer a tangible approach to diverting the development of substance use before it becomes a regular behaviour and develops into an addiction. The International Narcotics Control Board (2014) states that, while "the phenomenon of drug abuse requires societies to dedicate resources to evidence-based prevention, education and interventions ... [and] although such activities can be resource-intensive, studies have shown that for every $1 spent, good prevention programmes can save governments up to $10 in subsequent costs" (p. 1). Similarly, the 2016 United States Surgeon General's report indicated savings from $0.62 to $64.18 USD per dollar spent depending upon the type of prevention program implemented (United States Department of Health and Human Services [USDHH], 2016a). The route from experimentation to addiction is a complex interaction between individual biological and psychological factors, developmental maturation, family variables, and each individual's social context (Hays et al., 2003; Vimpani, 2005). Specific risk factors that have been identified for adolescents and young adults are:

- early initiation of substance use;
- early and persistent problem behaviour such as emotional distress and aggressiveness;
- rebelliousness against parental and other authority;
- favourable attitudes towards substance use;
- peer substance use;
- genetic predisposition;
- family conflict;
- favourable parental attitudes towards substance use;
- family history of substance use;
- academic struggles beginning in elementary school;
- lack of commitment to education and school attendance;
- low cost of alcohol in the community;
- high availability of substances in the community;
- positive media portrayal of alcohol, tobacco, and other drugs;

- low neighbourhood attachment;
- low socio-economic status; and
- high degree of transition and mobility (USDHH, 2016a).

In response, three distinct levels of prevention initiatives have arisen:

1. *Primary:* occuring before a person begins to use substances. The goal is to prevent or delay the onset of first use.
2. *Secondary:* occuring once a person has begun to experiment with drug use. The goal is to prevent more frequent, regular use.
3. *Tertiary:* occuring after substance use has become problematic. The goal is to reduce the harm associated with use or, if possible, achieve complete abstinence.

The goal of psychoactive drug prevention can be very narrow, as in complete abstinence. It can also be more broad and defined as a reduction in the prevalence of the misuse of drugs, or the reduction in the incidence, duration, or intensity of undesirable developmental outcomes, through a sustained change in drug-using behaviour (Dumka et al., 1995; Shepard & Carlson, 2003; Siegal et al., 2001). The use of psychoactive substances is a widespread phenomenon with a peak risk between the ages of 10 and 20. The preadolescent years from 10 to 12 are a particularly vulnerable period for the development of early substance misuse (Segal & Stewart, 1996; Skara & Sussman, 2003). In Canada, 60 percent of those between the ages of 15 to 24 are drug users (CCSA, 2008). Research indicates that even delaying alcohol use onset to age 13 can significantly reduce the risk of severe alcohol misuse or other problems in later adolescence, and that subsequent delays in onset of use provide additional protection from later problems, such as committing a crime or contracting a sexually transmitted disease (Odjers et al., 2008; Rioux et al., 2018; Werch et al., 2001). Those working to minimize this harm need to consider which level of intervention they wish to take. Is the focus of the psychoactive drug prevention program on

- those who chose to abstain from drug use;
- those who chose to postpone drug use;
- those already using drugs;
- those experiencing difficulties with their current drug use;
- those experiencing difficulties with the use of drugs by relatives or friends; or
- the larger family system (Griffin & Svendsen, 1992; UNODC, 2004)?

This section will explore not only what approaches have been shown to be effective with individuals and families but what does not work in prevention programming. The section concludes with a checklist to help you plan and assess your own prevention programming initiative.

CHAPTER 13

An Overview of Prevention Programming

Prevention efforts should start early and continue through adolescence and into adulthood. Prevention initiatives must also be repeated, for they do not work best in isolation or as stand alone programs. There are two principal prevention strategies, risk avoidance and risk reduction, that are used to influence three distinct sub-populations: non-users, low-risk users, and at-risk users (BCMCFS, 1996). The risk continuum illustrates the different types of strategies used to influence people's behaviour, depending on their level of risk for alcohol or other drug problems. The risk continuum is a useful tool to help understand the levels of risk and also to demonstrate the relationship between prevention and treatment.

There are three prevention focuses that can be adopted within the risk continuum: (1) universal, (2) selective, and (3) indicated or targeted (Figure 13.1).

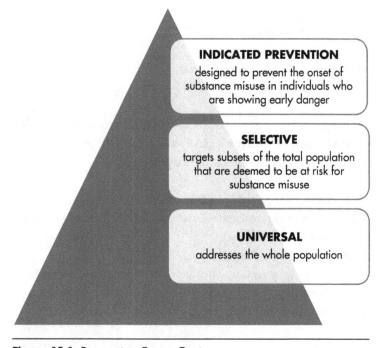

INDICATED PREVENTION
designed to prevent the onset of substance misuse in individuals who are showing early danger

SELECTIVE
targets subsets of the total population that are deemed to be at risk for substance misuse

UNIVERSAL
addresses the whole population

Figure 13.1: Prevention Focus Options

UNIVERSAL PREVENTION

These are activities that target the entire population, such as all Grade 9 students or all parents of high school students, with the aim of promoting the health of the population or preventing or delaying the onset of substance use (health enhancement). Activities are targeted to a general population that has not been identified or pre-selected on the basis of individual risk. There is generally no indication that any particular member of this group is using psychoactive drugs, or at risk of using, but engaging in this type of prevention has definite benefits compared to the costs (Dumka et al., 1995; Shenassa, 2002). Universal prevention consists of activities and intervention that are applicable to everyone in the group, so this approach avoids labelling (Bauman et al., 2000; Durlak, 1998; Foxcroft et al., 2002).

However, while the majority of adolescents are able to negotiate the transition to adulthood without major crisis, some are innately unable to handle the stresses and strains of the teenage years, especially when their environmental context is considered. Others lack adequate family support through this developmental stage, and some simply become involved with a higher risk peer group. These individuals will need different approaches than a basic universal prevention program (Tobler, 2000).

SELECTIVE PREVENTION

A more intensive approach targets specific subgroups deemed to be at greater risk (risk avoidance and risk reduction), including those with

- academic struggles;
- family issues and dysfunction;
- issues of poverty;
- problematic social environments; and
- a family history of substance misuse.

Program recipients are targeted not because of specific individual needs assessments or diagnoses, but because of epidemiologically and empirically established risk.

Compared to universal programs, selective programs have

- smaller numbers of participants per group;
- recipients who are known and who are specifically recruited to participate in the intervention;
- longer and more intensive structure;
- more intrusive intervention, with a goal of changing existing behaviours in a positive direction;
- a higher degree of skill among program leaders and staff;

- a greater cost per participant; and
- a greater likelihood of demonstrating change.

As selective programs do not individually assess participants, it is critical to be clear on the variables and characteristics being considered for group selection, and some general screening should occur (Kumpfer et al., 1998).

INDICATED PREVENTION

Indicated prevention is for those who are already using or involved with psychoactive drugs, but who are typically not yet dependent, though are at a high risk to be so in the future. This type of programming is individualized and can include a formal counselling component for the student and also for the family as warranted. Individual rather than group work is recommended with this population, as bringing individuals together who are using can normalize their behaviour and increase substance use. Indicated prevention also targets injection drug users (IDUs) and teaches them harm-reduction techniques with or without a goal of abstinence. These are the most costly types of programs (Catalano et al., 1993; Cuijpers, 2003; Greenberg et al., 2000; Kumpfer et al., 1998; Roberts et al., 2001).

Ultimately, the utility and feasibility of community intervention and prevention programs depend greatly on matching students to an appropriate program, as an indiscriminate application of a program to an entire community benefits only a few. The most comprehensive approach is a multiple gating intervention strategy (MGIS) that combines and integrates universal, selective, and indicated prevention programs to maximize their collective impact, though this requires a coordinated effort between multiple partners, including the school system, police, and community-based health and social services (Dishion & McMahon, 1998).

PROGRAM COMPONENT OPTIONS

Components of a psychoactive drug prevention program can be divided into three core areas: (1) knowledge, (2) attitudes and values, and (3) skills.

Knowledge

- the concept of abstinence and alternative behaviours to drug use
- definitions of drugs and psychoactive drugs, drug misuse, and drug dependency
- how different contexts and situations influence personal values, attitudes, beliefs, and behaviour in relation to drug use
- how different drugs can affect a person's ability to perform tasks
- the impact of media messages on the health behaviour of individuals and societies

- the importance of self-esteem, positive self-concept, and identity
- the rights and responsibilities of interpersonal relationships

Attitudes and Values

- a value stance regarding drug use and the confidence to act on those values
- the significance of the social and cultural influences on beliefs
- empathy and acceptance of a diverse range of people
- individual responsibility for health and universal health protection
- personal beliefs about drugs and their effects on decisions

Skills

- the ability to communicate constructively with parents, teachers, and peers
- giving and receiving care in a variety of health-related situations
- setting short- and long-term health goals
- demonstrating conflict, aggression, stress, and time-management skills
- identifying and assessing personal risk and practising universal protection
- developing assertiveness and dealing with influences from others; working effectively with others; and coping with change, loss, and grief
- problem solving (Minnesota Department of Education, 1992; Tobler, 1993; Tobler & Stratton, 1997; UNODC, 2004)

Prevention programming for youth may be classroom-based, school-wide, or applied in multiple settings, including the community. Prevention programs can be presented by appropriately selected and matched peers, teachers, program staff, outside speakers, police, parents, or professional counsellors. A thorough prevention program framework

- addresses protective factors, risk factors, and resiliency;
- seeks comprehensiveness;
- ensures sufficient program duration and intensity;
- uses accurate information;
- sets clear and realistic goals;
- monitors and evaluates the project;
- addresses sustainability from the beginning;
- accounts for the participants' stage of psychosocial development;
- recognizes youth perceptions of substance use and their community's recreational use of drugs;
- involves youth in program design and implementation;
- develops credible messages delivered by credible messengers;
- combines knowledge and skill development;
- uses an interactive group process; and
- provides sufficient attention to teacher/leader qualities and training (Roberts et al., 2001).

Again, the issue of program intent must be clearly specified, as the program should

- increase the knowledge about drugs in adolescents;
- increase the knowledge about drugs in adults;
- increase the knowledge about drugs within families;
- reduce the recreational use of drugs;
- delay the onset of first drug use;
- reduce misuse of drugs; or
- minimize the harm caused by the use of drugs (Cuijpers, 2003).

Actual prevention strategy options are quite broad and, of course, are not equally applicable to each of the three prevention focuses:

1. *Information strategies*: Teaching facts about the legal, physiological, and psychological consequences of psychoactive drug use and misuse using didactic presentations, discussions, and multimedia presentations.
2. *Normative education*: Adolescents and adults alike typically overestimate the level of drug use among their peers and the general population, which leads to inaccurate normative expectations and a set of expectations of drug use. Normative education makes students aware that most people do not use drugs and do not think drug use is "cool," countering the myth that everyone is doing it through use of local and national surveys.
3. *Perceived harm education*: Entails teaching participants about the risks and short- and long-term consequences of alcohol and other drug use. The message is best received when it comes from a credible source and is reinforced in multiple settings.
4. *Social influence education*: Teaches individuals to recognize external influences, such as social and peer pressure (role models, peer attitudes), who use and misuse drugs and to develop cognitive skills to resist these influences.
5. *Advertising pressures education*: Teaches individuals to recognize the purposes and effects of social media, advertising, and other media, and the cognitive skills to resist these influences.
6. *Protective factors*: Teaches, supports, and encourages the development of positive aspects of life, such as helping, caring, goal setting, and challenging students to live up to their potential and facilitating affiliations with positive peers.
7. *Resistance (refusal) skills*: Teaches students and adults how to recognize and resist pressure from others to use drugs, including learning to resist peers effectively and assertively while still maintaining friendships by using behavioural examples, homework, and even older peers. Common techniques include:
   - teaching students to recognize high-risk situations
   - increasing awareness of social and other media influences
   - developing direct refusal skills

8. *Competence enhancement skills training*: In this approach, drug use is viewed as a socially learned and functional behaviour that is the result of the interaction between social and personal factors. Those with poor personal and social skills are more susceptible to influences that promote drug use and are also more motivated to use drugs as an alternative to more adaptive but typically more difficult to master skills. This approach teaches generic social and personal skills.

9. *Persuasion strategies*: Influencing attitudes or behaviours regarding drugs through persuasive messages.

10. *Counselling strategies*: Peer, self-help, or professional counselling programs for those experiencing both drug- and non-drug-related personal and family problems (targeted prevention).

11. *Tutoring/teaching strategies*: Peer or cross-age tutoring or teaching to assist in enhancing academic achievement.

12. *Peer group strategies*: Attempts to strengthen or exploit natural peer group dynamics to inhibit drug use. This is primarily targeted at students.

13. *Family strategies*: Efforts aimed at strengthening parenting skills and family relationships to address student drug issues (see Chapter 15).

14. *Recreational activities*: Programs to occupy leisure time and provide alternative activity other than drug use.

15. *Harm minimization/harm reduction*: The goals of this approach do not focus on abstinence but rather on imparting information to reduce the harm stemming from substance use and to promote safer drug-using skills, though abstinence remains an option as the ultimate risk-reduction goal. This approach does not condone drug use but acknowledges that it exists and responds to it by providing accurate information about drugs, combined with the opportunity to learn appropriate skills to allow young people to become more discerning in their drug use, leading to the minimization of drug-induced harm. This includes the following:

    • decision-making and problem-solving techniques for handling situations in which a choice needs to be made

    • stress management to allow participants to learn how to recognize positive and negative stress and how to develop skills to manage stress

    • anger and anxiety management skills

    • communication skills and social competence to help students learn to listen, express themselves effectively, and to avoid being misunderstood; the importance of core verbal skills should not be underestimated here

    • personal and social skills to teach effective social interaction skills, including how to make friends and reduce anxiety when interacting with those they do not know or know well

    • assertiveness skills (peer resistance) in learning how to express needs, likes/dislikes, to stand up for oneself, and resist pressure to do things you do not want to do

16. *Affective education*: Focuses on enriching the personal and social development of prevention program participants by developing positive self-esteem, good interpersonal skills, and decision-making ability so that individuals will be less likely to use or misuse psychoactive substances. The intent is to increase self-understanding and acceptance through values clarification and decision making to improve interpersonal relationships by fostering effective communication. It can include both affective skill-building strategies, which are systematic efforts to improve affective skills related to drug use, such as communication skills, decision-making skills, and self-assertion, and affective experiential strategies, which are attempts to provide positive or growth-inducing affective experiences.

17. *Resilience development*: A selective prevention approach that entails achieving positive outcomes despite the risk situations in which people must live. It involves the development of social competence; increasing bonding; communicating high expectations for academic, social, and work performance; maximizing opportunities for students' meaningful participation in the school environment or employees in a work environment; and creating partnerships with families and community resources. Resilience is conceptually distinguished from risk reduction as it focuses on developing people's interests and strengths to promote their healthy development. Resilience education is the development of decision-making and affective skills within each person and connectedness among people in the context of a healthy and democratic learning environment. Resilience education can lead to higher levels of internal locus of control, concern for others, conflict-resolution skills and a fuller sense of school as community. At the curriculum level, young people show more participation, higher self-efficacy, better decision-making skills, and less involvement with outside negative activities. The educator becomes a facilitator of learning rather than only an imparter of knowledge as this approach is more problem solving and process-orientated. (Botvin, 1990, 2000; Botvin & Griffin, 2004; Brooks, 2006; Brounstein & Zweig, 1999; Brown, 2001; Griffin & Svendsen, 1992; Hawthorne, 2001; Poulin & Nicholson, 2005; Schaps et al., 1981; Shope et al., 2001)

As evidenced by this list, there are a plethora of mechanisms through which to offer prevention programming. Having knowledge of your target group, and their strengths, challenges, and dominant risk factors, will be crucial in deciding which of these approaches to employ. One final factor to consider when making programming decisions is how culturally and gender sensitive the program should be. Is there a need to include or enhance the program for those of minority status or those who face additional challenges? Cultural sensitivity in this field entails adapting prevention curricula to accommodate the intended audience, including surface structure, which involves matching curricula to superficial demographics, such as language. However, the more difficult component is adapting curricula for deep structure, which needs to take into account cultural, gender, social, historical, environmental, and psychological factors (Blake et al., 2001; Catalano et al., 1993; Davis et al., 2004; Foxcroft et al., 2002, 2006; Guthrie & Flinchbaugh, 2001; Hawkins et al., 2004; Hecht & Raup-Kreiger, 2006; Kulis et al., 2005; Resnicow et al., 2000; Schinke et al., 1988; Schinke et al., 2004; Schinke & Schwinn, 2005; Unger et al., 2004).

CHAPTER 14

What Works and What Doesn't

Results! Why, I have gotten a lot of results. I know several thousand things that won't work.
   —Thomas Edison

EFFECTIVE PROGRAMMING

Prevention interventions need to be intensive and extensive if you wish to achieve positive outcomes. Targeted programs do better than universal programs at obtaining specific objectives, with parental involvement making a significant difference in overall outcomes regardless of which approach is taken (Hayward et al., 1994). Effective programs for youth are typically led by teachers and supported by specialists from the treatment community (Allott et al., 1999). An effective global plan would have a balance between universal, selective, and targeted programs.

In general, effective comprehensive youth development programs should foster and promote the following:

- bonding
- resilience
- social competence
- emotional competence
- cognitive competence
- behavioural competence
- moral competence
- self-determination
- spirituality
- self-efficacy
- clear and positive identity
- belief in the future

- recognition for positive behaviour
- pro-social norms
- opportunity for pro-social involvement (Catalano et al., 2004; Nation et al., 2003)

Effective prevention programming is about much more than just drugs, as it needs to both reduce risk factors as well as enhance protective factors. Demonstrated prevention strategies include:

- helping students recognize internal pressures, such as wanting to belong to the group, along with external pressures, such as peer attitudes and advertising, which influence them to vape or use alcohol, tobacco, or other drugs
- facilitating development of personal, social, and refusal skills to resist the pressure to use
- teaching that using alcohol, tobacco, and other drugs is not the norm among teenagers, correcting the misconception that everyone is "doing it," and promoting positive norms through bonding with school and constructive role models (normative education)
- providing developmentally appropriate material and activities, including information about the short-term and long-term consequences of alcohol, tobacco, vaping, and other drug use
- using interactive teaching techniques, such as role play, discussion, brainstorming, and co-operative learning
- actively involving the family and the community so that prevention strategies are reinforced across settings
- including facilitator training and support to assure that curricula are delivered as intended
- containing information that is easy for facilitators to implement and both culturally and gender-relevant for participants
- being developmentally appropriate
- engaging parents in reinforcing ideas discussed in class, including refusal skills as part of family homework assignments
- promoting positive relationships between parents and children to enhance family norms, including communication skills to allow parents to communicate with their children as they move into adolescence
- teaching parenting skills, including positive discipline and adequate supervision
- including community resources to support and reinforce concepts being taught
- including school and workplace policies on alcohol, tobacco, vaping, and other drug use
- providing important health information that people need to make decisions about use and non-use

- encouraging and supporting drug-free activities and situations, emphasizing not only the skills required for participation but also the personal, social, and spiritual dynamics associated with choice
- developing guidelines for safe, healthy, and appropriate behaviour for family members
- encouraging broader skills beyond substance use refusal, including promoting positive, healthy lifestyles; development of positive personal, social, and spiritual support systems; and promoting healthy lifestyles that include good nutrition, stress management, and lifelong exercise and activity (Brounstein & Zweig, 1999; Griffin & Svendsen, 1992)

An Australian study conducted by Midford and colleagues (2002) indicates that effective school-based drug education should do the following:

- be evidence-informed
- involve parents and the wider community
- involve the entire school
- be taught sequentially in a developmentally appropriate school health curriculum
- be based on students' expressed needs and responsive to their developmental, gender, cultural, language, socioeconomic, and lifestyle differences
- be initiated before drug use begins
- be harm-minimization focused
- use interactive teaching techniques
- use trained peer facilitators to lead discussions
- utilize the classroom teacher as central in the education process; teachers should receive up-to-date teaching resources from community experts to guide their instruction
- include practical, immediate, relevant information on the harms associated with drug use, influences that promote drug use, and normative student drug use
- focus on general social skills training, including the values, attitudes, and behaviours of the broader community
- consider the interrelationship among the individual and the student's social context
- focus on drug use that is most likely to occur initially, to minimize experimentation that becomes integrated and ultimately excessive use

In response to the high rates of adolescent substance use during the 1990s, Iceland developed a nation-wide, coordinated approach to substance use that over the course of 20 years has led to a dramatic decrease in use among youth. The initiative, entitled the Icelandic Prevention Model (IPM), is a bottom-up collaborative approach to reducing drug use among young people based on sociological and criminology theory rather than health promotion. The view was that just about anyone is capable of engaging in deviant acts, but these are most likely to occur and become a regular pattern of behaviour only under specific environmental and social circumstances, including:

- lack of environmental sanctions by the social environment, namely parents, caregivers, and other adults;
- low individual and/or community investment in traditional and positive values, such as performing well at school; and
- lack of opportunities for participation in positive and prosocial development including organized recreational and extracurricular activities such as sports, music, drama, and after-school clubs.

The theoretical standpoint that has driven the IPM for three decades is that children are social products *not* rational individual actors, which makes alcohol, tobacco, and other drug use an outcome of the social environment rather than shortcomings of any individual child. Thus, the driving factors in prevention work should focus on social factors and not individual deficits. This means that, while programming does not ignore the individual, other factors that must be considered along with the school system are peers, the family, and functional, positive use of leisure time (Figure 14.1) (Kristjansson et al., 2019). Since the implementation of the IPM there has been a steady decrease of drug use in Iceland.

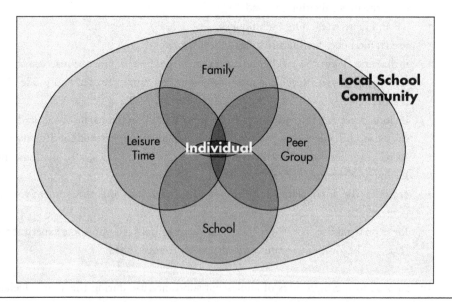

Figure 14.1: Domains of Community Risk and Protective Factors in the Icelandic Prevention Model

Source: Kristjansson et al. (2019).

Thirty-day drunkenness declined from 29.6 percent in 1997 to 3.6 percent in 2014, with daily smoking dropping from 17.0 percent to 1.6 percent (Kristjansson et al., 2016).

Effective school-based programs are also supported by policies that prohibit smoking, drinking, vaping, and any other drug use by students on school property and extend to teachers and other members of the community using the school for a function. The messages should be positive (school premises are drug-free) rather than negative ("Just Say No") with consequences for violation of the policy clearly presented. Fully comprehensive and integrated programs involve the entire community; make use of multiple strategies; design ongoing activities that target audiences from the very young through older citizens; allow adequate time for prevention efforts; and seek to integrate prevention strategies into family, school, religious, and other community environments (Paglia & Room, 1999; Wagner et al., 2004).

What has yet to be fully established by research studies is how technology and social media can be best incorporated into these initiatives (Schinke & Schwinn, 2017). A meta-analysis of school-based alcohol and other drug prevention programs facilitated by computers or online evaluated 10 distinct prevention programs. Of the seven programs with available data, six achieved reductions in alcohol, cannabis, or tobacco use at post-intervention and/or follow-up interviews. Two programs were associated with decreased intentions to use tobacco, and two significantly increased alcohol- and drug-related knowledge (Champion et al., 2013). Preliminary results from a small Australian universal online school-based prevention program found a reduction in students' intentions to use new psychoactive substances and did lead to an increase in knowledge about psychoactive substances in the short term (Champion et al., 2016). A web-based drug prevention program for 788 adolescent girls recruited through Facebook reported less past-month cigarette, cannabis, and illicit drug use within the control group. Three years after the commencement of the prevention program, those girls in the comparison group self-reported more cigarette and e-cigarette use, greater rates of peer drug use, higher anxiety and stress levels, and lower scores on drug refusal skills, self-esteem, media literacy, self-efficacy, and body image compared to those girls who were part of the active prevention group (Scwinn et al., 2019).

INEFFECTIVE PROGRAMMING

For young people, smoking, drinking, vaping, and other drug use are key to distinguishing their identities and their subculture from those of adults. Thus, even good prevention programming has much to overcome to prevent drug use. One of the difficulties with school-based drug education is that it is an attempt by the adult world to have an impact on youth. Most universal drug-prevention initiatives have not been able to demonstrate ongoing effectiveness; they simply have not shown long-term impacts, though it has been argued that some of this may be a result of how success has been conceptualized and how the evaluations have been analyzed. Most universal drug education initiatives have had, at best, minimal impacts on behaviour, with typical initiatives achieving only short-term delays in the onset of substance use by non-users and short-term reductions in use by current users. While there is a place for universal initiatives as general education, they do not produce substantive changes in those at greatest risk. Simple knowledge of drugs is insufficient to curtail misuse among adolescents and emerging adults. Applied prevention programs have also not worked because there is inappropriate initial selection of the program, inadequate stakeholder involvement (including the school system), insufficient attention to program fidelity, and improperly conducted evaluation (Case & Haines, 2003; Cuijpers, 2002; Derzon et al., 2005; Dusenbury et al., 2003; Faggiano et al., 2006; Foxcroft et al., 1997, 2006; Gorman, 1997, 2002; Hawthorne, 2001; MacKinnon & Lockwood, 2003; Voepel-Lewis et al., 2018; White & Pitts, 1998).

The seminal piece on what not to do regarding illicit drug prevention programming was written in 1975 by de Haes and Schuurman. They randomly assigned 1,035 Dutch youth ages 14–16 into four groups. Two groups involved one-shot approaches, led by outside experts. The first stressed the dangers and moral dimensions of illicit drug use and was called the "warning/mild horror" approach. The second was a factual psycho-educational approach that provided accurate information to participants. The third group consisted of 10 one-hour small group sessions led by teachers in which general issues of adolescence were discussed rather than only drug use and prevention. The fourth group of youth were a control group who received no additional education. Regardless of which approach was used, those already using drugs were not deterred and continued to use. However, three months after the initiatives were completed, follow-up questionnaires found significant differences between those who had not been using at the time they participated in the program. Control group use had increased 3.6 percent and was considered a baseline increase resulting from natural curiosity and experimentation. The "warning" group's drug-using rate three months after the intervention had increased at double the rate of the control group to 7.3 percent, while the "fact" group also had more new drug users than the control group, at 4.6 percent. Only in the discussion group was the number of new users less than that of the control group, one-third of that of the warning group (2.6 percent).

Similarly, evaluations of early intervention programs focused on information dissemination, alternative approaches, and affective education, typically in a non-integrated manner, have consistently failed to show any long-term effects, with some studies indicating, as was found by de Haes and Schuurman, that factual initiatives alone actually increased drug use (Foxcroft et al., 2002, 2006). Nearly half of all implemented drug education prevention programming focuses only on providing knowledge while alternative methods promoting risk and protective factors are much less used. Studies examining the effectiveness of drug education have led to the conclusion that neither information alone or affective programs nor social skills–alone programs, including the original DARE, Life Skills Training, the Seattle Social Development Project, ATLAS, SUCCESS, or Learning for Life, have had significant impacts (Allott et al., 1999; Brown, 2001; Clark et al., 2010;

Gorman, 2003; Lynam et al., 1999; Perry et al., 2003; Sobeck et al., 2006; West & O'Neal, 2004).

As well, there is no evidence that approaches promoting no use of any drug are more successful than alternative options, as most of the research has focused only on abstinence and not openly broached other strategies to reduce use. A focus on no-use drug education has resulted in decreased educator credibility, with students losing trust in adults because no-use programs have punitive zero-tolerance policies, but adults do not abide by the same guidelines. In a no-use context, young people cannot seriously engage with educators in the necessary and complex process involved in their own cognitive and emotional development regarding such a socially pervasive issue as drug use. Furthermore, less than one in five prevention programs have been actually implemented as designed. The main deficits are a lack of teacher training and materials, the use of some but not all lessons, and limited teaching strategies (Hallfors & Godette, 2002). While schools attempt to engage students by encouraging curiosity and risk taking as part of their personal development, when it comes to drug prevention, the typical message has been no, abstinence-only, and zero tolerance (Brown, 2001; Gorman, 1997; Marsiglia et al., 2000).

Another major issue is the complexity of a fully integrated prevention program. Canadian provincial and territorial education systems simply have not been constructed to be able to incorporate all the elements necessary to produce change in attitudes regarding drug use following best practice principles. A New Zealand study of 14,991 students aged 17 to 24 who participated in a web-based alcohol screening and brief intervention program found no significant reductions in the frequency or overall volume of drinking or academic problems (Kypri et al., 2014). Bruno and Csiernik (2018) examined drug prevention programming in elementary schools across Ontario. They found no consistency across schools nor within school boards as to which drug education program was offered, with well over one-third (37.6 percent) of surveyed schools not offering any type of prevention programming. In the remaining schools, a range of different programs were being offered, though neither of the two most prominent initiatives, DARE (30.1 percent) and VIP (16.5 percent), have been demonstrated to produce long-term change in drug use. The study's findings indicated a lack of provincial leadership in this area, with limited consideration of the effectiveness of the drug education programs being delivered.

Psychoactive drug-prevention programs shown not to produce significant changes include the following:

- single-shot assemblies and testimonials by former drug-dependent persons that reinforce a negative norm that everyone uses drugs
- programs presented independently and in a non-integrated manner
- projects with inadequate facilitator training, preparation, and instruction manuals
- sessions where there is inconsistency between presenters' messages

- initiatives that take a fragmentary approach and are not coordinated with other existing community prevention efforts
- undertakings in which abstinence is the only or primary criteria of success
- presentations that focus on fear arousal, using scare tactics and moralistic appeals that assume fear or negative consequences will prevent use, disseminating only information that using drugs is dangerous
- programs with curricula that rely solely on accurate information about drugs, their effects, and their dangers
- projects that focus only on affective education, working to promote self-esteem and emotional well-being without providing training in resistance skills and normative education
- undertakings with only a social influence component
- sessions that spend too much time focusing on those who are using drugs
- presentations based exclusively on strategies to enhance an adolescent's character or personality
- initiatives that do not respond to youth of varying ages, from different settings, and of different ethnic backgrounds
- programs that do not specifically identify and offer additional services to at-risk children and their families
- enterprises that start too late, as kindergarten is the appropriate starting point for school-based prevention programs
- projects with an inadequate or insufficient evaluative component
- programs with insufficient implementation, program fidelity, and curriculum (Bosworth, 1998; Botvin, 1990; Donaldson et al., 1995; Gorman, 2003; Griffin & Svendsen, 1992; Midford et al., 2002; Mohai, 1991; Resnicow & Botvin, 1993; Tobler, 2000)

What is common across these disparate approaches is that they tend to be either unidimensional or time limited or both. Historically, school-based programming has been too narrow. The process that local schools use in developing their own substance use curriculum includes high levels of involvement by a variety of personnel, but low levels of training, little use of resources outside of the school's immediate sources, and poor training of teachers who will be implementing the curriculum (Bosworth, 1998). As well, most of the literature supporting resistance training is American-based, and there is a different culture of violence and gangs in the United States than the one in Canada. Thus, the importance of resistance skills training may be overstated as is the importance of peers in determining drug use (Allott et al., 1999; Oster, 1983).

Resources used in conducting drug prevention programs should not do the following:

- glamorize drug use and drug users as cool or sophisticated
- exaggerate and misrepresent the dangers of drug use as these contradict participants' knowledge or belief based on their own experiences

- use graphic images that portray drug use as only dangerous
- present frightening case studies that are too far removed from the reality of participants' lives
- present emotionally loaded videos and personal anecdotes
- romanticize drugs using slang or street names without using the pharmacological names as this highlights a drug's positive side
- inform students on how to obtain, make, or use potentially harmful substances
- use images of drug use that can be appealing
- use one-off or standalone activities rather than activities that contribute to an ongoing comprehensive, developmentally appropriate programme
- use only passive participation, such as lectures and teacher-centred discussions and dialogues (UNODC, 2004)

There is no one best prevention strategy, and programs must be matched to the target. Thus, the first step in any programming plan should be a needs assessment to determine what is missing. To minimize the risk of a drug prevention program being ineffective, the goal should be clearly articulated from the commencement of the initiative.

WHAT WORKS

The impacts of drug education on drug use have historically been minor and short-lived. This is not only due to poor initiatives but also to inherent contradictions between the objectives of prevention and those of education. The first seeks to empower children and youth to think for themselves; the latter seeks to influence them to implement ready-made decisions. There are also inherent contradictions within prevention programs themselves. Some aim to limit young people's autonomy in their choice of friends and substances while others encourage conformity to non-drug-use values by discouraging conformity to drug-using peers. Programming often encourages the development of teamwork and social solidarity without acknowledging that youth may choose to accompany their peers as often as not, based on the specific circumstances of a situation. What appears to work best in keeping those who do not use drugs from starting to use are small, universal, interactive school-based programs that involve parents. Components that should be included are the following:

- *Knowledge*: Information about short-term and long-term health consequences
- *Attitudes about drug use:*
    feedback from school surveys of peer drug use
    analysis of media and social influences that promote pro-drug attitudes
    perception adjustment regarding actual peer use
- *Drug refusal–based interpersonal skills:*
    drug refusal skills
    assertiveness skills

communication skills

safety skills (ways to intervene in a drinking/drugging and driving situation)

- *Intrapersonal skills:*

coping skills

stress reduction techniques

goal setting

decision-making/problem solving

- *Active involvement:*

student-generated role plays

participation among peers

supportive comments from peers

peer modelling of appropriate behaviour

rehearsal of drug-refusal skills

sufficient practise time

developmentally appropriate activities (Bahr et al., 2005; Baker, 2006; Case & Haines, 2003; Ma & Thompson, 1999; Marsiglia et al., 2000; Midford et al., 2017; Piper et al., 2000; Sale et al., 2003; Tobler, 2000; Tobler & Stratton, 1997)

Successful universal prevention programs:

- strengthen social competency;
- strengthen emotional competency;
- strengthen behavioural competency;
- strengthen cognitive competency;
- strengthen moral competency;
- enhance self-efficacy;
- increase healthy bonding with adults, peers, and younger children;
- expand opportunities and recognition;
- are consistent in program delivery;
- are at least nine months in duration with booster sessions;
- deliver the same message in multiple settings (school, home, community); and
- have a social influence component that increases awareness of the social influences promoting drug use, alters norms regarding the prevalence and acceptability of drug use, and provides formal drug resistance skills (Catalano et al., 2004; UNODC, 2004).

However, in the majority of cases, drug problems gradually disappear as young people grow into adulthood. The proportion of adults with drug problems that continue past the age of 24 is small compared to the number of initial users, with those attending post-secondary institutions consuming far more than those who have graduated. Thus, it may be more beneficial to examine programs for those with continuing problems and to develop more intense prevention programs for those with a high risk of ongoing problems (Cuijpers, 2003). Universal programs that are theoretically sound with empirical support have distinct limits: they are unlikely to reach those youth at the highest risk of using drugs and in engaging in other anti-social behaviour, including those no longer in school, leading to a prevention conundrum. Those students at highest risk are often disconnected from the schools that offer the supports they require due to intellectual, academic, or family issues and are most likely to be absent or suspended from school (Cunningham & Henggeler, 2001). Thus, those most in need are least likely to benefit from universal prevention programs.

In the criminal justice literature, the offending population consists of two subgroups: a large group of individuals who experiment with illegal activities for a short period during adolescence who naturally or spontaneously stop; and a smaller group of offenders who begin earlier, continue for a longer period, and offend at higher rates, and are responsible for the majority of youth crime. A similar pattern exists among substance users, and thus targeting more prevention services toward higher risk youth has programming utility (Gottfredson & Wilson, 2003).

CHAPTER 15

Family Programming

The experiences and perspectives of children and young people regarding psychoactive drugs and their use are directly affected by their parents. This, in turn, is situated within the local social, geographic, and economic environments in which the family lives (Slemon et al., 2019). Parents can inhibit their children's substance use directly. They can reinforce their children's involvement in positive alternatives, yet many parents feel ill equipped to do so as there is no formal training in this skill, just as there is no formal training to become a parent (Dusenbury, 2000). Parents are powerful socializing agents in the lives of their children, and they are in a unique position to engage children in ongoing rather than singular dialogues about risky situations and decision making (Dufur et al. 2013; Miller-Day, 2002). Family-based prevention promotes healthy functioning in children primarily by addressing the risk and protective factors that characterize parents and families. Family interventions are generally the most effective strategy for changing the behaviour of high-risk young adolescents (Becker et al., 2002; Davis et al., 2004; Dusenbury, 2000; Hays et al., 2003; Kumpfer & Alvarado, 2003; Kung & Farrell, 2000; Montoya et al., 2003; Redmond et al., 1999; Vakalahi, 2001). Selective prevention initiatives have also shown promise in working to decrease the use of substances by pregnant women and after the birth of a child, continuing through the child's early education, including focusing on developing parenting skills. The goal of family skills programs is not only to decrease substance misuse, but to positively affect parent-child family relations by increasing family cohesion, decreasing family conflict, and decreasing family health and social problems overall. Such programs should provide parents with the skills and opportunities to strengthen positive family relationships and family supervision and monitoring and assist the family in communicating values and expectations. Though there is great range in the actual content of family skills programs, there are four primary approaches:

1. information only
2. parental skills
3. parent support
4. family interaction (Allott et al., 1999; UNODC, 2009b, 2013)

Box 15.1 provides a best practices program outline designed by the United Nations Office on Drugs and Crime to address this area.

Box 15.1: Principles of a Good Family Skills Training Program

Content and Skills for Parents
Parents should learn and practise how to

- display affection and empathy appropriately to each other, their children, and other people;
- use positive attention and praise, consistent with desirable behaviour that has been communicated clearly to the child, including telling children that they are behaving well at appropriate times;
- appropriately express their feelings and emotions, talk about their own and their children's feelings, and help their children to recognize and express their emotions;
- identify and model behaviour that corresponds to the values and norms they want to transfer to their children;
- learn new coping, resiliency, and anger-management skills to avoid further stress, and use fair-conflict strategies to eliminate verbal and physical fighting;
- use responsive play skills, allowing children to lead play activities and learn to manage their children while they lead in play; and
- have expectations that are appropriate to the age and developmental level of their children.

Teaching Parents to Provide Structure
Parents should learn and practise how to

- use age-appropriate discipline methods, including teaching children about the consequences of their behaviour;
- establish clear rules and values for appropriate behaviour and help children understand the rules and values of the family and community;
- recognize possible problems and problem situations in the family and in the community (excessive or inappropriate Internet/social media use, neighbourhood environment) and how to protect their children;
- recognize what their good qualities are as parents and build on these qualities;
- reach agreement with each other on core issues of child rearing, parenting style, and family life and put them into practice, or, in the case of a single parent, consciously decide on core issues by themselves;
- monitor children's whereabouts, activities, friends, and school and academic performance;

- support children in reaching the goals that both parents and children think are important and praise them for doing so;
- manage conflicts in the family, solve arguments, and demonstrate forgiveness;
- protect children from involvement in parental arguments and help them to understand the reasons for them; and
- provide structure for family life in general, including having meals together at certain times of the day and establishing times for doing homework and going to bed.

Teaching Parents to Become Involved in Their Children's School and Studies and in the Community
Parents should learn and practise how to

- monitor and assist their children in the school and with their homework; and
- co-operate and communicate with the school and recreation and health centres in the community on matters involving their children.

Source: United Nations Office on Drugs and Crime (2009b).

A significant issue is the level of parental participation, as universal prevention initiatives usually attract extremely few parents. As well, the greater the parental use of alcohol, tobacco, vaping, and other drugs, the lower the rates of participation in any type of drug prevention programming. Attempts at school-based initiatives tend to attract only the most motivated parents and to have high drop out rates (Allott et al., 1999; Toomey et al., 1996). Parents who engage in universal drug-prevention programs prefer those that promote communication with their child, do not require much time to complete, and can be completed at home, typically through joint homework assignments. In these instances, materials should be enjoyable, easy for families to use, complement school-based activities, provide information to parents, and strengthen family communication (Bickel, 1995; Biglan & Metzler, 1998). However, as children grow into adolescence, this approach becomes less attractive, and older adolescents are more hesitant and resistant to engaging in these types of activities, which also requires teacher co-operation and coordination with other classroom activities (Spoth & Redmond, 2000).

An alternative that is not as comprehensive but has been used with positive outcomes is direct provision of information, materials, and activities to parents for use in guiding discussions with their teenagers. A review of this method indicates that it did not alter parental behaviours, nor did the technique alone have a dramatic effect on adolescent drug use. However, it did enhance overall family functioning of those who chose to participate and opened up communication between parents and their teens (Bauman et al., 2000).

Recognized family factors that inhibit drug use include the following:

- close, mutual reinforcing parent-child relationships;
- positive discipline methods;
- monitoring, behavioural management, and supervision of children's activities outside the home (parental monitoring is the strongest preventative factor of any parenting variable); and
- family involvement and advocacy in the community (Bahr et al., 2005; Bry et al., 1998; Case & Haines, 2003; Dishion & McMahon, 1998; Griffin et al., 2000).

However, as much as most families work to prevent their children from engaging in drug use, a minority of families actually contribute to their children's substance use and misuse through a variety of dynamics. These range from genetic predisposition to environmental factors, including using themselves in front of their children, allowing children to use drugs in the home either alone or with peers, inconsistent, ineffective, or harsh parenting, family isolation, family instability, conflict, family disorganization, marital discord, criminality, and, of course, physical, psychological, and sexual abuse (Bahr et al., 2005; Bailey et al., 2018; Case & Haines, 2003; Dusenbury, 2000; Kumpfer & Alvardo, 2003; Kumpfer & Kaftarian, 2000; Lochman & van den Steenhoven, 2002; McGovern et al., 2018; Remes et al., 2019). In these instances, a universal prevention approach would not be appropriate. Rather a selective or targeted approach would be necessary that

- enhanced family functioning, including teaching stress management strategies and conflict resolution options;
- increased child/adolescent safety;
- addressed risky parenting behaviours, including discipline and increased monitoring of activities;
- included both mothers and fathers in the programming, along with the children; and,
- targeted decreasing parental use of psychoactive drugs (Bahr et al., 2005).

Research has indicated that in these circumstances, parental skills workshops, parent training, and family skills training have all decreased child substance use (Lochman & van den Steenhoven, 2002). These sessions have included resilience training, behavioural parent training, in-home family support, and family therapy. Decreasing youth drug use can also be produced by more simple means, such as regularly providing parents weekly information regarding their children's academic performance and achievements via text, phone, or e-mail (Bergman et al., 2019). However, there are significant barriers to obtaining family involvement, including:

- unclear definitions and expectations;
- lack of information;

- inherent family-school system tensions;
- fear of child welfare involvement;
- the family and/or school system's lack of acknowledgement of the significance of alcohol and other drugs in both the family and the school system;
- additional work for teachers and other school officials; and
- lack of coordination with other school events/educational efforts (Bickel, 1995; Biglan & Metzler, 1998; Perrino et al., 2001).

As well, most schools are not in a position to add a distinct family program to their curriculum. Thus, these initiatives, while they may begin within the school and should be coordinated with schools, usually occur in the community within a social agency. Despite the difficulties in establishing and implementing selective prevention programs that target high-risk families, these have been shown to have an impact on adolescent substance use. To be most successful, programs should begin work with high-risk families before and immediately following the birth of a child (Dusenbury, 2000).

The focus of successful selective programs has been on skill development and not only education. This allows for practise and feedback, assigning homework, and then helping family members refine skills that work while modifying those that are not improving (Etz et al., 1998). The most effective strategies include parents and children in individual and group training sessions. In these interventions, work is done individually with the parents and the children, and then the entire family is brought together to practise skills and strategies (Hogue et al., 2002). However, selective prevention programs are still not always sufficient, and the ability to incorporate targeted prevention programming with specific therapeutic interventions can be a valuable addition (Dusenbury, 2000).

Families least likely to engage in prevention programming are those that are disorganized with poor communication; have significant family conflict; have unreliable and inconsistent supports; and divergent expectations—exactly the group with the greatest need. High-risk families may not resist participating. However, the qualities that make their children susceptible to substance misuse are the exact ones that limit their participation in prevention programs (Garnier & Stein, 2002). Thus, families may need support to achieve a minimal level of health and positive functioning to allow them to even participate in prevention programs. Pre-intervention programs may be necessary in these cases, as the family may be facing more pressing stressors than the risk that a child may or is using drugs. This may necessitate crisis intervention or family therapy as a precursor to and component of the prevention program (Perrino et al., 2001).

Recommendations for engaging high-risk families in prevention programming are as follows:

- have a leader who is positive; who can remain hopeful and optimistic under trying circumstances; who is not into power and control; who is confident without being aloof; who focuses on family strengths, not deficits; and who has a high level of energy, creativity, and enthusiasm for the group

- clearly convey the purpose of the program to parents; why it is important to their children and to them
- build relationships of mutual trust, respect and equality; be sincere in the relationships built; and have a positive community profile—small things such as calling parents after a session, thanking them for attending, and asking if they had any questions were seen as critical to long-term parental commitment, as was dropping by the home when a session was missed to inquire if everything was okay
- create parent ownership and group bonding
- provide easy access to meetings, incentives, and reminders, including child care for those with younger children
- provide in-home sessions to those who missed some to keep them on pace with others in the group
- be flexible yet persistent (St. Pierre & Kaltreider, 1997)

Issues of race and culture are just as important when developing programs for families as they are when creating them for individual students or school systems (Holmes et al., 2018). However, the greatest preventative factor appears to be affectionate parents who are attentive to their children, spend time with them, are aware of their activities, and set boundaries with a degree of flexibility (Bahr & Hoffman, 2010; Turner, 2000; Turner et al., 2004). This parent-child engagement is even more crucial given the findings of a recent meta-analysis that stated that there were no clear benefits of any of the currently evaluated family-based programs for decreasing alcohol use among young people (Gilligan et al., 2019).

An interesting finding is that one of the most substantive ways for parents to decrease substance use among their children is to have dinner with them. As frequency of family dinners increases, reported drinking, smoking, and other drug use decreases. Compared to teens who participate in frequent family dinners (five to seven times per week), those who have infrequent family dinners (fewer than three times per week) were twice as likely to have used tobacco or marijuana, and more than one and a half times likelier to have used alcohol. Of course, this is a correlational finding and not causation, for the actual factor decreasing risk of use is family engagement. Being together is what decreases risk; speaking and listening to one another and giving children undivided parental attention. Cell phones and tablets need to be set aside and not only for dinner, but for regular, shared family activity. Children and youth need boundaries and established rules that are fair and consistently applied. They also need parents to set appropriate examples. The work in this area has led to the fourth Monday of September in each American state being proclaimed CASA Family Day: A Day to Eat Dinner with Your Children (National Center on Addiction and Substance Abuse, 2009, 2012).

One final debate involving families and prevention relates to harm minimization and alcohol and to setting appropriate boundaries and examples. An ongoing question in the field of prevention is whether parents should enforce an abstinence approach or provide alcohol and supervise their children's underage use, including for other drugs like cannabis now that it too is legal. While there is variance by culture, research examining adult-supervised drinking has found that parent sanctioned drug use at home tends to lead to higher levels of harmful alcohol use among children than in families where alcohol is not supplied by parents and children are not allowed to drink with their parents at home. While this runs contrary to some cultural beliefs, research findings provide little support for parental supervision of alcohol use as a protective factor for adolescent drinking. Providing opportunities for drinking in supervised contexts does not inhibit alcohol use or harmful use among adolescents in higher risk situations. Even after adolescents begin to drink, adult supervision of alcohol use appears to exacerbate continued drinking and the harms associated with drinking. Parental supervision of children's drinking at a young age can establish a developmental process by which progression to unsupervised drinking occurs more rapidly than in families where alcohol use is not openly supported. Alcohol use in a supervised setting and subsequent alcohol use outside a supervised setting both influence the progression to misuse in adulthood, compared to families where parents adopt a no-use expectation at home or set specific and strict alcohol consumption limits with their adolescent children and model that behaviour themselves (Gilligan et al., 2012; Komro et al., 2007; Koning et al., 2015; Kypri et al., 2007; Lundborg, 2007; McMorris et al., 2011; van der Vorst et al., 2010). Similar findings have also been noted with both tobacco (Gilligan et al., 2012; Mahabee-Gittens et al., 2013) and cannabis use (Vermeulen-Smit et al., 2015).

Section IV Closing Thoughts and Activities

School-based drug education remains the great hope for preventing unhealthy or illegal substance use. However, there is no single program that can prevent multiple high-risk behaviours. A package of coordinated, collaborative strategies and programs is required. Multifaceted system-wide interventions that target multiple risk and protective factors focusing on the influence not only of peers but of parents, siblings, and other adults are the most likely to succeed overall and with a higher risk population (European Monitoring Centre for Drugs and Addiction, 2019; Greenberg et al., 2000).

Program delivery is also important to consider. A tolerant atmosphere free of moralizing or scare tactics should be created in which an open dialogue between program leaders and students can occur. The program should be built around an active learning model that includes small-group discussions and role play rather than passive lectures and films. Presenters are best when participants can trust them and when they can present information in an accurate and unbiased manner. Teachers can also be assisted by peer leaders, though the peer's social group and who they are presenting to also need to be considered. Finally, anything taught in the school has greater impact when it is reinforced in the community by not only parents/caregivers, but also the media and health policies (Centre for Addiction and Mental Health, 1999).

The goals of alcohol and drug prevention programs for youth have to be realistic to be effective. The main thrust, especially with those at higher risk, should be preventing or reducing harms associated with alcohol and other drug use as opposed to preventing use completely, with resiliency-focused programming having great potential. An attainable positive goal is to delay a young person's first use, to limit overall use, and to shape their drug use in a safe way. Programming should be comprehensive and include school-based initiatives in combination with family programming and broader community campaigns, while also including special programs for those at greater risk or who are already using in a problematic manner. Whenever possible, young people should be directly involved in the program planning and implementation to identify the issues, develop solutions, and deliver messages to their peers. Zero tolerance and hardline approaches do not work and can be counterproductive, punishing students who are still in the experimental stage and discouraging students already using from seeking help to minimize harm or to seek counselling support (Centre for Addiction and Mental Health, 1999).

Before beginning a new program, answer the following questions:

- What is the purpose of the program?
- What is it that you are asking and wish to evaluate?
- Who is the population you wish to change?

- How will success be defined?
  - through abstinence
  - decreased/controlled use
  - harm reduction
  - psychosocial factors, such as coping
  - change in knowledge or attitudes
  - refusal skills
  - resilience
  - family functioning

The optimum evaluation has a pre-test and a post-test component. It includes both qualitative and quantitative data collection using a range of instruments, including, but not limited to, the following:

- questionnaire survey
- interviews
- direct observation
- analysis of institutional records (secondary data analysis)
- focus groups
- measure of actual drug use (and which drugs)
- measure of intended drug use (and which drugs)
- measure of attitude toward drug use (and which drugs)
- drug knowledge (which drugs)
- affect (attitudes toward oneself, family, and school)
- academic performance and attendance
- family cohesiveness

It is highly recommended that a triangulation approach be taken when evaluating any program with multiple measures from multiple viewpoints (Liddle & Hogue, 2000; MacKinnon & Lockwood, 2003; Schaps et al., 1981).

In determining what type of program to develop, the following five issues must be considered:

1. Outcome focus:
   (a) abstinence
   (b) harm minimization
   (c) harm reduction

	Fully in place	Partly in place	Under development	Not done
A. Assess the situation				
1. Determine youth substance use patterns and associated harms				
2. Learn factors linked to local youth substance use problems				
3. Assess current activities, resources and capacity to act				
B. Organize the team and build capacity				
4. Engage youth partners in the initiative				
5. Develop organizational structure and processes				
6. Build and maintain team capacity				
7. Clarify team members' perceptions and expectations				
C. Plan a logical and sustainable initiative				
8. Ensure the plan addresses priority concerns, factors and current capacity				
9. Develop a logic model showing how initiative will bring desired change				
10. Plan for sustainability of the initiative				
D. Coordinate and implement evidence-based activities				
11. Promote quality of existing and planned initiatives				
12. Strengthen coordination among local initiatives				
13. Give attention to community policies and processes				
14. Monitor the initiative				
E. Evaluate and revise initiative accordingly				
15. Conduct a process evaluation of the initiative				
16. Conduct an outcome evaluation of the initiative				
17. Account for costs associated with the initiative				
18. Revise initiative based on the evaluations				

Figure IV.1: Planning, Self-Assessment, and Action Sheet

Source: Canadian Centre on Substance Abuse (2010a).

2. Program focus:
    (a) universal
    (b) selective
    (c) indicated
    (d) multiple gating
3. Population focus:
    (a) students
    (b) families
    (c) adults
4. Program strategy:
    (a) adopt existing program
    (b) adapt existing program
    (c) develop own program
5. How will issues of gender and cultural sensitivity be addressed?

To aid with this process, the Canadian Centre on Substance Abuse (2010a) developed an evidence-informed tool that can be used when planning, implementing, or evaluating substance prevention initiatives (Figure IV.1).

DISCUSSION QUESTIONS

1. (a) Which of the prevention initiatives discussed in the chapter have you been previously exposed to?
   (b) Which did you find effective? Why?
   (c) Which did you find ineffective? Why?
2. What barriers would you anticipate in developing a prevention program for (a) grade-school children, (b) high school students, and (c) families?
3. Based on the readings, your experiences, and the barriers any prevention initiative faces, design an outline for an effective prevention program and the steps you would take to implement it.

SECTION V

TREATMENT OPTIONS

The history of medicine demonstrates repeatedly that unevaluated treatment, no matter how compassionately administered, is frequently useless and wasteful and sometimes dangerous or harmful. The lesson we have learned is that what is plausible may be false and what is done sincerely may be useless or worse.
—Enoch Gordis, Past Director, National Institute of Alcohol Abuse and Alcoholism, 1987, p. 582

Substance misusers are a heterogeneous group, necessitating different types of counselling and treatment approaches. As a result, matching a service user to the most appropriate program and counselling approach has taken on ever increasing importance. Some treatment facilities favour a medical model featuring the principles of Alcoholics Anonymous, others take a social support approach, while still others are more cognitive and behaviourally orientated. Many different methods have been proposed on how to best treat those addicted to psychoactive drugs, though some are slightly more enigmatic than others. Among the options that have been proposed are:

- acupuncture (Cho & Wang, 2009; Wu et al. 2016)
- animal-assisted therapy (Martin et al., 2009; Pugh, 2004)
- art therapy (Gorji, 2019; Holt & Kaiser, 2009; Waller & Mahony, 2012)
- brain stimulation (Salling & Martinez, 2016; Wang, Moosa et al., 2018)
- chiropractic care (Holder & Shriner, 2012; Nadler et al., 1998)
- e-intervention (Boumparis et al., 2017; Dedert et al., 2015)
- eye movement desensitization and reprocessing (Pilz et al., 2017)
- exercise (Linke & Ussher, 2015)
- horticultural therapy (Neuberger, 2012; Young, 2007)
- humour therapy (Arminen & Halonen, 2007; Ptaszik, 2007)
- hypnosis (Flammer & Bongartz, 2003; Green et al., 2006)
- laser therapy (Marovino, 1994; Zalewska-Kaszubska & Obzejta, 2004)
- logotherapy (Crumbaugh & Carr, 1979; Hart & Singh, 2009)

- music therapy (Navone & Carollo, 2016; Stamou et al., 2017; Vega, 2017)
- neurofeedback (Dehghani-Arani et al., 2013; Scott et al., 2005)
- spontaneous remission (Fillmore et al., 1988; Walters, 2000)
- subliminal audio tapes (Merikle, 1988)
- traditional Chinese herbal remedies (Lu et al., 2009; Zhu et al., 2017)

The lack of any agreed-upon best practice and the diversity of approaches may partially explain why addiction counselling is underutilized and characterized by high attrition rates (Gainsbury & Blaszcynski, 2011). It may also explain why one in six counsellors had service users whose substance use became worse after seeking counselling (Kraus et al., 2011), with observable clinical deterioration occurring in 7–15 percent (Ilgen & Moos, 2005; Moos, 2005). However, even more important is the question of what constitutes success.

Despite a distinct proportion of negative outcomes, that treatment works and that there are substantive quality of life, community, and economic benefits is no longer in question. Multiple studies have indicated positive cost returns, including reduced health care system use, reduced criminal justice costs, and increased workplace productivity (Asay & Lambert, 1999; Collins et al., 2017; Csiernik, 2011; Gastfriend, 2014; McCollister & French, 2003; Popova et al., 2011). At the height of the cocaine scare in North America, it was determined that $1 allocated to treatment caused the same decrease in the flow of cocaine as did $7 spent on enforcement (Rydell et al., 1996). The benefits of addiction treatment accrue not only to individuals but to society as a whole. However, this does not mean that we cannot stop asking the question of what works best and with whom. There are three myths regarding addiction treatment:

1. that nothing works,
2. that everything works, and
3. that all modalities work about the same.

Deciding if one approach tested under highly controlled conditions works better than another form of treatment is not the same as determining what works best for the next service user within the person's social context. Taking a person-centred approach, a treatment plan and a definition of what constitutes success should be based on each individual's needs and not the counsellor's or the facility's, and especially not exclusively on the latest trend. In their meta-analysis, Callahan and Swift (2009) found that individuals who were provided with their preferred treatment were 58 percent more likely to show greater outcome effects compared to those who were not. A synthesis of 52 qualitative studies based on the lived experience of those in recovery found that the treatment process needs to recognize the interpersonal, temporal, and community aspects that contribute to the development of addiction. The process of treatment needs to consider the fact that the process of developing an addiction deconstructs who the individual was, meaning that treatment needs to assist individuals in reconstructing their sense of self along with addressing physical healing (Kemp, 2019). In contrast, key factors contributing to dropping out of the counselling process are cognitive deficits, personality disorders, younger age, and low counsellor–service user alliance (Brorson et al., 2013).

The matching hypothesis suggests that treatment will be more effective when service users are fitted to an optimal intervention based upon their specific needs. This suggestion is both logical and has validity, and also has the potential of providing substantial savings if unnecessarily intensive and expensive treatment can be averted through an appropriate matching process. What is as important as the counselling provided is how it is delivered by the counselling professional (Gottheil et al., 2002; Thornton et al., 1998), along with the attributes of the counsellor. However, there are some factors that should be considered in determining which treatment approach might offer the best likelihood of success:

1. Treatment Setting: Where is treatment done?
   - community-based outpatient program
   - court-ordered (driving while impaired programs)
   - day treatment
   - in-patient hospital
   - non-medical residential facility
   - workplace-based (employee assistance program counselling)
   - voluntary or mandated setting
2. Treatment Regimen: What focus is taken in treatment?
   - harm reduction or abstinence focused
   - behavioural: controlling or changing maladaptive behaviours to increase or teach adaptive behaviours
   - cognitive: correcting maladaptive cognition
   - developmental: remedying structural deficits in ego development
   - exploratory: increasing understanding/resolution of intrapsychic conflicts and problems
   - pharmacological: using drugs to address the biological component of addiction
   - supportive: helping to manage problems in daily living by supporting service users' existing coping skills
   - systemic: structuring patterns of interactions, communications, and roles in the family social system

3. Treatment Format: With whom is treatment done?
   - educational groups
   - families/couples
   - individual
   - therapeutic group
   - professional and peer support
   - peer support
4. Treatment Frequency: How often is treatment done (also relates to the treatment setting)?
   - less than once per week
   - once per week
   - twice per week
   - daily
5. Treatment Duration: How long does treatment last?
   - less than one month
   - 21 to 42 days
   - three to six months
   - six to twelve months
   - open-ended
6. Treatment Process: Is there a relationship between the service user and therapist that promotes learning?
7. Treatment Readiness: Is the service user ready and/or receptive to treatment now?
8. Treatment Quality: How does the service user like the treatment process? How is it in terms of the following?
   - accessibility
   - availability
   - cost
   - counsellor characteristics
   - intensity
   - proximity to home and supports
9. Treatment (Therapy) Philosophy: Is the service user responsible for either the problem or the solution? (see Table V.1)

Table V.1: Treatment (Therapy) Philosophy

		Client Responsibility for Solution	
		High	**Low**
Client Responsibility for Problem	**High**	Moral	Enlightenment
	Low	Compensatory	Medical

Treatment philosophy may be the most important of all the variables in that it provides insight into what being person-centred truly means in the addiction field. During the assessment and matching process, it is critical to determine the extent to which individuals view the problem as being their responsibility and to what extent they believe it is due to circumstances beyond their immediate control. The counsellor also needs to assess how active a service user wishes and/or is able to be in the change process, and to what extent the person views the counsellor as needing to lead the change process. While we must always begin where the service user is, the fact that psychoactive drugs alter one's central nervous system and thus their cognitions and behaviours means that, in some cases, being person-centred will actually mean being more directive. Non-directive counselling approaches better suit individuals who are resistant or upset about having to attend counselling, as these persons generally do not believe that they have an addiction issue. Thus, service users who react against the directions of a counsellor will do best when the counsellor gives them little direction to react against. Individuals who externalize problem responsibility and resolution, who have an external locus of control, tend to do better with symptom-focused counselling that utilizes skill development and targets symptom change. Service users that internalize these two factors tend to do better when counselling focuses on providing insights and awareness regarding their drug misuse (Beutler et al., 2011).

Additional factors that have been found to be important in matching service users to a treatment program include:

- *Conceptual level:* Individuals with a low conceptual level prefer simpler constructs and rules and tend to do better in directive programs. Those with higher conceptual levels do better in non-directive intervention modalities.

- *Neuropsychological impairment:* It is believed that service users with greater neuropsychological impairments do poorer in treatment. These individuals would benefit from longer, more intensive treatment.

- *Severity of dependence:* The greater the dependency, the more intense therapy needs to be.

- *Family history:* Those with a family history of problematic alcohol or drug use require a distinct method of intervention from those without such a history (De Leon et al., 2008; Miller & Hester, 1986a; Minkoff, et al., 2004).

No one technique stands out as the panacea for substance dependency treatment or to be better than any other treatment in every case, which demonstrates that using matching techniques prior to prescribing an intervention method can improve treatment. As well, much of what one believes is successful depends on how success is defined. Cade and O'Hanlon

(1993) perhaps best summarized some of the differences we see in treatment in the following statement:

> Behaviourists see behaviour problems with service users, psychotherapists discover intrapsychic problems originating from childhood, while brief therapists discover self-reinforcing patterns of thought and action during the course of treatment. Thus, a good clinician in developing a treatment plan needs to work from a holistic stance and listen to the service user.

This section covers the wide range of treatment options available for those addicted to psychoactive drugs, including pharmacological therapies, individual counselling, confrontation and intervention, family and group counselling, behavioural approaches, harm reduction, the Transtheoretical Model of Change and motivational counselling, trauma-informed practice, and mutual aid/self-help.

CHAPTER 16

Pharmacological Therapies (Pharmacotherapy)

Pharmacological treatments were among the first approaches to emerge to address addiction, though with limited success as they only focus on one of the three dimensions of the condition. Codeine and heroin were substituted for morphine while cocaine was prescribed as an alternative during the 19th century. The further conceptualization of alcoholism as a disease in conjunction with the biological nature of excessive consumption of any psychoactive substance has led to and fostered the investigation of a large number of drugs as potential treatment methods for drug addiction.

ANTI-ALCOHOL DRUGS

These drugs, also referred to as antidipsotropics, have traditionally been prescribed to create an adverse physical reaction when the individual consumes alcohol. The basic paradigm is that of conditioned avoidance and conditioned aversion. When taken before alcohol ingestion, these drugs produce a strong and unpleasant aversive reaction that is intended to deter further drinking. Treatment with the alcohol-sensitizing drugs assumes that

- an aversive reaction will occur after alcohol ingestion;
- the reaction will be sufficiently unpleasant to deter further drinking; and
- the ensuing reduction in alcohol use will result in overall improvement in the behavioural and medical problems that led to excessive drinking or resulted from it.

The two drugs that were commonly employed for this purpose were Antabuse (disulfiram [tetraethylthiuram disulphide]), in use since the late 1940s, and Temposil (citrated calcium carbimide), both of which interfere with the breakdown of alcohol, though neither is now readily available. The human body has a good process for removing alcohol, which is a poison to it. When an antidipsotropic interacts with alcohol, a person's face and neck may become quite warm and flushed, and the individual can experience dizziness, a pounding heart, a throbbing head, and nausea. In essence, it is an exaggerated hangover effect. The severity of the reaction varies from person to person, but the more one drinks, the worse the reaction will become. If a person continues to consume alcohol, they can experience escalating unpleasant and dangerous symptoms such as vomiting, tachycardia, hyperventilation, shortness of breath, hypotension and, in severe instances, arrhythmias, unconsciousness, and even myocardial infarction, which explains why these drugs are no longer readily employed. It may take several days or even up to two or three weeks after the last dose of disulfiram before the body is able to handle alcohol without an unpleasant reaction. The effects of calcium carbimide may last up to two days after the last dose is administered (Douaihy et al., 2013).

The use of disulfiram and calcium carbimide seemed reasonable initially: the chemical effectively makes it impossible for anyone to drink any beverage with alcohol in it. Even the description of violent reaction can be enough to deter an individual from taking an alcoholic drink. Success, however, depends entirely on the alcohol consumer's willingness to take the protective drug consistently. The chemical provides a prop for a drinker who is already, for other reasons, strongly committed to abstention and to a schedule of doses. If a drinker does not have a desire to stop heavy drinking, the individual may resist a casual impulse to drink because of the drug already ingested but could still skip several doses and then resume drinking. Studies have indicated that even small pharmacologically inactive doses of Antabuse produced abstinence rates as great as that of a full active dose. The finding confirmed that the belief one is taking Antabuse or Temposil is as effective as taking the chemical itself. The therapeutic effects of anti-alcohol drugs derive primarily from a placebo effect (Roth & Fonagy, 2005). Thus, it is not surprising that these drugs are now used sparingly as a treatment or even as an adjunct to counselling.

Acamprosate is the newest drug used to prevent reoccurrence among alcohol-dependent patients. Taken orally three times a day, the drug ameliorates the symptoms of alcohol withdrawal and helps to limit reactions to alcohol drinking–related cues. It makes consuming alcohol less pleasurable, thereby potentially stopping a brief reoccurrence from becoming ongoing drug use. Acamprosate also has fewer side effects than other antidipsotropics. It is thought to stabilize the chemical balance in the central nervous system that is disrupted by both alcohol and benzodiazepine withdrawal, though the exact mechanism of action remains uncertain. Acamprosate has a significant but modest ability to decrease reoccurrence rates as compared to a placebo when combined with counselling at both three and twelve months after the conclusion of treatment. However, a proportion of those in clinical trials did return to their previous drinking patterns (Rösner et al., 2010). The American Psychiatric Association (2017) recommends the use of acamprosate with individuals who have moderate to severe alcohol related issues who have a goal of reducing alcohol consumption or becoming abstinent. Antabuse is recommended only when the service user asks for it specifically as part of their treatment regimen with both acamprosate and naltrexone, an antagonist, having better outcomes with fewer risks.

ANTAGONISTS

Antagonists are drugs that block the effects of misused drugs by occupying receptor sites in the brain. When used, antagonists extinguish the behavioural aspects of drug use. A drug user receives no positive reinforcement if the drug of choice is administered after the antagonist. However, as with the anti-alcohol drugs, the effectiveness of this method of intervention rests solely with the dependent person's willingness to self-administer the drug. As well, there is always a risk of overdose when using these drugs as some dependent persons will attempt to overcome the antagonistic effect by increasing the amount of psychoactive drug they consume.

The most prominent antagonist is naltrexone. It was initially developed as an opioid antagonist and has been shown to also have value as an adjunct therapy in treating alcohol dependency (Litten & Allen, 1998). When using naltrexone, which is marketed under the name ReVia, the pleasurable effects some people experience when they drink are diminished or do not occur. As well, there is no experience of nausea such as with the use antidipsotropics. However, unlike its interaction with heroin, naltrexone does not prevent one from becoming impaired or intoxicated with the use of alcohol, as alcohol does not attach itself to only one type of receptor site in the brain as do opioids.

Naltrexone is a competitive opioid antagonist that blocks the rewarding aspects of consuming alcohol through occupying opioid receptors. When naltrexone is present in the brain, alcohol cannot stimulate the release of dopamine. The use of ReVia has been demonstrated to reduce the frequency and intensity of drinking, to reduce the risk of reoccurrence to heavy drinking, and to increase the percentage of days abstinent (Garbutt, 2009). Naltrexone is usually well tolerated, and the most frequent side effects are mild nausea and headache. In a review of 29 studies where naltrexone was provided in conjunction with counselling, reoccurrence rates were one-third lower compared to individuals receiving counselling alone (Srisurapanont & Jarusuraisin, 2005).

DRUG SUBSTITUTION

Drug substitution is simply the replacement of one psychoactive agent with an alternative, less problematic drug or an alternative means of administering the psychoactive substance that has been deemed to be safer. The alternative drug is theoretically used to slowly withdraw the dependent person until a time when they neither crave the original drug nor require the substitute. Drug substitution was typically offered in conjunction with other treatment methods, though this has changed with a greater emphasis on methadone and Suboxone maintenance programs rather than methadone or Suboxone treatment.

Opioids

Drug dependence that involves heroin and other opioid agents is a chronic, relapsing condition with a generally unfavourable prognosis. The outstanding characteristic elements include an overpowering drive or compulsion to continue to take the drug and to obtain it by any means for pleasure or to avoid the extreme discomfort of withdrawal. The basic premise for opioid substitution therapy is that a suitable oral opioid agent that is administered daily is effective in suppressing withdrawal symptoms and reducing the use of illicit opioids. Methadone is still the most widely used pharmacotherapeutic agent for maintenance treatment, with a history dating back to the era of the Vietnam War (Dole & Nyswander, 1965). The World Health Organization considers it an essential medication for global health as it effectively reduces illicit drug use, treats opioid use disorder, and retains individuals in treatment, even if they do remain in a physically dependent state. Methadone is also a pain masker but does not produce the euphoria other opioids do.

No serious chronic side effects have been reported with the therapeutic use of methadone, though methadone itself is an addictive substance. As such, methadone should be used only with those who are unable to curtail their excessive opioid use and who are already physically dependent. While studies have indicated the use of methadone as a maintenance drug decreases the costs of criminal behaviour, health care, and employment (Zarkin et al., 2005), a major question with the use of methadone maintenance rather than methadone treatment is in whose interests is it used—the service user's or society's. The other pressing issue is at what point a person should be encouraged to move toward abstinence.

In 2007, Health Canada also approved Suboxone, a combination of buprenorphine and naloxone, for use with persons dependent on heroin, Dilaudid, and OxyContin. When Suboxone is administered sublingually, the naloxone remains inactive while the buprenorphine antagonizes the painful physical effects of opioid withdrawal. However, if the drug is injected, the naloxone blocks buprenorphine's effects and the person rapidly enters a very painful opioid withdrawal. This interactive mechanism greatly minimizes the improper use of the drug. When used as intended, Suboxone has fewer side effects, builds tolerance slower, and has less chance of overdose when compared to methadone. However, its greater financial cost has limited its use where opioid antagonists are paid for through universal health care (Fareed et al., 2012).

Like methadone, Suboxone has been regularly demonstrated to produce superior outcomes than placebo medication. Also, like methadone, individuals need to take buprenorphine on a daily basis or they will enter active withdrawal. Finally, while Suboxone blocks the effects of opioids, individuals who continue to use alcohol or benzodiazepines remain at risk for overdose as these CNS depressants will interact with the buprenorphine component to produce exaggerated sedation (Lee et al., 2018).

Opium continues to be used in some countries, such as Thailand, while medical-grade heroin is routinely made available, under medical supervision, to substance-dependent persons in several European nations. It is also available to a limited number of individuals in British Columbia, after successful clinical trials demonstrated its efficacy (see Chapter 21,

"Heroin-Assisted Treatment"). Lastly, there is growing interest in using cannabis to assist with opioid withdrawal and to mask pain; while there is great enthusiasm for cannabis as a panacea for many issues (Box 11.1), there is currently no evidence from either observational studies or clinical trials that cannabis is a viable option, especially for individuals who have been using more potent opioids (Humphreys & Saitz, 2019).

Nicotine

Nicotine replacement therapy (NRT) has become a prominent pharmacological treatment approach. There are several distinct approaches to NRT from patches (transdermal administration) to gum (mucous membrane) (Table 16.1) to the most controversial, e-cigarettes (see also Box 10.1). In each of these approaches one form of nicotine is simply being replaced by another, though all the other harmful side effects of smoking are eliminated, except with e-cigarettes where they are reduced. However, there are still other risks; for example, if a patch, particularly one for 21 mg per day, is ingested or applied to a child, potentially fatal poisoning can occur quickly due to peripheral or central respiratory paralysis or even cardiac arrest. Another much less severe but much more frequently reported side effect with the patches has been redness, swelling, and irritation at the administration site because nicotine, along with all its other negative effects, is also an

Table 16.1: Nicotine Replacement Therapy Options

Nicotine Replacement Therapy Option	Dose	Side Effects
Gum	2 mg or 4 mg 4 mg for those smoking more than 25 cigarettes daily 1 piece every 1–2 hours as needed for 12 weeks Maximum 24 pieces/day	mouth soreness jaw ache indigestion
Lozenges	2 mg or 4 mg 9 lozenges/day for 6–12 weeks then taper Maximum 20 lozenges/day	nausea heartburn coughing oral cavity irritation
Nasal Spray	0.5 mg dose to each nostril 1–2 doses/hour, increase until symptom relief 8–40 doses/day for 3–6 months	nasal irritation nasal congestion altered sense of smell
Sublingual Tablets	2 mg Minimum of 12 weeks, then taper	oral cavity irritation
Transdermal Patch	7 mg, 14 mg, or 21 mg Typically begin at 21 mg and wean down	local skin irritation insomnia

Source: Sachdev et al. (2018).

irritant to the skin. In 2003 the American Food and Drug Administration approved an over-the-counter lozenge produced by GlaxoSmithKline, called Commit. Smokers suck on a lozenge when they feel a craving, with the intent of gradually reducing use over a three-month period. A British study found lozenges more effective than either gum or patches, with a 25 percent smoke-free status six months after quitting (Alberta Tobacco Reduction Strategy, 2003).

The latest nicotine replacement alternative is e-cigarettes. Electronic cigarettes have the look and feel of cigarettes but do not burn tobacco. Instead, e-cigarettes use a battery and an electronic device to produce a warm vapour from a cartridge containing nicotine, often propylene glycol, and some flavouring additive. Cartridges can be refilled with different flavours and nicotine concentrations. E-cigarettes still contain some carcinogens (including nitrosamines), toxic chemicals (such as diethylene glycol), and tobacco-specific components that are harmful to humans, but they do deliver less nicotine per puff than tobacco cigarettes. E-cigarettes deliver nicotine to the blood more rapidly than nicotine inhalers, but less rapidly than cigarettes. As a result, the effect of the e-cigarette on nicotine craving is similar to that of the nicotine inhaler, but less than that of cigarettes. This has led researchers to report that e-cigarette use does lead to decreased tobacco consumption, among existing smokers (McKeganey et al., 2019). The issue has not been the reduction of smoking in established tobacco users but rather the number of new vapers, primarily adolescents and young adults.

E-cigarettes are not safe because the user is still consuming nicotine, and a variety of health issues arise, from minor mouth and throat irritation to airway obstruction, increased cardiovascular risks, and lung damage—but they have merit if being used as a form of NRT (Ghosh et al., 2019; Hartmann-Boyce et al., 2016). While there remain carcinogens in the product, the overall health effects are fewer than smoking a cigarette; here again, as with cigarettes and cigars, vapour in the air contains harmful irritants, though it is not yet known if these are as problematic as second-hand smoke (Sleiman et al., 2016). For individuals addicted to tobacco, completely substituting e-cigarettes for combustible tobacco cigarettes reduces the user's exposure to thousands of toxicants and carcinogens present in traditional tobacco cigarettes (Koval et al., 2018). E-cigarettes can be an aid in both reducing and entirely stopping the use of tobacco products (Brown et al., 2014; Manzoli et al., 2017), with the potential to decrease tobacco-related deaths (Levy et al., 2018). Preliminary studies have indicated that the use of e-cigarettes is more effective in promoting smoking cessation than other nicotine-replacement options (Hajek et al., 2019), though this has been undermined by the direct targeting of the product to non-smokers, primary adolescents.

Benzodiazepines

Benzodiazepines with long half-lives are used to assist persons to withdraw from dependencies on benzodiazepines with short half-lives. An optimal five-step intervention model incorporating benzodiazepine drug substitution with ongoing counselling would consist of the following:

1. For two weeks, service users monitor and record their daily drug consumption.
2. Eight one-on-one therapy sessions follow at a rate of one per week, examining psychosocial issues along with supporting the person in their goal to reduce use.
3. Gradual reduction of drug use begins by switching to drugs with longer half-lives.
4. Ongoing supportive care and reassurance continues until cessation of any drug use.
5. A one-year follow-up period commences, using a support group model.

Stimulants

No medications have yet been proven effective for treating either cocaine or methamphetamine addiction (Chan et al., 2019; Singh, Keer et al., 2016). Ritalin has been used in an attempt to improve brain function among those addicted to cocaine (Konova et al., 2013), while both dextroamphetamine and methylphenidate are being used to treat heavy amphetamine users, with some limited success (Elkashef et al., 2008). When given disulfiram for the treatment of their alcoholism, individuals who misused both cocaine and alcohol also reduced their cocaine use from 2.5 days per week to less than once per week (Whitten, 2005). Modafinil, a mild stimulant used to treat chronic fatigue, has been found to have some value in treating those physically dependent on crack. While several clinical trials have found those using modfinil to be far more likely to become abstinent and maintain a drug-free lifestyle, the vast majority, over three-quarters in the experimental group, eventually returned to drug use (Kampman et al. 2015).

UNDERLYING DISORDER TREATMENT

Co-morbidity is the occurrence of two or more disorders in the same person. Drug misuse is frequently found in association with a variety of mental health issues. Meyer (1989) reported that up to one-half of those receiving treatment for alcohol dependency had been diagnosed as having suffered from a major clinical depression or a major anxiety disorder in their lifetime. For these persons, drug use may be a form of self-medication. Alcohol or other drug misuse may be a secondary issue to the actual problem of anxiety, depression, neurosis, or psychosis. This belief system led to the unsuccessful trials of LSD with alcohol-dependent persons in the 1960s. The rationale for LSD use was that dependent individuals would have a psychedelic experience or would undergo an altered state of consciousness that would render them more amenable to personality change. Early uncontrolled studies enthusiastically reported positive results, with abstinence rates ranging as high as 94 percent (Smart et al., 1967). However, long-term studies repeatedly found no advantage in using LSD as a treatment method, and by the early 1970s, the use of LSD in alcoholism treatment had all but disappeared. Similarly, controlled research has provided no persuasive support for using benzodiazepines or other anti-anxiety agents to treat underlying disorders that possibly precipitate substance misuse. However, where psychopathology persists, particularly after initial sobriety has been achieved, a carefully chosen medication may be appropriate for treating these concurrent problems (Anton, 1994). While there had been some hope that certain antidepressants and lithium carbonate could reduce the desire for and consumption of alcohol, more recent studies have shown the limited effectiveness of antidepressants as a primary treatment for alcohol dependency (Miller et al., 2011). Interestingly, a renewed interest in hallucinogens has led to studies examining the usefulness of psilocybin, ayahuasca (dimethyltryptamine), and ketamine in resolving treatment-resistant depression (Denis-Lalonde & Estefan, 2020).

In the 1990s, with increasing knowledge of neurotransmitters, antidepressants began to be prescribed as smoking cessation aids. Among those was Zyban, the trade name for bupropion hydrochloride. Zyban was introduced in Canada in 1998 to aid tobacco users in dealing with their craving for nicotine once they stopped smoking. The drug was believed to work by stimulating the production of dopamine and noradrenaline, neurotransmitters associated with creating feelings of well-being. The drug's predominant side effects, dry mouth and insomnia, were deemed minor in comparison with the damage created by nicotine and tobacco (Douaihy et al., 2013). While pharmacotherapy alone cannot address the holistic nature of addiction, what is evident is that the biological aspect of this phenomenon is under-treated. While there is active use of drug substitution, other medications are hardly prescribed and this contributes to increased health care costs, hospital readmission rates, and issues of return to drug use (Holzbach et al., 2019).

CHAPTER 17

Individual Counselling Approaches

Individual counselling covers as much territory as almost all other forms of intervention combined. It ranges from neo-Freudian and Adlerian psychotherapeutic techniques to the breakthrough thinking of feminist therapy and the newer areas of brief, solution-focused, and narrative therapies. This short overview cannot cover all of these topics adequately, especially as many were not developed to deal directly with addiction issues. Nevertheless, a brief synopsis of some key approaches is provided. Regardless of the specific technique utilized by a clinician, therapeutic, individual counselling should always be purposeful and goal-centred, should only occur by mutual consent, and should have a specific beginning, middle, and end phase.

PSYCHOTHERAPY: AN OVERVIEW

Psychotherapy is a broad title that incorporates a host of talk therapies as opposed to pharmacological treatments. At its root, which dates back to Sigmund Freud's abandonment of hypnosis, is the belief that substance misuse is a function of some underlying psychopathology. Traditional psychodynamic therapy was a way of thinking about service users and clinicians that included unconscious conflict, deficits and distortions of intrapsychic structures, and internal object relations. The rejection and separation from an object, other people, produced frustration that was experienced as a primary source of anxiety. This anxiety presented in and of itself the conscious awareness of unconscious traumatic separations from existentially needed objects that lead to substance misuse (Korolenko, 2019).

Popular, contemporary psychotherapy deals primarily with the aloneness of modern life, the absence of purpose or meaning in our lives, the difficulty of knowing who you are, how you should behave, and what your obligations are (Specht & Courntey, 1994). Treatment focuses on identifying underlying unconscious or intrapsychic problems, redirecting patients' defences, ego strengthening, self-criticism, and helping to establish stable relationships within the service user's environment. Psychotherapy entails, by definition, an attempt to facilitate a major personality change through personal insights, relying on historic events, major life developmental stages, and traumas as a guide. At its core are the fundamentals of human personality and one's family position and role. Early psychotherapy saw oral dependency as being at the root of addiction. The notion of an addictive personality and the need to aggressively confront addiction are ideas that contemporary counselling has countered with alternative approaches. Psychotherapy has evolved and now views addiction as a stress or trauma response. Drugs are used to maintain and protect an existing sense of self, and suffering is further perpetuated by their continued and escalating use (Weegman, 2002). The role and significance of trauma as an antecedent event has taken on increasing prominence (see Chapter 23) (Kalsched, 2014).

Psychotherapists are expected to have certain personal qualities, such as warmth, expressiveness, genuineness, empathy, unconditional positive regard, and relative absence of emotional problems, but above all they must have professional training that will allow a consistently applied approach (Kolden et al., 2011). They also need to be able to effectively develop alliances with their service users to support the change process (Friedlander et al., 2011). The counsellors' training should be extensive, as they are the experts and the "knower" in most modalities, though this has begun to change with postmodernist approaches, such as feminist and narrative therapies. Several studies report that psychodynamic factors create internal conflicts within an individual's psychic structure, which predisposes the person to the development, maintenance, and reoccurrence of drug use (Khantzian, 2003). Studies assert that psychotherapeutic techniques addressing these internal conflicts can be successful in the cessation of substance use (Woody, 2003), with positive regard toward the individual being an essential aspect throughout the entire counselling process (Farber & Doolin, 2011). Examples of traditional psychotherapy systems are presented in Table 17.1.

A contemporary focus in the addiction field is that of the strength-based approach. Originating in the United States in the 1980s, the strength-based approach was a radical departure from traditional addiction counselling. Its emphasis is on an individual's existing abilities, competencies, and available social resources, rather than the pathology, deficits, and problems emphasized by the dominant view. The six principles of the model as they apply to the addiction field are as follows:

1. Service users with addiction issues can recover, reclaim, and transform their lives
2. The focus is on individual strengths, not deficits
3. The community is viewed as an oasis of resources
4. The individual is the director of the helping process
5. The worker-service user relationship is primary and essential
6. The primary setting for work is the community, not a residential facility

The strength-based approach is more than a philosophy or perspective, although it is both of these things. In its essence it is a set of values and principles, a theory of practice, and the explicit practice methods and tools that, once employed, help service users achieve the goals they set for themselves (Rapp & Goscha, 2006).

Table 17.1: Traditional Models of Psychotherapy

System	Therapeutic Goals	Methodology
Psychoanalytic therapy (Freud & Jung)	To reconstruct the personality; to promote insight; to make the unconscious conscious; to resolve internal conflicts; to understand the effect of early experience on adult functioning	Free association; dream analysis; interpretation; reconstruction of early experience and analysis of its present influence; study of client's feelings toward therapist as revealer of current interpersonal difficulties
Client-centred therapy (Rogers)	To experience and accept aspects of self formerly denied or distorted; to encourage personal growth; to trust the self and remain open to experience; to maximize self-awareness and self-actualization	Creation of a safe climate in which client can explore self-functioning; communicate qualities of the therapist (warmth, respect, genuine regard for client) to the client to promote realistic self-appraisal and personal growth; communicate empathic understanding to client to promote self-awareness
Existential therapy (May, Frankl)	To accept responsibility for one's own life and choices; to discover meaning in life; to gain freedom by removing block to self-awareness and fulfilling potential; to clarify values	Elicit client's being-in-the-world; establish a genuine encounter between therapist and client; examine choices client has made; lead client to make independent choices and adopt own unique values
Transactional analysis (Berne)	To re-examine decisions and to make new decisions based on accurate perceptions; to recognize the influence on behaviour and attitudes of parts of the personality; to improve interpersonal relationships	Analyze social transactions between individuals, especially games people play; psychodrama and role playing; explore consequences of commitment to adopting a rigid life pattern (script)
Reality therapy (Glasser)	To learn to appraise the self and the world realistically; to develop the capacity to make and carry out plans for reaching realistic goals	Therapists requires client to face reality and to make value judgments about his own behaviour; determine specific desirable behaviour changes; commit client to follow through on behaviour changes; promote sense of personal responsibility

Source: Lewis et al. (1988).

BRIEF SOLUTION-FOCUSED THERAPIES

Sigmund Freud practised short-term therapy with a few of his patients as early as 1908. In the 1940s serious challenges began to be made to the psychotherapy community's stance that longer treatment was better treatment. To this was added the work of Virginia Satir and Milton Erickson who continued to evolve individual counselling to a briefer, more problem-solving, solution-focused, strength-enhancing orientation. Erickson stated that one must keenly watch what a service user presents during the interview and urged counsellors to use the information provided by individuals during counselling to help them realize their potential for change. At the end of the 20th century, several prominent practitioners came to the forefront in systems theory and social constructionism, including Scott Miller, Insoo Kim Berg, and Steve de Shazer (O'Hanlon & Weiner-Davis, 1989; Berg & Miller, 1992; Miller & Berg, 1995).

In this form of individual counselling, various strategies are used to ameliorate the drug use and disrupt the trajectory of more serious issues. Brief interventions are useful primarily as early interventions for individuals without substantive physical or psychological dependency (O'Hare, 2005; Nilsen, 2010). Sessions are directed by the counsellor, focusing on the drinking or drug misuse and how it is maintained. It is postulated that the problem behaviour is perpetuated or maintained by ineffective or inappropriate solutions. There is no denial. Rather, the tactics individuals know and regularly use worsen or escalate the situation relating to their drug use. Individuals engage in behaviours that they believe will solve the problem but in fact do not. In the brief, problem-focused therapies, service users are supported to alter or reverse the way in which they have attempted to resolve problems thus far in their lives. The counsellors' language is positive and strength-based, and this person-centred approach provides individuals with choice at all stages of the process (de Shazer & Dolan, 2007).

Parsimony is important in this approach. Counsellors are encouraged to take the most direct route to a solution, keeping focused on the present and the future, using the simplest and least invasive treatment option. The major distinction between this approach and competing therapeutic models is the belief that no matter how problematic the situation, small changes in behaviour can make profound differences with a clear focus on solutions and not problems. Emphasis is on mental health rather than on mental illness, on personal abilities and strengths rather than weaknesses, while always maintaining a present and future orientation. There is a collaborative relationship between the worker and the service user. However, change remains the responsibility of the individual. Goals are typically practical and concrete, and they are based on the individual's description of the behaviours, thoughts, feelings, interactions, and relationships that will be present when the problem is resolved (de Shazer & Dolan, 2007).

There are several schools of brief therapy that share similar beliefs and processes. Obviously, a service user and counsellor meet for a limited time. While the counsellor initially tends to direct sessions, this approach is centered on determining how service users view their presenting situations and uses each person's unique strengths to build a solution. Regardless of how entrenched a situation may appear, the counsellor needs to look for ways in which the person is already building solutions, one of which is the ability to discern there is an issue and to seek formal help with its resolution. The counsellor's role is to find ways to best engage the service user to facilitate the change process (Lethem,

2002). Six common components of many brief interventions are known by the acronym FRAMES:

Feedback of personal risk due to alcohol use
Responsibility of the person
Advice to change drinking behaviour
a Menu of options to reduce drinking
Empathic counselling
Self-efficacy for the service user (Bien et al., 1993)

Miller and Berg (1995) developed a five-step method to working with problem drinkers that also applies to other substance misusers:

1. Develop a co-operative relationship in which the service user is actively engaged in developing the solution.
2. Set small, concrete, specific, behavioural, salient treatment goals that have a beginning rather than an end, and that are realistic and achievable.
3. Interview toward finding a solution using very specific questions, including the "Miracle Question":

    > While you are sleeping a miracle happens and the problem that brought you here is solved—just like that. Since you were sleeping you didn't know that this miracle has happened. What do you suppose will be the first small thing that will indicate to you tomorrow morning that there has been a miracle overnight and the problem that brought you here is solved?

    With scaling questions, the service user ranks the seriousness of the problem on a scale of one (worst) to ten (best). The counsellor then works at moving the person from one to two, two to three and upward, using the service user's ideas on what steps could be taken to improve the situation.
4. All solution-focused interventions, including interviews and homework assignments, are designed to elicit, trigger, and repeat new successful strategies for problem resolution.
5. In maintaining goals do not focus on high-risk situations; rather, focus on high-success situations.

De Shazer and Dolan (2007) offer counsellors a three-step framework:

1. If it ain't broke, don't fix it. In other words, if the service user does not present it as a problem do not spend time addressing the issue.

2. Once you know what works, do more of it.
3. If something is tried and it doesn't work, stop doing it and try something else.

Counsellors using this approach encourage individuals they are working with to continue to engage in actions that were functional during their misuse of a substance, increase the number of new actions that are functional, and not engage in any action that leads to a regression or return to drug use.

Figure 17.1 illustrates a brief solution-focused approach. In this model, the counsellor begins by asking: "Why today? What specific event or incident was the direct cause of your coming for counselling at this point in time?" The situation is then discussed, and one of three avenues is chosen. The first is to ask what the individual would like to change about their situation (wishes and complaints). In addiction counselling, this typically focuses on the drug use, though it does not need to initially. This establishes some concrete goals for the person to work toward. The second option is to explore what the service user does when the problem is not happening (exceptions frame). The counsellor then further explores the behaviours the person engages in when this occurs or what activities led away from the drug-using behaviours. This then gives the service user some specific targets to work toward or to do more of and also gives the person actual examples of things they did rather than drink and/or do drugs to illustrate that the service user has the capacity to control the use of the substance. The third option is the hypothetical frame. In this instance the counsellor has the service user imagine what activities they would be engaged in when they are no longer using drugs. A plan is then developed to start working in small ways toward this goal.

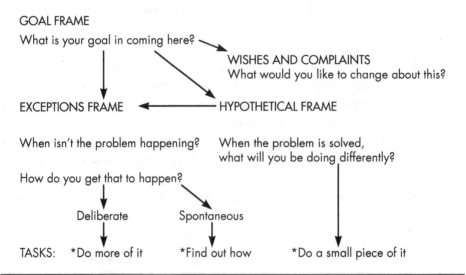

Figure 17.1: Pathways for Constructing Solutions

Source: Walter & Peller (1992).

A FEMINIST APPROACH

What the feminist approach brings to the addiction field is a new way to conceptualize the problem. It integrates the bio-psycho-social approach to addiction, with the person-in-environment context, along with empowerment principles and practice (van den Berg, 1995). A feminist perspective on addiction necessitates a greater appreciation of the roles of social and cultural factors in the development of substance misuse (Bepko, 1991). The feminist approach refocuses how we define problems and how we identify what is important to examine. It takes the perspective of examining problems of those who have not dominated the culture or societal decision making. It challenges not only the questions that have been traditionally asked, but also those that have not been asked. The goal is to provide women's explanations of social phenomenon, for the context of discovery is as important as the context of justification (Harding, 1987). The feminist perspective has a unique standpoint because of women's gender and their being part of a dominated class. At a basic level feminism is a recognition and critique of patriarchy and sexual politics, including historically within psychotherapeutic approaches. As opposed to pathologizing problems as individual deficiencies, the feminist approach broadens the scope, placing onus upon the inherent structures of society. Applying a feminist perspective forces us to examine the larger societal constructs that divide our society rather than focusing on individual weaknesses. It is a model that questions existing societal hierarchies and their role in creating addiction. Feminism challenges the concept that biology alone creates destiny (Abbott, 1994). While the feminist theory was originally developed exclusively with women in mind, over time the principles have been expanded as both men and non-binary individuals can benefit from the practices arising from this counselling approach.

There were three primary values that grounded feminist counselling thinking:

1. *The personal is political*: Each woman's personal experience and situation is a reflection of the position of women generally in our society.
2. *Choice*: Women have historically had limited choices as a result of their economic and social oppression and the internalized beliefs which stem from that oppression. Feminist therapy's goal is to help women become aware of their options and self-acutalize by developing greater psychological and economic autonomy.
3. *Equalization of power*: There needs to be a greater equalization of power among persons, and the counsellor needs to take care not to add to a woman's oppression through their actions.

There are four major approaches that are specific to feminist therapy:

1. *Consciousness raising*: A small group process examines how oppression and socialization have contributed to the distress and dysfunction experienced by women.
2. *Social and gender-role analysis*: Implicit and explicit sex roles contribute to the development of the addiction. Labels such as co-dependency are re-examined

and placed within a context that questions why traditionally socialized female characteristics have been pathologized and blamed.

3. *Resocialization*: The woman's belief system is reorganized based on new insights into the role of gender in creating excessive drug use. Women are taught to differentiate between what they have been taught and have accepted as socially appropriate and what may be more appropriate for them. This approach combines both an inward and outward examination of their social context.

4. *Social activism*: Incorporating the notion of "the personal is political" into the recovery process, this approach addresses structural inequalities in society that apply both to psychoactive drugs and to larger societal issues that oppress women and make them vulnerable to addiction (Dutton-Douglas & Walker, 1988; Jones-Smith, 2012).

Women have not been well served by all forms of counselling. Traditional approaches often negatively perceived women's functioning and contributions (Russell, 1984). Counselling in a feminist framework has several goals:

- symptom removal
- increased self-esteem
- improved interpersonal relations
- competence in role performance
- resolution of target problems through problem solving
- increased comfort with body image and sensuality
- encouragement of political awareness and social action, emphasizing independence, autonomy, and personal effectiveness

Powerlessness and despair are central to understanding women's addiction as a position of oppression within society. As women experience greater stigma with drug use, they tend to drink and do drugs alone more often than do men. Many women substance misusers have a history of physical and sexual abuse, and this trauma is highly correlated to substance misuse (Collins, 2002; Hiebert-Murphy & Woytkiw, 2017). Female substance misusers also tend to have a family history of misuse and have feelings of rejection stemming from childhood, depression, low degree of trust and self-esteem, along with high levels of anxiety. These characteristics can also often be correlated with a history of trauma (Wilsnack & Beckman, 1984).

Another feminist perspective views substance misuse as a result of the suppressed anger and self-hate that occurs in our societal context. Substance misuse numbs this anger, and thus cessation is only the initial step in the treatment process, not the end goal. The next step is to help women identify, respect, and appropriately direct their anger. An important consideration is the use of alternative resources. As Alcoholics Anonymous is a white, middle-class, Protestant, male-created form of helping, it is important to help women in recovery find a women's support group that recognizes their unique problems in recovery (Dutton-Douglas & Walker, 1988; Ettore, 1992). However, with its base in oppression, and with a focus on the role of larger societal factors, the principles of feminist intervention may be transferred to any population that is marginalized and has turned to drug use to cope with their situation.

NARRATIVE THERAPY

Narrative therapy, developed by Australian postmodernists Michael White and David Epston (1990), was heavily influenced by the work of Michel Foucault (1965). It is quite distinct from other forms of individual counselling pertaining to addiction issues. Postmodernists believe that there is no one reality but rather multiple interpretations of it, all of which have some legitimacy. What we take as truths are, in fact, social constructions, with the foundation of narrative therapy moving counsellors away from pathologizing drug misuse. Narrative counsellors are philosophically opposed to treatment ideas based on the disease model; instead, narrative therapy aims to help individuals explore their past experiences from different perspectives. This is done by aiding service users to discover new meanings, strengths, exceptions, and understandings of themselves through rewriting their personal stories in ways which will be more hopeful, empowering, and reflective of their self-written and preferred truths (Beres, 2017; Gardner & Poole, 2009; Garte-Wolf, 2011).

The goal of this form of individual counselling is to externalize the drug use. Service users are discouraged from seeing themselves as the problem and as an addict, an object with no other attributes. In narrative therapy, the individual's story is the base unit of experience. Labels are considered part of the larger mental health discourse that maintains rather than resolves the problems of daily living (Carr, 1998). The use of the label "alcoholic" or "addict" increases the importance of the substance to where it becomes the central focus and organizing principle of a person's life story. No other aspects are considered, especially their existing strengths in other areas. This focus draws attention away from the times when the person is not using and minimizes the person's attempts to not use or delay use. When engaged in narrative therapy, individuals begin to see themselves as other than simply an addict and as more than a problem. Their situation then ceases to represent the truth of who they are and allows them to focus on other options and resolutions to their excessive use of drugs (Beres 2017; White, 1995). Individuals examine what is occurring when they are not using and thus view themselves in another light. The process of "re-authoring the story" highlights the discrepancy between one's life story and one's actual lived experience in the development of an alternative, preferred story. By re-storying their experiences into alternative, life-improving, and empowering stories that overcome distressing narratives and identities, which were created and imposed upon them from external social, cultural, and political forces, individuals work to reclaim control of their personal narrative and thus their personal identities (Szabó et al., 2014).

In using narrative therapy, counsellors support individuals in replacing self-concepts of victimhood with self-images of survivors and fighters in order to positively shift their self-images and facilitate the process of recovery. A second core principle of narrative counselling entails searching for alternative meanings and conclusions from past experiences. During this stage of the change process, service users are supported in sharing their stories and examining their past behaviour from new perspectives in order to find alternative understandings, to connect their experiences in new ways, to find exceptions, and to ultimately regard themselves in a new light. New narratives are created through the counsellor assisting the service user in creating reconstructions of past experiences in order to develop new storylines based on their re-analysis of their past. Another principle of narrative therapy involves individuals discussing, reflecting on, and strengthening the new, positive, and preferred stories and narratives of their lives (Gardner & Poole, 2009; Szabó et al., 2014).

The role of the counsellor in narrative therapy is a collaborative one. The counsellor works with the service user to discover alternative storylines. They work as a team to find exceptions to the problem, thicken the story's plot, and link the presenting problem to the past as well as to the future. Examples of internalized and externalized problems are presented in Table 17.2. The newly constructed life narrative then becomes more powerful than the problem, and the individual becomes the author of a new identity. The counsellor addresses three areas during narrative therapy:

1. the meaning people make of their lives
2. the language used in creating meaning
3. the power relationships in which the service user is involved

Table 17.2: Comparing Internalized with Externalized Service User Issues

Problem Internalized within service user	Problem Externalized from service user
The person is the problem.	The problem is the problem.
The problem is something wrong with the service user.	The problem is external to the service user's self-identity.
Experts are needed to explain the service user's behaviour.	Service users can provide their own interpretation of self.
The counsellor is the expert.	Service users are the experts on their own lives.
Oppression is not a theme.	Counselling examines culture, race, gender, sex, class, ability, and sexual orientation.
The focus of counselling is the service user's problem.	Counselling focuses on distinguishing the service user from the problem.
Counsellor reorders the service user's personality.	Service users re-author their own stories.

Source: Jones-Smith (2012).

Also critical to this process is teaching the service user to be mindful. The individual must develop enhanced self-awareness, particularly of the thoughts and behaviours that lead to drug use as well as those that do not. Positive self-talk is stressed in this form of individual counselling, as is self-worth (Carr, 1998; White, 1995). One major caveat of the narrative therapy approach is its requirement for a high level of cognitive capacity to be able to engage in self-awareness and critical reflection. Narrative therapy also requires strong communication as a highly intensive talk therapy and, in some formats, will require strong reading and writing skills which may limit the populations that can be reached with this approach, particularly when compared with behavioural and psycho-educational approaches (Szabó et al., 2014).

CHAPTER 18

Confrontation and Intervention

PRINCIPLES OF CONFRONTATION AND INTERVENTION

Despite the contemporary focus on person-centred practice, there remains an undercurrent in the addiction field of mandating or coercing individuals into entering a formal treatment program. The reluctance of many drug-dependent persons to enter treatment, particularly those using illicit drugs, has led individuals and organizations to engage in confrontation and intervention and governments to legally coerce people with addictions into treatment by offering counselling as an alternative to imprisonment. Proponents argue that coerced addiction treatment is justified because it reduces the harm to people with addictions, the harmful effects of their addiction on families and friends, and their social and economic impacts on society. Critics argue that this practice is unethical, and yet the practice remains (Carter & Hall, 2018).

Some of the earliest espoused approaches for resolving issues of addiction involved coercion: confrontation or intervention. The initial justification for this was tied to Glatt's (1958) disease model construction of addiction (see Figure 5.1) that postulated an individual had to hit rock bottom and lose just about everything in order to be motivated to change. The belief was that some persons would remain at this level and that their excessive substance misuse would continue unless there were substantive consequences. These individuals were labelled as living in a state of denial that allowed them to minimize, intellectualize, and/or rationalize their drug use, for the thought of stopping was more overwhelming than the consequences of continuing to use. In many cases, individuals with an addiction issue truly do not perceive the damage they are creating and the chaos that surrounds them. Unfortunately, hitting rock bottom affects a person's entire system, meaning family members, particularly children, can be greatly affected. This approach believes that recovery from the bottom is always possible; however, the longer the drug use continues the greater the associated shame, making the recovery more difficult to overcome physically, psychologically, and socially.

The response for individuals trapped at this point in Glatt's model was the development of therapeutic confrontation. Confrontation involves the counsellor providing direct, reality-oriented feedback to an individual regarding the person's own thoughts, feelings, or behaviour relating to the use of psychoactive agents. Confrontation was not only widely accepted but was often a formal component of many treatment programs, particularly residential, until the 1990s. The format can vary in its intent, timing, intensity, and emotional content. However, the common belief is that drug misusers as a group tend to deny or fail to recognize the reality of their problems, and that it is therapeutic to confront them with reality through the use of a dramatic intervention.

Confrontation is also known as the Johnson model of intervention, after Vernon Johnson (1973) who believed that, while alcoholics could have insight into their situation, this did not occur without formal active assistance. He believed that it was only through the creation of a crisis state that people would be adequately motivated to change and that by precipitating a crisis by a forceful confrontation this process could be enhanced.

Therapeutic confrontation was premised upon four interrelated assumptions. First, the core belief is that addiction is rooted in an immature, defective character encased within an armour-plated defence structure. Second, the passive methods of traditional psychotherapies are hopelessly ineffective in penetrating this defensive structure and altering this deformity of character. Third, the addict or alcoholic can only be reached by a "dynamite charge" that breaks through this protective shield. And fourth, verbal confrontation is the most effective means of engaging and changing addictive behaviour (Bassin, 1975). The usual procedure in confrontation includes a forceful and factual presentation of evidence that the individual has a drug dependency and the refuting of the person's protestations to the contrary. Yet it is argued by proponents of this approach that confrontation need not be equated only with strategies of coercion and extrinsic control. Alternatives include soft confrontation, which resembles a gentle persuasion and a feedback model in which the service user is given information about their current health status. Minimal feedback procedures can have a substantial impact on behaviour and health, if the emphasis remains on an honest and caring presentation. Yet confrontational approaches must be undertaken with care because of their potential to precipitate drop out from the process, negative emotional states, lowered self-esteem, and potentially return to drug use. However, confrontation is often not compelling enough, and leads to the next level, intervention, which involves members of the individual's larger system.

CARRYING OUT AN INTERVENTION

Intervention in the addiction field is articulated as being a targeted, concern-based process by which a group of people present reality in a caring way to the substance user, who does not recognize the harm their drug use is creating. Those who carry out interventions believe individuals need to have their bottom raised through a formal, active process of specific feedback. While at its core intervention is a coercive process, it can take many forms, some far less formal: it can be as simple as a comment from a colleague or as complex as a structured intervention that includes not only family but friends or co-workers. In developing a structured intervention, choosing the correct participants is crucial. All involved in the process need to be willing to participant in the intervention and to be prepared to develop and practice a script that includes consequences for the individual if the person does not opt to seek treatment. As well, all those involved need to be able to contain their own anger, as an angry confrontation invites defensiveness on the part of the person receiving the intervention. A defensive person will have a hard time hearing what is being said, and the intervention will not be successful (Lawson, 2005).

Intervention in its simplest form is a direct conversation regarding another's inappropriate or excessive drug use. More typically, it is a formal structured group who delivers rehearsed scripts in an orchestrated fashion that has involved multiple rehearsals. During the actual intervention, which takes only 10 to 20 minutes, one person will have been chosen as the chairperson, typically a trained interventionist affiliated with a treatment agency, and this neutral person will introduce the reason for the person being targeted and ask that the individual just listen until all those assembled have finished reading their scripts. Each person who has agreed to participate in the intervention will have written down what they want to say, starting with a statement of positive regard and followed by the factual, non-judgmental reporting of two or three incidents pertaining to the individual's substance use and how it has personally impacted them and how that made them feel (Box 18.1). After everyone has spoken, the chairperson will ask that an assessment take place and will speak about the consequence of non-compliance.

It is important that the mood of the intervention be even, calm, and always caring. The group will have anticipated excuses ahead of time and have answers for them (for example, "I can't go to treatment now, I have a work project due next week"). The group should expect refusal to accept what has been presented and perhaps anger, threats, and hostility, and be prepared not to react or argue with the person. It should be expected that anyone confronted with the reality of their behaviour in this manner and who has their life summarized in this manner will experience anger. This is a normal response to intervention, and it is one of the tasks of treatment to assist the person in working through this anger. The person being confronted may try to bargain with the group or suggest that they can do it on their own without help. It is important that the assembled family, friends, and co-workers consider this ahead of time and decide on what is and is not negotiable. Some groups will leave it to the person to select a treatment centre, while others will have already made a tentative assessment appointment prior to commencing the intervention, typically in a residential facility. If the intervention is successful it is important that the person not be left alone, as the individual is usually in a vulnerable and fragile emotional state, quite shaken by what has just occurred, and will require support from those closest to them. Intervention is emotionally challenging and difficult, with significant treatment consequences. It should only be considered when all other methods of returning a person to health have been unsuccessful (Lawson, 2005; Stanger & Weber, 2018).

Box 18.1: Sample Intervention Scripts

Paula is a 44-year-old successful entrepreneur who has struggled in a male-dominated field to start a successful small business. Her business is stable but at a personal cost, as her alcohol consumption is equivalent to 14 standard drinks per day, which affects all aspects of her life. She also uses Z-drugs to assist in falling asleep at night and cocaine on occasion to help her get through long days.

Her intervention circle consists of:

Alex, Paula's wife of six years
Ben, Paula's business partner of 14 years
Debbie, Paula's childhood friend who brought her to the intervention
Mikaeli, Paula's younger sister by six years
Paul, Paula's father
Violet, Paula's mother
Rick, the trained interventionist and chair of the meeting

The Circle*

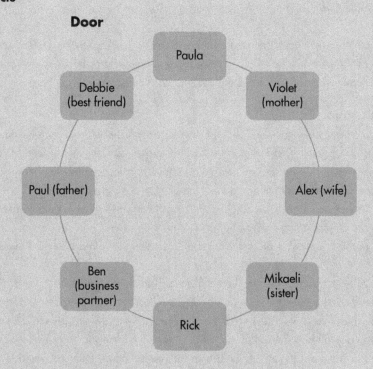

Paul's Script

Paula, I love and admire you, you were always the centre of my life, but now I am greatly concerned that you will fail to reach the potential I have always seen for you.

At Easter dinner at your home you were obviously impaired. You had volunteered to make dinner for the entire family, but nothing was prepared when we arrived, and you wouldn't let anyone help you. You yelled at your mother when she went into the kitchen to talk with you and ended up burning dinner. You did, however, have time to serve drinks before dinner and when your sister said no after her second drink you called her a name and said, "Okay I will drink for both of us." I left that night feeling frustrated, embarrassed for you, and sad that I couldn't help you in any way.

At our wedding anniversary party last year, you got up to say a toast but were slurring your words and spilled a drink on Alex as she went to help you sit down and then yelled at her to leave you alone, causing a scene. While I felt badly for you at the time, I later became upset because what should have been a celebration for your mother and me became all about you.

Because I love you so much, I have decided I will go to any length to stop you from killing yourself.

My bottom line: If you continue to drink and use drugs in spite of today's special effort that all the people who love you have made, I have decided to stop interacting with you in any way and will not allow you into our house until you get help.

Ben's Script

Paula, I have tremendous respect for your tenacity, abilities, and pure moxie. I would not be the person I am today if we had not grown our business together the last 14 years. However, over the last two years I have had to do more and more, and I no longer see you contributing in a meaningful way to our partnership.

When you come to work in the mornings I can smell alcohol on your breath, and you are almost falling asleep, but then some afternoons I can't get a word in as you talk and talk with wild project ideas that don't seem to relate to our business plan in any way.

At July's business meeting with the vice president of sales of DHL, you arrived late, under the influence of some type of drug, insulted our top salesperson, and told one of our best clients we didn't need their business if they wouldn't give us a better price and to piss off and get out of our office. It took me weeks to have him even take my call so I could apologize. I felt alarmed for you but angry that you would jeopardize our business in such a cavalier manner without thinking about all our employees or me in any way.

My bottom line: Please get help for your drug use. If you don't, I will take legal action to sever our partnership.

Alex's Script

Paula, I love you. You are an amazing person and I dream of us spending the rest of our lives together, but I fear your increasing drug use is going to end that dream. I fear for your life. You have gotten three speeding tickets and one DUI in the last two years. I had to go to a jail for the first time in my life. To see what you looked like after spending the night there made me sad, but then I got upset, having stayed up all night worrying about you and not knowing if you were alive or dead.

At our wedding after a beautiful ceremony you started drinking right away and right through dinner, and you were so drunk we had to leave early from our own reception. I felt embarrassed in front of our friends and my family and cheated out of a day I had been looking forward to for years.

My bottom line: If you don't get help I will be contacting a lawyer to ask about getting a divorce.

---

* Debbie, Mikaeli, and Violet would have similar scripts, all with an ultimatum as their bottom line for Paula to get help or their existing relationship with her would end.

The outcome literature has generally indicated that there is little efficacy in this approach, with more long-term harm than benefit (White & Miller, 2007). However, a study conducted in Vancouver between 2005 and 2015 examined changes in substance use and related outcomes before and after treatment in people coerced into treatment, voluntarily attending treatment, or not attending treatment who were using illicit drugs, primarily opioids. The study involved 3,192 persons with 399 (12.5 percent) participants reporting being coerced into addiction treatment. What was fascinating, and speaks to the fact that much work continues to be done in the area of addiction counselling, was that there were no statistically significant reductions in substance use outcomes for people coerced into treatment, voluntarily attending treatment, or not attending treatment. There were also no statistically significant differences in the before and after substance use patterns for those coerced into treatment versus those voluntarily attending treatment or not attending treatment (Pilarinos et al., 2020).

CHAPTER 19

Working with More Than One: Families and Groups

FAMILY COUNSELLING

Substance treatment has traditionally focused on isolating the drug user from the family. By the time most substance misusers seek some form of treatment, their drug use has affected not only themselves but also their entire social and family structure, producing profound social, economic, legal, and health changes. Addiction affects the emotional and physical intimacy of family members, isolates the family and its individual members, and increases the risk of mental health issues such as depression (Lander et al., 2013). Globally, it is estimated that more than 100 million adults are affected by their relatives' addiction issues. Affected family members experience multiple stresses, coping dilemmas, and a lack of information and support, making them vulnerable to their own health and social issues, both related and unrelated to the drug use (Orford et al., 2013; Rojas, 2015). As well, when the substance misuse ends, everyone within the family unit has become vulnerable and disequilibrium may ensue.

Issues associated with parental substance use include adverse health and child developmental outcomes, heightened risk of child maltreatment and neglect, attachment disruption, misreading or missing emotional cues from the child, the inability to respond to a child's cues and expressed needs, and general emotional unavailability. As well, when there are substance misuse issues within a family system the risk of interparental conflict is far greater, children are more likely to be exposed to interpersonal violence at a young age, and there is a greater likelihood of child welfare involvement. There are also dramatic differences in families where one or both parents use drugs (Table 19.1).

Family counselling, which emerged as a separate field in the 1950s, views the family as an organic whole. The family therapist explores with the family how substance use is embedded in a cycle of interaction within the family. The treatment interview is usually conducted with the caregiver(s) and children, but can include other persons who have a functional participant role in the ongoing life of the family group, like grandparents, aunts,

Table 19.1: Comparing Characteristics of Healthy Families with Drug Involved Families

Healthy Families	Drug Involved Family
Safety for all members	Emotionally unavailable parents Lack of emotional resolution of issues Failure to protect children from hazards Neglect and abuse
Open communication	Secrets kept to keep peace within the family Facade of normality maintained Feelings hidden Children made into parental confidants
Caring for children's needs	Scarcity economy places focus on parents' needs Children feel responsible for adults (parentification of children)
Individualized roles	Family's needs dictate roles Roles become rigid, especially during times of stress
Continuity	Chaos Arbitrariness Dissolution of the family
Respect for privacy	Parents become intrusive Secrets confused with privacy Diminished respect for the individual
Broad family focus	Family focus determined by needs of drug-using adult Drug-using parent's needs come first

Sources: Adapted from Mayes and Truman (2002), Niccols (2010), Rotunda et al. (1995), Shadur (2013), and Sharma (2016).

or uncles. In essence, the interview unit comprises all those persons who share the identity of a family and whose behaviour is influenced by the circular interchange of emotion within the group. The counsellor initiates the treatment process with the entire group but may excuse the children and concentrate on the marital and parental pair or on a parent-child pair (Steinglass, 1992). There are four distinct options when working with a family:

1. *Family orientation*: This involves informing family members about the rehabilitation program on which the identified service user is embarking. It is used to enlist family support in the service user's treatment.
2. *Family education*: This approach is used to inform family members about family-relation issues and how they may be relevant to substance misuse and the substance misuser.
3. *Family counselling*: This is employed to bring about the resolution of problems identified by family members as related to the substance misuse.
4. *Family therapy*: This method is employed to bring about significant and permanent changes to intractable areas of systemic family dysfunction related to the substance misuse. (Boudreau, 1997)

Family work in addiction counselling revolves around several themes:

- All couples and families have problems, but psychoactive drug use prevents resolution of these problems and creates new and more complex ones.
- No individual can force another to change.
- Personal change comes through accepting responsibility for one's own behaviour.
- All members of the family are involved in the problem, and all have responsibility in finding some form of resolution.
- Removal of drugs from the family system represents a necessary beginning in the recovery process, yet is incomplete in itself.

The three prominent stages of family counselling are: (1) the attainment of sobriety and unbalancing of the system; (2) the adjustment to sobriety and stabilizing the system; and (3) the maintenance of sobriety and rebalancing the system (Todd, 1991). Early family work in the addiction field arose from the disease model and had a sense of blame associated with it, particularly the idea of co-dependency. The theme of co-dependency typically explored how the spouse, typically the wife, enabled and supported the addiction of the husband and how the wife needed to be counselled in order for the husband to recover fully. The focus on co-dependency was typical of this era of mother-blaming theories (Prest & Protinsky, 1993).

Contemporary family system orientations provide a more comprehensive and meaningful approach to addressing underlying issues related to drug use. It is an integrated approach that views drug misuse and family functioning as interrelated. Among family counselling's goals is to help identify new skills and then coach family members in the practice of these new skills. One component that should not be overlooked in the process is the couple's sexuality, and sex therapy should be made available as one aspect of this type of intervention (Dowsling, 1980; Osmond & Kimberley, 2017). Family therapy, when incorporated with other treatment approaches, significantly increases the improvement observed at both short- and long-term follow-up intervals in interventions ranging from cognitive-behavioural to pharmacological (Alaggia & Csiernik, 2017; Fals-Stewart & O'Farrell, 2003; McCrady et al., 2009; Thomas, 1989).

Family counselling entails four distinct steps, beginning with family engagement, the process of enhancing all family members' involvement and investment in the treatment of the substance misuser. The second element is relational reframing, which consists of interventions designed to move away from individual ways of defining problems and generating solutions, and toward an understanding focused on relationships instead. These actions also aim to remove irrational descriptions and attributions for family members' behaviours, moving toward understanding motivations for the substance use and associated behaviour based on those relationships. The goal of the third core element is family behaviour change, which aims to teach concrete new skills and encourage individual behaviour changes that will allow for improved overall family relationships. New skills and behaviours are positively reinforced and coached, not only for the substance misuser but for the entire family system. The key here is to move the family from mutually punishing behaviours to mutually rewarding ones that enhance the relationships between members. The final component is family restructuring. Here the counsellor works with the family to change the way the family system is governed, examining the family's underlying beliefs, premises, and rules. In this final stage, family members are encouraged to understand the dynamics of their family, and how these dynamics are linked to problematic behaviours including but not limited to the drug misuse. The goal here is to promote changes in attachment and emotional processes between family members (Alaggia & Csiernik, 2017; Klostermann et al., 2011).

Specific approaches to family counselling in the addiction field have been developed, including Community Reinforcement and Family Training (CRAFT), a derivative of the Community Reinforcement Approach (see Chapter 20). CRAFT more actively engages non-using family members, typically partners and children, to affect the behaviour of substance misusers (Sisson & Azrin, 1986). CRAFT's goal is to improve both the quality of life and functioning of the entire family system, which occurs by reducing substance use. CRAFT arose from the dichotomy in the addiction field that many who would benefit from substance misuse treatment are strongly opposed in participating initially, whereas their families are often highly motivated to get help for them. CRAFT stresses the importance of relationships in the treatment process. This approach believes that focusing only on drug-using behaviours and not on interpersonal problems decreases the likelihood of change. Key to CRAFT is reciprocity: all participants need to be allowed to express themselves during counselling, avoid blaming each other, and are encouraged to speak in a positive, reinforcing manner. Issues need to be clearly stated by all participants, including an overt discussion of feelings (Roozen et al., 2010).

In CRAFT, families are taught that all behaviours make sense, and that they serve some function. As in any form of counselling, active listening is stressed, but here not between the counsellor and the service user but between all members of the family unit. Being able to listen to each other without immediately responding and without responding defensively are key skills that the family needs to learn. CRAFT involves a strength-based component, as there is also an attempt to positively reinforce positive behaviour rather than just focusing on the drug use and its negative ramifications. Looking for times the individual does not use drugs and how that is a positive to family functioning, and reinforcing these events and behaviours, is a core aspect of CRAFT. As well, when there are reoccurrences of drug use, the family is encouraged to allow for natural consequences, not to rescue the individual but to have the person deal with the implications and learn to resolve them without additional family support. There is also an emphasis on self-care in CRAFT, such that each family member is encouraged to examine their own needs and to focus on them, not only on the needs of the member misusing drugs (Roozen et al., 2010).

While family counselling is an integral component for addiction intervention, there are certain instances when it should not be applied. If there is an alcohol-related crisis that is of greater urgency, family counselling needs to be delayed. Similarly, if there is great potential for violence in the relationship, safety concerns override the value of this type of counselling. Lastly, if family counselling leads to blaming or labelling, a re-examination of this approach is required. Counsellor's need to be aware that when an individual returns to their family from treatment but no work has been done with the family, the family may attempt to return to the previous status quo to remove this uneasiness. This can entail sabotaging treatment and the ongoing recovery process, intentionally or unintentionally, because while one part of the system has been changed (the substance misuser), the more dominant part (the rest of the family) has not (Alaggia & Csiernik, 2017).

GROUP COUNSELLING

Group work with service users has been a preferred intervention model in the alcohol dependency field since the inception of formalized treatment programs in the 1940s, with early outcome studies demonstrating the utility of this approach (Ends & Page, 1957). This is partially due to the influence of Alcoholics Anonymous but also to the common experience of oppression of those with an addiction issue, despite the heterogeneity of this vast population (Csiernik & Rowe, 2017; Loughran, 2009). Group counselling is based on the recognition that, with proper guidance, those misusing psychoactive substances can help each other. Group counselling is also based on the universal human tendency to validate subjective experiences by comparing them with the experiences of others who are perceived as similar or share some common characteristic. In all forms of group coun-selling, service users and the group facilitator meet regularly to conduct specific, formal activities within the framework of a mutually acknowledged group structure and code. Interactions with the leader and between members are the foundation for change. This interactive process allows for insight into behaviour and correction of maladaptive actions such as communication problems, leading to improved social and personal functioning. Groups for substance misusers are particularly helpful in assisting members to recognize, anticipate, and cope with drinking or drug-using triggers. They also help members move through the stages of change and work through the action phase of the Transtheoretical Model of Change (see Chapter 22). The here-and-now orientation of groups is also an extremely valuable characteristic of this approach, as is a group's capacity to provide examples of drug avoidance and alternative coping methods. Groups are also safe havens for self-disclosure and provide opportunities for experimentation with new behaviours. The group process reduces social isolation and can provide wonderful opportunities for the development of insight into past and current behaviours (Flores, 1983; Hepworth & Larson, 2012). All groups provide a level of mutual aid where individuals both receive and give help, with this mutuality being essential to the change process. While each group is a unique entity, its membership is representative of the range of issues persons with addictions face outside the group, and of the broader issues they experienced during the development of their drug use and will continue to encounter during their recovery.

Finally, each group is a unique gestalt, which simply means that the group is greater than the sum of its individual members. What each person brings to the group makes it unique in its potential and outcome.

Many treatment programs utilize some form of small group experience with service users as a focus for change, especially given the flexibility of group formats and approaches. No single technique, type of group, or theoretical orientation succeeds for all group participants, and one cannot find a technique, type of group, or orientation that will not work with at least one person. However, no person should be expected to automatically be able to relate closely to whatever group they are asked to join. Consequently, a service user's wish to switch groups may indicate resistance to treatment, but it may also signify a quite healthy judgment of feelings and needs. It is therefore incumbent on the group worker to foster a sense of psychosocial belonging between members in the beginning stages of group development (Loughran, 2009).

The composition of the group is a powerful determinant to what happens and what gains the participants ultimately achieve. Consequently, the process of selection is critical, and if carried out ineffectively, can lead to poor group dynamics, interactions, and outcomes. On the other hand, effective and sensitive selection can be the principle determinant of successful outcomes. The following are key in creating a small group whose purpose is to change behaviour:

- A high degree of group interaction is required, and activities should keep group members interested in attending and facilitate development of the group.
- Group members need to be supported and protected to develop sufficient courage to speak about upsetting, problematic, and even traumatic aspects of their lives.
- Sufficient compatibility among group members is needed to increase personal attraction: "Can we actually like each other?"
- Adequate diversity and similarities among group members is necessary to provide examples to each other, so that the strengths and resources of each can be utilized. For example, some group members may be capable of expressing anger more easily than others or be able to manage financial matters more adequately. The question is what each person can teach others in the room.
- The group facilitator needs to prepare participants to engage with each other and provide them with clear and adequate information about the group treatment process. The group leader must always provide a safe environment, outline the group rules, and demonstrate the norms for appropriate participation at the beginning of the group process. Special attention should be given to pre-counselling training and in providing specific instructional materials about the nature, purpose, method, and goals of group exercises.

Attachment style of individual group members is another factor to consider, as this has been demonstrated to be a predictor of relationship quality, well-being, and ability to function well within a counselling group. Insecure attachment styles (see Chapter 6) are thought to be one underlying cause of addiction and represent a target for change in one-to-one counselling, but also affect an individual's ability to work well in a group setting. In a study examining the effects of attachment styles on reoccurrence of drug use and treatment retention, 58 volunteers, participating in group counselling, completed measures of attachment anxiety and avoidance. Participants were followed up with four weeks later and their continued treatment attendance and drug-using status were recorded. Those with high anxiety/high avoidant attachment styles were most likely to complete the entire counselling cycle. However, low anxiety/high avoidant participants had the lowest reoccurrence rates. Thus, attachment style is another factor for group workers to consider as they plan and organize group activities to maximize the likelihood of service users succeeding (Marshall et al., 2018).

An important decision to make prior to beginning an addiction-specific treatment group is whether it should be open or closed. Open groups allow new participants to enter at any time during the group's life, while closed groups do not allow for the addition of new members. An open group format provides the opportunity for new members to bring new perspectives to the group and offers immediate support for those in need. However, open groups are more prone to instability, are more disruptive, and their members often do not develop the same level of trust that occurs within closed groups. Regardless of which option is selected potential members should be informed prior to joining if the group is to be open or closed (Hepworth & Larson, 2012).

Group counselling is a social experience with a focus on both the group and each individual member. As such, an optimum size is from six to eight members. Counselling groups are intended to allow a safe opportunity for members to identify, express, and talk about their emotions. The group is a place where one is allowed and encouraged to search for and articulate feelings. The non-judgmental intent of groups also provides an ideal locale for practising newly acquired skills and behaviours. The here-and-now emphasis, the opportunity to gain insights from others' behaviours, and the opportunity for personal insights all speak to the value of including some type of group process in addiction treatment. However, while group counselling is a standard treatment approach in the addiction field, there is still only limited empirical evidence to demonstrate the long-term value of individual versus group interventions (Csiernik & Arundel, 2013; Csiernik & Troller, 2002; Lo Coco et al., 2019). Current economic realities are forcing more programs to use group interventions and the question must be asked as to whether this is in the individual's or the facility's best interest.

Counselling groups can serve one of several purposes. They can assist with socialization, or, in the case of substance misusers, re-socialization, so that the behaviours associated with drug use are minimized if not eliminated. Group counselling can also focus on self-concept formation, where members grapple with being a drug user or being outside societal norms or not feeling like a citizen. Group work can also aim to directly change behaviours through role play that examines antecedent events leading to drug use, or on learning avoidance or refusal skills. Group work may also function as a support to offer emotional and instrumental aid in becoming a non-user.

Educational groups tend to be larger than counselling groups as there is less one-to-one and counsellor-to-individual group member interaction. This type of group usually entails a series of lectures, films, readings, or discussions on a specific substance use–related topic. Members still share their experiences, though there is a greater emphasis on how-to. Specific how-to strategies include the following:

- how to problem solve
- how to self-monitor
- how to handle reoccurrence
- how to decrease consumption
- how to abstain

Yalom (2005) discussed 12 curative factors in detail that are associated with group work:

1. Provision of information
2. Instillation of hope
3. Universality: understanding that you alone are not affected by addiction
4. Altruism: offering help to others
5. Corrective emotional response to the primary group, one's family
6. Development of socializing techniques
7. Role modelling of alternative behaviours by other group members
8. Interpersonal learning
9. Group cohesion and the development of positive interpersonal bonds
10. Catharsis
11. Insight into existential factors of life, existence, and death
12. Acceptance, safety, and support

Group workers should also be aware of the distinct stages of group evolution, from initiation to termination. Two fundamental models, the traditional Tuckman (Tuckman & Jensen, 1977) and the alternative, feminist-premised Schiller (1997), outline this development. Tuckman observed that there tends to be five distinct though overlapping stages in the life cycle of a group (see Table 19.2). The opening stage, "forming," is predicated on an approach-avoidance conflict. Members new to each other and to the group leader assess the group and decide whether to commit their time but also their affect to be part of the process. This is followed by the "storming" phase, where group position and status is determined. Group members are most likely to react negatively to the group leader rather than against each other in this phase, especially if the leader has no recovery history or is still using a substance in an integrated manner. If this conflict can be satisfactorily

Table 19.2: The Tuckman and Schiller Models of Group Development

Tuckman	Schiller	Major Characteristics
Forming	Pre-affiliation	Approach-avoidance
Storming	Establishing a relationship base	Interpersonal relationship focus
Norming	Mutuality and interpersonal empathy	Working stage
Performing	Challenge and change	Moving forward
Mourning	Termination	Consolidating changes

Sources: Schiller (1997) and Tuckman & Jensen (1977).

resolved, the group will enter the "norming" stage. Group members will move toward intimacy, where mutual trust and cohesion begin to develop and superficial support is replaced with earnest social and emotional interaction. The fourth stage is "performing," in which the group becomes less dependent on the group worker and relationships become more realistic. Members take more risks, and social support between members becomes more evident and more genuine. The termination stage in Tuckman's model is called "mourning." The function of the group leader in this stage is to lessen the members' need for the group while ensuring that they take what they have learned from the group, both about their drug use and about themselves, beyond the confines of the group.

Linda Schiller offers a different perspective from the Tuckman model. For her, the group dynamics among women differ from men, the only individuals observed in Tuckman's and most other group development models. While Schiller's model also has five stages (see Table 19.2), the process varies in two key areas. After dealing with the discomfort of being in a new environment with unknown individuals, a stage she labels as "pre-affiliation," Schiller states that woman are not driven to establish social power and dominance. On the contrary, what women want is to form a "relational base" to work from, and to find common ground where trust and cohesion can develop. Once this is established, they can move to a state of greater openness, that of "mutuality and inter-personal empathy," when connections and similarities between group members become the overriding focus of the social exchange. At this point, women tend to become more comfortable in confronting each other to deal with the underlying issues that led them to a counselling group for addiction. Schiller calls this the stage of "challenge and change." Once a positive relationship is developed, it is easier, according to Schiller, for women to challenge each other regarding behaviours that led them to be part of the group.

Group work has distinct advantages over individual counselling. It more closely resembles everyday life than does one-to-one work. As well, being part of a group reduces the social isolation many persons with addiction issues face, especially if their peer group continues to use. Group counselling offers greater feelings of support and caring for others through the dynamic of mutual aid, as well as increasing self-esteem through the giving and receiving of positive feedback. It also offers a safe environment from which to learn from others and the opportunity to imitate successes through social learning.

CHAPTER 20

Behavioural Approaches

While Freud's ideas and work were laying the foundation for psychotherapy, the work of American John Watson was doing the same for behaviourism. Rather than looking at developmental stages and early psychological conflicts and trauma, Watson emphasized theories of learning and how the majority of behaviour originates through learning processes. Another early contributor to behaviour therapy was Edward Thorndike, whose law of effect stated that behaviour is shaped by the consequences it derives. To this was added Pavlov's ideas regarding classical conditioning, and Skinner's work on operant conditioning. Meichenbaum added the ideas of self-management, self-instructional learning, and stress inoculation to this practice area (Jones-Smith, 2012; Meichenbaum et al., 2007).

Within behavioural approaches, substance misuse is linked to varying degrees to maladaptive decision making. Drug use is a behaviour that produces immediate positive outcomes, while ongoing or extensive drug use produces long-term negative consequences. The ongoing misuse of drugs in the face of negative consequences indicates dysfunction in the cognitive mechanisms involved with decision making, which values greater risk options that lead to rewards, even if only temporarily. This cognitive dysfunction has three distinct stages: the formation of preferences involving the relative value of distinct decision options (using versus abstinence); choice implementation, including motivation for using, self-regulation, and the ability to inhibit one's behaviours; and positive and negative feedback to using or not using. Relative to non-drug-dependent individuals, those with substance use disorders value risky options more highly during the formation of preferences; have a greater appetite for superficially attractive rewards during choice implementation; and are both more efficient in learning from rewards and less efficient in learning from losses during feedback processing (Verdejo-Garcia et al., 2018).

Behavioural therapies apply to the full range of psychological events—attitudinal and emotional, as well as learned. These counselling approaches are based on the belief that drug use is a functional, socially learned behavioural pattern maintained by a wide variety of positive consequences and conditioned factors. Some forms of behavioural therapy bring about major changes in people's actions by modifying their emotional responses, while enduring changes in attitude can be most successfully affected through modifications in overt behaviour. Almost any learning outcome that results from direct experience can also come about through a vicarious basis through observation of other people's behaviours and the consequences they produce. Providing an appropriate model may accelerate the learning process, and thus one prominent method of social-learning therapy is based on modelling desired behaviours.

Although differing in application, the behavioural component for treating drug problems is based on a common belief system:

- It is assumed that drug-using behaviour and behaviours affected by drugs, such as risk taking or aggression, are learned. Further, it is assumed that the learned characteristics of this behaviour can be modified or unlearned.
- Drug use is usually dealt with directly, often by introducing the behaviour into the treatment strategy. Drug-use decisions are critical events; thus, the circumstances surrounding decisions to use a drug serve as a basis for determining their function.
- Emphasis is on operationally specifying treatment procedures and assessing treatment effectiveness by using empirical methods (Riley et al., 1985). In general, antecedent conditions (triggers) lead to behavioural responses (drug use). These lead to consequences in the form of initial positive reinforcement, which leads to continued drug use.

OPERANT METHODS

Operant conditioning techniques stress the relationship between behaviour and the environment, attempting to alter the interaction through modification of behavioural consequences. This behavioural approach assumes that individuals are conditioned by the consequences of their behaviour. Pleasant consequences reinforce some behaviours and punishment discourages them. First suggested as a treatment method in the mid-1960s (Ulmer, 1977), it is based on a community health approach that believes that the entire range of mental health disorders results from forces operating in the community on the individual. This suggests that treatment occurs through rearranging community influences on the service user in the community, not in a hospital or other closed institution. With alcohol- and drug-dependent individuals, reinforcement and punishment contingencies are used to influence drug use and drug-related behaviours. An extensive literature attests to the effectiveness of reinforcement contingencies in influencing drinking behaviour within laboratory settings (Cassidy et al., 2018; European Monitoring Centre for Drugs and Drug Addiction, 2016; Kirby et al., 2016; Miller & Hester, 1986a; Oluwoye, 2019; Pollack et al., 2002; Riley et al., 1985). In this model, antecedent behaviours leading to drug use are punished while behaviours that substitute for drug taking are positively reinforced.

One specific type of operant conditioning is contingency management. This method involves systematically arranging the individual's environment so that positive

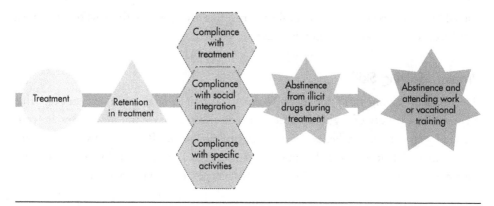

Figure 20.1: Targets and Potential Uses for Contingency Management

Source: European Monitoring Centre for Drugs and Drug Addiction (2016).

consequences follow desired behaviours, and either negative or neutral consequences follow undesired behaviours (Figure 20.1). This process is intended to weaken drug use reinforcement and strengthen abstinence. Initially rewards such as vouchers, clinical privileges, and prizes are used to positively support non-using behaviours. In the community, contingency management requires other persons, such as the partner and other family members, to enforce the contingencies and are often used as part of a multimodal or family treatment program. The core tenets of this approach entail monitoring of target behaviour, quickly rewarding desired behaviour and withholding rewards in the absence of the desired behaviour (Petry, 2012).

A second form of operant conditioning is behavioural contracting. Behavioural contracting is similar to contingency management. Essentially, the process is one of explicitly defining a set of behaviours and their associated consequences. The contract is usually negotiated between two parties and stated in writing, as often it is only through explicit written agreements that the foundations for change can be established. Behavioural contracting ensures that all parties agree to expected behaviours, appropriate reactions, and how behaviour change will be recognized and rewarded. Behavioural contracting is very helpful in the initial stages of treatment as it can build in early recognition of behaviour changes and thereby motivate service users to make continued life changes.

SKILLS TRAINING

Although most behavioural techniques involve the acquisition of skills, some focus on teaching specific adaptive behaviours that are presumed to be deficient prior to the individual's excessive drug use and may have been a major contributing factor to the alcohol or other drug issue. The main assumption underlying skills training techniques is that drug-dependent individuals have deficiencies in skills that are essential in achieving personal goals and solving interpersonal problems. If taught these skills, service users should be more successful in maintaining a drug-free lifestyle than those whose treatment focuses only on alcohol and other drug use.

Problem-Solving Skills

The problem-solving skills approach is a general behavioural treatment strategy that assures that a variety of highly specific and specialized behavioural procedures are considered by an individual whenever a problem situation arises. It focuses strongly on identifying and evaluating multiple opportunities, categorized as behavioural options, for treatment intervention. The training typically incorporates a four-stage procedure:

1. Problem identification
2. Description of behavioural options or alternative responses
3. Evaluation of each behavioural option for its possible outcome
4. Employing the best behavioural option based on the best probable outcome

The behavioural technique of problem-solving skills training analyzes treatment operations on a continuing basis and directly involves the service user in the treatment process. This approach involves the following:

1. Tailoring the treatment approach to the service user rather than vice versa.
2. Removing the judgmental aspect of what is and is not appropriate by matching the model to the person in treatment. This is because behavioural consequences are specific to individuals and circumstances.
3. Precisely defining and evaluating behaviours and situations.
4. Avoiding the use of vague terminology or labels, such as dependency needs, alcoholic or drug addict.
5. Increasing awareness of the powerful influence of the short-term consequences on perpetuating drinking and/or drug taking.
6. Increasing awareness that many other appropriate behavioural options have long-term rewarding consequences.
7. Recognizing that as service users become better able to define, evaluate, and understand the influences on their behaviour, their personal problems correspondingly become less mysterious and more capable of positive resolution. This is predicated on service users being active participants in their own treatment and life planning.

Social Skills

The excessive use of some substance misusers can be traced to a deficit in social skills. Controlled research clearly supports skills training as a valuable component of alcohol and drug treatment (Roth & Fonagy, 2005). Techniques useful in teaching social skills include role playing, modelling, social coaching, role reversal, and providing social rewards. Comparative findings suggest that focusing on assertiveness training and cognitive inhibitions is particularly helpful. Cognitive rehabilitation includes training in focusing, sustaining and dividing attention, discrimination between cues, inhibition, and differential responding to cues, along with problem solving (Fals-Stewart & Lam, 2010). The focus of cognitive self-change is to

- pay attention to thoughts and feelings;
- recognize that thoughts and feelings have risks leading to harmful behaviour;
- use new thinking to reduce the risk; and
- practice until proficient at the change (Barnett, 2009).

Interpersonal Skills

The evidence regarding deficits in interpersonal skills among drug misusers is extensive (Ferrari et al., 2014; Longabaugh & Morgenstern, 1999; Nixon et al., 1992; Roberts et al., 1999; Sacks et al., 2002). Some studies suggest that substance-dependent persons use drugs as a coping response to stressful interpersonal situations and reoccurrence is often initiated by stressful situations. Therefore, it is possible that interpersonal skills training may increase the individual's real control over the stressor(s) by compensating for skill deficiencies, or increase the individual's perception of control over the stressor(s), leading, in either case, to control over the consequent drug use. One reason that training in coping skills may be useful is that it increases self-efficacy, mobilizing skills they already possess but have not employed (Miller et al., 2011).

Vocational Skills

Training in vocational skills is based on findings that many misusers of psychoactive drugs have a poor employment history, and that employment status is a good predictor of treatment outcome. Vocational skills education usually involves assertiveness training and instruction in other skills for dealing with co-workers and employers. Generally, training in vocational skills has not been used alone but as one component of a multimodal treatment approach (Walton & Hall, 2016).

Stress Management

Stress has been hypothesized as an antecedent of drug use and reoccurrence of use after treatment. The theoretical rationale underlying the application of relaxation training techniques usually involves two assumptions: first, that the problem is caused or exacerbated by tension or anxiety and, second, that relaxation training can effectively deal with the problem either by reducing anxiety or by increasing the individual's sense of perceived control in stressful situations. Relaxation training can be particularly useful when it is used as part of a systematic desensitization treatment. Systematic desensitization is a well-defined procedure used to diminish specific fears. The person is gradually and repeatedly exposed to imagined or real aspects of the phobic situation. This is done under conditions that prevent or minimize the arousal of anxiety. Other popular relaxation training techniques include progressive muscle relaxation, meditation, and yoga (Back et al., 2007; Farhoudian et al., 2019; Noone et al., 1999).

COGNITIVE BEHAVIOURAL THERAPY

Cognitive behavioural therapy (CBT) combines theories about how individuals learn behaviours with theories regarding how they think about and interpret a life event. CBT has an extensive history of empirical support in treating substance misuse since this synthesis of cognitive and behavioural approaches was proposed in the 1980s (Bador & Kerekes, 2019; Carroll, 1996; Carroll & Onken, 2005; Gold et al., 2020; Marlatt, 1985; O'Hare, 2005; Pollack et al., 2002; Salehi & Alizadeh, 2018). The rationale behind using CBT is the assumption that the process of drug use, including reoccurrence, can be controlled by making new cognitive and emotional and, therefore, behavioural choices. While the foundation was laid by John Watson, Aaron Beck also contributed extensively to the development of the therapy. CBT also draws from Albert Bandura's social learning theory, being premised on the belief that all thoughts and behaviours are learned through the results of direct experience as well as through vicarious observation (Wills & Saunders, 2013). It also assumes that cognitive processes lead to drug craving, though research suggests that other neurobiological and physiological processes, which operate out of cognitively conscious awareness, may also influence behaviour (Waldron & Kaminer, 2004).

Cognitive behavioural therapy focuses on cognition as covert behaviour and holds the view that individuals' problems arise from their beliefs, evaluations, and interpretations regarding life events (Gabour & Ing, 1991). The first step in CBT is to take a functional analysis of the individual's behaviours associated with drug use, focusing on patterns of use and frequency. CBT is based on several assumptions, including that drug use is often the result of maladaptive cognition, that drug and alcohol misuse is an attempt to solve such problems, and that adaptive cognition will decrease alcohol and drug use (National Institute on Alcohol Abuse and Alcoholism, 1988).

Like all variations of CBT, the Beck model emphasizes the therapeutic relationship and case conceptualization, focusing on teaching service users psychological self-monitoring and self-change skills. Using the Beck approach, the clinician aids the service user in identifying and managing high-risk situations, modifying maladaptive automatic thoughts and beliefs, cravings, and situations where the person gives themself permission to use a drug. The process of learning entails developing tactics to resist acting on cravings and urges, thus disrupting established substance-related behavioural patterns, limiting the damage from reoccurrences, and learning adaptive, alternative, and healthier behaviours. The importance of the counsellor always responding empathically is stressed here, as it is in all CBT approaches. It is vital to appreciate that developing new cognitions and new behaviours is a slow process and thus counsellors using a CBT approach need to understand that service users can have great ambivalence about treatment, and instances when they are not fully engaged or co-operative are part of the process of change (Newman, 2019). This makes CBT counselling quite congruent with the stages of change approach (see Chapter 22).

Combining behaviour and cognitive therapies, CBT concentrates on the mental process mediating between stimuli and responses in the belief that a person's feelings and behaviours can be moderated by their thinking. Individuals have negative automatic thoughts (NATs), which are typically closely linked with their emotions and behaviours. As NATs develop, a person's interpretation of life can become skewed, creating a cycle of negative thought and self-doubt. Additional negative emotions and behaviours then reinforce the negative thoughts (Dryden & Branch, 2012). Skills training to break this cycle can be either intrapersonal (examining internal events) or interpersonal. In either case, the counsellor draws on daily life examples to address both the cognitions and the behaviour. Self-efficacy is enhanced to the point where individuals regain control over the active decision-making processes in their lives. This collaborative approach between service user and counsellor places the individual as active learner in the course of treatment, with the counsellor as teacher. Using positive reinforcement, the counsellor focuses on the assumptions that behaviour can change, based on how individuals think about themselves (Figure 20.2). If the thinking can become self-regulated, change can follow (Fisher, 1995).

CBT seeks to bring about change during the therapeutic process by altering an individual's established cognitions, errors, and schemas. However, rather than addressing only distressing thoughts and feelings, contemporary CBT has evolved to promote an attitude of non-judgmental acceptance as part of the process (Herbert & Foreman, 2011). Waldron and Kaminer (2004) add that, within CBT, substance use issues must be conceptualized as learned behaviours that are initiated and maintained in the context of environmental factors. Recovery is a learning process, and time must be spent examining, explaining, and discussing high-risk situations that trigger drug use to build self-efficacy

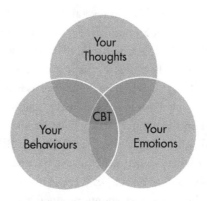

Figure 20.2: Intersection of Thought, Behaviour, and Emotion in CBT

in responding to them. Outcome studies indicate that becoming aware of these high-risk situations increases service user confidence and provides them with an element of control over their lives (Vedel et al., 2008).

DIALECTICAL BEHAVIOURAL THERAPY

Dialectical behavioural therapy (DBT) is an evidence-based form of skills training that has been classified as a third wave of cognitive behavioural counselling along with acceptance and commitment therapy (ACT) (Hayes et al., 2005; Ii et al., 2019). Developed by Marsha Linehan (1993), DBT involves the synthesis of both change and acceptance. Linehan found that individuals with suicidal ideation tended not to have the skills to solve their problem, which further exacerbated their suffering. As well, due to high levels of frustration, these individuals were extremely sensitive to criticism. When tasked with behavioural change options they could not successfully complete, their emotional state led many to either shut down or respond physically. Such service users would dramaticaly exit from counselling sessions or even forcefully confront their counsellors. Their distraught emotional state simply did not allow them to accept their circumstances. Linehan worked to bring about change in these persons using persuasion and by asking what had not been considered in prior work with them.

DBT was initially developed to treat the suicidal and parasuicidal behaviours of individuals diagnosed with borderline personality disorder (Linehan, 1993). Borderline personality disorder (BPD) is a complex mental illness characterized by fear of abandonment, impulsivity, self-harm behaviours, and emotional dysregulation (American Psychiatric Association, 2013). DBT is best characterized as a combination of CBT and mindfulness principles derived from Buddhist meditative practices. Its intent is to improve motivation to change, enhance capability, and generalize new behaviours through structuring the person's environment in a more positive manner. As with other behavioural approaches, the behaviours to be changed are placed in a hierarchy. Life-threatening behaviours are a priority for change, followed by those that interfere with the counselling process, and then by those that degrade the quality of life. In several studies, DBT has demonstrated that it may be the first effective treatment for borderline personality disorder (Kliem et al., 2010; Linehan et al., 1991, 1993). DBT is based on a dialectical worldview, meaning that in this version of behavior therapy there are two distinct perspectives. The first relates to the fundamental nature of reality as perceived by the service user while the second pertains to the persuasive dialogue and relationship created by the counsellor (Linehan, 2015).

The overlap between borderline personality disorder and co-morbid conditions precipitated the use of DBT with other clinical issues. In the BPD population, this often included substance misuse issues as well as homelessness, unemployment, and eating disorders (Hayes et al., 2004). In stage one of DBT, the focus is on the service user obtaining basic information and skills to decrease counterproductive behaviours. This begins with decreasing substance use among those presenting with this issue, followed by alleviating the physical pain of withdrawal, decreasing urges and temptations, and avoiding cues that could trigger a return to drug use (Dimeff & Linehan, 2008).

It has now been well established that a range of addiction treatment approaches work but that the greatest impediment remains drop out (Csiernik & Arundel, 2013), with evaluation studies regularly being compromised as drop out rates range close to 80 percent (Bornovalova & Daughters, 2007). In contrast, a major strength of DBT is its retention-enhancing strategies. DBT strategies that explicitly aim to increase treatment compliance may do so by

- increasing motivation to attend treatment;
- emphasizing the importance of the therapeutic alliance;
- emphasizing therapist availability through frequent contact or case management approaches; and
- focusing on equipping individuals with additional coping strategies in order to manage their intense feelings and allow them to regulate those emotions in a positive and healthy manner (Bornovalova & Daughters, 2007).

Many of the mindfulness-based practices in DBT have been demonstrated as having utility in addiction treatment (Brautigam, 1977; Monahan, 1977; Alexander et al., 1994). While the exact mechanism remains unknown (Bowen et al., 2006), it is likely that the focus on behaviour change combined with validation is responsible for improved compliance. One of the primary reasons that people drop out of treatment is because the traditional treatment paradigm views their actions only as dysfunctional and pathological (Linehan, 1993). However, DBT views their actions as problems to solve and not as an indicator of treatment failure, personal inadequacy, lack of desire to change, or moral failing (Dimeff & Linehan, 2008).

DBT's goals are to balance thoughts, emotions, and actions while restoring emotional regulation to interpersonal situations (see Box 20.1). The counsellor observes, describes, and participates in the process without judging to manage the substance use with strategies that are not self-punishing. The goal is to allow service users to become more patient and accepting of themselves, and thus the counsellor must accept the service users as they are while working to teach them the skills necessary for change. DBT is a modality of acceptance and gentle persuasion for vulnerable individuals with one or more of the following issues: emotional, behavioural, interpersonal, cognitive, or self-dysregulation. In DBT, tolerance of distress, emotional regulation, core mindfulness, and interpersonal skills are the priority (Dimeff & Linehan, 2008).

MINDFULNESS

Mindfulness is derived from Indo-Sino-Tibetan contemplative practices and philosophies relating to the development of a state of awareness characterized by an attentive

Box 20.1: Sample DBT Activities

Brief Mindfulness Activity
Observe your thoughts for 15 minutes. Lie back, release your tension, focus on your breathing, move your awareness to your body and then your thoughts. Resist the urge to label or judge your thoughts. Let them pass by.

Self-Soothe with Senses
Find a pleasurable way to engage each of your five senses. Doing so will help to soothe your negative emotions.

Vision: Go for a walk somewhere nice and pay attention to the sights.
Hearing: Listen to something enjoyable, such as music or nature.
Touch: Take a warm bath.
Taste: Have a small treat.
Smell: Find some flowers or spray some perfume or cologne.

Emotion Regulation: Identifying the Function of Your Emotion
Identify an emotional reaction lasting a few moments to a few minutes during your week and describe the following:

1. What was the prompting event?
2. What was the interpretation?
3. What was the emotion and the intensity (on a 1 to 100 scale)?
4. Use the following to identify the function(s) of the emotion:
   (a) Did the emotion communicate something to others or influence their behaviour? If so, describe.
   (b) Did the emotion organize or motivate you to do something? If so, describe.
   (c) Did the emotion give you information, colour your perception, or lead you to any conclusions? If so, describe.

Distress Tolerance Skill Development: ACCEPTS
Negative feelings will usually pass, or at least lessen in intensity over time. It can be valuable to distract yourself until the emotion subsides. Follow ACCEPTS to help with this.

Activities: Engage in activities that require thought and concentration. This could be a hobby, a project, volunteer or paid work, or school.
Contributing: Focus on someone or something other than yourself. You can volunteer, do a good deed, or engage in an action to help someone else.

Comparisons: Look at your situation in comparison to something worse. Remember a time you were in more pain, or when someone else was going through something more difficult.

Emotions: Do something that will create a competing emotion; if feeling sad, watch a funny movie; if feeling anxious, listen to soothing music.

Pushing Away: Do away with negative thoughts by pushing them out of your mind. Imagine writing your problem on a piece of paper, crumbling it up, and throwing it away. Refuse to think about the situation until a better time.

Thoughts: When your emotions take over, try to focus on your thoughts. Count to 10, recite song lyrics in your head, or read a book.

Sensations: Find safe physical sensations to distract from intense negative emotions. Wear a rubber band and snap it on your wrist, hold an ice cube in your hand, or eat something sour like a lime.

and non-judgmental monitoring of moment-by-moment cognition, emotion, sensation, and perception, without intrusion from thoughts from the past or of the future (Garland & Howard, 2018). Interest in mindfulness-based interventions (MBIs) has increased in the past decade, particularly as a reoccurrence prevention approach, though the concept was introduced to the counselling world in the late 20th century through the work of Jon Kabat-Zinn (1982, 1990). Kabat-Zinn argued that a purposeful control of attention can be learned, and promoted meditation as the mechanism through which this could be practised. MBI is also part of the third wave of behavioural therapy, designed to temper stress responses through increased awareness and non-judgmental attention to oneself and one's internal experiences. The practice of mindfulness consists of three core elements: intention, attention, and attitude. Intention entails knowing why we are doing what we are doing; attention involves focusing fully on the present moment instead of allowing ourselves to become preoccupied with the past or future; and attitude is the process of how we pay attention. These three elements are interconnected, each informing the others (Shapiro & Carlson, 2009). During mindfulness practice, service users intentionally focus their attention on the current moment, making it possible to enhance their awareness, which in turn helps develop kindness and compassion toward themselves. The process typically begins by concentrating simply on breathing. Individuals start the process by focusing on inhaling and exhaling deeply through the nose, followed by slowly disengaging and ultimately disregarding all other thoughts and feelings (Garland & Howard, 2018).

Mindfulness training programs originally concentrated on reducing emotional distress, with the aim of helping individuals increase awareness of their experience in the moment, learning to respond gradually rather than reacting immediately to emotions or situations. Mindfulness practice gradually expanded to also include a focus on emotional regulation and self-control through increasing sensitivity to and awareness of affective cues that may be triggering and producing a craving to return to drug use (Bautista et al., 2019). Mindfulness-based reoccurrence prevention targets three facets of mindfulness: acting with awareness, being non-judgmental toward oneself, and non-reactivity (Karyadi et al., 2014).

Along with being part of DBT practice, there are several other approaches that include mindfulness as the primary or secondary focus (Bowen et al., 2011; Zgierska et al., 2009):

1. Vipassana meditation: Based in Buddhist traditions, this is what other contemporary forms of MBI are based on. Vipassana meditation is typically taught as a group-based course over two weeks. This practice is conducted in silence and entails upward of 10 hours per day, which is one reason it has not gained widespread popularity in North America.

2. Mindfulness-based stress reduction (MBSR): Adapted for the addiction field from work originally done with individuals suffering with chronic pain and stress-related disorders, MBSR training consists of eight weekly counsellor-led sessions of approximately two hours and daily home assignments. MBSR combines meditation with more traditional cognitive therapy strategies to attempt to prevent drug use reoccurrence.

3. Spiritual Self Schema (3-S) therapy: An eight- to twelve-week course that was originally designed for individuals at risk for or who had HIV. This approach teaches meditation and mindfulness skills in the context of comprehensive psychotherapy, integrating Buddhist principles with modern cognitive self-schema theory that is tailored to each person's faith or spiritual orientation.

4. Acceptance and commitment therapy (ACT): A positive psychological approach whose goals are to increase psychological flexibility. ACT incorporates both mindfulness and acceptance, as well as commitment and behaviour change processes to help service users gain the ability to control behaviour to achieve their valued end goals. There are six core processes in ACT:
   (i) contact with the present moment, which means being aware of your experience in the present moment;
   (ii) acceptance, which requires the service user to be actively connecting to their psychological experiences without needless defences;
   (iii) defusion, including looking *at* thoughts rather than *from* thoughts, noticing thoughts rather than being caught up in thoughts, and seeing thoughts as what they are, not as what they seem to be;
   (iv) self-as-context, which is a transcendent sense of self observing the self, being aware of being aware of oneself;

    (v)   value-chosen life directions, which is seeking out your deepest desires for the sort of person you want to be and the things you want to do in your lifetime; and

   (vi)   committed action, which is acting in the service of your values (Hayes et al., 2009).

5.   Mindfulness-Based Reoccurrence Prevention (MBRP): Also founded on the principles of self-compassion and acceptance, including cravings and urges to use again, MBRP combines three components: mindfulness-based stress reduction as originally proposed by Kabat-Zinn, mindfulness-based cognitive therapy, and the reoccurrence prevention work of Alan Marlatt. MBRP is also a group modality that is taught over eight sessions, but can be used in one-to-one counselling as well; in either approach the service user is expected to complete homework exercises and practise on their own between sessions.

6.   Mindfulness-Oriented Recovery Enhancement: Developed by Eric Garland (2013), this consists of 10 two-hour group sessions of formal mindfulness meditation, debrief and group process, psychoeducation/didactic material, and experiential exercise, along with ongoing homework activities. Garland's original 10 sessions were:

    (i)   mindfulness and the automatic habit of addiction;

   (ii)   mindful reappraisal;

  (iii)   shifting the mind to refocus on savoring;

  (iv)   seeing through the nature of craving;

   (v)   overcoming craving by coping with stress;

  (vi)   walking the middle way between attachment and aversion;

  (vii)   mindfulness of the impermanent body;

 (viii)   defusing relationship triggers for reoccurrence;

  (ix)   interdependence and meaning in recovery; and

   (x)   looking mindfully toward the future.

Several systemic reviews have been completed examining the various approaches to MBI summarized above and all have found mindfulness to have a degree of utility as a tool to decrease the risk of reoccurrence, superior to no counselling but not necessarily superior to other systemic approaches (Bautista et al., 2019; Black, 2014; Garland & Howard, 2018; Karyadi et al., 2014; Öst, 2014; Zgierska et al., 2009).

COMMUNITY REINFORCEMENT APPROACH (CRA)

According to Miller and Hester's (1986a) detailed analysis of treatment effectiveness, the community reinforcement approach model is among the strongest interventions possible, though also one of the most labour-intensive. CRA is based on the belief that environmental contingencies can play a powerful role in drinking or drug use, and that substance misuse is heavily influenced by social and occupational environmental stress-ors. CRA is designed to restructure family, social, and vocational factors in a manner that reinforces a drug-free lifestyle while discouraging future drug use. In CRA, a group of behaviourally based procedures designed to alter the contingencies for drug use are implemented so that sobriety is rewarded and drinking or drug use results in a "time out" from positive reinforcement. The intent is to increase satisfaction in major life areas, such as relationships, work, and recreation, so that the need to obtain positive reinforcement through alcohol or drugs is minimized (Azrin, 1976; Hunt & Azrin, 1973; Meyers et al., 2011).

The first step in the process is a comprehensive functional analysis to determine when drug misuse occurs and outline the chain of events that lead from non-drug use to a state of dysfunctional impairment. This entails identifying external antecedents, including with whom, where, and when the drug is used, as well as the physical and psychological triggers. The quantity and frequency of drug use, positive and negative outcomes, and legal, occupational, educational, and relationship factors are all part of the functional analysis. Understanding positive reinforcement is essential if a full range of actions, to alter both psychological and environmental factors reinforcing drug use, are to be employed to address the individual's drug misuse. Otherwise, the behaviour will not be fully addressed, and the likelihood of a reoccurrence of drug use increases. The CRA treatment plan is itself framed during a period of sobriety. However, while absti-nence may be the ultimate goal, the service user is initially asked to remain sober only during this planning phase and not indefinitely. The "Happiness Scale," which examines 10 areas of a person's life, is the foundation of the treatment plan. The service user and counsellor identify areas that need focus. Strategies for goal development and a feasible time frame are then determined. The counsellor uses a positive reinforcement frame-work to establish reasonable goals that the individual can obtain, which underscores how the treatment process aids the person in obtaining rewards important to the individual (Myers et al., 2005).

A key initial focus in the CRA assessment is behavioural skill deficits. The three main training components of CRA are problem solving, communication skills, and refusal skills that emphasize assertiveness in uncomfortable and difficult settings. These are supplemented with social and recreational counselling and job skills, given that many individuals with addiction issues are either unemployed or their existing employment is a substantive drug-using trigger. Mood monitoring and cognitive restructuring are important components of the counselling process, as is relationship counselling. CRA was among the first treatments to recognize the importance of family members in main-taining ongoing sobriety, and to stress the inclusion of other significant people in the counselling process. Interestingly, the CRA process begins by anticipating reoccurrence, and thus the functional analysis immediately begins by identifying future risks for use. Homework is an ongoing part of the treatment process. A major caveat is to not create a plan that is so complex or has so many goals initially that it cannot successfully be carried out. Along with avoiding high-risk situations, every step in the plan should be one over which the service user has input and control (Myers et al., 2005). In CRA, supportiveness, empathy, and a genuine caring attitude are critical to establishing the therapeutic alliance with the service user. CRA requires the counsellor to be directive, energetic, and engaging, encouraging the service user and pointing out all the successes in the change process, regardless of how small they may seem initially (Myers & Miller, 2001; Roozen et al., 2010).

AVERSION THERAPY

Aversion therapy, the least favoured form of behavioural therapy, was among the earliest approaches to treating addiction. Aversion therapy induces a state of mind in which attention to an object is coupled with repugnance and a desire to turn away from it. Historically, it has been produced by drugs or electric shock, though the most recent format uses verbal conditioning, forming a new relationship between an aversive stimulus and an undesirable response through the use of words. On presentation of the stimuli, either alcohol or another drug, the response is punished. When the response becomes infrequent or disappears, the repugnant stimuli are reduced or terminated.

The common goal of aversion therapies is to alter the individual's attraction to a drug. Through counter-conditioning procedures, the substance being misused is paired with any of a variety of unpleasant experiences. If the conditioning is successful, the individual shows an automatic negative response when later exposed to the drug alone, much like the protagonist in Stanley Kubrick's *Clockwork Orange*. Aversion therapies should not be confused with pharmacological interventions where the intended effects rest not on conditioning by repeated aversive pairings but rather on suppression of fear of immediate aversive consequences. Aversion therapy is a form of classical (Pavlovian) conditioning procedure.

Four variants of aversion therapy appear in the literature. The oldest form of aversion is a procedure that typically paired either alcohol or heroin with the experience of nausea. With alcohol, several sessions are typically held where nausea is induced, usually through injection or oral consumption of a noxious substance while the individual drinks their favourite alcoholic beverage. The nausea effects may linger for several hours after the "intervention." Apnea was a short-lived experiment in aversion therapy during the 1960s. In the procedure the aversive stimulus was an injection of succinylcholine, which induced total paralysis of movement and breathing for an interval of up to 60 seconds. During this interval, alcohol was placed on the lips of the paralyzed patient. If the patient did not begin breathing after 60 seconds, they were ventilated. Not surprisingly, individuals reacted quite negatively to the bottle containing alcohol after the trial. However, in one reported study, 17 of 23 males were again drinking regularly less than eight months after their last apnea session. Ethical factors, the severe nature of this treatment, and the lack of positive results quickly discouraged its application (Elkins, 1975).

Electric shock was also first employed in attempting to treat alcohol-dependent persons during the late 1960s. In one common procedure, individuals received several sessions of electric shock, usually applied to the forearm, paired with the smelling or tasting of alcoholic beverages. At the direction of the therapist, service users poured themselves a drink and then tasted it without swallowing. Shocks were applied randomly throughout the process. Sessions ran over a 10-day period and lasted from 20 to 45 minutes, depending on the person's level of alcohol misuse (Jackson & Smith, 1978). Outcome studies painted a confusing picture, as some noted strong and significant effects, while others found virtually no long-term benefit of this technique. The apparent lack of long-term success with this procedure led a young researcher named Alan Marlatt to one of the most important addiction insights of the late 20th century: the need for reoccurrence prevention training as integral to maintaining sobriety (Marlatt, 1973; Marlatt & George, 1984).

The newest addition to the repertoire of aversion techniques is covert sensitization. This technique occurred entirely in the person's imagination and entailed pairing aversive scenes with drug-use imagery. Covert sensitization using nausea scenes operates by establishing a conditioned aversion response. The procedure is related to that used in hypnosis.

The fact that aversion techniques, especially chemical aversion, produce substantially superior outcomes with older subjects who were of higher socio-economic status suggests that the principal benefits of these techniques may relate to factors other than classical aversive conditioning, including motivation, social stability, and a stable support system. In general, aversive conditioning procedures appear to be effective largely with those individuals who have a relatively good prognosis at the outset. However, because of the relatively poor long-term effectiveness of aversion techniques, it is difficult to justify their use, especially in light of their highly invasive nature. Reduction of consumption rather than total abstinence is a common observation following aversion therapies, and thus the success of these approaches would not be well reflected if complete abstinence were used as the primary criterion of success (Miller & Hester, 1986a).

CHAPTER 21

Harm Reduction

Harm reduction is a form of treatment that has multiple possible successful outcomes, one of which is the drug user becoming abstinent. At the 2001 meeting of Canadian provincial and federal health ministers, which formally established a new drug strategy for Canada, harm reduction was recognized as an important and distinct component of the addiction treatment continuum (Health Canada, 2001). Harm reduction is so distinct that not only is it a way to intervene to aid those with addiction issues, it is also officially one of the four pillars of Canada's drug plan and involves any strategy or behaviour that individuals use to reduce the potential harm that may exist for them (Figure 21.1). In the

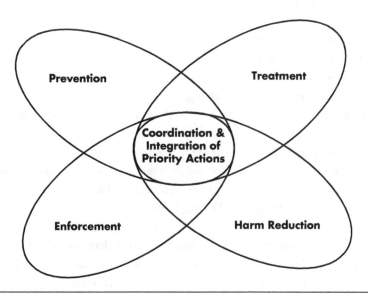

Figure 21.1: Canada's Four Pillar Model

Source: MacPherson & Rowly (2001).

field of addiction, this translates into a range of options from safer drug use techniques, to using licit rather than illicit drugs where the quality and purity of the product is better known, to decreasing either the amount of drugs administered or the frequency of administrations or both, to moving toward abstinence. Specific programming initiatives include needle exchange programs, methadone/Suboxone maintenance and treatment, heroin-assisted treatment (HAT), supervised consumption sites, and controlled drinking. While initiatives such as controlled drinking, designated drivers, contracts for life, and methadone treatment have been available for decades, it was the emergence of AIDS and HIV that formally brought harm-reduction initiatives to the forefront of the addiction field and shifted the focus more toward strategies relating to decreasing injection drug use (Collin, 2006; Thomas, 2005).

Harm reduction is more than just a treatment option, as it relates to "any policy directed toward reducing or containing adverse health, social and economic consequences of alcohol, other drug use and gambling without necessarily requiring a reduction in consumption or abstinence from substance use or gambling strategy or behaviour that an individual uses in their life to reduce the drug related harm which may exist for them in their life" (Alberta Alcohol and Drug Abuse Commission, 2001, p. 3). By adopting a harm-reduction perspective, we are obligated to also adopt a new philosophy toward users of drugs, including those who primarily use illicit drugs. While historically substance misusers have been judged through a moral model lens, and intervened with primarily using the criminal justice system, harm reduction offers a much different perspective. It rejects the belief that increasing law enforcement is the optimal approach to decreasing drug misuse. Instead, this philosophy embraces the following beliefs:

- All humans have intrinsic value.
- All humans have the right to comprehensive non-judgmental medical and social services.
- Licit and illicit drugs are neither good nor bad.
- Psychoactive drug users are sufficiently competent to make choices regarding their use of drugs.
- Outcomes are in the hands of the individual.
- Options are provided in a non-judgmental, non-coercive manner. Harm reduction practitioners acknowledge the significance of any positive change that individuals make in their lives (Hagan, 1999).

Harm-reduction interventions are facilitative rather than coercive, grounded in the needs of individuals. Small gains are viewed as success, just as abstinence is, for in the process of change, individuals are much more likely to take many small steps rather than one or two huge leaps. Harm reduction begins with the most feasible changes to keep people healthy as they slowly move toward abstinence, knowing that many will never reach that end goal. However, keeping people alive and preventing irreparable damage is regarded as the most urgent priority. International health bodies, including the World Health Organization and the Joint United Nations Programme on HIV/AIDS (UNAIDS), recommend harm-reduction programs as best practices and as crucial for reducing HIV infection among those who inject drugs.

NEEDLE-EXCHANGE PROGRAMS

Needle-exchange programs allow injection drug users (IDUs) to trade used syringes for new, sterile ones and related injection works. In recent years, many of these fixed and mobile outreach programs have also begun to offer pipes and straws for cocaine and methamphetamine use as well. Needle exchange is a harm-reduction strategy that arose as a direct result of the blood-borne infections of HIV, hepatitis C (HCV), and hepatitis B (HBV), which were unintended outcomes of injection drug use. However, this is not only a form of intervention for IDUs but is also part of a broader public health model. Funding for these initiatives is intended to limit the transfer of these diseases into the general population. Needle-exchange programs have been empirically demonstrated to reduce the spread of blood-borne infections and also to create supportive relationships between IDUs and the health and social services systems, often for the first time in their lives (Hankins, 1998; Hyshka et al., 2012; Stimson, 1995, Vertefeuille et al., 2000).

METHADONE AND SUBOXONE TREATMENT AND MAINTENANCE

Both subjective and health-related quality of life are relatively poor among opioid-dependent individuals compared with the general population, and also when compared to people with other medical illnesses (De Maeyer et al., 2010). Methadone, a synthetic opioid analgesic with a long half-life (Chapter 9), was first widely used as a drug substitute (Chapter 16) for those dependent on heroin in the 1960s. Most programs were of limited duration, and it was discovered that once users were weaned off methadone, many returned to heroin use. Methadone produces morphine-like actions and cross-tolerance but does not produce significant euphoria. As it is administered orally, its use as a drug substitute eliminates the associated risks IDUs have when injecting heroin, Oxycontin, fentanyl, and other opioids. However, methadone is not without its limits, as tolerance and withdrawal do occur, and with extended use, addiction does arise to this psychoactive drug. Both methadone maintenance (MM) and methadone treatment (MT) consist of an individual drinking a sufficient dose of methadone on a daily basis to eliminate withdrawal symptoms from other opioids. The basic premise for opioid substitution therapy is that methadone administered daily by mouth is effective in the suppression of withdrawal symptoms and in the reduction of the use of illicit opioids. MM involves determining a correct dose for each individual and providing regular health care and treatment for other addiction issues.

MT programs also entail the provision of counselling and support, mental health services, health promotion, disease prevention and education, along with advocacy and linkages to community-based supports and services, such as housing. Unfortunately, for many individuals living with opioid addiction, the damage that has occurred to their bodies as a result of prolonged drug use may not allow them to ever withdraw completely from methadone (Csiernik, Rowe et al., 2017).

Opioid-dependent individuals who receive treatment with methadone or who enter a MM program do use fewer illicit drugs (not only heroin), have better health than those not in a program, access health care more readily, develop a greater sense of wellness, have higher rates of employment and lower rates of social assistance, report better interpersonal relationships, including parenting and child rearing, and have overall better social functioning. As with needle-exchange programs, the benefits of both MM and MT extend to the general community by reducing the spread of infectious diseases (Methadone Strategy Working Group, 2001; Sun et al., 2015). Methadone substitution programs also have a positive effect on quality of life, especially during the first months of treatment, as the crisis or symptoms that precipitated it recede. Initial gains tend to be maintained over time, though they do typically fall back unless the underlying reasons for drug use are addressed. Drug use is not always the reason that people seek treatment, but rather as a result of problems they experience in other life domains (De Maeyer et al., 2010).

Suboxone has become an alternative to methadone as a drug substitution option for those addicted to opioids. Suboxone is an opioid agonist-antagonist composed of the partial μ-opioid receptor agonist buprenorphine, in combination with the opioid antagonist naloxone (Narcan) in a 4:1 ratio. When this combination drug is taken sublingually, it takes from 2 to 10 minutes to dissolve. When administered this way, the naloxone exerts no clinically significant effect, leaving only the opioid agonist effects of buprenorphine. However, when buprenorphine is administered in combination with naloxone through any form of injection, the opioid antagonism of naloxone causes the user to go into withdrawal immediately. This overwhelmingly negative physical response greatly reduces the misuse potential of the compound drug (Orman & Keating, 2009). Suboxone has been found to be an effective maintenance therapy for opioid dependence when administered orally and has generally similar efficacy to methadone, even when it is administered less often (Handford et al., 2011). Additionally, Suboxone users reported more clarity of thinking, greater confidence, and lower stigma compared to those using methadone (Tanner et al., 2011). A recent study in the United Kingdom found that Suboxone users suffered fewer poisonings and had a lower risk of mortality than did methadone users, though on average the period of usage was shorter for Suboxone than for methadone (Hickman et al., 2018). The major limitation of Suboxone is that it is approximately three times more expensive than methadone per dose.

The evolution and growing prominence of opioid maintenance programs, rather than opioid treatment programs, raises the troubling question of who is being helped the most: the user who remains addicted to a psychoactive drug, the general public, or those manufacturing, prescribing, and distributing this socially acceptable opioid drug?

It is acknowledged that longer treatment periods are associated with improved outcomes, including reduced use of other opioids and reduced criminal activity. Grella and Lovinger (2011) reported that 40 percent of methadone users achieved stable remission after five to eight years, with one year being considered the minimum to achieve better and sustained benefits. A 2010 economic study completed in Ontario found that the average daily cost of treatment was only $15.48 CAD per day, which consisted of physician billing (9.8 percent), pharmacy costs (39.8 percent), and urine toxicology screens (46.7 percent), with the methadone itself costing only $0.59 per day. On average, the annual cost is $5,651 or the equivalent of an annual three-week hospital stay (Zaric et al., 2012). This is eight times less than the average health, social, and criminal costs associated with an untreated person using illicit opioids, which was estimated to be $44,600 CAD per year (Health Canada, 2008). However, over the course of the next 35 years, with inflation factored in, the cost of keeping each person legally addicted in a methadone maintenance program will total over $250,000. If Suboxone continues to cost three times more than methadone, the equivalent Suboxone maintenance program would cost three-quarters of a million dollars per person. This long-term cost could be substantially offset if counselling were incorporated throughout the process to help individuals achieve abstinence. Even though the process of opioid treatment often takes two to four years, it is of much shorter duration and is much less costly, both economically and personally, than the 3.5 decades currently spent regularly ingesting an addictive substance. However, this is not a new idea: as early as 1993, research indicated that methadone alone, even in substantial doses, was only effective for a minority of program participants, though even with basic short-term counselling and service user engagement on an ongoing basis, major improvements in functioning and outcomes arose (McLellan et al., 1993).

HEROIN-ASSISTED TREATMENT (HAT)

Some individuals do not respond well to methadone or Suboxone. These drug substitutes may not ease the physical or psychological pain of withdrawal, or negate the craving, or an individual may have a negative reaction to their synthetic nature. Historically, these individuals either endured a cold turkey withdrawal or more typically went back to using street opioids. By returning to use, they again put themselves at risk for life-threatening health issues, including drug overdose, blood-borne viral infections, and endocarditis, as well as the violence that accompanies illicit drug transactions. One controversial alternative is heroin-assisted treatment (HAT). Under a HAT protocol, street opioid users are prescribed pharmaceutical quality heroin, which is injected in safe, clean specialized medical clinics. Service users typically attend up to two to three times per day to self-inject their dose of heroin. Average heroin dosage ranges from 400 and 600 mg/day, with supervised consumption being administered on average at around 150 to 300 mg/dose. Clinical staff can also supplement this further with a small 20 mg to 60 mg oral methadone dose as needed. Methadone administration is prevalent as a means to prevent withdrawal between the administrations of heroin. The heroin-assisted programs are usually supported by access to psychological support in the form of counseling and group work, as well as general social welfare support from social services (Hill, 2016).

In 2005, a randomized controlled trial was conducted in Vancouver and Montreal to evaluate the feasibility and effectiveness of HAT in Canada. The results showed that participants were less likely to use street drugs than those in a MM program, and they were also less likely to engage in criminal activity, increasing the likelihood of an eventual move toward abstinence (Nosyk et al., 2010). A follow-up study compared prescription heroin with hydromorphone. It too reported superior outcomes among those using the prescription heroin, which further reinforced earlier findings from studies in the United Kingdom, Germany, the Netherlands, and Switzerland (Ferri et al., 2011). The results of the two Canadian studies led to a recommendation by Health Canada to allow prescription heroin use among individuals who could not successfully use methadone. However, Conservative Health Minister Rona Ambrose objected to Health Canada's approval and introduced regulations to make prescribing the drug outside clinical trials illegal. In turn, Supreme Court Chief Justice Christopher Hinkson ruled against the then minister of health, stating that risks associated with the severe heroin addiction of the 202 follow-up study participants would be reduced under this specialized medical program. However, the court ruling allowed only for the study's initial participants to continue to receive the pharmaceutical-grade drug and sterilized supplies with which to inject it (Woo, 2014). Despite decades of national and international research indicating the economic and health utility of various harm-reduction initiatives, the Stephen Harper government continued to oppose programs that offered choices to Canadian citizens with addiction issues. However, with the election of the Trudeau Liberals in 2015, Health Minister Ginette Petitpas Taylor indicated that removing barriers to treatment was crucial in dealing with the opioid crisis affecting Canada and that legal changes would be made to allow some individuals to access prescribed heroin from approved community-based clinics.

The overall value of heroin-assisted treatment remains inconclusive, in part due to a lack of multiple outcomes studies. Existing research suggests that the majority of dependent users seeking treatment can use either methadone or Suboxone and these options should be offered first. However, heroin-assisted treatment can be considered as a secondary option for those who fail to make significant progress with the standard options. Research that has been completed on heroin-assisted treatment programs has found that program participants demonstrated improved:

- use of structured drug treatment programs;
- physical and psychological health outcomes;
- social integration, including improved capacity for work, better living conditions, and debt management; and
- pro-social behaviours highlighted by a significant reduction in offending-related activity (Hill, 2016).

SUPERVISED CONSUMPTION SITES (SCS)

Supervised consumption sites (SCS) began as supervised injection sites (SIS) in Canada, clinics that were designed to provide IDUs with clean single-use needles and sterilized "works" to inject their drugs safely. SCS provide individuals with a healthier environment in which to inject, inhale, and intranasally or orally consume drugs, while also providing related health and social services, all in one location. While the first Canadian supervised consumption site opened in Lethbridge, Alberta, in 2017, Switzerland, Germany, and the Netherlands adopted the concept of supervised injection rooms during the 1970s, again as a general public health initiative. Since then, the strategy has been demonstrated to decrease new HIV and HCV infections and reduce the number of overdose related deaths while providing access to primary and emergency health care for a traditionally oppressed population. After the opening of a new site, after the public backlash has subsided, there is generally a decrease in public nuisance issues related to drug use, including public injecting, discarded syringes, and injection-related litter (Rowe & Rapp, 2017).

Supervised consumption sites offer a safe place for drug-dependent individuals to administer drugs under the supervision of trained multidisciplinary health and social services staff who can provide education regarding safe practices, as well as respond appropriately in the event of an overdose. Each SCS varies in the way it operates. However, in general, individuals bring pre-obtained drugs to the site, are provided with sterile equipment to use, and consume their drugs with nurses and other trained staff nearby. Typically, needles, syringes, candles, sterile water, paper towels, cotton balls, cookers/spoons, ties, alcohol swabs, filters, ascorbic acid, and bandages are available in the injection-specific areas. SCS allow substance users to have their privacy while also offering the comfort of knowing that trained medical staff are available to respond in case of an emergency. SCS do not allow the sharing of drugs or equipment and prohibit assisted injection. SCS leads to a reduction in syringe sharing among users, which also reduces the spread of diseases and infections. It is critical to note how SCS differ markedly from illegal shooting galleries operating in many cities, where drug users pay a small fee for a few minutes in a private or semi-private room. The latter are profit-motivated, may be littered with trash and/or needles, violent, controlled by drug dealers, allow participants to share dirty needles, and show little regard for the user's health and safety. In contrast, SCS attempt to protect and promote the health of drug users by employing a non-judgmental, person-centred approach rooted in a harm-reduction philosophy (Rowe & Rapp, 2017).

A major social and community issue regarding SCS is the misconception that these sites bring with them an increase in drug dealing, using, and other crimes to the neighbourhood in which they are located. Interestingly, the risk of crime in a neighbourhood is more causally linked to the location of a convenience store than a SCS or any other type of harm-reduction program. The benefits of SCS on public drug use have not come at the cost of increases in criminal activity (Boyd et al., 2012). In addition, SCS can actually enhance public order through a decrease in public drug use, and the introduction of SCS has led to an increase in addiction treatment and detoxification service use in most communities where they have been established, as well as increased use of social and health services. There is also no evidence to suggest that the presence of SCS leads to more individuals initiating injection drug use or that using SCS increases reoccurrence rates.

Initial concerns of residents regarding SCS primarily stem from a fear of the unknown, a feeling of uncertainty, and a lack of knowledge regarding SCS, such as what they are and how they operate, rather than actual events or evidence. As with other forms of harm reduction, SCS benefit a hard-to-reach population by offering services with minimal barriers to access and avoidance of interactions with the criminal justice system. Contact with these hard-to-reach persons can lead to important social and health referrals and treatment opportunities, which ultimately result in positive social and community opportunities. The introduction of SCS has contributed to individual improvements in health, social functioning, and stabilization along with a decreased number of overdoses and premature deaths (Coppel, 2015; Kennedy et al., 2019; Wood, Kerr et al., 2004a, 2004b; Wood, Tyndall et al., 2006). Further, in a qualitative study of Danish users of a newly opened supervised injection facility, respondents indicated that they felt less rushed and less stressed while using, engaged in less public injecting, and were no longer sharing needles as a result of being able to access the agency (Kinnard et al., 2014).

CONTROLLED DRINKING

In 1973, Americans Sobell and Sobell introduced a highly controversial concept to the addiction field: controlled drinking. Seventy alcohol-dependent men in an in-patient program were assigned either to experimental or control groups. Two experimental groups received individual counselling and behaviour therapy, with one group having abstinence as their outcome and the second, a goal of controlling their alcohol consumption. The two control groups received standard treatment, with one group having an outcome goal of abstinence while the goal of the second group was to control their drinking. At both six-month and one-year follow-ups, the treatment groups were doing better than the control groups but there was no significant difference in the outcome measures between the two experimental groups. This led to the idea that controlled drinking was as effective as abstinence in treating alcohol addiction, which in turn brought waves of protest from Alcoholics Anonymous proponents, who believed it sent a message to its members that it was permissible to drink again. In 1974, Sobell and Sobell followed up their initial contentious study with an article claiming that "more than 600 total studies ... have reported that some alcoholic individuals have successfully resumed some type of non-problematic moderate drinking" (p. 10).

This furor was intensified when a study by Armor, Polich, and Stambul (1978) indicated equivalent reoccurrence rates between those following a program of abstinence compared with those following a regiment of controlled drinking. Pendery, Maltzman, and West (1982) further heightened the controversy with a retrospective review of Sobell and Sobell's study participants. They found that many members of the original controlled drinking group had returned to heavy drinking, with four having died due to alcohol-related causes. These authors, proponents of the abstinence approach, used their study to claim controlled drinking had no merit. However, what Pendery, Maltzman, and West failed to do was conduct a follow-up with the control groups to determine if in fact controlled drinking provided better outcomes than the traditional treatment.

Controlled drinking is an adapted behavioural technique with a specific defined goal. When the view of alcoholism broadened to incorporate the concepts of alcohol dependence, alcohol misuse, and alcohol-related disabilities, a wider range of treatment goals began to be considered. For those persons experiencing low levels of alcohol misuse, a treatment goal of controlled drinking can potentially be recommended. The assessment of the individual's level of alcohol dependence is necessary to assist in the selection of a goal of either controlled drinking or total abstinence. As controlled drinking is a component of the behaviourist school of treatment, it follows that training in drinking skills is viewed as a learned response that has short-term effectiveness for the drinker in specific situations, particularly when the individual lacks effective non-drinking responses. Thus, drinking skills training is used with alcohol misusers to teach them to drink in a non-abusive manner as an alternative to abstinence, and usually forms part of a more broad-based treatment program. Matching for controlled drinking is targeted at individuals with a lack of control rather than a loss of control (Donovan & O'Leary, 1979; Glatt, 1980; Miller & Hester, 1986a).

The first step in controlled drinking is determining whether an individual is misusing alcohol or is alcohol dependent. This is accomplished by first imposing a two- to three-week period of abstinence on a potential program participant. If the person can go without drinking, the individual is moved into the next phase of the controlled drinking program. Those who cannot abstain during this baseline period generally do not qualify for this treatment option. In the program itself, participants are provided with a set of goals and rules to guide them in controlling their alcohol intake. A common drinking goal of a set number of standard drinks per week is established, with numerous limitations. For a young healthy male approximately 1.8 m tall and 81 kg, the following regimen might be applied:

- no more than two standard drinks per day (one for women)
- no more than one drink per hour
- sip drinks and avoid carbonated beverages
- drink only on a full stomach
- two days per week must be set aside where no alcohol is consumed
- limit weekly intake to 14 standard drinks per week for men (seven for women)

Controlled drinking is a specific type of behavioural self-control training, requiring individuals to implement their own treatment. The primary advantage of these procedures is that they can maximize the generalization of treatment effects during and after treatment. The main problem with such techniques, however, is that they are likely to be feasible with only highly motivated individuals. Self-management programs generally consist of behavioural strategies, such as the following:

- self-monitoring
- goal setting
- specific changes in drug-using behaviour
- rewards for goal attainment
- functional analysis of drug-using situations
- learning alternative coping skills (Hester et al., 1990)

Low-risk or reduced drinking is achievable for some individuals with lower dependence severity, less baseline drinking, fewer negative mood symptoms, and fewer heavy drinkers in their social networks. Reduced drinking may also be a viable alternative for those who do not have alcohol-related physical damage, and who have not experienced any serious personal, financial, legal, or employment problems as a result of their drinking. Abstinence does not have to be the only treatment goal (Witkiewitz, 2017). However, controlled drinking training is not an alternative for those who are physically and psychologically dependent on alcohol or on any other psychoactive substance.

For several decades now, there has been a move to include a "warm turkey" approach to addiction treatment. This is a middle-ground tactic for moving toward abstinence using a controlled drinking philosophy. The 1996 National Institute on Alcohol Abuse and Alcoholism (NIAAA) instituted a program simply called "How to Cut Down on Your Drinking." It is a basic three-step approach, accompanied by alternatives to drinking. The NIAAA's first step is to have someone considering reducing their alcohol intake to write down the reasons to cut down or stop. The second step is to set the drinking goal: one standard drink per day for women and a maximum of two for men. It is recommended that the person write down the goal and place it in a conspicuous spot so that the person is regularly reminded of the goal. The third step is to keep a weekly drinking diary that lists the day, the number of drinks consumed, the type of drink, and where it was consumed. In closing, advocates of this method of intervention advise those considering modifying their drinking pattern to not keep much alcohol at home, drink slowly when they choose to drink, try to abstain for a week or two, learn to say no to a drink, stay otherwise active, and seek additional social supports to stay focused.

CHAPTER 22

The Foundations of Contemporary Addiction Counselling: The Transtheoretical Model of Change and Motivational Interviewing

THE TRANSTHEORETICAL MODEL OF CHANGE

Prochaska and DiClemente (1982) revolutionized thinking regarding addiction treatment with their integrative model of intentional change, based on their original work with tobacco smokers who stopped without any formal or self-help assistance. They took the idea of motivation as being a characteristic exclusively of service users and made it into an active counselling skill. Rather than being located exclusively within the individual with an addiction issue, they argued that motivation was an interpersonal, interactional process within which the probability existed for behaviours to occur that led to positive outcomes. Numerous studies have identified service user motivation as having a substantial positive effect on program retention and individual outcomes (Heather et al., 2009; Nidecker et al., 2008; Prochaska, 2008). Prochaska and DiClemente identified six specific steps necessary for any type of radical change to occur, which represented a natural process of change that could be adapted by counsellors to assist anyone (Figure 22.1).

The idea that drug use was a steady downward track that, with abstinence, became a steady upward track (see Figure 5.1) was replaced with the spiral model of change (Figure 22.2). For Prochaska and DiClemente, change unfolded through a series of stages. This perspective provides a more realistic representation of the change process, not only for drug use but for any behaviour. The spiral model of change demonstrates that there can be dramatic positive change interspersed with setbacks, not necessarily reoccurrences but rather periods of time when the change process becomes more difficult and counselling for the service user becomes tedious. However, further advances are possible if the counsellor continues to support and work with the service user and if both partners in the process are patient and diligent. The Transtheoretical Model of Change (TTM) is divided into six distinct stages: pre-contemplation, contemplation, preparation, action, maintenance/adaptation, and evaluation/termination.

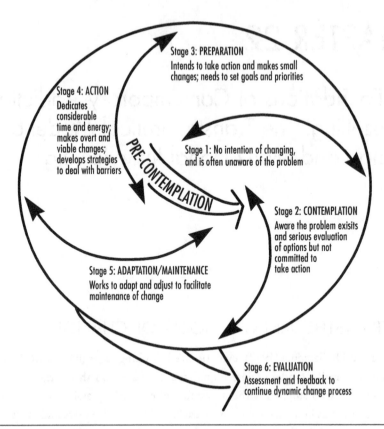

Figure 22.1: The Stages of the Transtheoretical Model of Change

Source: Addiction Studies Institute (2010).

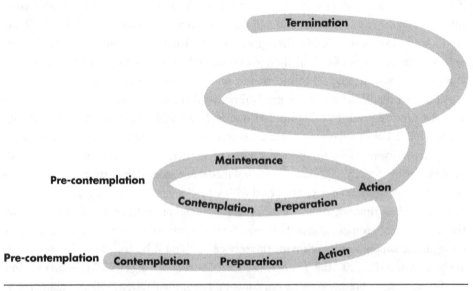

Figure 22.2: The Spiral Process of Change

Source: Adapted from Lalazaryan & Zare-Farashbandi (2014).

Pre-contemplation (Not Ready)

In the first stage of the model, it is recognized that an individual will resist change and typically has no intention of altering behaviour in the near future; the person does not recognize that any problem exists. This idea had historically been called denial. Critical to the entire premise of the Transtheoretical Model of Change was the replacement of the longstanding idea that service users were in denial regarding their addiction with the concept of pre-contemplation. Prochaska and DiClimente (1982) reconceptualized the idea of denial, framing it so that service users are not viewed as wilfully deceiving themselves and, in the process, destroying themselves or their families. Rather, these individuals were truly unaware of the impact of their behaviour on those around them. People with substance use disorders are often ambivalent about changing their harmful behaviour. They may continue their drug use because they are attracted to a particular lifestyle or wish to be included in a particular peer group, or simply to cope with life's daily stresses. When the destructive effects of their behaviour become obvious, they are faced with giving up many of the people, places, and things they have come to enjoy and rely on, and with which they may strongly identify. Without a clear view of other options, these individuals may be reluctant to change. A considerable effort is thus required not only by individuals with a substance use disorder, but by their family members, friends, and helping professionals, to become willing to make a commitment to change.

In the pre-contemplation stage, service users are not searching for solutions or looking to change, as they typically do not recognize the nature or severity of their substance misuse. Their drug use has become so normalized, so much a part of their everyday lives, that it is not viewed as a problem. Rather, it is a part of who they are. In this model, individuals who may well be demoralized and ill are assisted in gaining insight into their behaviour and situation using facts and information. The counsellor's role is to move a person to a point where they will consider change. Readiness to change is not a service user trait, but a fluctuating product of interpersonal interaction. Pre-contemplation does not entail confrontation or advice. Rather, alliance building is critical, as is the use of cognitive dissonance (Box 22.1). Counsellors assist service users in distinguishing between how they see their circumstances and the reality of their situation. This is accomplished by providing information on the physical consequences of substance use and discussing the history of drug use and its personal and interpersonal consequences. Counsellors need to raise doubts and increase service users' perceptions of the actual risks and problems associated with their drug use (DiClemente, 2007).

Contemplation (Getting Ready)

In the second stage of the model, service users become aware that they are stuck in a situation and must decide whether they wish to change or remain where they are. They are supported in gaining understanding of the consequences of their alcohol or other drug use, but the counsellor does not force them to make a commitment to change. This is the stage where the counsellor must help balance in the service user's mind the delicate equilibrium between the desire to change and the fear of changing and the associated

Box 22.1: Cognitive Dissonance

To be able to fully appreciate and utilize both the Transtheoretical Model of Change and motivational interviewing, it is important to have an understanding of Leon Festinger's (1957) cognitive dissonance theory. Festinger argued that individuals are always striving to obtain a balance or consistency within their cognitions. For Festinger, cognitions not only include our thoughts and beliefs but also our opinions about the environment, about ourselves, and about our actions and behaviours. Consistency occurs when our cognitions align with each other. If a homeostatic balance is not obtained, an individual will experience a state of tension or inconsistency between their opinions, attitudes, beliefs, and actions. This inconsistency places pressure on the individual to reduce this tension, which creates discomfort and motivates individuals to alter their thoughts, bringing their beliefs and perceptions closer together. Festinger labelled this inconsistency *dissonance*, while he used the term *consonance* to describe when a person's thoughts and actions are aligned with each other. Dissonance is a negative emotional state, disturbing to people as it produces a non-conforming internal relationship within a person. This is in contrast with consonance, which exists when there is a fitting relationship between a person's cognitions.

Festinger argued that individuals need to achieve cognitive consonance between what they believe and what they do, as dissonance produces a negative emotional state that is accompanied by autonomic arousal including anxiety and distress. Individuals will work hard to reduce dissonance or avoid situations or information that increases dissonance. This can be done by changing attitudes, by adding a consistent cognition or subtracting an inconsistent one, or by reducing the significance of a dissonant cognition. However, the most common method for reducing dissonance is by changing attitudes to be more consistent with actions or behaviour. Change is dependent on the level of discomfort (dissonance) and benefit, and how resistant these beliefs are to change. The greater the cognitive dissonance individuals experience, the more likely they are to change. It is for this reason that cognitive dissonance is an important tool in the change processes of both the Transtheoretical Model of Change and motivational interviewing.

unknown consequences. Counsellors need to reflect this ambivalence to help service users move forward to the next stage while recognizing and acknowledging the fear associated with change. Ambivalence is a normal response when facing potential change. In many ways, individuals know they need to change and want to change, but at the same time they want to maintain the previous status quo of their lives; any change, even change to benefit oneself, is difficult. Counsellors also need to be aware that some service users will drop out at this highly stressful stage, so there must be a willingness to work with these individuals in the future when they are ready and able to move forward again. This is why the TTM is a spiral rather than a linear model.

During the contemplation stage, counsellors assist service users in weighing the pros and cons of change, while working to aid the service user in tipping the scales toward change by exploring the person's ambivalence and alternatives to the current drug-using behaviour. Discussing reasons for change and the risks of not changing are also important, as is increasing the person's confidence in their ability to change.

Preparation (Ready)

The third stage, preparation, which is also known as the determination stage, is when service users consider changing their drug-using behaviour and anticipate what this future action will entail. However, the counsellor needs to be aware that there may still be much ambivalence to the idea and process of actual change. During the preparation phase, probing, reviewing consequences, and self-evaluation are areas of work with service users. A specific time frame, with a maximum target of one month, is established when the service user agrees to begin changing existing practices and actions. The counsellor needs to support service users as they develop ways to replace what they are about to give up and begin to acquire new skills—such as assertiveness, relaxation, anger control, and problem solving—if they are to make the successful transition to changed behaviour during the next stage, the action phase. The main task of the preparation stage is to identify and resolve barriers to success, including friends and family who may still benefit from the service user's drug-using behaviour, along with activities associated with their drug use. Areas to explore in preparing for success are the consequences for the individual and those around them when change occurs, and what the reactions to the change process will be. Clear goal setting and assisting the service user to develop realistic plans that can be easily implemented with minimal risk of failure are crucial during the preparation stage. This stage involves small steps rather than leaps.

Action (Doing)

In this stage of the TTM, the work and behavioural change begins, with a heavy emphasis on problem solving and problem-solving skills. However, action also entails changing awareness, emotions, self-image, and thinking. Support of positive decisions and positive reinforcement dominate this stage of moving forward by the service user, which can last as little as one day or as long as six months. Emphasis is on the positive: what the service user is doing, rather than what the service user is *not* doing, which is using drugs. Service users need to be reminded that they have reached the mid-point when they are in the action stage, with two steps remaining. Planning for drug use reoccurrence is also a critical aspect of the action stage. This involves identifying and exploring times that may lead to use, such as when faced with unpleasant emotions, physical discomfort, pleasant emotions, urges, cravings, social pressure, or pleasant times socializing with friends, colleagues, or family.

Maintenance/Adaptation (Sticking with It)

Stage five focuses on supporting and consolidating the gains made during the action stage and avoiding brief or longer drug use reoccurrences. The focus is on social skills training at this time of continued change. Another benefit of the TTM is that during the maintenance stage counsellors may draw upon any number of different counselling approaches to support the service user in adapting to not using drugs and in developing new strategies to avoid reoccurrence.

Evaluation/Termination (Solidifying Learning)

The final stage of the Transtheoretical Model of Change sees the service user move beyond problem solving, with a focus on preventing reoccurrence and dealing with the reality of sobriety. During this phase, service users assess their strengths and areas that may be problematic in the future as they develop a reoccurrence-prevention plan that can be undertaken on their own (Hall et al., 2012; Prochaska et al., 1994).

Techniques

A variety of techniques are used in the TTM. Consciousness raising, dramatic relief, and environmental re-evaluation are all critical during both the pre-contemplation and contemplation stages. Consciousness raising involves increasing information to service users about themselves and their problem by using observations, interpretations, feedback, education, reading materials, and challenges to what service users believe they are doing versus what they are actually doing. Dramatic relief entails experiencing and expressing feelings about one's problems and solutions, grieving losses, and partaking in role play to appreciate the impact of the changed behaviour on oneself and others. The intent of this technique is to produce increased emotional experiences followed by reduced affect if appropriate action can be taken. Psychodrama and personal testimonies can also move people forward emotionally. Environmental re-evaluation assesses how the presence or absence of a personal habit affects one's social and physical environment and entails empathy training. It can also increase awareness that one can serve as a positive or negative role model for others. Empathy training is a critical component of this technique.

As a service user moves from contemplation to preparation, self re-evaluation becomes important. Service users need to assess how they think and, even more importantly, feel about themselves with respect to their use of substances and clarify their values, often engaging in corrective emotional experiences. Self re-evaluation combines both cognitive and affective assessments of one's self-image. Value clarification, healthy role models, and imagery are techniques that are used in self re-evaluation. Self-liberation is the crucial step that helps to move a service user from preparation through to the action phase. Individuals choose and commit to change through both their beliefs and actions—it is both the belief that one can change and the enduring commitment to act on that belief.

Here it is vital that the counsellor also believes in the service user's potential and ability to change. Motivation research indicates that people with two options to choose from have a greater commitment to change than do those with only one option; those with three have an even greater commitment, though beyond this there is no further enhancement (Miller & Rose, 2009; Prochaska et al., 1994).

The remaining five tactics are used through both the action and maintenance steps:

1. *Reinforcement management* entails providing consequences for taking steps in a particular direction. While reinforcement management can include the use of punishments, rewarding oneself or being rewarded by others for making changes is far more powerful. Contingency contracts, overt and covert reinforcements, positive self-statements, and group recognition are procedures for increasing reinforcement and the probability that healthier responses will be repeated and maintained. This is similar to the contingency management process that arose from operant conditioning (see Chapter 20).

2. *Helping relationships* involves combining caring, trust, openness, and acceptance, as well as support for the healthy behaviour change. Rapport building, counsellor calls, and buddy systems can be sources of social support, though regardless of the technique employed, being open and trusting about problems with someone who cares will help maintain the change, especially when the service user suffers a setback. The therapeutic alliance that has been established with the service user is key during this part of the process to continue to assist the person moving forward.

3. *Counter-conditioning* involves substituting healthier alternatives for problem drug-using behaviours. Relaxation can counter stress; assertion can counter peer pressure; nicotine replacement can be a substitute for cigarettes. With this technique, the focus is on substituting alternatives for problem behaviours with an emphasis on self-care. Counsellors should consider all three dimensions of addiction—biological, psychological and social—in developing counter-conditioning approaches.

4. *Stimulus control* entails removing cues for drug use and replacing them with prompts for healthier alternatives. Avoidance, changing one's environment, and participating in self-help groups (Chapter 24) can provide stimuli that support change and reduce risks for a return to drug use.

5. *Social liberation* involves increasing engagement in non-drug-related behaviours, progressing emotionally so that the service user considers the needs of others, and becoming involved in broader issues such as policy change. This late-stage technique requires an increase in social opportunities or alternatives, especially for those who are relatively deprived or oppressed. Advocacy, empowerment procedures, and appropriate policies can produce increased opportunities for marginalized individuals and groups (Prochaska et al., 1992; Prochaska & Velicer, 1997).

Table 22.1: Service User Issues and Counsellor Strategies to Employ in the Transtheoretical Model of Change

Stage	Service User Issue	Counsellor Strategy
Pre-contemplation	Nothing needs to change.	Build rapport and trust; increase problem awareness; raise the sense of the importance of the change.
Contemplation	I am considering change.	Acknowledge ambivalence regarding the difficulties associated with change; explore the discrepancy between present behaviour and the service user's personal values and goals; discuss pros and cons of change; talk about ways to experiment with changing behaviour.
Preparation	I am figuring out how to change.	Build confidence; talk about timing of change; provide information, options, and advice; don't rush; work at the individual's pace.
Action	I am working on reaching my goals.	Offer planning assistance; provide support around the change process; develop attainable goals; monitor progress and assist the service user in self-monitoring; help develop plans in co-operation with the client to maintain the changes over time.
Maintenance/ Adaptation	I've made my changes. I need to keep up my changes.	Support and encourage new behaviour; talk about possible trouble spots and develop plans to address triggers that can lead to lapse or relapse.
Evaluation/ Termination	How do I maintain my new behaviour?	Reinforce new skills, new knowledge, and the positive changes produced; review triggers that can lead to lapse; develop strategies on how to return to the new behaviour if a lapse occurs rather than returning to previous behaviours that led to drug use.

Source: Waiters et al. (2007).

Throughout all stages of the TTM, service users are continually asked to weigh the pros and cons of change. This is referred to as decisional balance. Decision making on the part of the service user is not always fully conscious or rational, but by openly discussing options, unrecognized thoughts and feelings can be more judiciously examined and assessed. Critical issues that arise during the change process and techniques to counter them are presented in Table 22.1.

MOTIVATIONAL INTERVIEWING

"What do you make of all of this?"

"Where does this leave you?"

"What do you want to do next?"

Motivation is an interpersonal and interactional process wherein which there ex-
ists the probability of behaviours occurring that are intended to lead to positive
outcomes.
    —William Miller, 1983(b), p. 147

A key question that might have been even better to ask at the beginning of this section
is why don't people change their drug-using behaviour when it becomes evident to them.
There are a variety of possible reasons for this:

- the nature of the necessary change is misunderstood
- change is forced or mandated
- hard work is required to change what you have been doing for a long time
- new skills and knowledge are often required
- changing threatens one's competence
- too many changes are asked for all at once
- the outcome is not viewed as worthwhile
- the goal is not seen as achievable

A tool for counsellors to help them respond to this question was developed by
William Miller: motivational interviewing (MI). MI is a collaborative conversation style
for strengthening a person's own motivation and commitment to change. It is closely
associated with the Transtheoretical Model of Change and is integral to its success.
While developed by William Miller (1983b), MI also draws upon the work of Carl
Rogers. MI is a brief, person-centred, directive method for enhancing intrinsic motivation to change. It explores and resolves service user ambivalence using the ideas of
empathy, attribution, cognitive dissonance, and self-efficacy. People often get stuck, not
because they fail to appreciate the downside of their situation, but because they feel at
least two different ways about it. In MI, motivation is conceptualized not as a personality trait, but as an interpersonal process. The model de-emphasizes labelling, replaces
confrontation with empathy, and places a much greater emphasis on individual responsibility and internal attribution for change. Cognitive dissonance (Box 22.1) is created
by contrasting the individual's ongoing problem behaviour with salient awareness of
the behaviour's negative consequences. Empathic processes, motivation, and objective
assessment feedback are used to channel this dissonance toward a behaviour change,
being cognizant of and avoiding the typical barriers of low self-esteem, low self-efficacy,
and pre-contemplation. MI is a strength-based counselling style in which the counsellor
works with the service user, rather than doing things for or to the person. The focus is
on locating natural motivating issues within a person's life or the person's system. The
counsellor needs to anticipate and respond to a service user's genuine hesitation and
insecurity to engage in a fundamentally life-altering change in behaviour. Simply giving individuals advice to change is typically unrewarding and ineffective. Motivational
interviewing is non-confrontational in nature and acknowledges that creating conflict,

rather than ambivalence, in the therapeutic relationship is counterproductive and is more likely to create resistance than change. MI seeks to increase a service user's awareness of their problematic behaviour, along with unrecognized strengths and opportunities for change (Miller, 1983b; Rosengren & Wagner, 2001).

Motivational interviewing has become an integral aspect of addiction counselling and is a core component of counsellor practice. As such, a series of rules have emerged around it that are discussed below: the four principles, four components, and four attributes of motivational interviewing.

The Four Principles of Motivational Interviewing

The four principles that guide the practice of motivational interviewing are known by the acronym RULE: resist, understand, listen, and empower. First, there is a natural inclination, especially in the addiction field, to be directive, as is practised in confrontation and intervention (see Chapter 18). In practising MI, counsellors need to resist providing suggestions to service users and telling them how to fix their problems. While this may be well-intentioned, it moves the counsellor into the expert role, and takes away the service user's motivation for change. The second principle is understanding the person's motivation to change. This begins by being a curious listener and attempting to elicit the service user's own underlying motivations for change, rather than suggesting reasons for changing. Third, when listening, counsellors should also provide feedback on discrepancies between what the individual wants and how current actions are allowing or not allowing those goals to be achieved. Listening intently is a mandatory aspect of any form of strength-based counselling, and this is no different for MI. Empathy is another key attribute in MI, and it should begin with the counsellor creating an environment where the service user feels heard and can begin to promote positive personal change. The final MI guiding principle is empowerment. While this may seem a standard contemporary practice, in 1983 when MI was first formally proposed, it was a radical change from the mainstream approaches, which promoted humility and giving oneself up to experts and higher powers. While counsellors can provide approaches to change it is the service user who must decide to change and then take action. Empowering service users also involves encouraging and supporting them in their capacity for change (Miller & Rollnick, 2012).

The Four Components of Motivational Interviewing

There are four distinct components to motivational interviewing that are collectively known as PACE: partnership, acceptance, compassion, and evocation.

1. *Partnership* underscores the importance of working in collaboration with service users with the goal of being supportive and persuasive, working with rather than against. Autonomy of the service user is key to the entire process of MI, as is minimizing, as much as possible, power differentials in the therapeutic

relationship. In creating partnerships, the counsellor collaborates with the service user's existing and established knowledge and skills.

2. *Acceptance* is divided into four points:
    (i)   Absolute worth: In creating a relationship with a service user, the counsellor needs to value the inherent worth and potential of the service user.
    (ii) Autonomy and support: Accepting and confirming the service user's irrevocable right to self-determination and choice. This means that the responsibility for change is the service user's, with the counsellor showing respect for their resourcefulness and ability to make choices, including the decision to change.
    (iii) Affirmation: Demonstrating positive behaviours and actions to service users. This involves finding strengths in what the service user has or has not previously done that can assist in the change process.
    (iv) Accurate empathy: The skill of perceiving and reflecting back another's meaning. It is about conveying to service users that you are really trying to understand what's going on with them and what this problem means to them.

3. *Compassion* means working with service users in a non-judgmental, non-blaming, non-shaming way, always striving to be empathic. In being compassionate, the MI counsellor is trying to understand what this problem is like for the service user from their perspective and what it means for the individual. The counsellor acts benevolently to promote the service user's welfare, giving priority to the service user's needs.

4. *Evocation* involves drawing out a service user's own perceptions, goals, and values, which means counsellors using MI believe that the resources and motivation for change already reside within service users. The goal is to elicit the service user's own perspectives and motivation. Thus, the counsellor works to draw knowledge and options from service users rather than imparting information or opinions (Miller & Rollnick, 2002).

The Four Attributes of Motivational Interviewing

Four attributes are specifically stressed in motivational interviewing:

1. *Express empathy*: To be successful in motivational interviewing, a counsellor must be able to readily express empathy. Regardless of which counselling approach is employed, this is a critical helping skill, entailing the ability to feel what the service user feels and see the situation from their perspective. Even more importantly, empathy underscores the counsellor's understanding of the person's motives so that new motivational strategies can be utilized in the future. Empathy with a service user also sets the stage for acceptance of efforts to facilitate change.

Carl Rogers (1959) hypothesized that accurate empathy, congruence, and positive regard are critical therapeutic conditions that create an atmosphere of safety and acceptance in which service users are free to explore and change. These relational factors were predicted in and of themselves to provide the foundation to promote and maintain positive change (Miller, 1983a).

2. *Develop discrepancies*: The service user always needs to take responsibility for finding reasons to change. However, it is crucial for the counsellor to support this process, particularly early on in counselling. A list of the perceived values of drinking or using drugs in the person's life needs to be contrasted with the actual behaviours and outcomes of the drug use. This process, if successful, will unveil some negative insights that the person had not considered or fully recognized, and counsellors need to be in a position to support service users as they discuss who the drug use has led them to become. The change process is predicated on service users' ability to perceive the discrepancy between their present behaviour and the important personal goals and values they hold for themselves. A safe environment is a necessity for service users to be able to openly express the discrepancies and often the shortcomings of their lives. It is critical for the counsellor to distinguish between the service user and the service user's behaviour. Thus, being a person addicted to drugs or a drug user, rather than a drug addict, may appear to be simply semantics, yet it can be critical in helping individuals distinguish between themselves and their use of drugs, which is only one component of who they are.

3. *Roll with resistance*: Ambivalence, the hesitancy to change a well-established behaviour, is a normal state for individuals to experience when they are on the verge of giving up the most important thing in their lives for some uncertain outcome, such as abstinence or a decreased or altered pattern of drug use. Pushing or arguing against resistance is usually quite counterproductive, evoking defensiveness instead of enhancing the therapeutic alliance a counsellor is attempting to create. This, is turn, can further strengthen the service user's existing pattern of behaviour. Thus, a guiding principle of MI is to have the service user, rather than the counsellor, voice the arguments for change. The counsellor needs to avoid arguing with the service user and understand that any new perspectives they have to offer need to be invited by the service user. A service user's resistance to change is simply an indicator that the counsellor has to switch tactics and approach and respond in a different manner. If it is not working, try something else; if it is working, do more of the same.

4. *Support self-efficacy*: Belief in the possibility of change is an incredibly important motivator. Thus, not only must service users believe that they can change, but so must the counsellor (see Figure V.1). Hope, but not false hope, is another critical aspect of this process. The counsellor's belief in the individual's ability to change can become a self-fulfilling prophesy. Counsellors are responsible for finding

factors that motivate a service user to change, but it is the service user who is ultimately responsible for the change process and the speed of that process (Miller & Rollnick, 1991).

Often when a service user is urged or commanded to stop drinking or using drugs, the person is being told to give up the most important aspect of their life—their best friend. As a result, the counsellor should not be surprised by and, in fact, should expect hesitancy from anyone who is being asked to give up what can be their one great love, and perhaps longest and only love. A focus on the reasons to change is irrelevant if the individual is not motivated to work toward achieving an outcome (Rollnick et al., 2008). This has led to the development of the OARS approach in motivational interviewing:

O—Ask open-ended questions, allowing the service user to guide the conversation and do most of the talking. This allows you to assess what the person cares about, and the values and goals that can be employed in creating motivation to change.

A—Make affirmations. This is a strength-based approach where you compliment the service user on behaviours they may not appreciate as strengths, and indicate appreciation for the efforts made to change behaviour, including attending the counselling session. This process helps in building rapport and validates the service user taking the first step in the change process.

R—Use reflections. The practice of MI has evolved to incorporate asking open-ended questions, followed by two or three reflections, rephrasing statements to capture implicit meaning, and, just as important, the affective component of the service user's responses. This can aid in amplifying beginning desires for change.

S—Summarize. During initial conversations, as well as throughout the entire counselling process, links, discussions, and check-ins with service users ensure mutual understanding of the discussion and aid in underscoring discrepancies in meaning. This active form of listening also enhances trust and the therapeutic relationship (Hall et al., 2012).

Behaviour change through the use of MI is promoted by supporting individuals in verbalizing arguments for change, the very simple cognitive concept of "change talk" (Table 22.2). Encouraging change talk allows service users to openly discuss the new idea and thus think in a new way that is different from how they thought while misusing drugs. In contrast, "sustain talk," which is typically the conversation that active drug users and drug seekers engage in, favours the status quo and not changing. Proficient use of the techniques of MI will increase service users' in-session change talk and decrease sustain talk, which, in turn, is correlated with the likelihood of changing drug-using behaviours. One of the most important themes of positive self-talk, in terms of predicting positive behaviour change, is the strength and frequency of commitment language. The strength of expressed desire, ability, reasons, and need for change all positively relate to the degree

Table 22.2: Examples of Change Talk

Change Talk Options	Questions to Create Change Talk	Example of Change Talk
Disadvantages of the status quo	What worries you about your relationship with your children? What difficulties have resulted from your cannabis use? In what way does your health concern you?	I'm worried that if I don't cut down on my drug use I may lose my job.
Advantages of change	What would you like your grades to be like? What are the advantages of reducing your use of alcohol? What would be different in your life if you smoked less weed?	If I improved my grades I would be less guilty of all the money my parents are spending on me to be away at school.
Optimism for change	When have you made a significant change in your life before? How did you do it? What strengths do you have that would help you make a change?	I did stop drinking every weekend my first year at school and I felt way better. It wasn't easy and I lost a couple of people who I thought were friends, but I did have more money at the end of the year in my bank account.

Sources: Miller & Rollnick (2002, 2004).

of commitment to change and the ability to move into a stage of contemplation and action within the TTM. Increasing commitment language during counselling sessions is also associated with moving toward abstinence or less frequent use of drugs. However, commitment language that begins high and then decreases or plateaus early in the counselling process is not as strong an indicator of a person's commitment to change as is a slow build-up over time (Miller & Rose, 2009). In contrast to change talk are disengagement traps, approaches that negate the value of MI (Table 22.3).

There are four distinct processes associated with motivational interviewing that incorporate the concepts of OARS and change talk:

1. *Engaging*: Establish a mutually trusting and respectful helping relationship.
2. *Focusing*: Also called the "what" phase. It entails clarifying a particular goal or direction for change and also exploring the ambivalence to change.
3. *Evoking*: The "why" stage of the MI process. During this stage, the counsellor assists service users to find, nurture, and implement their own reasons to change.
4. *Planning*: A formal component of the MI process, in this stage the counsellor helps the service user to develop a specific change plan that the service user is willing and able to implement.

Table 22.3: Examples of Disengagement Traps

Assessment trap	When you begin and focus only on information gathering rather than exploring the service user's motivation for change.
Question and answer trap	Asking too many questions and not letting the service user lead the discussion.
Expert trap	Assuming and communicating that you have the best answers to resolve the service user's challenges.
Premature focus trap	Focusing the discussion before fully engaging with the service user.
Labelling trap	Defining the service user through a label.
Blaming trap	When the discussion shifts to blaming or finding faults with others rather than on the change process.
Chat trap	Engaging in small talk that is not action orientated.

Sources: Miller & Rollnick (2004, 2012).

In the MI counselling process, you are always looking to catch the service users doing something right and positively reinforce it—shamelessly if need be. Look for strengths at all times and recognize even small steps that illustrate their ability to change. Affirm their hard work and perseverance through the process, ask them to recount their most successful efforts and also their most difficult, and genuinely praise their success. Summarize their progress and look for further evidence that change is possible while still acknowledging, but not dwelling on, difficulties that service users have with the new learning they are experiencing (Miller, 1983b; Miller & Rollnick, 2002; Moyers et al., 2005).

Motivational interviewing is not merely a series of techniques or micro-behaviours linked together. Rather, it is a distinct philosophy on how service users are viewed and how the process of change is conceptualized. It entails both a relational component, focused on empathy and interpersonal interaction, and a technical component, centred on developing change talk and implementing ideas generated by the service user. This aligns with the knowledge that how we practise is critical to successful service user outcomes (Miller & Rose, 2009). Clinicians who are the most successful in producing change are those who capture the spirit of the intent of motivational interviewing, as well as being adept at the various specific skills. Decreased drug use as a result of using MI has occurred when counsellors demonstrate acceptance, make more comments consistent with a motivational approach, and elaborate and expand on service users' comments rather than simply reflecting them back or asking more questions (Jensen et al., 2011). All counsellors studied who were using MI were found to be able to assist already motivated service users to decrease their psychoactive drug use, while those who applied the principles in a consistent manner were also able to assist those who were much more ambivalent about their drug use, who were initially much less motivated to change, and who openly expressed more doubts. A counsellor's belief in the individual's ability to change is crucial to the success of MI, as is the ability to engage the person in the change process (Gaume et al., 2009). Outcome evaluations have consistently demonstrated that motivational interviewing is an effective approach that positively contributes to counselling efforts, though its utility is still dependent on the counsellor's ability to engage the service user (Betrand et al., 2015; Britt et al., 2004; Lundah et al., 2010; Satre et al., 2016; Shepard et al., 2016; Vasilaki et al., 2006).

CHAPTER 23

Trauma-Informed Practice[1]

WHAT IS TRAUMA?

There has been increasing interest in the addiction field in adding a trauma-informed practice approach to counselling (Brown et al., 2013; Goodman, 2017; Harris & Fallot, 2001a, 2001b; Mills 2015; Mills & Teeson, 2019). Trauma consists not only of the traumatic event itself, but also the response to the traumatic event, which includes both the experience of the trauma and its ongoing effects. Collectively, this is referred to as the three E's of trauma (Figure 23.1) (CCSA, 2014c; Goodman, 2017; Levenson, 2017; Yeager & Roberts, 2003).

The first E, the traumatic event, can be any type of incident that negatively affects individuals at any point in their lives. Levenson (2017) defines the event as an "extraordinary experience that presents a physical or psychological threat to oneself or others and generates a reaction of helplessness and fear" (p. 105). This can include, but is not limited to, experiences of violence, sexual assault, natural disaster, neglect, and emotional abuse (Levenson, 2017). Trauma also refers to the psychological experience that follows the event. It represents an experience "that overwhelms an individual's capacity to cope"

EVENTS
CIRCUMSTANCES
CAUSING TRAUMA

EXPERIENCES
PERSONAL RESPONSE TO
THE EVENT

EFFECTS
PHYSICAL, EMOTIONAL,
BEHAVIOURAL,
COGNITIVE, SPIRITUAL

Figure 23.1: The Three E's of Trauma

(CCSA, 2014c, p. 1). The response to the traumatic event (the second E) can occur directly after the event or much later (Yeager & Roberts, 2003). Furthermore, the traumatic event has a lasting effect on the individual's ability to function in everyday life (Goodman, 2017). Marcellus (2014) has identified five ways in which trauma can be expressed (the third E):

1. Physical: eating and sleeping disruptions
2. Emotional: depression or anxiety
3. Behavioural: drug misuse and other related self-harming behaviours
4. Cognitive: attention impairments or memory loss
5. Spiritual: guilt, shame, and/or withdrawal from community interactions

In addition, the US Substance Abuse and Mental Health Services Administration (2014) identified a series of key issues in trauma-informed practice, which are known as the four R's of trauma-informed care (Figure 23.2). The first step is to realize the widespread impact of trauma and to understand potential paths to recovery. Second, counsellors need to recognize the signs and symptoms of trauma not only in service users but also in the families of service users, in colleagues, and within organizations. The third step, respond, requires fully integrating knowledge about trauma into policies and procedures, moving the process to an integrated trauma-informed care approach. Fourth and finally, counsellors need to resist the re-traumatization of service users through their work with them or the way agencies interact with them.

RESPONDING TO TRAUMA

The response to the growing recognition that trauma is a major contributing factor to substance misuse has been the inclusion of specific trauma-informed practices into agency counselling protocols. In fact, Mills and Teeson (2019) argue that addiction service providers should assume that all service users have experienced some level of trauma that contributes to their misuse of psychoactive substances. This means that during every

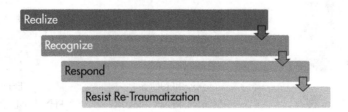

Figure 23.2: The Four R's of Trauma-Informed Care

Source: Substance Abuse and Mental Health Services Administration (2014).

assessment counsellors should be inquiring, in a respectful and safe manner, about the nature of the trauma service users have experienced and what connection they see between that trauma and their use of substances.

Levenson (2017) outlines five key practice provisions when offering trauma-informed-care:

1. Safety: Providing a protected physical and emotional environment where the service user feels welcome, that is accessible, well lit, and provides an ambiance that creates a foundation for developing a therapeutic alliance with the counsellor.
2. Trust: A feeling of trust between the service provider and the service user begins by establishing clear expectations regarding what the service user wants and what the agency can provide, along with listening in a non-judgmental, empathetic, and compassionate manner.
3. Choice: It is important that service users feel a sense of control and autonomy throughout the entire treatment process.
4. Collaboration: Working alongside service users throughout the treatment process to diminish power imbalances, collaboration is premised on the belief that the majority of service users have experienced power imbalances, both in their experience of trauma and in the types of services they have previously received that did not consider the impact of trauma on their substance misuse.
5. Empowerment: The outcome of the counsellor adopting a strength-based approach that reframes symptoms as adaptation and focuses on a service user's resilience rather than on deficits and pathologizing and labelling behaviours. Taking an empowerment stance in trauma-informed care means understanding drug use as a functional coping mechanism in response to the overwhelming feelings produced by the traumatic incident.

The Canadian Centre for Substance Abuse (2014c), in their best practice recommendations, added one additional element to Levenson's list: strength and skill building. The CCSA recommends building on the abilities of service users and using these to develop alternative healthier coping strategies.

Fallot and Harris (2009) provided eight reasons for grounding substance misuse counselling within a trauma-informed practice framework. They begin by simply arguing that, given how prevalent trauma is among substance misusers, this lived reality necessitates always applying a trauma-informed approach, regardless of the agency setting. Second, they emphasize that trauma touches so many lives and that trauma exposure is associated with such a range of negative life outcomes that substance misuse is only one negative consequence. Thus, if only the addiction is addressed in counselling without exploring the underlying trauma, other negative behaviours may manifest in other life domains, which may be even more problematic than substance misuse. Third, trauma affects individuals' perceptions of both themselves and their environment, leading to perceptions of themselves as less than and their environment as inherently dangerous. Without addressing trauma in the counselling process, service users can become trapped and unable to move forward due to their false perceptions. Fourth, those who have experienced violent trauma are more likely to perpetuate the violence. Thus, from a personal and community safety standpoint, taking a trauma-informed practice approach is an ethical imperative.

Fifth, Fallot and Harris argue that "trauma is insidious and preys particularly on the more vulnerable among us" (2009, p. 2). Those who belong to marginalized populations due to their sexual orientation, ability status, race, or other related attributes, who also have addiction issues, are at a greater risk of experiencing ongoing trauma in their lives. This can further perpetuate the use of substances as a functional coping response. Sixth, trauma affects the manner in which those impacted by trauma approach helping relationships. The experience of trauma is a major barrier to seeking support and in developing a therapeutic alliance with a counsellor. Therefore, a trauma-informed practice has the capacity to alleviate some of the stressors survivors experience accessing services. Seventh, trauma often occurs within the context of societal institutions like schools, places of worship, and workplaces, and thus the more institutional the agency appears the less likely some people are to access available services. This historical context makes it even more imperative to be mindful of trauma in service agencies, especially larger, more bureaucratic ones. Finally, the eighth and last reason to adopt a trauma-informed approach is that "trauma affects staff members as well as consumers in human services programs" (p. 2). It is possible for staff to experience secondary trauma from hearing service users' stories or to experience trauma themselves through threats or acts of violence from service users (Chechak & Csiernik, 2014; Darnell & Csiernik, 2014). For this reason, adopting a trauma-informed philosophy and approach is beneficial not only to service users but also to service providers.

Trauma-informed practice is a natural fit in the addiction field in part because of the prevalence of trauma in the lives of those who develop a substance misuse issue, but also because the risk of developing substance dependence increases with each traumatic experience a person has (Mills & Teeson, 2009). There is also extensive evidence of a relationship between childhood trauma or adverse childhood experiences and substance use disorders (Foster et al., 2018; Forster et al., 2018; LeTendre & Reed, 2017; Shin et al., 2018; Stein et al., 2017). Additionally, a co-occurrence of trauma and substance use disorders has been linked to high rates of suicide ideation and suicide attempts, high rates of psychiatric illnesses, physical health problems, and lower quality of life (Goodman, 2017). By failing to acknowledge the trauma experienced by service users, treatment is likely to be incomplete, with the lack of trauma-informed care being a contributing factor to a risk of both treatment drop out and return to drug use (Brown et al., 2013).

Nevertheless, there remains a degree of resistance in parts of the addiction field to making a trauma-informed approach standard practice. The most common reasons for this resistance are:

1. reluctance to ask about potential experiences of trauma, including fear that the service user will be unable to cope with discussing the trauma and that the counselling will worsen the situation;
2. the inadequate education and training of counselling staff in trauma-informed practice; and
3. a fear among some counsellors of experiencing secondary trauma as an outcome of hearing about and empathising with a survivor's experience of trauma (Mills & Teeson, 2019).

Despite these concerns there is growing evidence that trauma-informed care has value as a core practice component of addiction counselling (Covington et al., 2008; Markoff et al., 2005; Roberts et al., 2015; Shier & Turpin, 2017).

TRAUMA-INFORMED CARE

Becoming trauma informed also requires an organizational response to integrating trauma-informed care into the helping process. In treating trauma, the goal is to reduce symptoms, promote healing, and teach skills. Counsellors work to bring an awareness of the trauma to the service user and to create a trauma lens. While this is vital, it is not adequate—the goal should be to infuse trauma-informed care into all facets of the process, especially given how pervasive trauma is among those with substance misuse issues. Trauma-informed care moves beyond practice to agency policies and procedures.

Figure 23.3 is one example of a trauma-informed care process developed by Trauma Informed Oregon (2016) that consists of four distinct stages. Trauma awareness entails recognizing that trauma exists not only among service users but also service providers. Along with underscoring issues of transference and countertransference,[2] this means being aware that the counselling process itself can be re-traumatizing, including the physical setting and the way one's counselling space is used. Thus, becoming trauma-informed means becoming aware that the counsellor and agency themselves can be activating agents.

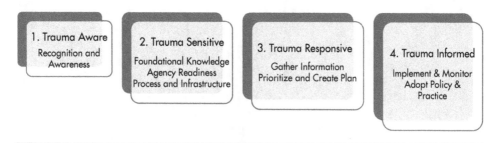

Figure 23.3: Roadmap to Trauma-Informed Care

Source: Adapted from Trauma Informed Oregon (2016).

Trauma sensitivity requires that the organization ensures that all staff have acquired a foundational knowledge of key themes associated with trauma. This includes being educated about adverse childhood experiences and the prevalence of trauma in individuals served by the agency, as well as a basic understanding of the neurobiology of trauma. Issues of power, oppression, and microaggression, and an appreciation of historical, collective, and intergenerational trauma, are vital to becoming trauma-informed, as is an awareness of trauma in the workplace and what produces secondary and vicarious trauma among helping professionals. Becoming trauma-informed also requires agency readiness such that all staff believe in the importance of providing trauma-informed care and that its principles are a component of the agency's mission, vision, and strategic plan. Trauma responsiveness requires gathering information and prioritizing the inclusion of trauma-informed practices such that they become part of the core helping process. This needs to pervade agency governance and leadership, policy, and the physical space the organization occupies.

NOTES

1. This chapter was written by Andrée Schuller and Rick Csiernik.
2. Transference is a process of redirection of feelings about a specific person onto someone else. In counselling, this refers to a service user's projection of their feelings about someone else onto the counsellor. In contrast, countertransference is the opposite, the redirection of a counsellor's feelings toward the service user.

CHAPTER 24

Mutual Aid/Self-Help

Self-help groups are informal, voluntary, small group structures for mutual aid and the accomplishment of a special purpose. They are usually formed by peers who have come together for mutual assistance in satisfying a common need, overcoming a common life-disruption and bringing about a desired social and/ or personal change. The initiators and members of such groups perceive that their needs are not or cannot be met by or through existing societal institutions. Self-help groups emphasize face-to-face social interactions and the assumption of personal responsibility by members. They often provide material assistance, as well as emotional support. (Katz & Bender, 1976, p. 9)

Self-help may be defined as a process, group or organization comprising people coming together or sharing an experience or problem with a view to individual and/or mutual benefit. As empowerment commonly means "becoming powerful," self-help may thus be viewed as one form of empowerment. (Adams, 1990, p. 1)

INTRODUCTION

Self-help is an informal method of social support providing informational, effective, and instrumental support. Self-help groups give their members an anchorage, a reference point, companionship, and even a sense of belonging. These groups employ three major ingredients of social learning: (1) instruction, (2) reinforcers, and (3) models (Kurtz & Powell, 1987). Mutual aid is a process in which people who share common experiences, situations, or problems can offer each other a unique perspective that is not available from those who have not shared these incidents (Self-Help Clearinghouse of Toronto, 1991).

The one thing that self-help is not is a unitary phenomenon. It is a non-professional practice in which the role of consumer is that of producer of service. Self-help is based on the principle of reciprocity: of both giving and taking. A central axiom of self-help is the helper-helpee principle. The foundation of this principle is that the more one helps others, the more the person is helped, and thus those who help most are helped most. Great value is placed on shared experience, with minimal social distance between the helper and helpee. Social support is paramount, as help is not a privilege. Rather, it is a right to be shared with others.

> Initially new members receive support from other group members. As they discover their own capacity for helping they develop a feeling of equality with other members. By participating in the group they are able to play the role of helper-helpee, a person who, being conscious of his/her own capacities and needs and those of others knows how to give and receive help at the same time. It is through the practice of mutual aid that the self-helper in his helper role is able to accept the person receiving help as a true equal; there is no place for feelings of superiority or inferiority. (Romeder, 1990, p. 32)

Other characteristics commonly associated with mutual aid/self-help groups include the following:

- free membership and participation
- the voluntary nature of all activities
- its not-for-profit approach, with members controlling all resources
- the lack of financial support from external sources
- a membership based on individual circumstances and situations
- the structuring of meetings for mutual benefit of those participating
- a constructive action toward shared goals
- an egalitarian philosophy, including a belief in participatory and not just representative democracy
- equality of status and power within the group
- shared leadership and co-operation in decision making
- groups are member-led and organized
- a lack of reliance on professional helpers
- individual decision making by each member, with the group as a whole responsible for its own decisions
- the confidential nature of groups' proceedings
- participants move toward improving control over their own circumstances, and giving themselves more control over their own lives
- a general avoidance of hierarchical and bureaucratic patterns of organization
- a lack of importance of outside societal status within group proceedings; instead status is conferred by personal involvement in the group (Adams, 1990; Gartner & Riessman, 1977; Katz & Bender, 1976; Pape, 1990; Silverman, 1980)

Self-help has become a recognized process to deal with all types of problems in a setting where members are treated as equals. It entails openness, informality, friendliness, and getting involved as the norm (Hill, 1983). Professional service providers may participate in the self-help process at the request and sanction of the group but usually remain in an ancillary or consultative role. Self-help has no pre-appointed hours. Many groups operate so that if there is no formal meeting, there is a contact person or personal buddy or sponsor to call. Self-helpers are not separated by education, class, or experience (Robinson & Henry, 1977). Typically, persons join self-help groups to overcome feelings of rejection, isolation, and powerlessness and to break free of societal stereotypes. However, in many groups, members must identify themselves as having a specific problem, with many of these problems being compulsive behaviours (Katz & Bender, 1976). Gartner and Riessman (1977) claim that one of the most significant characteristics of mutual-aid groups is that they are empowering and thus potentially de-alienating. They are empowering as they allow members to feel that they have greater control over their lives. To move from an external to internal locus of control is a significant achievement, but whether this affects the distribution of power in the community or society remains in question.

Katz and Bender (1976) proposed a variety of typologies in attempting to classify the myriad of self-help groups:

1. (a) self-fulfilment or personal growth (Recovery Inc.)
    (b) social advocacy (#MeToo)
    (c) alternative patterns of living or solidarity (women's groups)
    (d) outcast havens (X-Kalay)
2. (a) groups conforming to society's norms; also known as self-reforming (Alcoholics Anonymous)
    (b) groups wishing to reform society (LGBTQ2IA+ groups)
3. (a) inner-focused (Parents Without Partners)
    (b) outer-focused (wishing to change public policies—Fortune Society)
4. (a) anonymous groups (Alcoholics, Gamblers, Overeaters)
    (b) living with groups (Cystic Fibrosis, Cerebral Palsy)
    (c) life transition groups (widows' support groups)
5. (a) rehabilitative (Stroke Club, United Ostomy Association)
    (b) behaviour change (Narcotics Anonymous)
    (c) primary care (disease where there is no cure, but care is required) (Arthritis Association, Diabetes Association)

What becomes evident from the creation of this typology is that a myriad of self-help programs exist for a variety of different purposes.

Adams (1990) discussed four perspectives that attempted to explain the growth of self-help/mutual aid:

1. *Traditionalist*: A conservative view of history that claims that self-help has existed since humans first lived together. All that the 20th century introduced was a focus away from economic issues to deviance and problem-solving groups.
2. *Functionalist*: This viewpoint regards self-help as an automatic response to a changing society. It arises naturally between gaps left by existing services and complements other types of helping and social support. It is an inevitable consequence of the inability or unwillingness of the state, professionals, and agencies to meet needs.
3. *Liberal*: The liberal perspective claims that self-help is an alternative to existing forms of professional helping and grows because need is inadequately or incorrectly met, rather than because it is unmet.
4. *Radical*: Self-help is a response to wide spread alienation in society and acts by fulfilling many of people's affiliation and identity needs. Negative consequences of industrialization and urbanization that are associated with the decline in the extended family have led to the rapid growth of self-help groups. Mutual aid has also grown because of rapid technological development, depersonalized and dehumanized institutions, and the alienation of people from communities, institutions, and each other.

Hoehne (1988) attempted to explain the growth of self-help in North America as the consequence of four critical factors:

1. the fiscal crisis of the state leading to cutbacks in volume and quality of the services provided by governments at a time when demographic trends are leading to an increase of sectors of the population that are the most dependent on government services (unemployed, working poor, homeless, single parent families);
2. a rise in the proportion of chronic diseases due to increasing life spans;
3. the erosion of the traditional extended family network; and
4. health care and social service systems that are still rooted in 19th century models.

Hoehne (1988) claimed that increasing self-help use equates to deficiencies in existing health care and social service systems. While health problems are seen as individual problems, social problems are individual only in their consequences; in their causes, they are collective. However, the state still tends to equate social problems with each individual's shortcomings. Social self-help groups pose a greater threat to the legitimization efforts of governments than do health-focused self-help groups. By becoming organized, those involved in social self-help groups take the first step in countering the "blaming the victim" strategy of the ruling ideology. Thus, government funding is primarily targeted to groups that have cost-cutting goals and seek to legitimize the status quo, rather than to those advocating for system change.

While having great potential, self-help groups are no panacea. Their proliferation needs to be examined in context. The availability of self-help can be used to justify the curtailing of services, with the risk of poorer individuals being shunted off to self-help groups while more affluent individuals receive private professional services. Self-help groups can also become the dumping grounds of professionals whose service users' problems are hard to resolve or for cases where insurance and/or employer-financed counselling conclude yet more assistance is required. Self-help can thus become an inappropriate referral, replacing required professional interventions. Self-help groups focused solely on person-centred approaches tend to de-emphasize larger societal issues and take pressure off the need for societal changes. The issue of hitting rock bottom before becoming better, associated with anonymous groups, can create even poorer self-esteem and self-image in some participants. An overemphasis on self can lead to escapism and narcissism, with the potential to foster dependence and the need for a lifelong commitment instead of a focus on getting better, or moving forward, for some. Those attending meetings may be able to participate but not necessarily obtain assistance. Self-help groups have also been called limiting because they only examine issues at the symptom level, looking at small-scale solutions and providing only marginal alternatives to existing systems (Gartner & Riessman, 1977). A functioning self-help group should follow six fundamental principles with which it can be assessed and evaluated:

1. the social support it provides members,
2. education and information sharing it offers participants,
3. new identity formation,
4. affiliation and development of a sense of community,
5. personal growth and transformation, and
6. advocacy and collective empowerment.

These factors should all be taken into consideration when examining any form of mutual aid group and its efficacy.

ALCOHOLICS ANONYMOUS

The initial and most prominent form of mutual aid/self-help in the addiction field has been, and remains, Alcoholics Anonymous (AA). Alcoholics Anonymous is not a treatment modality, though it remains an excellent reoccurrence prevention resource (Clark, 1995). When AA arose, the moral model was the prevalent attitude toward persons who were misusing alcohol. This led members to conceal their participation during the initial development of AA due to the stigma and oppression that remained associated with alcohol misuse.

AA consists of individuals who are recovering from alcohol misuse and who provide help to other active users as one of the key steps in maintaining their own sobriety and commitment to not consuming alcohol. This informal banding together rests on a cornerstone of common experience. The members seek to promote, through continuing support, the hope and determination of each other to achieve and maintain the sobriety on which they believe their recovery depends. Non-political, non-sectarian, and non-reformist in any way, AA neither espouses nor opposes any cause or movement. It exacts no dues and imposes no assessments. Each group supports itself by means of voluntary contributions within its own community and is loosely associated with other similar groups (Alcoholics Anonymous, 2001).

The AA program is based on the 12 suggested steps and on the 12 traditions. They embody the thinking and beliefs regarding the functioning of an individual in the program, and the functioning of AA as a unique fellowship and method of mutual aid. The following are the 12 suggested steps of Alcoholics Anonymous:

1. We admitted we were powerless over alcohol—that our lives had become unmanageable.
2. Came to believe that a Power greater than ourselves could restore us to sanity.
3. Made a decision to turn our will and our lives over to the care of God as we understood Him.
4. Made a searching and fearless moral inventory of ourselves.
5. Admitted to God, to ourselves and to another human being the exact nature of our wrongs.
6. Were entirely ready to have God remove all these defects of character.
7. Humbly asked Him to remove our shortcomings.
8. Made a list of all persons we had harmed and became willing to make amends to them all.
9. Made direct amends to such people wherever possible, except when to do so would injure them or others.
10. Continued to take personal inventory and when we were wrong, promptly admitted it.
11. Sought through prayer and meditation to improve our conscious contact with God as we understood Him, praying only for knowledge of His will for us and the power to carry that out.
12. Having had a spiritual awakening as the result of these steps, we tried to carry this message to alcoholics and to practice these principles in all our affairs. (Alcoholics Anonymous, 2001)

The 12 AA traditions are:

1. Our common welfare should come first; personal recovery depends upon AA unity.
2. For our group purpose there is but one ultimate authority—a loving God as He may express Himself in our group conscience. Our leaders are but trusted servants; they do not govern.

3. The only requirement for AA membership is a desire to stop drinking.
4. Each group should be autonomous except in matters affecting other groups or AA as a whole.
5. Each group has but one primary purpose—to carry its message to the alcoholic who still suffers.
6. An AA group ought never endorse, finance or lend the AA name to any related facility or outside enterprise lest problems of money, property and prestige divert us from our primary purpose.
7. Every AA group ought to be fully self-supporting, declining outside contributions.
8. Alcoholics Anonymous should remain forever non-professional, but our service centers may employ special workers.
9. AA, as such, ought never be organized; but we may create service boards or committees directly responsible to those they serve.
10. Alcoholics Anonymous has no opinion on outside issues; hence the AA name ought never be drawn into public controversy.
11. Our public relations policy is based on attraction rather than promotion; we need always maintain personal anonymity at the level of press, radio and films.
12. Anonymity is the spiritual foundation of all our Traditions, ever reminding us to place principles before personalities. (Alcoholics Anonymous, 2001)

Underpinning AA's 12 steps and 12 traditions is a strong spiritual dimension, as all 12-step groups require members to express earnest humility in order to be successful. For many members, this is a mechanism that allows them to think about and envision a future that does not involve alcohol use (Timmons, 2010). Attending AA meetings is also intended to address core issues in the emotional growth of the alcohol-dependent person. Telling and understanding one's life story, repairing past misdeeds, recognizing and correcting false beliefs and cognitive distortions, and shifting focus from unhealthy rumination to a consideration of appropriate actions are fundamental issues that participation is intended to address. The emphasis on humbling oneself is premised on the belief that alcohol-dependent persons are, at their core, narcissists and that their self-absorption does not allow them to earnestly address their alcohol misuse. Narcissists so love themselves that they cannot love others. Thus, in addressing this character flaw, AA allows individuals to open themselves up emotionally to others (Sachs, 2009).

Though it inspires worldwide acclaim and great enthusiasm among many North American alcoholism treatment personnel, and has led to the development of Narcotics Anonymous (1987) and other related 12-step fellowships, AA lacks universal support for its efficacy and is viewed as rigid by some. Responses to this rigidity can be found in specific adaptions of the 12 steps and traditions, such as a First Nations adaption, the 12 Steps of Walking the Red Road (White Bison, 2002):

1. We admitted we were powerless over alcohol—that we had lost control of our lives.
2. We came to believe that a power greater than ourselves could help us gain control.
3. We made a decision to ask for help from a Higher Power and others who understand.
4. We stopped and thought about our strengths and our weaknesses and thought about ourselves.
5. We admitted to the Great Spirit, to ourselves and to another person the things we thought were wrong about ourselves.
6. We are ready, with the help of the Great Spirit, to change.
7. We humbly ask a Higher Power and our friends to help us change.
8. We made a list of people who were hurt by our drinking and want to make up for these hurts.
9. We are making up to those people whenever we can, except when to do so would hurt them more.
10. We continue to think about our strengths and weaknesses when we are wrong and we say so.
11. We pray and think about ourselves, praying only for strength to do what is right.
12. We try to help other alcoholics and to practise these principles in everything we do.

Likewise, a Millati Islami (2010a, 2010b) version of the 12 steps has emerged, based on Islamic principles:

1. We admitted that we were neglectful of our higher selves and that our lives have become unmanageable.
2. We came to believe that Allah could and would restore us to sanity.
3. We made a decision to submit our will to the will of Allah.
4. We made a searching and fearless moral inventory of ourselves.
5. We admitted to Allah and to ourselves the exact nature of our wrongs.
6. Asking Allah for right guidance, we became willing and open for change, ready to have Allah remove our defects of character.
7. We humbly ask Allah to remove our shortcomings.
8. We made a list of persons we have harmed and became willing to make amends to them all.
9. We made direct amends to such people wherever possible, except when to do so would injure them or others.
10. We continued to take personal inventory and when we were wrong promptly admitted it.
11. We sought through Salaat (a prayer service) and Iqraa (reading and studying) to improve our understanding of Taqwa (proper love and respect for Allah) and Ihsan ("though we cannot see Allah, He does see us").

12. Having increased our level of Iman (faith) and Taqwa, as a result of applying these steps, we carried this message to humanity and began practising these principles in all our affairs. (Millati Islami World Services, 2010a)

The 12 traditions of Millati Islami are:

1. Shahadah—We bear witness that there is no God but Allah, and Muhammed is the last messenger of Allah.
2. Personal recovery depends upon Millati Islami unity. Believers are friends and protectors of one another.
3. For our individual and Jamaat (group) purpose there is but one ultimate authority which is Allah (God, the source from which all originates).
4. Requirements for participation are a desire to stop using and willingness to learn a better way of life.
5. Each Jamaat (group) should be autonomous except in their adherence to these traditions.
6. Our primary Jamaat (group) purpose is carrying out Al-Islam as the message of recovery to those who still suffer (Dawah).
7. Problems of money, property, and prestige must never divert us from our primary purpose.
8. Every Millati Islami Jamaat (group) should be self supporting but may accept sadaqa (voluntary charity) without attached obligations or promises to donating parties.
9. We may create service boards and committees directly responsible to those we serve.
10. The Millati Islami name aught never be drawn into public controversy.
11. Our public relations policy is based upon attraction before promotion. The criterion for both are decided by Jamaat (group), Taqwa, and Ihsan.
12. Iman (faith) is the spiritual foundation of all our traditions, reminding us to place principles before personalities. (Millati Islami World Services, 2010b)

AA has grown from an organization of two in the 1930s to one that boasts millions of members globally. It has been incorporated into many treatment programs in both the United States and Canada (MacMaster, 2004) with some positive outcome evaluations (Costello et al., 2019; Humphreys et al., 2014; Sharma & Branscum, 2010). Despite its shortcomings, it remains a widely used resource because it is well known, inexpensive to join, accepting and tolerant of new members, open to everyone, and teaches by example. AA appears to be most effective for a specific subpopulation, though recent research has shown that it benefits non-traditional members as well (Csiernik & Jordanov, 2017). However, it should not be considered a remedy for all issues pertaining to alcohol misuse, nor for all issues persons in recovery face.

ALTERNATIVES TO 12-STEP GROUPS

As a response to concerns with the structure and message of 12-step groups, such as Alcoholics Anonymous, Narcotics Anonymous, Cocaine Anonymous, and even Nicotine Anonymous, other forms of addiction-specific mutual aid/self-help groups have arisen.

Women for Sobriety (WFS)

Women for Sobriety is an organization composed of self-help support groups for women with a dependency on alcohol. It was founded to meet the recovery needs specific to women drinkers and may be viewed as both an alternative to AA and as a complement to it, depending on the comfort level a woman has with the original 12-step program. Women for Sobriety was founded in 1975 by Jean Kirkpatrick and was influenced by a mix of the medical model with feminist principles. WFS encourages women to take charge of their alcohol misuse and embark on a path of self-awareness, as alcohol-dependent women have fundamentally different needs in recovery than do men. Interestingly, Men for Sobriety (MFS) groups have emerged due to the success of WFS and in response to the limits of AA.

Four central themes form the foundation of Women for Sobriety:

1. No drinking
2. Positive thinking
3. Believing one is competent
4. Growing spiritually and emotionally

While still premised on the overly rudimentary disease model, WFS differs from Alcoholics Anonymous. Rather than moving toward God for help in overcoming the compulsive use of alcohol, women are asked to discover why they initially became so dependent. Rather than being humble, participants are helped to become self-empowered and to change their thinking. Reoccurrences are more tolerated in WFS, with no need to begin again at day one of sobriety. Openly talking to other members during meetings is allowed, unlike in 12-step groups that have "no crosstalk" rules. Another significant difference is in the greeting. Rather than announcing and labelling oneself as an alcoholic, members introduce themselves by stating, "Hi, I'm ———, and I'm a competent woman." There is no emphasis on reducing ego or on being humble. For most women with an alcohol problem, there is a need for empowerment and increasing their self-worth (Kaskutas, 1989). The 13 affirmations of WFS are:

1. I have a life-threatening problem that once had me.
2. Negative emotions destroy only myself.
3. Happiness is a habit I will develop.
4. Problems bother me only to the degree I permit them to.

5. I am what I think.
6. Life can be ordinary or it can be great.
7. Love can change the course of my world.
8. The fundamental object of life is emotional and spiritual growth.
9. The past is gone forever.
10. All love given returns.
11. Enthusiasm is my daily exercise.
12. I am a competent woman and have much to give others.
13. I am responsible for myself and for my sisters.

SMART Recovery: Self Management and Recovery Training

SMART Recovery, which began in 1994, consists of facilitator-led, structured peer discussion groups that are premised on CBT counselling techniques. SMART Recovery was
founded by Joe Gerstein, an American clinical professor of medicine, to counter the myth
that addiction is a disease that leaves its victims powerless and needing to stay in permanent recovery. Instead, Gerstein used Rational Emotive Behaviour Therapy (Box 24.1)

Box 24.1: Rational Emotive Behaviour Therapy (REBT)

REBT is a behavioural form of counselling whose function is to assist the service user
identify self-defeating thoughts and feelings, challenge the rationality of those feelings,
and replace them with healthier, more productive beliefs. REBT is a present-focused
approach to help individuals understand how unhealthy thoughts and beliefs create
emotional distress which, in turn, produces unhealthy actions and behaviours such
as substance misuse. It is hypothesized that individuals who develop addiction issues
have low frustration tolerance around these irrational beliefs that lead to substance
misuse. Once identified and understood, these specific negative thoughts and actions
can be changed and replaced with more positive and productive behaviour, allowing
individuals to develop alternative approaches and more successful relationships in
general. Examples of irrational beliefs include the following:

- I cannot avoid having a drink
- I can't fall asleep without smoking weed
- I'm not strong enough to avoid using cocaine
- I'm deprived without having a cigarette
- I must always be happy
- I should never be upset
- If I am drunk I am worthless
- I'm not a good person so I might as well get high (Ellis, 1982, 1985, 1995)

as the foundation for this form of mutual aid. Rather than steps, SMART Recovery is premised on a four-point program and a toolbox that supports the framework:

1. Building and maintaining motivation
2. Coping with urges
3. Managing thoughts, feelings and behaviors
4. Living a balanced life (SMART Recovery, 2015)

All meetings are open, lasting approximately 90 minutes. Participation is voluntary, and any member may choose not to contribute on the topic being discussed. Unlike Alcoholics Anonymous, SMART Recovery focuses on self-empowerment rather than surrendering to a higher power, believing that human beings have the capacity within themselves to overcome even severe addiction. SMART teaches participants how to disrupt their irrational belief system by helping them understand why they act as they do and then challenging that thinking. Unlike 12-step groups, crosstalk is permitted after the initial group check-in. Members are also encouraged to openly discuss reoccurrence of drug use to help both the individual and the group understand what triggered the event and how to better respond in the future. Individuals who have been using may attend meetings but are asked to observe rather than participate. Members are invited to stay involved with the group after gaining independence but are not expected to attend indefinitely, for in SMART Recovery, the end goal is to become recovered. In a pilot project in England, results from six SMART groups indicated that this mutual aid group addressed service gaps. It serves as a valuable alternative to AA while also being extremely cost-effective (MacGregor & Herring, 2010).

Secular Organization for Sobriety (SOS)

The Secular Organization for Sobriety was founded by Jim Christopher in 1985 in Hollywood, California, as an alternative recovery method for either alcohol- or drug-dependent persons who were uncomfortable with the spiritual component of 12-step self-help groups. SOS, which is also called "Save Our Selves" by participants, takes a secular approach to recovery and maintains that sobriety is a distinct issue from either spirituality or religion. The credit for recovery, as in WFS and SMART Recovery, belongs to the individual, without reliance on a higher power. SOS supports healthy skepticism and encourages the use of the scientific method to understand alcoholism. SOS tends to attract members who wish to separate their recovery from their religious affiliation. Members are welcome to attend both SOS and traditional AA- or NA-type meetings, however, if it assists in their recovery (White, 2012).

SOS groups, whose members now number over 100,000 in North America, encourage those who attend meetings to acknowledge that they are alcohol- or drug-dependent and that abstinence is their only solution. SOS maintains that members have the ability to obtain a better quality of life only by abstaining, and they are asked to resolve not to drink or consume drugs regardless of circumstances, feelings, or conflicts. Groups tend to consist of 20 members who take turns acting as the moderator, with new members being asked to attend once per week for six months and as needed after that for booster meetings (Secular Organization for Sobriety, 2014).

The following are the SOS Suggested Guidelines for Sobriety:

- To break the cycle of denial and achieve sobriety, we first acknowledge that we are alcoholics or addicts.
- We affirm this truth daily and accept without reservation—one day at a time—that as clean and sober individuals, we cannot and do not drink or use, no matter what.
- Since drinking or using is not an option for us, we take whatever steps are necessary to continue our Sobriety Priority lifelong.
- A quality of life, "the good life," can be achieved. However, life is also filled with uncertainties. Therefore, we do not drink or use regardless of feelings, circumstances, or conflicts.
- We share in confidence with each other our thoughts and feelings as sober, clean individuals.
- Sobriety is our Priority, and we are each responsible for our lives and our sobriety.

Rational Recovery (RR)

Rational Recovery describes itself as a mutual aid group for self-empowered recovery from substance dependency. RR, founded in 1986, views addiction as primarily a behavioural problem. It is affiliated with the American Humanist Association and also with the principles of Albert Ellis's Rational Emotive Behaviour Therapy (Box 24.1). RR has its own guidebook, written by Jack Trimpey, entitled *The Small Book*. In RR members learn that their use of alcohol and other drugs is an irrational choice. They also learn to listen, hear, and resist their internal irrational "Beast," a voice that urges them to drink and use. Rational Recovery believes in self-mastery rather than self-surrender and is also popular with those who have trouble or no interest in grasping the intent of a higher power, which is the foundation of the 12-step philosophy. Rational Recovery is described as a task-centred self-help group where one can totally recover (Self-Help Canada, 1992). RR believes in empowering members and Trimpey (1992) stated that Rational Recovery does not believe in the one-day-at-a-time philosophy, as this keeps the idea of drinking constantly before oneself, which reinforces one's lack of power. In Rational Recovery, to be successful is to be powerful, and in creating a state of mind for success, in creating motivation, guilt is the least effective of all mechanisms.

Moderation Management (MM)

Moderation Management is a support group for individuals who wish to reduce their drinking and make other positive lifestyle changes. The group advocates a minimum 30 days of abstinence, followed by a personal assessment that assists the person select either an abstinence or harm-reduction approach. Among proponents of this model are Frederick Glasser and Stanton Peele (Kishline, 1994).

Moderation Management (2014) provides a professionally reviewed nine-step program with information about moderate drinking guidelines and limits, exercises to monitor one's drinking, goal-setting techniques, and related self-management strategies. The goal of MM is to assist members in finding balance in their lives. This self-help group is not intended for those who have a significant physical or psychological dependency on alcohol, but rather for moderate drinkers who feel that alcohol is becoming too prominent in their lives. MM believes that people can change their behaviours and that a moderation-training program is effective for problem drinkers. Moderation Management is a non-disease model that believes in empowering participants and having members take personal responsibility for their own behaviour.

The nine steps toward moderation and balance are:

1. Attend meetings and learn about the program of Moderation Management. For those who do not want to go to a support group, the program can be followed without attending meetings.
2. Abstain from alcoholic beverages for 30 days and complete steps three through six during this time.
3. Examine how drinking has affected your life.
4. Write down your priorities.
5. Take a look at how much, how often, and under what circumstances you used to drink.
6. Learn the MM guidelines and limits for moderate drinking. This information is provided at meetings and in MM literature.
7. Set moderate drinking limits and start weekly small steps toward positive lifestyle changes.
8. Review your progress and update your goals.
9. Continue to make positive lifestyle changes, attend meetings for ongoing encouragement and support, and help newcomers to the group.

Refuge Recovery

A new mutual aid group to North America, but one based in long-standing beliefs, is Refuge Recovery. Unlike the Christian principles that ground 12-step groups, Refuge Recovery draws upon Buddhist philosophy to address substance misuse. The underlying principle is that everyone has the capacity to free themselves from the suffering produced by addiction. Refuge Recovery espouses four truths:

1. Addiction creates suffering.
2. The cause of addiction is repetitive craving.
3. Recovery is possible.
4. The path to recovery is available.

Refuge Recovery is an abstinence-based approach that incorporates eight factors. These factors, or steps, do not have to be followed sequentially but rather are to be developed, experienced, and sustained individually and throughout one's entire lifetime.

1. *Understanding*: We understand that recovery begins when we renounce and abstain from all substances or addictive behaviours regardless of specific substances, we have become addicted to. Forgiveness, non-harming actions, service and generosity are a necessary part of the recovery process. We can't do it alone; community support and wise guidance are an integral part of the path to recovery. We begin to open to and acknowledge the reality of our situation and come to terms with the reality that life is an ongoing process of change, on-going difficulties and we begin to see this process as something that is not happening to "us"; we move from being in a state of reacting to developing an awareness that can respond to the ups and downs of our lives. We begin to take responsibility for the relationship that we have to our own life experience.
2. *Intention*: We begin to move towards a lifestyle that is rooted in non-harming by establishing clear intentions and work to change our relationship towards the mind's unwholesome tendencies and habits. We intend to meet all pain with compassion and all pleasure with non-attached appreciation. The practices of non-harming both internally and externally become a foundational part of daily life.
3. *Communication/Community*: We take refuge in the community as a place to practice wise and skillful communication and to support others on their path. We practice being honest, wise and careful with our communications, asking for help from the community, allowing others to guide us through the process. Practicing openness, honesty and humility about the difficulties and successes we experience.
4. *Action*: We abstain from all substances and behaviours that could lead to suffering. We practice forgiveness toward all people we have harmed or been harmed by, including ourselves, through both meditative training and direct amends. Compassion, non-attached appreciation, generosity, kindness, honesty, integrity and service are our guiding principles.

5. *Livelihood/Service*: We begin to look at our relationship to money. We try to be of service to others whenever possible, being generous with our time, energy, attention and resources to help create positive change. We try to secure a source of income/livelihood that causes no harm.

6. *Effort*: We commit to the daily disciplined practices of meditation, yoga, exercise, wise actions, kindness, forgiveness, generosity, compassion, appreciation and moment-to-moment mindfulness of feelings, emotions, thoughts and sensations. To develop these skills requires time and patience. It is important to begin to understand how to apply the appropriate action or meditation practice in any given situation or circumstance. We will need to develop the willingness and discipline that is required to stay with it, and to keep going when we make mistakes.

7. *Mindfulness/Meditations*: We develop wisdom and understanding through practicing formal mindfulness meditation. This leads to seeing clearly and healing the root causes and conditions that lead to the suffering of addiction. We practice present-time awareness in all aspects of our life. We move towards taking refuge in the present moment; to engage whole-heartedly in our lives as it unfolds in the here and now. We begin to develop a daily sitting practice of mindfulness and heart practices. We make a commitment to sitting at home and with others.

8. *Concentrations/Meditations*: We develop the capacity to focus the mind on a single object, such as the breath or a phrase, training the mind through the practices of loving-kindness, compassion and forgiveness to focus on the positive qualities we seek to uncover and we utilize concentration at times of temptation or craving in order to abstain from acting unwisely. (Refuge Recovery, 2019)

The Buddha recognized addiction issues and spoke of them, providing guidance to his followers. Nations such as Japan and Thailand have developed Buddhist responses to addiction and contemporary writing has looked to find intersections between Buddhist and 12-step approaches to recovery (Griffin, 2004; Groves, 2014). However, at this time no outcome studies have been produced examining the effectiveness of Refuge Recovery.

Section V Closing Thoughts and Activities

Although few would argue that what one does in addiction treatment is immaterial, outcome studies tend to find small to no difference when specific treatment methods are compared with each other or with treatment as usual. In contrast, there are usually substantial differences among therapists in client outcomes, and relational factors such as therapist empathy and therapeutic alliance can be significant determinants of addiction treatment outcome.
    —Miller & Moyers, 2015, p. 401

While there is no one perfect treatment approach, and controversy remains among treatment professionals regarding which method is "best," addiction treatment in general does produce positive outcomes, both for individuals and society (Babor & Del Boca, 2002). Studies from the United States (Ettner et al., 2006; Lipton, 1995; McCarty, 2008), Australia (Manning et al., 2019), and the United Kingdom (Davies et al., 2009; UKATT Research Team, 2005, 2008) have indicated that individuals receiving treatment not only get better, but the economic returns are five to seven times greater than the cost of providing the treatment (McCollister & French, 2003). As well, the average cost of treatment, even in the United States with its private health care model, and now in Canada with its drift away from universal health care for addiction treatment toward more privatized care providers, is less costly than acute hospital care, incarceration of users, and placing children in foster care (National Treatment Agency, 2012).

No single counselling method has been found to be universally successful in the treatment of those misusing or abusing psychoactive substances, though in virtually every study, counselling was superior to no treatment. For many, a combination of several types of counselling will be more successful than recourse to any one alone. Two things are certain: that the therapy employed must be tailored to meet the specific needs of each individual, and that no service user should be forced into a particular type of therapy simply because of the counsellor's convenience or prejudicial choice. The following critical factors should always be considered:

- the service user choosing to enter treatment with an expectation of being helped to change their behaviour, thus having the motivation to change
- the empirical credibility of the technique being used to both the therapist and the service user
- the counsellor being adept at the practice model being used
- consistent application of an evidence-informed approach
- the ability to create optimism for a successful outcome

- the ability to create a foundation so that change may occur
- counsellor discretion, flexibility, and emotional support
- the ability of the counsellor to create a supportive environment

Regardless of which approach one uses, it should always be consistently applied and person-centred so that the focus is on the individual in relation to their needs and wants, both perceived and actual (Imel et al., 2008; Magill & Ray, 2009; Wampold et al., 1997). Perhaps most important in considering these factors is your definition of success, as a counsellor, and the definition of success for the service user sitting across from you.

Decades of research indicate that the actual intervention employed, while important, is far less vital than the process (Smedslund et al., 2011). The counsellor–service user relationship, service user expectation, model employed, and other extra-therapeutic factors, such as the service user's attributes, social system, and social environment, and the treatment environment, all contribute to creating change (Figure V.1). The counsellor's personality, background, understanding, and patience all play significant roles in the success of the treatment, as the better the reported relationship at all stages of therapy, the better the outcome for the service user and the service user's system. As well, the counsellor's capacity to structure the treatment matters more than the type of treatment, as does the expression and discussion of empathy and emotion during the counselling sessions (Elliott et al., 2018; Peluso & Freund, 2018) and the ability to create a strong therapeutic alliance. Regardless of the method or model used, if the service user feels heard and supported, the treatment outcome is more likely to be positive—for hope and the bringing of hope are crucial parts of the counselling process (Koehn et al., 2012). What the service user expects, believes, and wants to happen in treatment contributes substantively to its final outcome. Research indicates that what motivates people to change is positive, not negative, thoughts. The more one focuses on problems, the more stuck one feels. It is hope that causes people to change, not the pain of addiction or the losses it brings to them.

Most critically, social factors account for the greatest proportion of change, which reinforces the need to view addiction through a bio-psycho-social lens. This includes all aspects of service users' environments that facilitate recovery, including social support and social capital. Thus, to provide the best person-centred care, environmental factors must be considered and responded to in the counselling process. Effective addiction counselling can no longer consider only the individual, but must always look at the person-in-environment. A personalized and creative approach, based in a service user's specific needs and considering their choices, should be the counsellor's guiding principles over rigid adherence to any one counselling approach (Flückiger et al., 2018; Holroyd & Luca, 2019; Hubble et al., 2010; Magill, 2015; Norcross & Lambert, 2018).

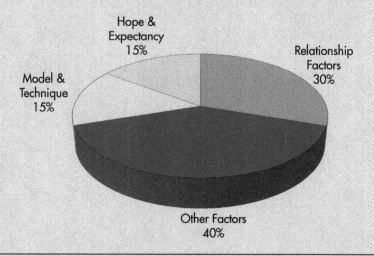

Figure V.1: Contributing Factors to Positive Counselling Outcome

Source: Adapted from Hubble et al. (2010).

DISCUSSION QUESTIONS

1. Compare and contrast harm reduction with self-help. What are the major differences and similarities between these two approaches?

2. (a) As an addiction counsellor, which of the different treatment approaches do you think would be most effective in your practice?
   (b) What attracts you to those approaches?
   (c) What evidence informs your decision of the usefulness of these approaches?

3. Of the various treatment options listed, which do you think is the single strongest and the single weakest? What leads you to those choices? What factors did you consider? How much emphasis did you place on outcome studies versus your own experience?

4. What are the advantages of using the Transtheoretical Model of Change as the foundation for your counselling practice?

5. How does Motivational Interviewing differ from other counselling approaches that did not originate in the addiction field?

6. What role do you see mindfulness having in the addiction field?

7. How will you use self-help groups as part of your practice as a counsellor?

8. What are the implications of Hubble and colleagues' (2010) findings on the way we should conduct counselling in the addiction field?

SECTION VI

TREATMENT RESOURCES

The implications are glaringly obvious; we do not provide adequate services for individuals with addiction issues. As a community we need to begin by identifying the individuals needing treatment in our schools, churches, workplace, hospitals, and families, we need to lobby the government for increased funding for addiction related programming and shore up gaps in services and reduce wait times.
—Annual Report of the Office of the Auditor General of Ontario, 2008, p. 1

Unfortunately, there have not been substantive improvements over the past decade in Ontario and elsewhere in Canada since the Ontario Auditor General's indictment of the addiction treatment system over a decade ago. Common barriers to access include wait lists, stringent admission requirements, stigma, the existence of private treatment, the cost for private treatment, and simply the anxiety of attending a treatment program. Studies have found that as few as one in three individuals suffering from addiction are able to readily access treatment in Canada (McPherson & Boyne, 2017). A study from the University of Alberta found that almost 50 percent of survey participants who met criteria for a past-year addiction or mental health problems reported unmet service needs (Wild et al., 2014). As well, the further a person has to travel to access addiction treatment services the less likely they are to attend or complete counselling (Morton, 2019).

Alcohol and other psychoactive drug treatment continues to be delivered by a diverse network of programs with administrative and fiscal linkages to government ministries, public institutions, private organizations, and lay groups that vary from province to province. The Canadian federal government is responsible for dealing with addiction on two fronts. First, it has a direct responsibility for specific groups of Canadians: military personnel and veterans, inmates at federal penitentiaries, the RCMP, and First Nations, Métis, Inuit, and Innu. Second, it is responsible for providing a national strategy for dealing with addiction, including transferring funds to provincial governments for data collection, research, and treatment (Kirby, 2004). The actual treatment of addiction in North America was initially organized and governed by groups of lay persons in recovery who were responding to the blatant neglect by helping professionals to this area of practice. By 1955, only 20 alcoholism treatment centres existed in all of Canada (Green, 1980). Prior to then, treatment was dominated by the moral model, with only a few psychiatric facilities or prison-based opioid-related programs in existence. Physicians were often forced to admit alcohol-dependent persons under false pretenses to get them any type of hospital care. The middle of the 20th century was dominated by the influence of Alcoholics Anonymous, with federal and provincial efforts leading to the development of treatment systems loosely connected to the health care system (Room et al., 2006). This began to change during the 1970s, when both public agencies and private insurance companies began to recognize the need for formal treatment programming based on humanitarian and fiscal grounds. In Canada, nearly 300 specialized addiction services were established during the first half of the 1970s, with expenditure on treatment services growing from $14 million to $70 million CAD. In 1978 the government of British Columbia legislated the first mandatory treatment in Canada with Bill 18, the Heroin Treatment Act, stating that compulsory treatment for heroin users was justified on economic grounds. This initial professionalization of the addiction field partially replaced the dominant role played by those using AA recovery principles as their foundation for helping. However, tension grew between those with more formal post-secondary education and those with personal recovery histories who had been the primary helping resource in Canada for decades, a tension heightened with the increasing focus on harm reduction and a decrease in residential abstinence-based programming (Kirby, 2004; Rush & Ogborne, 1992).

The 1980s were marked by the specialization and diversification of services, and the beginning of a research-informed approach. The War on Drugs mentality of the era, though, stymied some of the empirically based ideas regarding treatment system development. With the emergence of AIDS and the fear that first accompanied HIV, another struggle arose between those supporting an abstinence-only approach and the often vocal advocates of nascent harm-reduction-focused organizations to deliver services to those with addiction issues (Roberts et al., 1999).

The economic downturn of the 1990s saw the consolidation and integration of programs and the slow emergence of two-tier addiction care. For-profit agencies were established, and existing residential programs were no longer being fully funded, allowing those who could pay the full cost of care to no longer wait to receive treatment. A greater emphasis on neurobiological research in this century has contributed to a renewed interest in the pharmacological treatment of drug use. By 2002, an estimated $1.2 billion of funding was being allocated to specialized addiction treatment programs across Canada, with another $3.5 billion being directed toward medical and social issues arising from addiction (National Treatment Strategy Working Group, 2008; O'Connell, 2002). Research and experience have shown that a continuum of care (see Figure 25.1) is needed to serve the spectrum of drug-dependency-related problems (Csiernik, 2002, 2017; Csiernik & Troller, 2002). Both community- and institutional-based programs are needed, as are programs that serve specific groups such as women, youth, minority populations, and persons with concurrent disorders. Despite a demonstrated need, funding for new addiction facilities is slow, particularly for residential programming.

From April 1, 2014, to March 31, 2015, a total of 150,222 different adult Canadians used publicly funded substance use treatment services across seven provinces that collect this information (Alberta, Saskatchewan, Manitoba, Ontario, Nova Scotia, Prince Edward Island, and Newfoundland and Labrador), which accounted for 203,629 treatment service events. There were also 464 First Nations and Inuit youth who attended treatment centres under the National Youth Solvent Abuse Program. Of these, 63.8 percent identified as male, 35.9 percent as female, and 0.3 percent as transgender. Nearly 30 percent of those seeking treatment were between the ages of 25–34 with nearly 25 percent being 24 years of age or younger. The most prominent reasons for seeking treatment were alcohol, cannabis, and cocaine use. The most prominent form of publicly funded treatment was delivered through non-residential settings (67.4 percent), followed by withdrawal management (23.6 percent), with public residential services providing services to less than 14,000 of the 150,000 individuals seeking assistance (9.0 percent) (CCSA, 2017).

This section begins with an overview of the addiction continuum of care and its entry points, followed by an exploration of the various treatment resources available, including both addiction-specific and adjunct resources.

CHAPTER 25

Entry into the Addiction Continuum of Care

There are two primary entry points into the addiction continuum of care in Canada: withdrawal management (detoxification services) and assessment. Once entry has been established, depending on the complexity of addiction issues, ongoing case management to help navigate the continuum of care is often required but not always available. The opening chapter of this section examines these three resources in greater depth.

WITHDRAWAL MANAGEMENT SERVICES: DETOX AND DAYTOX

Withdrawal management, or detoxification services, is often a first step in the treatment process, especially given the biological consequences of prolonged psychoactive drug use. Detoxification entails total abstinence from not only the drug of misuse, but often all other drugs, including, in some facilities, tobacco. This strict rule created an issue for decades in Canada, as individuals who also had a mental health issue, concurrent disorder service users, could attend a detox program only if they discontinued use of their other psychotherapeutic medications, which would, in turn, place them at risk for other serious behavioural issues. The detoxification process should be of sufficient length to allow all psychoactive drugs to be eliminated by the body, which means anywhere from 3 to 14 days for acute use, though chronic issues can last upwards of six months. A service user's safety is the first priority of all withdrawal management staff, though once an individual becomes more stable, staff also typically offer social and environmental support during the stay.

The effects of withdrawal can range from mild to severe and can, on occasion, be life-threatening. It is the function of a detoxification program to manage this withdrawal process in a safe, caring, non-threatening, and empathetic atmosphere. Initially detoxification occurred exclusively in hospital emergency settings if it was a severe case; otherwise an impaired individual was usually incarcerated. In Ontario in 1965, the Addiction Research Foundation was commissioned to undertake an examination of chronic drunken offenders.

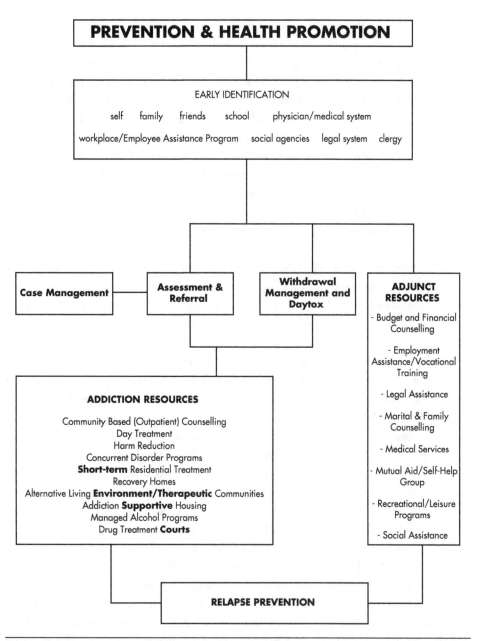

Figure 25.1: Addiction Treatment Continuum of Care

There was at this time a growing belief that alcohol misuse was more of a public health concern than a criminal justice issue. This process led to the formation of an inter-ministerial committee in 1970 to develop policy and programs to deal with issues created by individuals who were constantly in conflict with the law because of their misuse of alcohol.

Bill 101 led to the creation of non-medical detoxification centres in Ontario. These centres provided care and rehabilitation in judicial districts having more than 1,000 arrests per year for public intoxication as an alternative to incarceration. Non-medical meant staffed by specially trained paraprofessionals, rather than by medically trained personnel, with no administering of medication to assist with the pain of withdrawal. This is the pattern most provinces eventually followed across Canada, though British Columbia, Quebec, and Prince Edward Island still use primarily medical withdrawal management programs staffed by nurses and related health care professionals. These facilities provide not only addiction-related psychosocial support, but also pharmacological intervention (prescription medications) for distressing withdrawal symptoms. The remainder of the Canadian withdrawal management programs are located in close proximity to a partnered hospital, so that any necessary backup medical support is immediately available if a crisis situation arises.

The choice of a non-medical detoxification process occurs essentially for two reasons. First, it became apparent that most people could be detoxified safely in a non-medical facility, and second, with the removal of public drunkenness from the criminal statutes, it became necessary to provide a relatively inexpensive alternative to the historical remedy of the "drunk tank." Detoxification centres were intended to provide a link in the continuum of care for chronic alcohol-using offenders by receiving people, typically men, from police and, when possible, referring them to recovery homes that would provide longer-term shelter and rehabilitation. However smaller communities with no major public drunkenness issues were forced to make other arrangements for detoxification services, usually on an ad hoc basis. Typically, persons in these situations are detoxified in local community hospitals, but often without the benefit of a carefully designed withdrawal management program. Initial detoxification programs were designed exclusively for men, and it took over a decade in Ontario, once withdrawal management programs were established, to begin to include women and to develop women-specific resources for this component of the continuum of care (Watt et al., 1988).

Withdrawal management centres are crisis-care units that operate 24 hours a day, 7 days a week, 365 days a year. In most cases they have evolved to become much more than simply places to "dry out." They are now a core component in the continuum of care, acting as a gateway to other services, as well as remaining a safe haven. The overall population of detoxification centres is considerably different from that envisioned and experienced in the early 1970s. Whereas the original residents were largely chronic users, residents now represent a greater range of social and economic strata and age groups, as well as both sexes.

This integral component of the treatment system, while rudimentary in its approach, has continued to grow and evolve. As a result of increasing demand but reduced ability to meet the needs of individuals, in-home detoxification emerged as an experiment in some communities, particularly in rural and more isolated areas. This programming option is actually now more common in larger urban centres that also have specific withdrawal management facilities. Daytox is also a non-medical withdrawal management alternative that treats individuals in an outpatient setting during the course of the day, allowing service users to return home each evening only to return the next day to continue to receive assistance and social support until they are fully detoxified (Alwyn et al., 2004). As well as being an option where there is no residential withdrawal management program available, daytox can be used with individuals who do not experience severe withdrawal symptoms and who have a relatively stable environment and supportive social network (Williams, 2001). Not surprisingly, the lower operating costs associated with outpatient care seemed to drive the emergence of such programs, and this is expected to continue as health care costs continue to be scrutinized (Bischof et al., 2003). However, non-residential arrangements such as daytox can allow parents to continue to care for their children when they are not in treatment, diminishing the risk that they will be taken into care. Similar arguments can be made for maintaining employment. However, family support and relative stability in life are essential in an individual being assessed for a home detoxification program (Zinn, 1997).

In 1996, the Timmins Withdrawal Management Project was created as a partnership among social service agencies, the Ontario Addiction Research Foundation, and corrections services to provide a mobile, in-home outreach detoxification program. During the first two years of operation, the program was able to attract hard-to-reach populations, including women, Indigenous persons, youth, and the elderly, all of whom had traditionally exhibited reluctance toward in-patient care. In fact, 40 percent of the entire treatment population consisted of these demographic groups, compared to just 17 percent in the Timmins in-patient detoxification centre (Stuart, 1998). Vancouver opened a daytox centre in 2002 that continues to operate. Originally intended as a pilot project, the facility has been able to maintain operations due to its promising outcomes and fiscal structure: the centre costs approximately 60 percent less to run compared to traditional residential detoxification centres (Kent, 2002). In 2008, following the success of Vancouver's operation, a similar program opened in Surrey, where Fraser Health officials estimated that one-third of all individuals receiving detoxification services could be appropriately treated in an outpatient setting. Both of these programs offer education, counselling, treatment, and follow-up support, with nurse case managers providing initial assessments, treatment planning, and case management to service users as they move through the program. By incorporating alternative therapies, individual and group supports, and reoccurrence prevention strategies, the program encourages participation by individuals who have not succeeded in traditional program models. Similarly, the flexible hours and individualized treatment allows service users to maintain employment or continue academic pursuits that may otherwise be abandoned during hospitalization (Fraser Health, 2018). Key factors that indicate daytox is not an option are

- a lack of social support;
- a lack of safe housing;

- a history of delirium during withdrawal;
- other serious health issues; and,
- a risk of self harm (Davis, 2018).

A related initiative arose in the three Prairie provinces, Manitoba, Saskatchewan, and Alberta, and more recently in Newfoundland, in response to concerns raised by increasing methamphetamine use. Each of these provinces created legislation and new facilities to allow parents to forcibly send and confine their teenage children in youth detoxification centres for a limited stay, a measure called "involuntary confinement." In Alberta, the legal process is driven by parents who bring evidence to the courts and, in turn, if the judge finds in favour of the parents, the teenager can be confined for detoxification for up to 15 days. In Manitoba and Saskatchewan, the courts have more limited powers. Judges can order a youth to be taken for assessment, with an addiction specialist and/or physician making the final decision on whether the youth will be confined. In Saskatchewan, two doctors must assess the youth, and both must agree that involuntary confinement is necessary. Otherwise, the teen is released. The maximum length of confinement is also 15 days. Similarly, in Manitoba, the teen's drug problem is assessed by two addiction specialists. Those experts then decide whether to issue a stabilization order to confine the youth for up to seven days. In Alberta and Manitoba, only parents can seek a court order for their child, while in Saskatchewan, police officers and youth workers can also order a youth assessment.

Another withdrawal management option that has become more established with the emergence of the most recent opioid crisis is rapid detox/ultra-rapid detoxification. This treatment was initially only offered at private clinics with a cost ranging from $3,000 to $10,000 CAD. Normally, withdrawal from opioids results in severe flu-like symptoms, with pain reported to be as severe as that experienced by those with bone cancer. These symptoms peak two to five days after the last administration of the drug, and then gradually diminish over seven to ten days. In rapid detoxification, only a one-night residential stay is required. In this program, withdrawal is precipitated by opioid antagonists, either naltrexone or naloxone, after the individual is sedated. The most severe withdrawal phase is thus compressed to just hours, and the entire process, into only two days. The discomfort is avoided by deeply sedating the person in rapid detox, or anaesthetizing the patient in ultra-rapid detox, during the worst phase of the withdrawal period (Gevirtz et al., 2011). It has been found that for many who undergo ultra-rapid detoxification and experience a diminished use of opioids in the short-term, the initial gains fade with time and many users return to use patterns similar to before the procedure, particularly if no counselling component accompanies the post-treatment period (Hamilton et al., 2002; Krabbe et al., 2003; McGregor et al., 2002; Rothenberg et al., 2002). A publicly funded alternative that has emerged is Rapid Access Addiction Medicine (RAAM) clinics or Rapid Access Clinics (RAC). RACs and RAAMs are located in larger urban centres where non-medical detox programs exist. Their mandate is to see an individual within 24 hours after referral, provide pharmacological support for the addiction such as methadone or Suboxone to lessen cravings, assist with withdrawal, and connect individuals to the formal addiction counselling continuum of care.

ASSESSMENT

Once an individual has been identified as having a substance misuse issue, the depth and breadth of the situation needs to be determined. Assessment agencies provide services that use specific instruments and processes to determine the major issues, as well as the strengths and supports of the person with a substance issue. These agencies develop individualized plans for assistance, sometimes providing the counselling in-house but also referring to other organizations for more intensive or residential treatment. A standardized assessment procedure can take anywhere from two to three hours to complete. Currently there is no national consensus on what constitutes comprehensive assessment, with different provinces using different tools. An assessment typically includes a history of the use of alcohol and other drugs, including age of onset, duration, patterns, consequences of use, and use of alcohol and drugs by family members, along with types of and responses to previous treatment initiatives. It is also recommended that assessments determine a person's physical health, environmental supports (including partner and family), accommodation, employment and/or school status, leisure activities, legal problems, sexual orientation, and any history of sexual or other physical abuse or trauma. It is also essential to initially assess the level and intensity of withdrawal management and stabilization services required. This systematic process must also identify service users' strengths and take into consideration what they actually want.

The principal function of assessment is to act as the entry point into the treatment system and to provide a comprehensive portrait of the service user and their current situation. The assessment should culminate in an individualized treatment plan, including referral into the community's treatment service network when required. Some models for community-based assessment programs also include a case management role for assessment workers, thereby providing continuity to the service user from assessment to treatment to aftercare, highlighted by a reoccurrence prevention plan.

Specialized assessment services have been promoted as an integral part of a comprehensive local treatment system and have become a vital resource in many communities. Staff at assessment centres should possess the following:

- in-depth knowledge of effects of alcohol and/or other psychoactive drugs on physical and mental health, employment, financial, and legal difficulties; marital and family relationships; and social, religious, and cultural identity
- in-depth knowledge of treatment resources available to deal with service users' problems, including resources specific to treating alcohol and other drug issues
- knowledge of assessment tools specific to identifying drinking and/or drug-using activities

- access to psychological testing to determine the extent of damage from alcohol and/or drugs and thus the ability of service users to respond to treatment and interact in a treatment community
- ability to assess strengths and resources that would be a base for service users to begin to resolve their situation
- ability to identify environmental factors that might adversely affect treatment
- ability to prioritize service users' treatment needs
- ability to work co-operatively with service users and other stakeholders in the treatment system to design an appropriate treatment plan
- attitudes and specialized knowledge regarding needs of particular groups, such as youth, women, elderly, Indigenous, minority, and newcomer groups
- specialized knowledge of resources directed specifically to the above groups

CASE MANAGEMENT

Case management is a service user–focused strategy to improve coordination and continuity of care. Service users are provided a designated primary worker whose responsibilities include the ongoing assessment, treatment plan adjustment, coordination of required services, monitoring and support, and ultimately development of a discharge plan. In many instances, service users with addiction issues need to be linked to several different agencies to deal with the range of issues that have arisen due to the addiction (see Chapters 26 and 27). The case management role involves the counsellor serving as a referral agent, facilitator, and advocate for the service user, ensuring that the individual's assessment is accurate and up to date. The purpose of case management is to expedite the use of resources available in the community, consistent with an overall treatment plan, through a single, consistent point of contact. Without case management, the potential for inefficient use of limited resources increases. There may be misunderstandings among agencies as to who will deal with what problems, especially if the service user begins to develop additional issues after the initial assessment has been completed. Some issues can potentially be addressed by more than one organization, leading to duplication of services, while other problems may be missed altogether by all agencies unless there is one person responsible for coordinating the overall treatment plan in conjunction with the service user. In Canada, when case management does occur, it is often taken on by staff at assessment agencies or by counsellors within opioid-treatment programs. The tasks of a case manager can include the following:

- providing continuity of care for the alcohol/drug-dependent person
- facilitating contact with appropriate treatment resources
- assisting the service user in entering the appropriate treatment centre
- monitoring service users' changing needs and problems

- periodic assessment of service users' progress in terms of the agreed-upon treatment plan
- providing crisis intervention and ongoing support to service users and their families in solving immediate problems
- encouraging service users who leave treatment prematurely to return for further appropriate assistance
- facilitating, within the bounds of confidentiality, information sharing with all concerned parties, including other agencies, family, the Employee Assistance Program, and/or family physician
- providing aftercare or follow-up care after discharge from treatment to ensure that service users receive continuing encouragement and, where necessary, additional services
- assessing the risk of reoccurrence

Case managers can also become involved in helping service users learn social and relationship skills, developing constructive coping skills, and developing constructive leisure activities. Active case management increases treatment participation, decreases reoccurrence rates, and is a cost-effective use of a counsellor's time (Saleh et al., 2006; Vanderplasschen et al., 2004). In a study conducted in Philadelphia, a case manager was attached to a withdrawal management program. Before case management was fully operative, two-thirds of the treatments received by service users began and ended with detoxification. Afterwards this proportion more than halved, and instead there were increased referrals to residential programs. Average stays in treatment improved from one week to approximately one month (McLellan et al., 2005). Unfortunately, in Canada, case management is one of the largest gaps in the addiction continuum of care.

CHAPTER 26

Addiction-Specific Resources

As highlighted in Figure 25.1, there are several addiction-specific resources for the addiction continuum of care. The continuum of care consists of the following:

- community-based (outpatient) treatment
- day treatment
- harm reduction
- concurrent disorder programs
- short-term residential treatment
- recovery homes
- alternative living environment and therapeutic communities
- addiction supportive housing (ASH): Housing First
- managed alcohol programs: non-abstinence residential programs—the "wet shelter"
- drug treatment courts

COMMUNITY-BASED (OUTPATIENT) TREATMENT

This treatment is provided on a non-residential basis, usually in regularly scheduled sessions of one hour per week, though sometimes two times per week. Treatment may entail individual and/or group sessions to explore all aspects of the person's substance misuse and related issues. Sessions offer information and strategies to assist individuals in their recovery process. This is the least intense and intrusive treatment intervention option, primarily offered by non-medical, community-based counselling agencies. Appropriate matches for this service include individuals who

- are free of any significant medical problems;
- are self-motivated;
- have a support system in place, including family, friends, or work;
- live within easy access to the facility; and
- have not had their personal or work life extensively affected yet by their substance use.

DAY TREATMENT

This more intensive, structured non-residential treatment is typically provided five days per week or four or five evenings per week for three to four hours per session. The concept of using day treatment as an alternative to short-term residential programs emerged in the late 1960s, but it has never been prominent in Canada. Treatment involves group activities ranging from formal treatment sessions to education to recreational activities. As service users are home weekends, evenings, and/or days, the home environment must be stable with support from family and friends. This treatment option allows the social aspect of addiction to be acknowledged and addressed early and throughout the treatment process.

Day treatment is appropriate for individuals who are able to maintain social competence despite their dependency. Day treatment programs operate under a philosophy that attempts to develop a sense of community support and responsibility so that a person may attain balanced health and wellness. Day treatment is one means of providing a short-term, intensive, and structured period of treatment while keeping treatment costs down, especially in comparison to an in-patient stay in a more institutional setting.

An option that has traditionally received much less attention but has great merit as an alternative is evening-care programming. Intensive treatment programs offered in the evening may be desirable given the high proportion of people in addiction programs who are employed. Intensive evening programs may be more responsive to the time constraints of particular service users than programs operating during normal business hours. This option also appeals to those who do not wish their workplace to know about their personal problems or who need to continue to work throughout their treatment.

HARM REDUCTION

Harm reduction has always been practised as part of the addiction continuum of care, but as it has become more prominent it has also become more controversial. While methadone maintenance programs existed as early as the 1960s, harm reduction became more established in Canada as a response to AIDS and HIV in the late 1980s, when the mandate was to reduce the spread of potentially deadly communicable diseases, reduce drug overdose deaths, increase contact with health care services along with more traditional drug treatment programs, and reduce the consumption of illicit drugs. The most common forms of harm-reduction programs found in Canada are:

1. *Drug substitution—maintenance programs:* Methadone and Suboxone (see Chapters 9 and 16) are both opioids that are given orally to individuals physically and psychologically dependent upon other opioids, as a means of decreasing problematic opioid use. These two opioids do not produce the same euphoria as others in this family of drugs such as morphine, Oxycontin, heroin, or fentanyl, and are safer as they are not injected, given in standardized doses with no impurities, and do not

have to be taken as often. The use of methadone and Suboxone eliminates withdrawal, though the drugs need to be taken every day because if a person misses a dose they will experience the same withdrawal effects as any other opioid.

2. *Drug substitution—treatment programs:* Methadone and Suboxone treatment (MT/ST) also begins by switching an opioid dependent person from the drug they were using to one of these two alternative substances. However, along with receiving the drug, individuals in treatment programs receive counselling and a treatment plan that entails a gradual decrease of the drug to a lower level and in many instances to a point of abstinence. While early methadone maintenance programs claimed this process could be completed in weeks, currently treatment programs are more gradual. An individual will be maintained on the substitute drug and, once stabilized, there will be a decrease in the daily amount consumed, followed by another stabilization period, followed by another decrease. This process can take two to three years, during which the psychological and social issues associated with the initial drug use are also addressed.

3. *Heroin-assisted treatment (HAT):* Heroin prescription entails a physician providing identified drug users, who do not respond well to methadone or Suboxone, with daily prescriptions of medical-grade heroin. This controversial approach was first implemented in 1926 in the United Kingdom, long before methadone or Suboxone were synthesized, as a result of the addiction issues arising after World War I. HAT operates under the same premise as methadone maintenance, with the same benefits and risks. Heroin-assisted treatment evaluations, including those conducted in Canada, have shown a decrease in use of other opioids and involvement in the criminal justice system, as well as increases in health and social contacts, for those involved in the program.

4. *Needle exchange programs:* These are services that allow individuals to trade old, used syringes for new, sterile ones, along with related supplies to provide safer intravenous injection. These programs exist as fixed sites, street outreach initiatives, and mobile delivery vans. They may also offer crack pipes and straws for individuals using drugs through insufflation (administering the drug via the mucous membrane of the nose).

5. *Supervised injection sites (SIS):* Supervised injection sites, or supervised injection facilities (SIF), are clinics that allow injection drug users to obtain clean needles and sterilized supplies and that provide a clean, private setting in which to inject drugs. The goal of SIS is not only to provide individuals a safer environment but also to provide related health and social services, all in one location.

6. *Supervised consumption sites:* Supervised consumption sites provide the same services as SIS but also provide support for drugs that are inhaled and taken across the mucous membrane (insufflation) (Csiernik, Rowe et al., 2017). Caulkins, Pardo, and Kilmer (2019) reported that there has yet to be a documented case of a drug poisoning or overdose death in a professionally operated supervised consumption site in Canada.

CONCURRENT DISORDER PROGRAMS

Another specialized form of community-based counselling entails work done by agencies whose service users have both an addiction and a mental health issue. Services offered by institutional and community-based psychologists, psychiatrists, social workers, and nurses have long been a part of the extended continuum of care. Traditionally, these helping professionals dealt with either the mental health issue or the addiction issue alone, rarely together. However, beginning this century, many more specific programs have begun to emerge that address both issues simultaneously (Kimberly & Osmond, 2017).

Concurrent disorder programs move beyond working only with the addiction issue and provide counselling that also addresses issues such as depression, psychosis, loneliness, suicidal ideation and attempts, paranoia, and violent behaviours. Whether these behaviours are primary or secondary to the use of psychoactive agents is no longer an issue. Rather, the mental health problems are categorized as coexisting with the drug misuse, and vice versa, and thus treatment focuses on both. Mental health agencies had traditionally provided a wide range of individual and group counselling techniques, including behaviour modification, assertiveness training, leisure counselling, relaxation techniques, communication skills, and, when needed, pharmacological interventions. However, they did not typically directly address any addiction issues their service users had, and thus long-term outcomes were not as favourable as they could have been. Agencies providing concurrent disorder programming work with individuals who historically fell through the gaps of the addiction and mental health systems, as one system often did not wish to work with the person until the issues relating to the other system were resolved. This, of course, left service users with both issues typically receiving no care and thus deteriorating both with respect to their mental health and their drug misuse.

SHORT-TERM RESIDENTIAL TREATMENT

The first formal treatment environments to emerge in North America, after Alcoholics Anonymous, were three in-patient treatment programs: Pioneer House (1948), Hazelden (1949), and the Willmar State Hospital (1950). Prior to these, the only type of residential programming that treated those with alcohol issues were sanatoriums or rehabilitation farms, where alcohol-dependent individuals were sequestered from their environments for health reasons. These early programs were founded on the principles and philosophy proposed by AA, and took on the moniker of the Minnesota Model, following the same guidelines:

- Alcoholism is an involuntary, primary, chronic, progressive biopsychosocial, spiritual disease.
- Recovery is contingent upon abstinence from all non-medical drugs.
- Recovery is best achieved through the Twelve Steps of AA and immersion in a community of shared experience, strength, and hope.

- Focus of the residential rehabilitation process should be on the direct treatment of the disease.
- Addiction needs to be treated in an environment of dignity and respect.
- Motivation, or lack of motivation, at point of intake is not a predictor of outcome success, and motivation is as much the responsibility of the treatment setting as the individual (Cook, 1988; McElrath, 1997).

Success entailed not only attending AA meetings as an integral part of the residential treatment process, but also continued attendance on completion of rehabilitation.

Currently these treatment services are provided for less than 42 days, though average program length in Canada is typically 21 to 28 days. These short-term intensive treatment programs are either affiliated with hospitals and take a medical orientation or operate as community-based programs that still follow the Minnesota Model principles. Programs are not restricted to particular groups, though there are men- and women-specific programs, and they receive referrals from all segments of the health and social service network and also the workplace. Given the range of expertise within these facilities, they are capable of providing comprehensive assessments and offer a wide variety of treatment modalities. Almost all programs now also provide aftercare support in the form of reoccurrence prevention or alumni groups, with many offering family information nights on weekends. Unfortunately, the residential component of hospital-based programs makes them much more expensive in comparison to day treatment or community-based outpatient options, though 12-step-based programs and other non-medical programs remain less expensive to operate.

In-patient residential treatment offers a wide variety of services, including medical evaluation, assessment of the extent of the drug dependency, detoxification in some facilities, individual and group counselling, drug education, spiritual guidance, family involvement, vocational guidance, and even employer involvement. The centres provide a safe, relatively stress-free environment in which the person can recover from the physical and emotional effects of prolonged drinking and/or substance misuse. Planning for rehabilitation on return to the natural environment is also typically part of the process. Education regarding the effects of drugs varies from centre to centre, but usually includes the short- and long-term effects of drug use physiologically, socially, spiritually, and psychologically. There is also often attendance at a 12-step group that is either recommended or mandated, even in programs not premised on the philosophy of Alcoholics Anonymous.

Treatment staff's efforts to involve families and employers in the intervention process reflect the increasing awareness of the social-emotional environmental aspects that affect and are affected by residents' behaviour. This logical extension of increasing involvement of the resident's social world in the intervention process has also encouraged a significant increase in the options for help available following the in-patient experience. For example, in some institutions, service users are informed that a successful recovery process can involve two full years of active participation while individuals are living in their home community. Even more progressive residential programs have developed specific information and counselling programs for family members of those in residence.

In Canada, as a result of treatment costs, standardized provincial assessment outcomes recommend that only those with severe or chronic addiction issues be referred to residential programs. This has forced many programs to develop two-tier admission policies: one for those who are receiving treatment through universal health care and one for those who are paying for the treatment through workplace or personal extended health care benefits. This, in turn, has led to the slow but steady growth of private fee-for-service short-term residential programs that operate without formal oversight, with costs running as high as $40,000–$50,000 CAD.

RECOVERY HOMES

For many struggling with ongoing issues in their recovery, the ability to avoid a reoccurrence is often jeopardized by untenable housing or an unsupportive living environment. Recovery residences, also called social model recovery, or sober living houses, are designed to provide safe and supportive housing to help individuals initiate and sustain recovery, primarily through peer-to-peer interactions guided by a staff who themselves have recovery histories. These are gender-specific residential programs in which the goal is to provide a safe, supportive, therapeutic program of addiction education and life skills counselling. Interestingly, a recent qualitative study of 19 women with complex drug use histories, all of whom also had histories of physical or sexual abuse, and reoccurrences of drug use linked to relationships with men, reported that they did not necessarily want or perceive benefit in women-only residential treatment (Neale et al., 2018).

Recovery homes provide an array of services to individuals with addiction problems within a structured environment, either prior to or after the person has attended a withdrawal management program and/or received more intensive treatment from a short-term residential program. In some jurisdictions, these homes are classified as supportive housing programs (Polcin et al., 2014). Programs are developed to assist the recovering person in personal growth and positive lifestyle change. Recovery homes have a comparatively long history, with many facilities first developed in the 1960s and early 1970s (Ogborne et al., 1978).

In the United States, the use of AA as the foundation for programming in this environment became known as the Oxford House approach. Recovery homes are centres from which individuals can re-establish themselves in the community. A typical stay can range from three to six months. Therapeutic efforts are focused on providing social support and linking this with the social reality of the living circumstances, working with the residents through the actual living problems as they present themselves. The intent is for the facility to provide a bridge between initial intensive treatment and returning to the community. Residents assume a major share of the daily chores and functions of the house and are encouraged and assisted in finding employment in the local community, thereby contributing financially toward their own room and board. Recovery homes also offer group and individual counselling that focuses on physical, emotional, educational, and employment objectives. Alcoholics Anonymous and Narcotics Anonymous meetings also tend to be a core feature of recovery home programs. Staffing is frequently conducted by recovering persons who share their own life experiences with new residents and who act as role models and sounding boards (Polcin, 2009).

Typical sessions offered within a recovery home setting can include the following:

- education on the process of drug dependency
- exercise, nutrition counselling, and information pertaining to health issues
- problem-solving and decision-making skills
- information on retraining and job search skills
- appropriate use of leisure time
- goal setting
- communication and assertiveness
- stress management
- avoiding reoccurrence

Recovery homes also place an emphasis on knowledge gained through one's recovery experience. Residents draw on that experience as a way to help others. As well, for those who retain family supports, weekly family education sessions may be a component to aid family, friends, and significant others in learning how to deal with their feelings and to help them provide support for service users during their ongoing recovery. Numerous recovery homes also provide non-residential services, indicating a willingness to diversify and serve individuals for whom a completely residential service may not be appropriate. As well, many offer follow-up programs for individuals who have returned to the community to live. Costs of staying at a recovery home are typically geared to an individual's income, with subsidies often provided through local social-assistance programs if an individual is unable to pay.

ALTERNATIVE LIVING ENVIRONMENT AND THERAPEUTIC COMMUNITIES

For many persons with a substance misuse issue, the environment they live in is counter-productive to their successful treatment and recovery. These persons have unstable home lives and/or no support from family and friends. Others who come into treatment have no real home, no role models for healthy living, or need to relearn or learn socialization skills. Alternative living environments and therapeutic communities provide a protective living environment for people whose substance misuse is not an isolated problem but a major disruption of their entire lives. Therapeutic communities are community-led living and learning environments designed to promote social, psychological, and behavioural change. They are intensive structured programs, operating 24 hours a day and 7 days a week, where individuals live together and are encouraged to confront and un-learn addiction-related and anti-social patterns and behaviours. A defining feature of therapeutic communities is the use of the community itself as an agent of change. As with recovery homes, these programs tend to be gender specific (Aslan, 2018).

The objectives of a therapeutic community are to maintain abstinence and promote social rehabilitation. Unlike some other residential facilities in these communities, the therapeutic system is based on stages of treatment change that provide residents with increasing degrees of personal and social responsibility for the running of the community. Peer influence mediated through group processes is used to help individuals develop social norms and develop social skills, while social rehabilitation is promoted through daily activities. Residents have the opportunity to progress in the hierarchy to managing group activities as a peer leader. These programs help in setting limits and defining behaviour while satisfying daily needs and desires in a quasi-home setting. Relationships that develop provide a basis on which the members can learn or relearn how to live with others. Real-life issues of daily existence take precedence at these facilities (Malivert et al., 2012). Many alternative living settings are affiliated with a religious order, with the most prominent being the Salvation Army.

Although the term was first used in 1946, the therapeutic community (TC) movement evolved mainly during the 1960s as an alternative to institutionalized psychiatric care (Main, 1946; Manning, 1989). In the United Kingdom, TCs originally provided an optional form of treatment for addiction, but also for personality disorders and related mental health diagnoses. In the United States, they evolved as an alternative to involuntary detention under civil commitment laws (De Leon, 1988). A major proponent was Charles Dederich, who developed Synanon in an attempt to provide a safe haven for chronic opioid users within a positive living environment. Recovering drug-dependent persons viewed the therapeutic community treatment modality as a mutual aid endeavour to treat the whole person, whose criminal thoughts and lifestyle were at the root of drug use. They believed that the best way to counter antisocial thinking and exploitative social interaction was to immerse formerly drug-dependent persons, mainly heroin users, in a community-based therapeutically oriented social environment. In this setting, every aspect of maladaptive behaviour and thinking would be exposed and subject to correction by other recovering persons, who would recognize the distorted ways of thinking and social interaction that are common in drug addiction. Therapeutic communities were seen as a viable treatment alternative for individuals whose substance use made them eligible for detention in the criminal justice system. Their originators saw programs evolve that had an intense structure, peer-enforced values, and active confrontation of any behaviour deemed disruptive or regressive. The intent at Synanon in particular was to change the personality so that the individual remained drug- and crime-free (Barnett, 2009; Mandell et al., 2008).

Contemporary therapeutic communities operate from the perspective that substance use is a problem of the whole person. The goal of the TC is not just to eliminate the substance use behaviour, but to refocus the individual. Thus, all activities are designed to be psycho-educational, emphasizing personal behavioural, attitudinal, and value change to support lifelong abstinence (De Leon, 1997). These facilities focus on the here and now, on truth and honesty, and on personal responsibility and community involvement. Participants contribute to all activities of daily living in the TC. As a result, they adopt various social roles and become active participants in the process of changing themselves and others (Barnett, 2009). A number of contextual factors contribute to the delivery of an effective recovery community: fostering community, a sense of belongingness and personal space, peer support, options regarding community routine and structure, a sense of fun, and a person-centred focus not only providing support on a typical Monday-to-Friday business model (Eckley et al., 2016).

Peer membership provides the primary source of instruction and support within therapeutic communities. Participants have a shared responsibility to observe and authentically react to each other's actions. Each participant aims to model the change process. Not only do they provide feedback about what others can change, but they also model change behaviour in themselves. Group formats are used for education, training, and other therapeutic activities. Shared norms, values, rules, and regulations serve as explicit guidelines for mutual aid and teach how to live in a healthy manner. Participants must reinforce these guidelines. Learning occurs not only through skills training but also by adhering to the procedures and systems of the TC (De Leon, 1995). While connection with peers is vital, a formal evaluation conducted in the United Kingdom found that success also included being able to rebuild connections and trust with family members and demonstrate that program participants were now responsible for their behaviour. Likewise, members in contemporary therapeutic communities also wanted to work on their overall communication skills in order to reconnect with members of society not in recovery (Eckley et al., 2016).

ADDICTION SUPPORTIVE HOUSING (ASH): HOUSING FIRST

Addiction supportive housing programs are another component of the treatment continuum that recognizes the importance of safe and sustainable housing in the recovery process. Part of the Housing First initiative, these programs provide longer support in a therapeutic environment than do short-term residential programs or recovery homes. The goal is to encourage program participants to develop long-term skills that are necessary to maintain their own residence. Increasingly, the value of supportive housing initiatives is being recognized across service sectors, as addiction is frequently intertwined with issues of poverty, homelessness, and mental health (DiLeo, 2003; Rickards et al., 2010). In fact, substance misuse is a primary predictor of homelessness (Dickson-Gomez et al.,

2007; Edens et al., 2011). By providing housing supports, ideally in conjunction with, but not contingent on, addiction treatment, service providers can increase the probability that someone who is marginally housed or homeless will follow through with addiction treatment. This is particularly crucial after a person receives their initial assessment and is placed on a waiting list due to a lack of available resources (O'Connell et al., 2013; Winn et al., 2013). Individuals who have participated in supportive housing programs have demonstrated a reduction in contact with the criminal justice system and residential treatment while improving their income levels, access to food, and housing stability (Hickert & Taylor, 2011). However, not all service users will be successful in this model either, and thus matching is key here as well.

Housing First programs can be considered a component of the harm reduction approach to addiction treatment (Collins et al., 2012; Larimer, 2012; Pauly et al., 2013), as permanent housing is viewed as a human right and not an earned privilege contingent on abstinence or treatment participation (van Wormer & van Wormer, 2009). What distinguishes some Housing First programs is that they do not make admission contingent on sobriety or treatment attendance but rather target chronically homeless people who are high users of publicly funded health and criminal-justice resources. In fact, though Housing First programs effectively end homelessness, randomized controlled trials have shown that they do not reduce daily substance use among homeless adults who also are experiencing mental illness (Henwood, 2015), though a Canadian study found that while drug use did not decrease among residents, alcohol use did (Kirst et al., 2015).

A study in Seattle, Washington, reviewed the use and cost of services before and after program admission among 95 participants in a Housing First program, 39 of whom were wait-listed and all of whom had severe alcohol problems. The results revealed the following:

- Monthly median costs among admitted participants decreased from $5,360 CAD in the year before admission to $1,967 after six months in housing and $1,263 after twelve months in housing.
- Even after accounting for housing program costs, total mean monthly spending on housed participants compared with wait-listed participants was $3,228 lower after six months.
- Both costs and crisis-services use decreased the longer the person remained housed.
- The number of drinks per day among housed participants decreased from 15.7 prior to housing to 14.0 at six months, 12.5 at nine months, and 10.6 at twelve months.

Both costs and alcohol consumption further decreased the longer participants were in supportive housing. This indicates that the provision of supportive housing for chronically homeless individuals can substantially reduce the cost of and burden on health and criminal justice services (Larimer et al., 2009).

In the Ontario ASH initiative, two living options are available to service users who have typically completed an addiction treatment program yet still remain at risk of homelessness. One is the transitional house option, which is gender-specific communal living with up to four individuals per house. Individuals are required to attend weekly house meetings, be involved in a community support program, such as a 12-step group or an aftercare program, and participate in the general upkeep and chores of the house. This very much resembles an alternative living environment, though under much smaller parameters and less direct supervision. The other option is independent living in a single unit. Service users are required to attend a weekly one-to-one counselling session with an ASH counsellor. The single units are, however, a harm reduction–based approach and the requirements for remaining in the program are much more individualized and person-centred, though all service users must participate in the program and actively work on some type of change goal. Both the transition home and single units are subsidized, geared-to-income rental units. The initial six-month evaluation of this initiative indicates that the program is reaching a group that had historically been hard to serve. Improvements were found in increased levels of health and functioning and in reductions in substance use, use of emergency departments, hospital admissions, and encounters with the criminal justice system (Johnston Consulting, 2014).

MANAGED ALCOHOL PROGRAMS: NON-ABSTINENCE RESIDENTIAL PROGRAMS—THE "WET SHELTER"

Harm reduction initiatives have historically been outpatient and community-based with the goal of reducing negative health, social, and economic outcomes. Until the early 1990s, the policy throughout Canada was to confiscate any drug, including alcohol, from an individual seeking a shelter bed for a night. This precluded many chronic alcohol users from using the shelter system, including during cold Canadian winters. Influenced by harm-reduction advocates, staff at Seaton House, a large shelter in Toronto, adopted a policy where any alcohol coming into the shelter would not be confiscated and poured down the drain, but rather collected, labelled, stored, and then returned to the owner the next morning when the individual left the shelter for the day. After a coroner's inquest into the freezing deaths of three homeless men in Toronto, Seaton House expanded their approach to include one area of the facility that allowed for supervised consumption of alcohol on site, an ongoing initiative in which residents are provided with a regulated amount of alcohol each hour. The idea was to keep residents from leaving the shelter and putting themselves at risk in order to find an alcoholic beverage, and also to reduce the consumption of harmful alcohol-based products such as hand sanitizer and mouthwash.

Two other communities in Ontario, Ottawa and Hamilton, followed Toronto's lead in establishing addiction-related residential programs where the consumption of alcohol is a core part of the daily routine, and by 2019 there were 22 programs located across five provinces: British Colombia (4), Alberta (7), Saskatchewan (2), Manitoba (2), and Ontario (7).

At Shepherds of Good Hope in Ottawa, service users are individually assessed to determine the appropriate amount and frequency of alcohol to be administered to meet their health needs. Individuals have a choice of 12 percent white or red wine. No more than five ounces is provided at one time, with the exception of the first drink of the morning, which can be up to seven ounces. Between 7:30 a.m. and 9:30 p.m., participants can receive a maximum of 14 drinks, which by standard levels seems excessive. However, some individuals in the program had consumption levels as great as 48 standard drinks a day (Inner City Health, 2010). Claremont House in Hamilton has moved to the point where residents are involved in brewing their own alcohol as part of their residential responsibilities, with the enhancement of the quality of life of residents being the ongoing mission of the organization.

The primary purpose of managed alcohol programs (MAPs) is to offer continuing health and housing services for individuals who have a history of homelessness and alcohol misuse along with chronic health issues, and who are often deemed to be near the end of their lives and remain unwilling or unable to participate in an abstinence-based residential program. The aim of this component of the continuum of care is to integrate social support with individualized humane treatment to reduce harm to service users by eliminating the need to binge drink and to drink non-beverage alcohol products (Brooks et al., 2018). Nursing, medical, and rehabilitation care are provided, along with a regular but limited amount of alcohol. MAPs provide residents with permanent rather than transient housing, similar to the Housing First philosophy, though some, like The Annex at Seaton House, remain shelters. Some MAPs offer private rooms, though the standard is shared accommodation, with all programs staffed 24 hours per day. The majority of MAP service users are male. Care plans are individualized and include a recreational component and access to primary health care. The overall goal is to improve the quality of life of service users while allowing them to live in a respectful, supportive environment (Podymow et al., 2006). Involvement in a MAP has also been shown to lead to fewer emergency department and hospital admissions due to a lower incidence of alcohol-related harm, fewer detox episodes, and fewer police contacts leading to custody. MAPs are also more cost-effective than acute and crisis use of the health care system (Larimer et al., 2009; McMaster Health Forum, 2019; Pauly et al., 2013). A summary of the benefits and risks of managed alcohol programs are outlined in Table 26.1.

DRUG TREATMENT COURTS

Another progressive addition to the addiction continuum of care in Canada has been the development of drug courts or drug treatment courts (DTCs), which aim to reduce substance use and provide rehabilitation to persons who resort to criminal activity to support their addictions (Canadian Association of Drug Treatment Court Professionals

Table 26.1: Risks and Benefits of Managed Alcohol Programs

Risk	Single Heavy Drinking Episode	Non-Beverage Alcohol Consumption	Drinking in Unsafe Settings	Chronic High-Volume Alcohol Consumption
Potential Harms	violence, injury, poisoning, seizures, legal issues	exacerbates chronic diseases, poisoning	violence, injury, freezing, conflict with the law	cirrhosis, cancer, housing and social problems
MAP Benefits	smooths drinking pattern, fewer injuries and seizures, secure housing, improved relationships	reduced consumption of non-beverage alcohol	shelter from cold, protected supply of alcohol, personal safety, food	housing security, reduced consumption, improved nutrition
MAP Risks	higher blood alcohol concentration if drinking continues outside of program	increased ethanol consumption if drinking continues outside of program	less exercise and weight gain	fewer days of abstinence contribute to liver disease risk

Source: Stockwell et al. (2013).

[CADTP], n.d.). First established in Miami, Florida, in 1989, the inaugural Canadian drug treatment court opened in 1998 in Toronto. DTCs are premised on the theory that substance use and criminal behaviour can perpetuate a vicious cycle. To break this cycle, treatment and rehabilitation outside the traditional prison system is often required. In this way, DTCs represent a partnership between the criminal justice and addiction treatment systems (Barnes, 2011).

Justice Barnes (2011) identified the following principles and objectives of DTCs:

- increase *public* safety
- help participants reduce or eliminate drug use
- help participants reduce or eliminate criminal behaviour
- help reunite participants with their families
- help participants become productive members of society
- have participants experience an overall improvement in personal well-being

Although historically unstandardized and with no universal model (UNODC, 2005), there are established international guidelines that each drug treatment court strives to uphold. There is also recognition that they can and should be tailored to individual jurisdictional needs (CADTP, n.d.). The guidelines include:

- integrating addiction treatment services with justice system case processing

- using a non-adversarial approach to allow prosecution and defence counsels to promote public safety while protecting participants' Charter rights
- identifying eligible participants early in their contact with the criminal justice system so that they can be placed in the drug treatment court program as promptly as possible
- providing access to a continuum of drug, alcohol, and other related treatment and rehabilitative services
- monitoring compliance by frequent drug testing
- developing a coordinated strategy governing drug treatment court responses to participants' compliance and non-compliance
- applying both sanctions and rewards, swiftly, certainly, and consistently, for both non-compliance and/or compliance
- ongoing judicial interaction with each drug treatment court participant
- monitoring and evaluating the achievement of program goals and gauging their overall effectiveness
- continuing interdisciplinary education promoting effective drug treatment court planning, implementation, and operations
- forging partnerships among courts, treatment and rehabilitation programs, public agencies, and community-based organizations to generate local support and enhance program effectiveness
- ongoing case management providing the social support necessary to achieve social reintegration
- being appropriately flexible in adjusting program content, including incentives and sanctions, to better achieve program results with particular groups, such as women, Indigenous people, and racialized minorities

The first meta-analysis on drug treatment court outcomes indicated that participation had a modest, though statistically significant, impact on decreasing recidivism. Those involved in regular court proceedings had a 50 percent rate of recidivism whereas those adjudicated in the drug court system were likely to reoffend 37.5 percent of the time across the studies reviewed. However, success rates are far greater when non-violent crimes were associated with the drug charge (Mitchell et al., 2012). There are also substantive cost savings with treating rather than incarcerating individuals with drug-related crimes, particularly those that are non-violent in nature. Savings ranged from $1,000 to $15,000 AUD per participant in an Australian study, to a 75 percent cost return across five drug treatment courts in Washington state, to a study in St. Louis, Missouri, that found drug treatment court participants cost less to monitor than those on probation (Duggal, 2016).

In Canada there are currently 23 drug treatment court programs. Upwards of 90 percent of DTC participants have a lengthy history of prior convictions, with 86 percent reporting drug use prior to turning 18 and two-thirds also having a mental health issue ranging from depression to PTSD. Nearly all participants are unemployed, with high levels of risk to reoffend and acute or chronic health needs. Canadian drug treatment courts provide intensive treatment services, case management, and judicial supervision, and participants are released with strict bail conditions, including rules for curfew, living arrangements, and limitations on who they can interact with and where they can live. In many instances, these conditions are more restrictive than probation rulings. DTC participation also requires the provision of random urine drug tests at least once or twice per week. To graduate, participants must have an extended period of abstinence, no new criminal charges, stable housing, and be employed, in school, or engaged in active volunteer work. An evaluation study completed on one Ontario DTC found a total savings of approximately $12 million CAD, with frequency of drug use declining from an average of 28.5 days per month to 0.8 days per month during participation in the program. As well, nearly half of DTC participants re-established a connection with supportive family members after entering the program (Budd et al., 2019).

Although drug treatment courts are already recognized as specialized initiatives, an even more specific court process is the family drug treatment court (FDTC). In addition to the need for substance use treatment, FDTCs also recognize the role of trauma in both addiction and child welfare contexts (Drabble et al., 2013). FDTCs aim to improve outcomes for children by assisting parents whose alcohol or other drug use puts their children at risk. While improved family relations and family reunification are the goals, the court does not always reunite children with their parents, depending upon parents' treatment outcomes. One evaluation conducted in England reported that parents found the FDTC process fairer and more empowering than typical child welfare court interactions, where they felt they had little voice and little understanding of the process. While more children are returned to parental care in FDTC compared to typical court proceedings, more than half are still placed into permanent non-parental care (Harwin et al., 2016).

Lastly, it is important to note the potentially preventative role that DTCs play, especially among juvenile populations. Criminologists have historically maintained that conflict with the law among young offenders is a strong predictor of adult criminal behaviour, as 68 percent of adult crimes are committed by individuals formerly involved in the youth justice system (Kempf-Leonard et al., 2001). The overlap with substance misuse is also relevant, as individuals chronically misusing substances are three to four times more likely to commit a crime (Bennett et al., 2008).

IN-PATIENT VERSUS COMMUNITY-BASED OUTPATIENT CARE

Many controversies exist within the addiction field. Among the most prominent and long lasting has been the community-based versus in-patient treatment argument. The traditional approach, especially with long-term substance misusers, had been in-patient residential programming. However, research over the past five decades has tended to indicate that this is not the most efficient method of intervention and it is definitely not the most cost-effective.

The first studies to explore this issue occurred in the Maudsley Hospital in London, UK (Edwards & Guthrie, 1966, 1967; Edwards et al., 1977). A one-year follow-up study of men dependent on alcohol reported that there was no significant difference in outcome between those who had received community-based outpatient counselling and those who had received several months of in-patient treatment. Helen Annis (1984), of the Ontario Addiction Research Foundation, conducted an extensive review of the in-patient versus community counselling question at that time. Her conclusions were quite decisive:

- In-hospital alcoholism programs of a few weeks to a few months duration show no greater success in producing abstinence than do periods of brief hospitalization of a few days.
- The great majority of alcohol-dependent persons seeking treatment for alcohol withdrawal can be safely detoxified without pharmacotherapy and in non-hospital-based units.
- Detoxification with pharmacotherapy on an ambulatory basis has been demonstrated to be a safe alternative at one-tenth the cost.
- Partial hospitalization (day treatment) programs have been found to have equal or superior results to in-patient hospitalization in producing abstinence among individuals at one-half to one-third the cost.
- Controlled trials have demonstrated that community-based outpatient programs can produce comparable results to in-patient programs. One estimate placed the cost savings at $3,700 CAD per person (1984 dollars) compared with the typical course of medical in-patient treatment.

Another major critique of residential programming was that moving to a special treatment environment, where the individual's residence is temporarily changed, brings with it a set of limitations on the impact of the treatment. It is argued that the residential shift is an artificial one, and the impact of the treatment is heavily affected by this limitation. It is further contended that the transfer of an individual's treatment into the natural world needs to occur for the impact to be most successful. However, in-patient programs do provide environments where there are fewer urges or opportunities to use drugs, and limit the negative social issues associated with drug use. Nance (1992) agreed that there were shortcomings to in-patient care including cost, lack of matching service users to level, intensity, and duration of treatment, and overly simplistic treatment regimens. However, he stated that in-patient care offered several significant advantages as a treatment format by providing the following:

- protection from further drug use
- the opportunity for individuals to focus solely on their substance misuse problem

- a focus on ego strengthening and learning how to control compulsive behaviours
- maximum treatment retention

The short-term protection of a residential setting also enables those individuals with the greatest needs and most substantive environmental pressures to do as well as those with more initial strengths, often by eliminating the extra environmental risks faced in the community (Witbrodt et al., 2007). Residential treatment has been demonstrated to assist in moving service users along in their preparedness to change and also in instilling a sense of hope and resiliency (Shumway et al., 2013). A qualitative study of 36 men and 24 women completing residential treatment uncovered five dominant themes, underscoring the value they found in this treatment resource:

1. the creation of positive therapeutic changes in relation to their drug use;
2. development of emotional regulation;
3. increased mindfulness and self-awareness;
4. feeling positive about being able to do well after treatment; and,
5. establishing changes in how they approached important relationships (Yang, et al., 2019).

As well, a meta-analysis of 23 residential treatment outcome studies found this treatment resource to be effective in reducing substance use, improving mental health, improving social inclusion, and decreasing criminal justice involvement (de Andrade et al., 2019).

With the emergence of daytox options in Canada, controversy has also arisen in withdrawal management. As previously discussed, although the primary consideration of community-based detoxification programs is their cost-effectiveness when compared to in-patient settings, some suggest that the service user's personal characteristics may be more important than setting in predicting treatment success (McLellan et al., 1983; Hayashida, 1998; Hayashida et al., 1989). This contention is supported by research that finds no difference in reoccurrence rates among those receiving alcohol detoxification in hospitals, recovery homes, or community-based agencies (Smart et al., 1977). One clinical audit of an at-home detoxification program in the United Kingdom found that 96.6 percent of suitable candidates completed their programs successfully, but results were very much contingent on the individual having a suitable social support in the home and not having a severe mental health issue (Callow et al., 2008). Another contention is that home-based detoxification succeeds when primary care physicians actively support these endeavours (Roche et al., 2001), which is not the norm in Canada. In interviews with general practitioners in Australia, study participants did not feel that the necessary policies, infrastructure, or remuneration strategies were in place to support effective and widespread at-home detoxification. Similar studies in Wales, however, found that physicians were supportive of such treatment, and some even volunteered their time to provide in-home detoxification services to appropriate service users (Middlemiss, 2002; Stockwell et al., 1986; Stockwell et al., 1990).

Residential rehabilitation is a vital component of the addiction treatment continuum of care, not as an alternative to community treatment, but as one potential element of a successful recovery journey. However, unless there are pressing reasons for residential care, community-based counselling results are typically equivalent, at a much lower cost and with far less disruption to a person's life. Shorter and less-intensive approaches are not only most cost-effective but are more effective in absolute terms (Miller & Hester, 1986b; Witbrodt et al., 2007). An exception is concurrent disorder treatment programs, where longer residential care is associated with longer periods of abstinence and lower risk of homelessness (Brunette et al., 2001). Of course, it makes little sense to talk about length or intensity of treatment without considering what kind of treatment is being offered. Some modalities lack evidence for effectiveness at any length or level of intensity.

It is tempting to assume that more treatment is better treatment, and that longer or more intensive interventions will yield superior outcomes. However, the evidence clearly suggests that if service users are properly matched on clinically significant dimensions to a range of treatment alternatives, much higher overall improvement rates in the addiction treatment field would be observed. Thus, there needs to be a continuum of care in place to allow for the widest possible range of services. A balance is required between community and institutional treatment. A service user's needs must always be the first item on the agenda, and individuals should be matched to their specific needs. This becomes even more pertinent when the growing empirical evidence continues to indicate that there is no one single best approach in the addiction field, but that a variety of interventions are effective, as is the need for a variety of venues for treatment delivery (Polcin, 2009). Interestingly, for both community-based and residential care, the longer the contact with counsellors the more positive outcomes are reported (McPherson et al., 2017). As well, drawing from the concluding ideas presented in Section V, service user satisfaction with treatment is as much about the relationship developed with the counsellor as it is with the intervention or the treatment resource (Andersson et al., 2017).

CHAPTER 27

Adjunct Resources

Addiction disrupts an entire person and an entire family's homeostasis. As such, treatment often begins when treatment ends. While this last statement may seem confusing and contradictory, what it means is that there is often other counselling initiatives that are necessary once addiction counselling has concluded, with many individuals needing to work on issues beyond those that deal exclusively with psychoactive drugs. This is one reason case management services (see Chapter 25) are an important part of the addiction continuum of care, because the case manager can help the individuals, and their family members, connect with a broader range of community resources. Additional services that individuals with an addiction issue can often benefit from include the following:

- budgeting and financial counselling
- employment assistance/vocational training
- legal assistance
- marital and family counselling
- medical services
- mutual aid/self-help groups
- recreational/leisure programs
- social assistance (see Figure 25.1)

ADJUNCT RESOURCES

Budgeting and Financial Counselling

Individuals who develop addiction issues often accumulate significant debt by diverting much of their money toward purchasing their drug of choice, or simply through financial mismanagement or neglect. As part of the entire recovery process, attention may need to be concentrated at some point on budget counselling and assistance in debt management or consolidation. This type of assistance is generally free through registered credit counselling services, which are most often affiliated with family services agencies or financial institutions such as credit unions. Regardless of the service provider, ensure that the credit counsellor has completed the Accredited Financial Counsellor of Canada (AFCC) certification program.

Employment Assistance/Vocational Training

Individuals recovering from drug addiction often face challenges in returning to the job market and in maintaining employment. Many of them feel they have no choice but to do entry-level work, and they are often unsure about their work ability and vocational choice (Siu et al., 2019). During the course of treatment, others will come to the realization that they need to enter a new field of employment or look for a more stable employment option, as the job that they held or the workplace environment were themselves triggers leading to substance use. Of these service users, a proportion will also require additional assistance because of physical or psychological limitations that played a part in their becoming drug dependent or are a result of chronic misuse. Other individuals will benefit from aptitude testing, additional education, or specific skills training or retraining. Thus, the vocational segment of a service user's initial assessment can help establish an employment plan, or the need for retraining or additional education as part of the treatment plan. Having regular employment has been shown to not only provide recovering substance misusers income but also to assist with social reintegration as part of the recovery process (Sumnall & Brotherhood, 2012).

Legal Assistance

Unfortunately, many persons become involved in the addiction treatment system as a direct result of coming into conflict with the law. For others, the dramatic changes they personally undergo as a result of treatment lead them to significant life changes that necessitate legal action. Thus, a high rate of separation, divorce, and child custody claims can occur among substance misusers before, after, and during their recovery process, especially if family counselling was not part of the formal treatment process. Other frequent legal problems include driving while intoxicated, assault, and civil litigation claims, as well as theft and break and enter charges for those who committed crimes to support a drug dependency. As many substance misusers often require legal advice but do not have sufficient funds to pay for a lawyer, counsellors should also be aware of good legal aid lawyers and community and legal clinics that will provide legal counsel without charging a fee.

Marital and Family Counselling

Additional therapy beyond addiction counselling is often required for families, especially if it was not part of the formal addiction treatment process. This may entail couples counselling, sex counselling, sessions on parenting, grief counselling, and, for some, separation and/or divorce counselling. Support for partners and children of substance misusers should be a core feature of any community's continuum of care. Typically, in

North America, family treatment occurs outside the addiction treatment system, though in some nations, such as Norway, family members of the person with the alcohol or other drug problem are also entitled to take sick leave from work to accompany the person to treatment and receive counselling. Appropriate family counselling remains a major gap in the addiction continuum of care, and an area of need that anyone working in the addiction field should inquire about during the assessment process.

Medical Services

Too often persons suffering from an addiction have poor health, and thus part of the recovery process is dealing with the physical aspect of wellness. Medical attention may be required for emergency treatment of injuries or severe medical conditions, such as hepatitis or HIV, as part of a comprehensive assessment. However, often service users have more common problems, such as gastrointestinal complications, liver disorders, a cardiovascular issue, or even cancer due to their historic drug use, which has not been properly addressed. As well, medical support may be necessary to facilitate a complete recovery from substance misuse problems or in dealing with issues as fundamental as nutrition and fitness counselling. Addiction medicine is a specialized area of practice, one that not many physicians are well versed in, and one for which not all hospitals have dedicated staff, so being aware of physicians who specialize in this area will be an asset to your practice and to making appropriate referrals.

Mutual Aid/Self-Help Groups

Self-help groups hold a unique distinction: not only are they a method of peer-based helping, but, for some, a cultural experience. The original substance-related self-help group and the association responsible for the growth of addiction services in North America is Alcoholics Anonymous. From it has sprung Narcotics Anonymous, Nicotine Anonymous, Gamblers Anonymous, Overeaters Anonymous, Cocaine Anonymous, and many other similar 12-step recovery groups. As well, a series of addiction-specific non-12 step groups has arisen in response to the limitations of AA, thus further enhancing the support offered by this adjunct component of the continuum of care. Self-help groups can be used as an entry point into treatment, including non-addiction-specific groups, as well as a maintenance and reoccurrence-prevention service. In communities where there are few or no drug-specific services, there is still likely to be an AA group. In larger communities, AA groups meet seven days a week. Membership is voluntary and fees are based primarily on a "pass-the-hat" pay what you can format. However, self-help groups have moved beyond AA and addiction-related themes and offer support in areas ranging from mental health to physical health to parenting support groups. Those involved in providing assistance should be familiar with the continuum of care offered by mutual aid/self-help groups (see also Chapter 24).

Recreational/Leisure Programs

Quitting or moderating the use of a drug often constitutes a major change in a person's lifestyle, as individuals need to adapt to a new routine that revolves around recovery and abstaining from substance use. Part of this adaptation requires developing constructive uses of leisure time to replace the time spent seeking out, using, and recovering from drug use, as free time can be a trigger, especially in the early stages of recovery. Research has reported that participating in sober recreational activities is correlated with ongoing sobriety six months post-treatment (Zemore & Kaskutas, 2008) and with reported improved quality of life (Muller & Clausen, 2014). Appropriate use of leisure time can also aid in both the healing process and in reoccurrence prevention (Lacsán et al., 2017) and has been found to not only help with recovery and conferring physical benefits, but also participants feeling that they are part of the community (Stevens et al., 2019). Low-cost recreational options include the YMCA/YWCA, where subsidies are often available, local recreation centres, and board of education programs offered through high school facilities. Leisure counselling may help a person choose an appropriate activity or to engage in activities initially only with other recovering persons. As well, some communities have developed leisure activities and clubs specifically for those in recovery.

Social Assistance

Social assistance refers to the provision of monetary supports to low-income individuals to achieve a minimum income standard established by law or convention. While this is most often associated with financial support, employment support, child care, food subsidies, and transportation assistance are also subsumed under this category. The relationship between social assistance and addiction is complex. First, social assistance is certainly not a resource everyone with an addiction issue requires. In fact, it is a major myth that addiction only occurs to those with economic issues or challenges. However, addiction certainly can lead to the loss of economic supports, and there is a correlation between poverty and addiction. Social assistance is therefore an adjunct resource to support some people undergoing addiction treatment and to aid in their re-establishing themselves financially on treatment completion. A quasi-experimental study in 1998 demonstrated that when people receiving substance treatment had access to social assistance caseworkers to assist with "medical screenings, housing assistance, parenting classes and employment services," they showed "significantly less substance use, fewer physical and mental health problems and better social function at 6-months" compared to the control group (McLellan et al., 1998, p. 1489). Social assistance recipients typically also receive drug benefit coverage, which has important implications for treating addiction. A number of pharmacological therapies for smoking cessation, opioid dependency, and alcohol misuse are also covered for social assistance recipients under drug formularies.

REOCCURRENCE (RELAPSE) PREVENTION

Long-term recovery is not a straight line and is preceded by periods of flux and discontinuity before change is stabilized. These periods can last longer than the length of time the individual was actually in treatment. This reality has placed increasing importance and emphasis upon follow-up, aftercare, and relapse prevention, which is now being called reoccurrence prevention in some programs. Reoccurrence, which is a return to previous drug use patterns, poses a fundamental barrier to the treatment of addiction. Reoccurrence events are viewed as learning opportunities around a specific event or trigger (Kougiali et al., 2017).

Depending on the definition one uses for recovery, statistics indicate that upwards of 90 percent of individuals have the potential to return to using (Brandon et al., 2007; Carroll, 1996; Marlatt, 1985). Historically, reoccurrence had been attributed to factors such as cravings or withdrawal symptoms arising from the disease of addiction. However, reoccurrence is a complicated, multi-faceted process, rather than a discrete event, and is now generally considered a setback rather than a failure. Thus, aftercare needs to be a continuation of work begun during the initial treatment regimen, with a focus on resettling and reintegrating individuals back into society. The goal is to provide continuing encouragement, support, and additional services as needed following a service user's completion of a treatment plan. Preventing reoccurrence or minimizing its extent is a necessity for successful, long-term change (Guenzel & McChargue, 2019; Hendershot et al., 2011).

The contemporary approach to relapse prevention also rejects the idea of a person being either successfully abstinent or failing and being a drug misuser. Rather, the transition is viewed as a process where drug use is not an end point but rather a learning opportunity. If a reoccurrence occurs, it is considered a temporary setback that is not unique to the individual but a common part of the process. It is simply another learning opportunity, which, when resolved, becomes part of the person's behavioural repertoire. Primary goals of treatment are functional analysis, determining triggers and consequences of use, and skill building.

Specific relapse prevention models have been a mainstay of addiction treatment for over 30 years. While vital to understand and practise, they are limited in that they view relapse only as a specific event, or a series of events, rather than part of the entire change process (Miller, 2015). Relapse prevention as an intervention is a tertiary strategy, intended to reduce the likelihood and severity of reoccurrence following the cessation or reduction of problematic substance misuse. In Marlatt and Gordon's original model (1985), the basic belief was that reoccurrence events were immediately preceded by a high-risk situation, defined as any context that places a person at risk of engaging in unwanted drug-using behaviour. These high-risk situations can be emotional or cognitive, such as negative feelings or a decrease in self-efficacy. As an example, if a person returns to a club where they used to buy drugs, whether they use in this situation will depend upon their ability to enact an effective coping response, either cognitive or behavioural, to counteract the trigger that led to the psychological desire to use again.

Cognitive-behavioural principles continue to guide evidence-informed reoccurrence prevention models (Figure 27.1). Marlatt and Witkiewitz's (2005) model views reoccurrence as a complex, circular process in which various factors interact and create the opportunity for the person to return to regular drug use. The key is to assist service users in recognizing and quickly addressing high-risk situations in their lives. There are two sets of variables that need to be considered. The first, "tonic factors," are constants in a person's life, and the second, "transient influences," are phasic. Tonic processes include personality, genetic, and familial risk factors, including drug sensitivity, metabolism, neurotransmitter levels, and the effects produced by physical withdrawal. Tonic processes also include cognitive factors that show relative stability over time, such as drug-related outcome expectancies, a person's degree of self-efficacy, and personal beliefs about one's ability to remain abstinent. Tonic processes provide a baseline of risk, but it is typically phasic responses that produce the reoccurrence event. Phasic processes can be both cognitive and affective, including urges and cravings often triggered by an event or mood, both negative (distress) or positive (eustress). Transient changes in outcome expectancies, self-efficacy, and an individual's level of motivation are also phasic risks (Hendershot et al., 2011),

Applying the Marlatt and Witkiewitz (2005) model to prevent reoccurrence, counsellors need to make service users aware of their tonic risk factors, including which ones they can control and which ones they simply need to be aware of when managing their

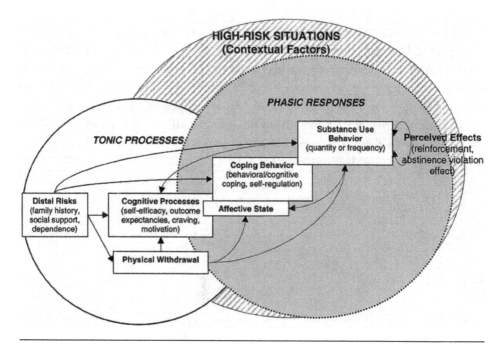

Figure 27.1: Marlatt and Witkiewtiz's Cognitive-Behavioural Model of Reoccurrence

Source: Adapted from Marlatt & Witkiewtiz (2005).

recovery. Counsellors can support service users by strengthening self-efficacy, demonstrating hope that abstinence or controlled use can be maintained, and reinforcing this belief in service users. As well, counsellors can assist service users in becoming aware of social risk factors that serve as triggers, including friends, recreational situations, workplace stressors, family relationships, and both negative and positive mood states. Key in relapse prevention is to have ongoing social supports, and this requires not only professional counselling but also appropriate referrals to mutual aid groups (Hendershot et al., 2011).

However, the process of reoccurrence prevention is not only the application of one approach or model; rather, it entails supporting the service user after treatment and monitoring progress so that if an issue does arise, an appropriate referral can be quickly made. Reoccurrence prevention programs also offer service users contacts and a support system after treatment so that an early intervention can take place in the event of reoccurrence. The actual length of the follow-up period will vary in how often contact is made and for how long it is kept, with the most significant restriction being staff resources. A minimally acceptable aftercare program would be a monthly contact for one year, with the provision that the service user can contact a counsellor whenever needed. A two-year follow-up is preferable, though some programs have moved to a five-year plan, encouraging those with longer recovery histories to facilitate reoccurrence-prevention groups for more recent service users, as well as to join alumni groups for their own growth and development (Linley & Warren, 2019; Noone et al., 1999).

Various studies have demonstrated the utility of reoccurrence prevention (Bennett et al., 2005; Blodgett, 2014; Glasner et al., 2017; McKay et al., 2011; Witkiewitz & Bowen, 2010) or regular check-ins with service users (Walker et al., 2015) as means to support ongoing recovery. However, it can be difficult empirically to disentangle the effects of aftercare itself from what motivated the service user to participate in it. Despite the potential for aftercare to sustain treatment gains, not all treatment providers routinely include it as part of their continuum of care, and service users must often seek out this care separately at the end of their treatment program.

Section VI Closing Thoughts and Activities

What do you know about aeronautical engineering? Does this matter to you when you get on a plane? What about how the internet works—does that matter to you until your network goes down? Similarly, why should we expect individuals to be aware of the addiction continuum of care or adjunct treatment services when they are unlikely to ever need to know about them? When an addiction-related crisis does occur, this knowledge will become essential, and just like we count on engineers and computer specialists to aid us when we have issues, individuals and their families count on us to know what resources exist and how to access them. Thus, of all the discussion questions posed to you in this book, the following are the ones you should make a priority to complete.

DISCUSSION QUESTIONS

1. (a) Identify, from your own community, one example of each of the addiction-specific treatment resources discussed in the chapter.
    (b) What service user attributes would lead you to refer a person to each of those resources?
2. Identify one example of each of the adjunct resources (Chapter 27) from your community.
3. From your perspective, which are superior, in-patient or outpatient/community-based programs? Specify the needs that each kind of program addresses.
4. What agencies offer reoccurrence prevention counselling in your community? Which modalities are used in the different programs?
5. What gaps exist in your community's continuum of care that need to be addressed with additional resources?

SECTION VII

BECOMING A COMPETENT ADDICTION COUNSELLOR

The field of addiction is truly multidisciplinary in nature. A range of medical professionals work in this field: nurses, psychiatrists, and physicians (including those with specialized practices in addiction medicine), along with counselling professionals including social workers, addiction counsellors, social service workers, mental health specialists, psychologists, psychotherapists, correctional staff, clergy, and individuals with lived experience. There is no one profession, but multiple professions that work with individuals and their families who have addiction issues. This, however, can lead to overlapping jurisdictions and practice approaches. Regardless of the educational foundation that brings a professional into the addiction field, there are parameters within which they must all work to provide competent care for those affected by addiction. This section explores those parameters that everyone working in this area of practice should be aware of and are bound by.

CHAPTER 28

Psychoactive Drugs and the Law

HISTORY

Since the early 1970s drug offences have accounted for more than one-third of the growth in the incarcerated population in Canada, with the rate for drug arrests increasing 1,000 percent between 1980 and the end of the century. Over the past two decades, Canada has the highest number of drug arrests per capita of any nation other than the United States (Grant, 2009; Motiuk & Vuong, 2002; Riley, 1998) with 225 drug related offences per 100,000 people in 2018. This, however, was the lowest rate in the 21st century, dropping from a peak of 278 in 2015 as a direct result of the legalization of cannabis (Government of Canada, 2019a). Contemporary Canadian drug legislation traces its origins to the Opium Act of 1908, which created the first drug prohibition of the 20th century while also formally regulating alcohol and tobacco sales. Other opioids and cocaine were added in 1911, with cannabis being made an illicit substance without any parliamentary debate in 1923. Six years later, the Opium and Narcotic Act was introduced and became Canada's primary drug legislation of the 20th century. Since then Canada has become a signatory to all three major international drug laws, which prohibit and regulate psychoactive substances: the Single Convention on Narcotic Drugs (1961), the Convention on Psychotropic Substances (1971), and the Convention against Illicit Traffic in Narcotic Drugs and Psychotropic Substances (1988) (the Vienna Convention). These treaties significantly determine which drugs will be allowed to be legally used and which are to be banned, not only in Canada but around the globe. For example, the Single Convention, which limits the production and trade in prohibited substances to the quantity needed to meet the medical and scientific need of each nation, has incorrectly labelled cannabis as a narcotic and thus purposefully shaped international drug policy regarding this drug for over half a century (Solomon et al., 1989).

In 1961, in response to the Single Convention on Narcotic Drugs, the Canadian government introduced the Narcotic Control Act, which made the simple possession of cannabis an indictable offence along with drugs such as heroin and cocaine, while increasing the maximum jail sentence for trafficking to 14 years from 7 for all narcotic substances. Between 1969 and 1973, the Commission of Inquiry into the Non-Medical Use of Drugs (the Le Dain Commission) examined the use of psychoactive drugs in Canada and recommended changes to the legislation that took on a more public health orientation rather than an exclusive criminal justice focus. Despite some sympathy for the Committee's paradigm-shifting recommendations, Canada's drug laws remained unaltered.

In 1987, in response to the Reagan administration's reaffirmation of the War on Drugs in the United States, which actually officially began during President Nixon's time in office, Canada's federal government introduced a new drug strategy in an attempt to address not only the supply, but also the demand component of the drug equation. Not only were new enforcement initiatives introduced, but funding was also provided for new treatment and prevention programs. As well, a decision against random drug tests for civil servants was made, and instead, employee assistance programs were introduced for all employees and their family members, establishing a new timbre for the era (Standing Committee on National Health and Welfare, 1987).

However, nearly a decade later, much more conservative legislation was passed to close the 20th century. In a ploy used over time in numerous local and national jurisdictions, the Chrétien Liberals, in attempting to demonstrate to the Canadian electorate that they were "tough on crime," opted to revert to a less progressive philosophical stance and return to viewing drug use primarily as a criminal rather than a health or social issue. This led to the development of the Controlled Drugs and Substances Act (CDSA), which moved Canadian drug policy back toward a prohibitionist orientation, with the CDSA only minimally addressing the long-term financial and human costs of treating drug users primarily as criminals. The importation, exportation, production, distribution, and possession of drugs and substances in Canada, including obtaining multiple prescriptions from one or more physicians (double doctoring), all became governed by the provisions of the CDSA, which replaced the Narcotic Control Act and parts III and IV of the Food and Drugs Act on June 20, 1996 (Riley, 1998). In 2012, additional amendments were made to the law by the Harper government, the most contentious of which was the addition of mandatory minimum sentencing for an accused convicted of serious drug-related offences including trafficking, possession for the purpose of trafficking, importing and exporting, and production of drugs listed in Schedule I and Schedule II of the CDSA. The legislation also moved GHB and Rohypnol, as well as all of the amphetamine drugs, from Schedule III to Schedule I so that the new harsher penalties could be applied. Fortunately, since 2012, the majority of legislation pertaining to drugs has focused on cannabis as its use moved from being prohibited, to allowed for specific medical conditions, to becoming legalized across Canada with the passing of Bill C-45. A major exception to this legislative focus on cannabis pertained to vaping, with the introduction of the federal Tobacco and Vaping Products Act (TVPA) in 2018 and a range of related provincial enacted policy between 2015 and 2020.

PENALTIES

The Controlled Drugs and Substances Act allows for three different charges to be laid pertaining to drugs: (1) summary conviction, (2) indictable, and (3) hybrid or Crown election offences. Summary conviction offences encompass the most minor offences in the Criminal Code, with the penalty typically being a fine of up to $5,000 CAD or six months in jail or both. If an individual is convicted of a summary offence as an adult, the person may be eligible for a pardon three years from the time the sentence is completed, typically at the conclusion of probation. Indictable offences are harsher, with lengthier incarceration periods and greater financial penalties. If you are prosecuted by indictment, you are entitled to trial by jury for most offences. If convicted of an indictable offence, the individual may still apply for and receive a pardon but must wait a minimum of five years once the sentence is completed. Drug-related offences maybe prosecuted either by summary conviction or indictment, depending upon the discretion of the Crown prosecutor. These are referred to as hybrid offences.

Under the Controlled Drugs and Substances Act, unlawful possession of either heroin or cocaine is a criminal offence punishable on indictment by imprisonment for up to seven years or on summary conviction for a first offence to a fine of up to $1,000 or imprisonment for up to six months, or both. A subsequent offence is punishable on summary conviction by a fine of up to $2,000 or imprisonment for up to one year, or both. Trafficking, possession for the purpose of trafficking, possession for the purpose of exporting, production, import, and export are indictable offences punishable by up to life imprisonment. In contrast, amphetamines, their derivatives, and most hallucinogens are punishable on indictment by imprisonment for up to three years and on summary conviction to a fine of up to $1,000 or imprisonment for up to six months, or both (Table 28.1). Trafficking, possession for the purpose of trafficking, possession for the purpose of exporting, production, import, and export offences are punishable by imprisonment for up to 18 months or on indictment by imprisonment for up to 10 years, while for khat it is a maximum of only three years (Government of Canada, 2015). However, regulations within the legislation do allow for the prescription of some otherwise illicit drugs for treatment or therapeutic purposes, including both methadone and heroin (Riley, 1998). This clause allowed the North American Opiate Medication Initiative (NAOMI), which evaluated the feasibility and effectiveness of heroin-assisted treatment (HAT) in the Canadian context, to proceed.

Benzodiazepines and barbiturates are governed by Schedule IV of the CDSA, and convictions pertaining to trafficking and possession are similar to khat. Psychotherapeutic agents, including all of the tricyclics, MAOIs, and SSRI antidepressants, are subject to the provisions of the Food and Drugs Act and Food and Drug Regulations applicable to drugs listed in Schedule F to the Regulations. The Regulations generally require that the sale or distribution of Schedule F drugs be made pursuant to a prescription. Violation of the act or regulations is an offence punishable on indictment by a fine of up to $5,000 or

Table 28.1: Penalties Pertaining to Illicit Drugs

Offence	Summary Conviction Maximum Penalty	Indictable Offence Maximum Penalty
Possession of cocaine or heroin	6 months imprisonment $1,000 fine	7 years imprisonment
Possession of amphetamines, LSD, mescaline, or psilocybin	6 months imprisonment $1,000 fine	3 years imprisonment
Trafficking cocaine or heroin or possession for purpose of trafficking	1–2 years imprisonment	life imprisonment
Trafficking barbiturates or possession for purpose of trafficking	1 year imprisonment	3 years imprisonment
Importing or exporting > 1 kg heroin or cocaine		life imprisonment
Trafficking amphetamines, mescaline, LSD, or psilocybin	$5,000 fine	10 years imprisonment
Production of cocaine or heroin	2–3 years imprisonment	life imprisonment
Production of amphetamines, mescaline, LSD, or psilocybin	$5,000 fine	10 years imprisonment
Production of barbiturates	1 year imprisonment $5,000 fine	3 years imprisonment

Source: Government of Canada (2015).

imprisonment for up to three years, or both, and on summary conviction for a first offence by a fine of up to $500 or imprisonment for up to three months, or both. A subsequent offence is punishable by a fine of up to $1,000 or imprisonment for up to six months, or both (Health Canada, 2009).

With a few minor exceptions in northern Canadian communities and Alberta, possession and sale of inhalants are not regulated. However, the misuse of a solvent may be taken into consideration when dealing with young offenders and children found in need of protection under provincial legislation. As well, gammahydroxybutyrate (GHB) is governed by the provisions of the Controlled Drugs and Substances Act, with its possession punishable by imprisonment for up to three years on indictment or on summary conviction to a fine of up to $1,000 or six months imprisonment, or both for a first offence, and a fine of up to $2,000 or up to one year imprisonment, or both for a subsequent offence. Offences of trafficking, possession for the purpose of trafficking, possession for the purpose of exporting, production, import, and export of GHB are punishable on indictment by imprisonment for up to 10 years and on summary conviction by imprisonment for up to 18 months (Health Canada, 2009).

ALCOHOL

The sale and use of alcohol is subject to federal, provincial, and territorial legislation, including the sale to minors and use in public places. In the Northwest Territories, alcohol use is restricted by the municipality and not by the territorial government, with individual communities having the right to ban alcohol completely if the local government wishes. Distinct offences exist relating to underage drinking include possessing, consuming, purchasing, attempting to purchase, or otherwise obtaining liquor outside of the home. In some jurisdictions, parents or guardians may legally supply liquor at home to an underage person, but in others, supplying liquor or selling liquor to a minor is an offence regardless of the relationship between provider and consumer. Currently, in all provinces and territories, the legal drinking age is 19 with the exception of Alberta, Manitoba, and Quebec, where the legal drinking age remains 18 (Table 28.2).

While the laws respecting alcohol are determined by the province or territory and not by the federal government, alcohol is still governed by the Criminal Code of Canada. Impaired driving applies to all conveyances, which means motor vehicles such as cars, trucks, snowmobiles, all-terrain vehicles, boats, aircraft, and railway equipment. As of

Table 28.2: Legal Age for Drug Use and Year of Vaping Legislation

Jurisdiction	Alcohol Use	Cannabis Use	Tobacco Use	Year Vaping Legislation Introduced
Alberta	18	18	18	2020
British Columbia	19	19	19	2016
Manitoba	18	19	18	2015
New Brunswick	19	19	19	2015
Newfoundland & Labrador	19	19	19	2017
Northwest Territories	19	19	18	N/A
Nova Scotia	19	19	19	2015
Nunavut	19	19	18	N/A
Ontario	19	19	19	2017
Prince Edward Island	19	19	19	2015
Quebec	18	21	18	2015
Saskatchewan	19	19	18	N/A
Yukon Territory	19	19	18	N/A

Sources: Government of Canada (2019a, 2019b).

December 18, 2018, police no longer require a reasonable suspicion to demand a breath sample from a driver. Anyone operating a conveyance who is lawfully stopped by police can be required to provide a breath sample to detect potential alcohol in their blood. Failure to comply with this demand will also result in criminal charges that carry the same, or greater, penalties as driving while impaired (Table 28.3). Any driver legally stopped by a police officer is obligated to:

- provide a sample of breath on an Approved Screening Device;
- provide an oral fluid sample on Approved Drug Screening Equipment; and
- participate in Standardized Field Sobriety Testing.

Table 28.3: Penalties for Drug-Impaired Driving

Penalties			
Charge	1st offence	2nd offence	3rd offence
Alcohol-impaired driving • having a BAC at or over 80 mg per 100 ml of blood within 2 hours of driving	**Mandatory minimum:** $1,000 fine **Maximum:** 10 years imprisonment	**Mandatory minimum:** 30 days imprisonment **Maximum:** 10 years imprisonment	**Mandatory minimum:** 120 days imprisonment **Maximum:** 10 years imprisonment
Drug-impaired driving • having 5 ng or more of THC per ml of blood within 2 hours of driving • any detectable level of LSD, psilocybin, ketamine, PCP, cocaine, methamphetamine, or 6-mam within 2 hours of driving • having 5 mg or more of GHB per 1 litre of blood within 2 hours of driving			
Combination • having a BAC of 50 mg per 100 ml of blood and 2.5 ng or more of THC per 1 ml of blood within 2 hours of driving			
Refusal to comply with demand for sample	**Minimum:** $2,000 fine		
Drug-impaired driving—summary conviction • having over 2 ng but less than 5 ng of THC per ml of blood within 2 hours of driving	**Maximum:** $1,000 fine		
Impaired driving causing bodily harm	**Summary conviction**: Maximum 2 years imprisonment less a day **Indictment**: Maximum 14 years imprisonment		
Impaired driving causing death	**Indictment**: Maximum life imprisonment		
First offence and BAC of 80–119mg	**Mandatory minimum**: $1,000 fine		
First offence and BAC of 120–159mg	**Mandatory minimum**: $1,500 fine		
First offence and BAC of 160mg or more	**Mandatory minimum**: $2,000 fine		

Source: Government of Canada (2019a).

After providing a breath or oral fluid sample, the results of that test will determine what, if any, further actions are taken. Performing poorly on any of these tests can lead to an arrest. An individual who submits a breath sample in the "warn" range can be subject to administrative penalties such as a roadside suspension or an immediate roadside prohibition. An individual who submits a breath sample and registers a "fail" will be required to provide further breath samples at a police station. With regards to alcohol, a subsequent breath sample that meets or exceeds the legal blood alcohol content (BAC) limit of 80 mg means that the person may be charged under section 320.14 of the Criminal Code of Canada—having a blood alcohol concentration that is equal to or exceeds 80 mg within two hours of ceasing to operate a conveyance. If an individual is in the driver's seat of any conveyance, whether it is in motion or not, and a police officer reasonably suspects that the person has consumed alcohol, drugs, or a combination of alcohol and drugs, the police officer may make a demand to submit to a Standard Field Sobriety Test (SFST). Failure, or refusal, to comply with the SFST demand can also result in criminal charges that carry the same, or greater, penalties as impaired driving (Government of Canada, 2019d).

TOBACCO

The federal Tobacco and Vaping Products Act (TVPA) was enacted on May 23, 2018, to regulate the manufacture, sale, labelling, and promotion of tobacco products and vaping products sold in Canada, replacing the 1997 Tobacco Act. While it is known that tobacco and tobacco products cause a vast array of illnesses (Chapter 10), tobacco remains a legal product in Canada, as it is also well known that prohibition does not prevent people from using psychoactive substances. The TVPA provides the legislative framework for how tobacco products can be sold, labelled, produced, and promoted. The TVPA also states that vaping products are not to be sold or given to anyone under 18 years of age, and outlines how vaping products can be marketed, how they are to be packaged, what can be included in a vaping product, and what health messages must be on the label (Government of Canada, 2019b).

Each province also sets its own standards regarding tobacco and vaping within the guidelines provided by the federal government, including the legal age to purchase these products, who may sell them, where they can be used both indoors and outdoors, and how they can be promoted. Most provinces introduced initial vaping legislation prior to the TVPA being passed, but have since made amendments in response to new concerns regarding underage vaping and the serious health implications that started to surface in 2019 (Table 28.2).

CANNABIS

Canada was among the first nations to prohibit the use of cannabis and now has become one of the first to legalize its use. Bill C-45, the Cannabis Act, along with its companion legislation Bill C-46, An Act to Amend the Criminal Code, was passed by the House of Commons in late November 2017 and by the Senate on June 7, 2018, with minor revisions accepted on June 19 and royal assent on June 21, 2018. This legislation made Canada the second country in the world to legalize recreational cannabis nationwide, after Uruguay. The Cannabis Act also created a formal legal framework for controlling the production, distribution, sale, and possession of cannabis, with three stated goals:

1. to keep cannabis out of the hands of youth;
2. to eliminate the illegal market of cannabis sales; and
3. to protect public health and safety by allowing adults access to legal cannabis with known and stated THC levels.

Under Canada's confederated model of governance, the federal government is responsible for overall regulation of cannabis, including licensing and production, while the provinces and territories are responsible for retail sales and distribution. Each province and territory has established its own model of private, government, or hybrid sales. Legal age of possession in the majority of provinces and territories is 19, though it is 18 in Alberta and 21 in Quebec (Table 28.2). Each individual of legal age is allowed to possess up to 30 grams of dried cannabis or equivalent in non-dried form in public, to share up to 30 grams of legal cannabis with other adults, and to buy dried or fresh cannabis and cannabis oil from a provincially licensed retailer. The federal law stipulates that 1 gram of dried cannabis is equal to:

*   5 grams of fresh cannabis,
*   15 grams of edible product,
*   70 grams of liquid product,
*   0.25 grams of concentrates (solid or liquid), or
*   1 cannabis plant seed.

Individuals are also allowed to grow up to four cannabis plants per residence for personal use and to make their own homemade products using dried cannabis. In October 2019, edibles were also legalized, allowing for a range of foods and beverages to also be infused with cannabis. The regulations for cannabis edibles, extracts, and topicals use packaging and taxation to promote lower-risk use, applying the public health approaches developed for tobacco products. Edibles are taxed based on the amount of THC they contain, making lower-risk products more affordable. As well, cannabis for medical purposes remains legal, with employers required to offer modified work accommodation for those using cannabis to address health issues.

While cannabis is now a legal product in Canada, there remain a range of penalties for cannabis offences, including warnings and fines for minor offences such as possession of small amounts over the limit, and a maximum sentence of 14 years for illegal cultivation and distribution and selling cannabis to a minor (Table 28.4). As with alcohol, there are also specific penalties for cannabis-impaired driving (Table 28.3). There are two prohibited levels for THC: a less serious offence of 2–5 nanograms (ng) of THC per ml of blood, and a more serious offence of 5 ng of THC or more per ml of blood. The prohibited levels of alcohol and cannabis, when found in combination, is 50 mg or more of alcohol per 100 ml blood and 2.5 ng or more of THC per ml of blood, while having any detectable amount of LSD, psilocybin, ketamine, PCP, cocaine, methamphetamine or 6-mam (a metabolite of heroin) in your system within two hours of driving is also prohibited. Additionally, each province and territory may add their own penalties, including administrative costs, licence suspensions, training to renew your licence, and vehicle seizure, if an individual is charged with impaired driving due to consuming cannabis (Government of Canada, 2019e).

Table 28.4: Cannabis Related Offences

Offence	Summary Conviction Maximum Penalty	Indictable Offence Maximum Penalty
Unauthorized possession in public by adult of cannabis > equivalent 30 g	6 months imprisonment $1,000 fine	5 years less a day
Possession by an adult of illicit cannabis	6 months imprisonment $1,000 fine	5 years less a day
Possession in public of cannabis plants that are budding or flowering	6 months imprisonment $1,000 fine	5 years less a day
Possession of more than four cannabis plants that are not budding or flowering	6 months imprisonment $1,000 fine	5 years less a day
Distribution or cannabis > equivalent 30 g that is illicit or to an organization	6 months imprisonment $5,000 fine	14 years
Possession for the purpose of distributing or unauthorized sale	6 months imprisonment $5,000 fine	14 years
Unauthorized cultivation, propagation, and harvesting	6 months imprisonment $5,000 fine	14 years
Distribution or sale by adult of cannabis to a young person	18 months imprisonment $15,000 fine	14 years

Source: Government of Canada (2019e).

CHAPTER 29

Ethical Considerations

Ethics is a branch of moral philosophy concerned with human conduct and moral decision making; of being a good person and doing the right thing. An ethic is a statement of the most fundamental principle of professional counselling conduct. It is an attempt to answer the question of what is right and wrong in a consistent and systemic manner. The study of ethics is a discipline examining our values, beliefs, morals, and the justification of these. Ethics frame the rules of conduct by which we live our lives and conduct our counselling practice. When thinking about ethics, the question typically arises: How should we think? The role of ethics is to ask us: What are the values and attitudes that should shape the concepts through which we define ourselves, the world in which we live, and thus our work as professional counsellors?

To join a profession entails subscribing to some common ethical values, yet values do not always lead to desired behaviours, and counselling professionals can have their values depart greatly and gravely from societal values or even the values of other professions. We see this in conflicts regarding right-to-life decisions, reproductive freedom, minority rights around fundamental issues of what is a family and who should be considered eligible for marriage, and, of course, in addiction around issues such as harm reduction, mandated detoxification treatment for youth, and the imprisonment of individuals because of behaviours caused by their drug use. Ethics are also often closely linked to societal values and are reflected in statutes, policies, and the criminal justice system.

The following are examples of unethical counselling behaviour:

- violation of confidentiality
- exceeding one's level of professional competence
- negligent practice
- claiming expertise one does not possess
- imposing one's values on a service user
- creating dependency in a service user
- conflict of interest
- questionable financial arrangements/financial exploitation of a service user

Lastly is one that appears totally obvious, yet is one that is still too frequently violated:

- sexual harassment of or activity with a service user

In essence, any activity by a counsellor that leads to exploitation, insensitivity, incompetence, irresponsibility, or abandonment of a service user is unethical behaviour. Most counselling professions have prescribed ethical codes, as does the addiction field, and a formal college to protect the public from unethical and unprofessional behaviour. However, in the case of addiction, there is no mandatory association to which one must belong to qualify as an addiction counsellor. Nor is there a uniform ethical code that all counsellors working in the addiction field are obligated to follow or an association that members of the public can turn to if they have concerns regarding the practice of an addiction counsellor, though a voluntary association and ethical code are in place.

There is also a more subtle ethical issue in the addiction field that relates to how voluntary the consent is to treatment. The subtle coercion that often precedes seeking treatment may be an invisible barrier to forming a therapeutic alliance with a service user. There are three distinct forms of constraint that may affect the counselling relationship: (1) judicial, (2) institutional, and (3) relational. The coercive aspect of treatment can consist of any one or a combination of all three of these forms of constraint. Judicial constraint refers to any mandate from the criminal justice system to seek treatment or a specific form of treatment, either as a condition of sentencing or to avoid sentencing. This can take different forms, such as therapeutic remands, conditions of a probation order, conditions of a conditional sentence of imprisonment, or coercive treatment mandates ordered through drug treatment courts. Institutional constraint is coercion exerted within any institutional setting, such as a workplace to preserve employment, or a school to maintain enrollment. The third form of coercion, relational, applies to any form of constraint in which the drug user is encouraged or pressured to seek treatment by people in their immediate environment, such as family members, friends, or workplace colleagues (see Chapter 18). Even if this form of constraint is not as obvious as those exerted by a court or correctional facilities, it must be considered by practitioners who are evaluating the motivation of the person seeking treatment. The recognition of these three forms of coercion is vital for practitioners to incorporate into their assessment of the service user's environmental context (Quirion, 2014).

TELEOLOGICAL VERSUS DEONTOLOGICAL ETHICAL DECISION MAKING

While competent practitioners easily avoid ethical problems, ethical dilemmas are more likely to create a lose-lose situation in which any action will have some negative consequences. There are two basic approaches to ethical decision making when one is faced with an ethical dilemma: (1) teleological, and (2) deontological.

Teleological ethical decision making is goal directed and is consequentialistic in its approach. The focus is on the anticipated outcome of a given situation or action. It operates from the perspective that we have only one moral duty: to do as much good as possible. This approach is most concerned with overall consequences rather than the outcome for a specific individual, thus making it utilitarian in its orientation. Teleological ethics draws its name from the Greek *telos*, which refers to an archery target. A teleological approach is one that orients each action or activity toward a goal or a target that is deemed to be good. A telelogic ethic orients actions to ends and chooses those means that lead to a desired outcome identified with "the good." Thus, actions taken under this ethical decision-making framework are good by virtue of the consequences they produce. We should act in a certain manner because it will produce the most positive results. Teleological ethical approaches, being consequential in nature, focus on the expected outcomes, leading to cost-benefit and cost-effectiveness–based courses of action. This model has been regularly followed by health care and social services professionals as it fosters general benevolence.

In contrast, deontological ethical decision making is concerned with balancing rights and duties and tends to reject purely outcome-orientated considerations. The root *deon* comes from the Greek meaning that one must, which implies that there are several distinct duties that must be considered in making an ethical decision. While not ignoring outcomes entirely, this philosophical approach states that certain kinds of actions are either inherently right and good, or wrong and bad. It proclaims that we do the right thing because it is in fact the right thing to do. The right thing to do is typically based on an external authority, such as the Ten Commandments, or the code of practice of a professional body, such as social work, psychology, or addiction counselling. This approach is orientated less to goods or harms produced by actions and more toward the basic principles of right and wrong. In and by themselves, the consequences of an action do not determine whether the action is ethically right or wrong. Rather, this perspective maintains that whether an action is ethical depends on whether it is in accordance with, and is performed out of respect for, certain absolute and universal principles.

The classic though simplistic example illustrating the difference between these two approaches is found in the scenario in which one has the opportunity to return in a time machine to murder Adolf Hitler's mother, so that Hitler is never born. From a teleological perspective, this could be argued as ethical behaviour, as it would prevent the murder, death, and suffering of millions. However, from a deontological viewpoint, the argument would be that murder is wrong regardless of the situation and cannot be justified even under these circumstances.

Few of us are purely teleological or deontological ethical decision makers, but rather follow both paths at different times and in different situations. What is critical is to appreciate which philosophical approach we are using and why, and to be able to document the process of our decision making. Ethical guidelines are just that, guidelines, and at times counsellors are faced with lose-lose situations in which ethical implications are unavoidable.

Box 29.1: Situation One—The Limits of Confidentiality

Debbie Woods calls your agency and asks to speak to an addiction counsellor. You arrange to meet with Debbie the next day and find out that she does not personally have an addiction issue but is looking for your assistance in obtaining a divorce from her husband of 12 years. During the course of your assessment, Ms. Woods confides that she wants a divorce because of her husband's excessive drinking. She states that he drinks heavily four to five times a week even if he has a scheduled flight. Ms. Woods tells you that her husband is a commercial pilot and recently returned from a 21-day "vacation" during which time he entered an in-patient treatment facility under an assumed name. He did not complete the program but left after two weeks. As the counsellor, you are aware of aviation regulations that forbid a pilot from drinking for several hours prior to a flight.

You further explore the issues of Debbie's husband causing harm if he drinks and flies. Ms. Wood becomes quite agitated and says that this session is confidential. "I don't want you reporting anything to anybody. We're here to discuss my problem. If he loses his job, he won't be able to support himself let alone provide assistance for me and our children."

What action can you take?
What will you do?

Box 29.2: Situation Two—Testing the Limits of Confidentiality

Violet Woodlands calls your agency and asks to speak to an addiction counsellor. You arrange to meet with Violet the next day and find out that she does not personally have an addiction issue but is looking for your assistance in obtaining a divorce from her husband of 12 years. During the course of your assessment, Ms. Woodlands confides that she wants a divorce because of her husband's excessive drinking and behaviour toward their children. She states that he drinks heavily four to five times a week, even if he has a scheduled flight. Ms. Woodlands tells you that her husband is a commercial pilot and recently returned from a 21-day "vacation" during which he entered an in-patient treatment facility under an assumed name. He did not complete the program but left after two weeks. He returned home, and during a drinking episode, hit the oldest child, age nine, so hard that the child's shoulder was partially separated. As a professional counsellor, you are aware of aviation regulations that forbid a pilot from drinking for several hours prior to a flight and about the need to protect children.

You further explore the issues of Violet's husband causing harm when he drinks excessively. Ms. Woodlands becomes quite agitated and says this session is confidential, and that it says so in everything she has every read about counselling. "I don't want you reporting anything to anybody. We're here to discuss my problem. If he loses his job or goes to jail, he won't be able to support himself, let alone provide assistance for me and our children."

What action can you take?
What should you do?
Were there any differences in the course of action you took with Debbie as compared to Violet?
Why? How does this speak to teleological and deontological ethical decision making?

ETHICAL DECISION-MAKING APPROACHES

Ethical dilemmas arise when there is a conflict in the following:

- problem definition
- goal setting
- priority setting
- decisions on means
- decisions on strategy
- decisions on outcomes

Ethical dilemmas can be proposed by the following:

- the service user
- the counsellor
- the family system
- the criminal justice system
- the employer/school

Each relates to different assumptions about the following:

- human nature
- values
- criminal justice/workplace/school issues
- the personal/work/school interface

Along with determining if you are a teleological or deontological decision maker, a variety of ethical decision-making formats have been proposed to assist practitioners in making good ethical decisions. Kitchener's model (1984) is a bottom-up process based on the assumption that some clinical decisions cannot be made only by simple reasoning. Its intent is to provide counselling professionals with a systematic ethical decision-making process. The model proposes that ethical decision making always begins by thoroughly examining the particular facts of a situation, and that the more experience a counsellor has with potential ethical dilemmas, the more likely the counsellor will be able to act appropriately using ordinary moral and common sense. It is a hierarchically tiered model, so that if a decision cannot be made at a lower level, one can move up and engage in ethical reasoning at a higher level of abstraction (Figure 29.1).

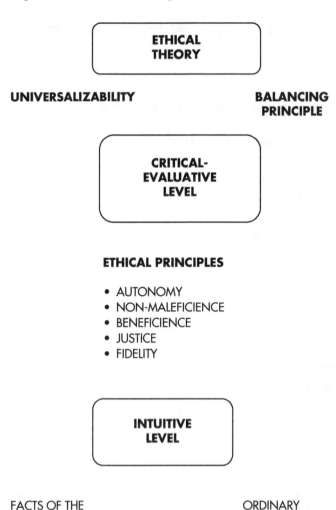

ETHICAL THEORY

UNIVERSALIZABILITY   BALANCING PRINCIPLE

CRITICAL- EVALUATIVE LEVEL

ETHICAL PRINCIPLES

- AUTONOMY
- NON-MALEFICIENCE
- BENEFICIENCE
- JUSTICE
- FIDELITY

INTUITIVE LEVEL

FACTS OF THE SITUATION   ORDINARY MORAL SENSE

Figure 29.1: Kitchener's Model of Ethical Justification

Source: Adapted from Kitchener (1984).

The intuitive level is derived through a counsellor's post-secondary education in combination with one's immediate personal response to a situation. It is what "feel's right" based on an individual's values, ethical behaviour, life experiences, education, and supervisory experiences. This is the most biased and responsive level of reasoning and occurs at the lowest level of abstraction or at a pre-reflective state. Relying solely on intuition does not allow individuals to critically evaluate their decisions.

The critical-evaluative level consists of a series of options to provide a clearer rationale when making ethical decisions, with the goal of protecting the interests of all persons involved in the decision-making process. Generally, these are organized using a deontological process established by a governing professional body and presented in a formal set of rules or guidelines. Counsellors are urged to follow these guidelines and sanctions are typically applied if they are not adhered to. The ethical principles arising from the ethical rules component of the critical-evaluative level are established beliefs about specific modes of conduct, and are somewhat more general than ethical rules found in codes of ethics. Autonomy is the basis for the preferred rights of service users found in ethical codes, including such concepts as self-determination, confidentiality, and informed consent. Autonomy does not imply unlimited freedom, as people do not have the right to infringe on the rights of others or to cause them harm. Non-maleficence is the process of doing no harm, while beneficence entails promoting the wellness of others. Justice is the principle of treating people equally by treating them according to their needs, while fidelity involves loyalty on the part of the counsellor to the service user's best interests. Of course, these principles are all prima facia, meaning none are absolute or perfect. While always relevant in every situation, a principle must be overturned when a stronger ethical one is in conflict with it.

Finally, if one is still uncertain of how to act, the counsellor can move to the top of Kitchener's model, to ethical theory. This tier is applied when intuitive thought, ethical codes, and ethical principles fail to resolve an ethical dilemma: when the lose-lose situation leads to a stalemate. There are two principles in this final and top tier. Universalizability is the broad-based use of a principle that can be applied fairly similarly in all cases, implying that an act is ethical only if it can be generalized to all similar cases. In contrast, the balancing principle, derived from teleological thought, states that the potential for good in all aspects must be balanced against the potential for harm. Thus, the final stage also allows the counsellor to include consideration for what action would bring about the most good for the most people in the decision-making process.

Loewenberg and Dolgoff (2008) have proposed a much simpler process—one that allows practitioners to compare the source of the conflict and determine which course to take based on its level. The higher levels take precedence over the lower when a counsellor is faced with a lose-lose scenario.

The following are listed from most to least important when resolving an ethical dilemma:

Ethical Principle 1: Principle of the protection of life
Ethical Principle 2: Principle of equality and inequality
Ethical Principle 3: Principle of autonomy and freedom
Ethical Principle 4: Principle of least harm
Ethical Principle 5: Principle of quality of life
Ethical Principle 6: Principle of privacy and confidentiality
Ethical Principle 7: Principle of truthfulness and full disclosure

---

Box 29.3: Situation Three—Self-Determination

Mary Popovich was born on August 10, 1959. During her childhood, she moved several times before her family settled in St. Catharines, Ontario. Her father died when she was six and her mother remarried. Mary completed Grade 8 and then obtained an office job. She was 22 when she was first admitted to St. Michael's Hospital in Toronto. Her case history described her as "pale, underweight, preoccupied and vague." Her diagnosis was possible schizophrenia. Electroconvulsive therapy was ordered, which was the acceptable standard of the time.

Mary lived in a boarding house for one year but ended up in the North Bay Psychiatric Hospital. Her prognosis did not appear favourable. During the 1980s, Mary was in and out of hospital. She gave birth to a healthy baby boy, whom she put up for adoption. Mary's symptoms were controllable with psychotherapeutic drugs, but without supervision, she stopped taking her medication and began drinking. She began slowly, but over time has developed a serious substance dependency.

In the 1990s, Mary became an active outpatient. She did well for several years, but in the early part of this century, she stopped attending clinic appointments to get her medication and began self-medicating with alcohol and street drugs. She was finally evicted from her accommodation in 2017 and began to live on the street. She became a permanent fixture around the corner from the women's withdrawal management program, and once or even twice a year, she would admit herself to be detoxified before returning to the street. These self-admissions have tended to occur during the winter months and have increased in recent years. Her homelessness also caused her to be admitted to the hospital with breathing problems. She was also suffering from liver problems, kidney problems, and cardiovascular problems and was malnourished. She was transferred to the Queen Street Mental Health facility in Toronto, and then to the Hamilton Psychiatric Hospital. Once there, she refused to accept any ongoing treatment. She was subsequently released.

On her return to the community, she occasionally dropped in to the Centre for Hope for companionship, the occasional meal, and even for a place to sleep when it got too cold outside. One day, Mary suddenly refused to go inside. Already street-weary, she became even more short-tempered and difficult to interact with. Some days she would talk with anyone, but at other times, she would refuse to communicate. The Centre's alleyway soon became her permanent home.

In the mornings, staff from the withdrawal management centre would hose down the area where she had slept because of the smell. They grew increasingly concerned as she appeared to be ill with a chronic cough, but Mary continued to refuse assistance. It is now early November and winter conditions are quickly encroaching. Mary has not given any indication that she will be moving indoors.

What is your course of action?

Box 29.4: Situation Four—Dual Relationships

John Kowalski, who began his recovery as a result of your intervention, is a volunteer with your facility. He has an excellent reputation as a caring volunteer and is considering taking early retirement to formally study addiction counselling. He is held in high regard by board members, staff, fellow volunteers, and service users.

Cheryl Hillwards voluntarily sought counselling. She has worked for Union Chemical for five years, since completing college. She has a variety of problems, including inappropriate use of prescription drugs and interpersonal issues, all which appear to stem from a lack of self-confidence and self-esteem. After an initial assessment, Cheryl is assigned to John Kowalski's voluntary peer-led group for ongoing support as part of a larger professional treatment program. John notices that Cheryl has difficulty in establishing friendly relationships with any of the men in the group. During the course of her ongoing group sessions, he publicly compliments her on her appearance to bolster her self-esteem and provides supportive hugs at the end of sessions. After one particular session, Cheryl admits that she is attracted to him. John immediately transfers Cheryl to another group.

After six months, John calls Cheryl to see how she is. He then asks her if she would like to go out with him on a date.

Are there ethical dilemmas arising out of this situation?
What additional issues would arise if John were a paid staff member rather than a volunteer?

CANADIAN ADDICTION COUNSELLORS CERTIFICATION FEDERATION'S CANON OF ETHICAL PRINCIPLES

Despite the lack of professional college, many practising in the addiction field in Canada have voluntarily joined the Canadian Addiction Counsellors Certification Federation (CACCF) and ascribe to the Federation's Canon of Ethical Principles (2019). CACCF promotes, certifies, and monitors the competency of addiction specific counsellors in Canada, using current and effective practices that are internationally recognized. This association serves as a voluntary professional body that certifies professionals working in the addiction field and offers a Canon of Ethical Practice consisting of 12 principles:

1. Believe in the dignity and worth of all human beings, and pledge my service to the well-being and betterment of all members of society.
2. Recognize the right of humane treatment of anyone suffering from alcoholism or drug abuse, whether directly or indirectly.
3. Promote and assist in the recovery and return to society of every person served, assisting them to help themselves, and referring them promptly to other programs or individuals when in their best interests.
4. Maintain a proper professional relationship with all persons served, assisting them to help themselves, and referring them promptly to other programs or individuals, when in their best interests.
5. Adhere strictly to established precepts of confidentiality in all knowledge, records, and materials concerning persons served, and in accordance with any current government regulations.
6. Ensure that all interpersonal transactions between myself and persons served are non-exploitive and essential to their good recovery.
7. Give due respect to the rights, views, and positions of any other alcoholism and/or drug counsellors and related professionals.
8. Respect institutional policies and procedures, and co-operate with any agency management with which I may be associated, as long as this remains consistent with recognized standards, procedures, and ethics.
9. Contribute my ideas and findings regarding alcoholism and other drug addictions and their treatment and recovery, to any body of knowledge, through appropriate channels.
10. Refrain from any activities, including the abuse of alcohol, drugs, or other mood-altering chemicals where my personal conduct might diminish my personal capabilities, denigrate my professional status, or constitute a violation of law.
11. Avoid claiming or implying any personal capabilities or professional qualifications beyond those I have actually attained, recognizing that competency gained in one field of activity must not be used improperly to imply competency in another.

12. Regularly evaluate my own strengths, limitations, biases, or levels of effectiveness, always striving for self-improvement and seeking professional development by means of further education and training.

CONCLUDING THOUGHTS

In closing, let's return to the four case studies presented in this chapter. Debbie Woods has provided you with only hearsay evidence and thus your only course of action is to work with her and support her working toward engaging her husband in the counselling process, as well as deal with his addiction issue. While you may have felt that you needed to act to protect innocent people, you neither have the authority nor sufficient information to proceed. However, in the case of Violet Woodlands, you are ethically, legally, and hopefully morally compelled to contact your local child welfare agency, or, even better, to support Violet in making that contact herself, for when a minor is at risk, there is no alternative but to intervene regardless of what the service user asks of you. The issue becomes less clear if the child is 17 rather than 9.

Mary's case asks you to reflect on service user self-determination. Historically, the addiction field was very directive, and service users were told what was best for them. That has now changed, with a greater focus on service user rights, harm-reduction approaches, and options other than abstinence. However, when does the need to protect your service users supersede their right to act in a manner they wish to? Do you have a moral obligation to intervene when someone is doing harm to themselves? What can you do if a person refuses your aid? Perhaps more importantly, how do you deal with your feelings and sense of professional responsibility when you are not allowed to provide the assistance you deem necessary?

Finally, there is the question of John's boundaries. The power differential that exists in professional counselling relationships quickly answers the question of whether one can have a relationship with a former service user: the simple answer is no, and with a current service user, the answer is always, definitely no. However, John is not a professional counsellor. He does not belong to a professional association, nor is he bound by a college's rules and regulations. There is no government censure regarding his behaviour, a similar situation to what currently exists for addiction counsellors, and thus why having a professional body is essential to the future of the field.

Situations like those described above will always bring a challenge to working in the addiction field. However, this a difficult yet vastly rewarding, noble, and gratifying calling that you are entering into as long as you take care of yourself first so that you can take care of others.

CHAPTER 30

Practice Considerations: Addiction Counsellor Competencies

Frontline addiction counsellors have difficult and stressful positions. However, not only are there no mandatory ethical guidelines to support them in their practice, as discussed above, there are also no national educational or practice standards required for those working in this field. Canada's substance use workforce continues to be unregulated, meaning that persons working in the field of substance use and misuse are not required to conform to any standardized qualifications or professional standards. However, in this century, in both Canada and internationally, there has been an increasing interest in workforce development issues stemming from a growing need to ensure services are being delivered in accordance with the highest possible standards and practices, while creating supportive and satisfying work experiences for those who are employed in this demanding arena (CCSA, 2007, 2014b; Pernell-Arnold & Finley, 2012). This led the Canadian Centre on Substance Abuse (CCSA), a national agency that was created as part of the 1987 Drug Strategy, to take a lead in coordinating a workshop and national survey to identify the needs of the addiction workforce (Ogborne & Graves, 2005), a process that was reviewed and revised beginning in 2019.

A National Advisory Group on Workforce Development (NAGWD) was struck in 2006, whose responsibilities included development, implementation, and ongoing evaluation of a broad national strategy on workforce development across the continuum of services related to substance use. A primary focus of the committee was to identify core knowledge and practice competencies needed by the substance use workforce, with a goal of enhancing professionalism within the field by supporting the adoption of evidence-informed practice and supporting the hiring and retention of skilled practitioners (CCSA, 2007).

The result has been the development and subsequent revision of a set of core knowledge and practice competencies that any professional working in the addiction field should become familiar with and adept at (CCSA, 2010b, 2014b). Competencies are essential skills, knowledge, attitudes, and values, with competency-based education being an approach that advocates for and attempts to provide precise measurable knowledge, skills, and behaviours by the end of a course or educational program (Richards & Rodgers,

2001). Competencies are specific, measurable skills and/or knowledge needed to effectively perform a particular function or role (Marrelli, 2001; Mirabile, 1997). They do not equate to increased job performance but rather are areas in which addiction counsellors should have expertise during their professional careers (Boyatzis, 2008). No one counsellor can be expected to have expert proficiency knowledge in all competencies. Some competencies will not pertain to the responsibilities of every counsellor, but rather they are areas pertinent to the entire field of addiction.

Technical competencies are the specific, measurable knowledge and skills required when applying specific technical principles and information in a job function that are typically learned in an educational environment or on the job. They are considered to be the hard skills of the profession. Complementing these are behavioural competencies, which are the abilities, attitudes, and values required to perform effectively in a specific position. These soft skills involve performing in the role of an addiction counsellor and complement the technical competencies (CCSA, 2010b, 2014b).

The CCSA developed (and revised in 2019–2020) 17 technical (Box 30.1) and 18 behavioural (Box 30.2) competencies that those working in the addiction field should become adept at. The aim of these competencies is not to be proscriptive but rather to enhance professionalism within the field by providing tools and resources to identify knowledge and skill sets for allied professionals, support employers in hiring and staff development, and assist educators and trainers in developing strategies for learning to provide Canadians with a more consistent quality of service delivery from the addiction workforce. To further this goal, a joint initiative has been undertaken by CCSA with the Canadian Addiction Counsellors Certification Federation to address the need for the regulation of addiction counsellors, and to create a certification process not only for the benefit of those working in the field but for the protection of the public.

Box 30.1: Technical Competencies

As the CCSA reminds us, "Understanding substance use and understanding concurrent disorders are the two foundational technical competencies upon which the others rest. If one does not grasp the key points for these two competencies, one will be less effective in implementing the other technical competencies."

1. *Understanding substance use:* Background or contextual knowledge of substance use, as defined in the Competencies, required to properly inform more specific aspects of a professional's work with service users and their families.
2. *Understanding concurrent conditions*: Knowledge and skills required to properly inform more specific aspects of a professional's work with service users with co-occurring substance use and mental illness, or substance use and mental health issues.

3. *Case management*: Facilitating a substance use service user's movement within and between service providers. It includes maintaining accurate documentation, sharing service user information appropriately and collaborating with other service providers.

4. *Referral*: Collaborating with substance use service users, services, and supports to identify and access the best available resources to meet service users' needs.

5. *Community development*: Working together to identify community needs and resources, and to plan and support or guide collective action.

6. *Counselling*: Applying a comprehensive range of evidence-informed counselling styles, techniques and methodologies aimed at improving the overall well-being of substance use and concurrent disorders service users.

7. *Crisis intervention*: Recognizing and responding effectively when a substance use or concurrent disorders service user, or associated group or community, is in an unstable, risky, dangerous, or potentially dangerous situation.

8. *Family and social support*: Working with service users and individuals and groups most affected by the person's substance use and most able to either support or undermine the service user's treatment goals.

9. *Group facilitation*: Using evidence-informed approaches to work effectively with substance use and concurrent disorders service users in group settings.

10. *Medications* (formerly pharmacology): The knowledge and skills required to understand and use medications in the treatment of service users with substance use or concurrent disorders and to understand and respond to the impact that medications could have on the service user.

11. *Outreach*: Designing and delivering substance use and concurrent disorders services in the community to a broad range of service users, including those who might otherwise not seek or have access to those services.

12. *Prevention and health promotion*: Engaging with substance use and concurrent disorders service users, their families, and their communities to encourage the adoption of knowledge, behaviours, values, and attitudes that promote personal and community well-being.

13. *Program development, implementation, and evaluation*: Developing and implementing new substance use programs, modifying existing programs to respond to identified needs, and evaluating the outcomes of new or revised programs.

14. *Record keeping and documentation*: Creating and maintaining accurate, up-to-date, comprehensive service user records able to withstand legal scrutiny.

15. *Screening and assessment*: Selecting, administering, and interpreting the results of evidence-informed tools and methods to measure a service user's substance use and related concerns, and inform the care and treatment plan.

16. *Trauma- and violence-informed care*: Interacting with substance use service users to identify and consider the impact that overwhelmingly negative events have on functioning and the ability to cope, and then developing and delivering interventions that emphasize safety, choice, and personal control.

17. *Treatment planning*: Collaboratively developing a treatment plan based on screening and assessment findings, ensuring that activities and resources reflect the service user's needs, strengths and goals. The process also includes monitoring, evaluating, planning for discharge, and updating the treatment plan so that it reflects the person's evolving needs and goals.

Source: Adapted from Canadian Centre on Substance Abuse (2014b).

Box 30.2: Behavioural Competencies

1. *Adaptability/flexibility*: Willingly adjust one's approach to meet the demands and needs of constantly changing conditions, situations, and people and to work effectively in difficult or ambiguous situations.

2. *Analytical thinking and decision making*: Gather, synthesize and evaluate information to determine possible alternatives and outcomes and make well-informed, timely decisions, including critical thinking and reasoning.

3. *Person-centred change*: Enhance, facilitate, support, empower, and otherwise increase service user motivation for positive change. Positive change is achieved by co-creating and collaborating with people using services in the change process and encouraging individuals to take responsibility for the outcomes they achieve. People using services may include individuals, families, groups, communities, or organizations.

4. *Person-service orientation*: Provide service excellence to people who use services (which can include individuals, families, groups, communities, and organizations). Includes providing trauma-informed care, making a commitment to serve service users and focusing one's efforts on discovering and meeting their needs within personal, professional, and organizational capacities and boundaries.

5. *Collaboration and network building*: Identify and create informal and formal interdisciplinary networks and allied community groups, including people with lived experience, their families, and communities, to support the provision of service delivery and achievement of the organization's objectives.

6. *Continuous learning*: Identify and pursue learning opportunities to enhance one's professional performance and development and the delivery of high-quality programs and services.

7. *Creativity and innovation*: Use evidence-based and evidence-informed practices in innovative and creative ways to initiate both effective new ways of working and advances in the understanding of the field of practice. Innovation and creativity are achieved by collaborating with stakeholders to optimize improvements in service delivery and professional practice.

8. *Developing others*: Facilitate and motivate sustained learning and create learning opportunities and resources, as well as promote and respect others' ownership of learning outcomes. Includes creation of a continuous learning environment that fosters positive growth in both work and public contexts among peers, individuals, families, communities, and other groups (recipients).

9. *Diversity and cultural responsiveness*: Provide respectful, equitable, and effective services to diverse populations, as defined by culture, age, gender, language, ethnicity, socio-economic status, legal status, health, ability, sexual orientation, and type and mode of substance use. Affirm and value the worth of all individuals, families, groups, and communities, and protect the dignity of all.

10. *Effective communication*: Articulate both verbally and in writing across a range of technologies including texting and social media, in a manner that builds trust, respect, and credibility. Checks with audiences to ensure the message is received and mutually understood. Includes active listening skills (attending, being silent, summarizing, paraphrasing, questioning, and empathizing) and communicating with cultural humility and congruent non-verbal communication.

11. *Ethical conduct and professionalism*: Provide professional services according to the principles and values of integrity, competence, responsibility, respect, and trust to safeguard both self and others. Includes the development of professionalism and ethical behaviour in self and others (individuals, families, groups, organizations, communities).

12. *Interpersonal rapport*: Establish and maintain relationships based on mutual respect and trust, appropriate sensitivity and transparency, empathy, and compassion with people using services, colleagues, professional associates, and the greater community. Encompasses skills of tact, engagement, and sensitivity in all encounters with others.

13. *Leadership*: Help others achieve excellent results and create enthusiasm for a shared vision and mission, even in the face of critical debate and adversity.

14. *Planning and organizing*: Identify and prioritize tasks, develop and implement plans, evaluate outcomes, and adjust activities in order to achieve objectives.

15. *Self-care*: Deliberately and continuously apply professional and personal self-care principles to oneself and, at times, others to sustain optimal productivity while maintaining physical, mental, spiritual, and emotional health.

16. *Self-management*: Appropriately manage one's own emotions and strong feelings; maintain a calm and respectful composure under a broad range of challenging circumstances; and think clearly and stay focused under pressure. Encompasses self-regulation and mindfulness.

17. *Self-motivation and drive*: Remain motivated and focused on a goal until the best possible results are achieved, with both passion for making a difference in the substance use field and persistence despite confronting obstacles, resistance, and setbacks.

18. *Teamwork and co-operation*: Work co-operatively and productively with others within and across organizational units to achieve common goals; demonstrate respect, co-operation, collaboration, and consensus-building.

Source: Adapted from Canadian Centre on Substance Abuse (2014b).

Section VII Closing Thoughts and Activities

At first people refuse to believe that a strange new thing can be done, then they begin to hope it can be done, then they see it can be done—then it is done and all the world wonders why it was not done centuries ago.
—Francis Hodgson Burnett, *The Secret Garden*

Of all the fields of counselling, perhaps there is none that faces as many stereotypes as the field of addiction. Prejudice is the pre-judgment of an individual and negative attitudes expressed toward them based entirely on their membership in a group. For those facing the stigma of addiction, prejudice and oppression also run the gamut of demographic differences, including race, ethnicity, sex, sexual orientation, gender identification, ability, age, geographic location, and class. Thus, beyond the legal and ethical issues that are essential for any counsellor to understand, and the competent practice we should also endeavour to achieve, there needs to be additional focus given to addressing issues of heterogeneity among those who seek assistance.

Thus, a final area to consider is that of inclusion and cultural competency. Historically, culture was defined simply by either the race or ethnicity that was shared by a group, but we have come to appreciate that, like addiction, culture is a far more complex phenomenon. One contemporary definition of culture states that it is "the shared identity or identities of a group of people based upon common traits, customs, values, norms and patterns of behaviour that are socially transmitted and highly influential in shaping beliefs, experiences and worldviews" (Azzopardi & McNeill, 2016, p. 283).

In attempting to understand how individuals and groups respond to cultural diversity, a continuum of cultural competency has been developed containing six distinct levels (Figure VII.1) (Srivastava, 2008; Victorian Aboriginal Child Care Agency, 2008):

1. *Cultural destructiveness*: Intentional attitudes, practices, and policies that are destructive to the individuals within the culture and thus to the culture as a whole.
2. *Cultural incapacity*: The inability to help members of any minority group that does not belong to the mainstream in any demographic attribute, due to biased beliefs or attitudes that the person or group should be more like members of the majority.
3. *Cultural blindness*: The belief that the counselling you employ with members of the dominant culture, or the majority in society, can also be used in the same manner with members of a demographic minority, with no need to adapt your helping approach in any way.
4. *Cultural precompetence*: The desire to deliver quality counselling and a commitment to diverse service users through hiring staff representing minority demographic groups, training and recruiting members of minority demographic groups for

leadership positions but not fully integrating agency practices and policies in an intentional manner, risking the development of tokenism rather than inclusion.

5. *Cultural competency*: Acceptance and respect for demographic differences, continuing self-assessment, mindfulness of the dynamics demographic differences create in the therapeutic relationship, and continuous expansion of knowledge and resources, along with agency adoption of services that better meet the needs of diverse service user populations.

6. *Cultural proficiency*: Holding all cultures in high esteem, seeking to continually add knowledge regarding distinct demographic minority groups, influencing approaches to care, and promoting self-determination of these individuals and groups.

However, one critique of the inclusion continuum is that it gives a sense of completion, that once someone is culturally proficient, they could move on to address other issues in their professional practice without further reflection on the role of culture in the helping process. The response to this has been to add another layer, "cultural humility," which, while important for everyone, is of particular relevance to those who belong to demographic majorities (Tervalon & Murray-Garcia, 1998). The practice of cultural humility begins with being open and self-aware, understanding yourself and working to understand those different from you, and engaging in supportive interactions. The next step is to recognize the prejudices that exist in our society and that you have been subject to unconsciously since birth. All of us have developed cultural misperceptions and stereotypes that we are not even aware of, many of which relate to those misusing psychoactive substances. Being culturally humble asks you to engage in continuous self-reflection, as you would in any other dimension of your practice— to be the fish that sees the water you swim in. In this reflection, however, you are asked to go one step further and incorporate the competency of advocacy and empowerment by challenging the power differentials in your relationships with service users, as well as in your organization's relationship with service users (Foronda et al., 2016). The ultimate outcome in cultural humility is appreciating the fact that you cannot know everything about every group of people, nor should you expect yourself to, but that as a helping professional your learning never ends. That learning process comes not only from research and books, but from engaging daily in the lives of service users and learning from them, just as they learn from us.

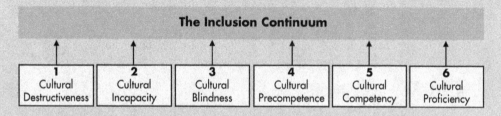

Figure VII.1: The Inclusion Continuum

Source: Adapted from Victorian Aboriginal Child Care Agency (2008).

DISCUSSION QUESTIONS

1. (a) What are your views on Canada's current drug laws?

    (b) If you had the opportunity to make a presentation to Parliament, what recommendations would you offer to change the current drug laws?

    (c) Knowing that your opinion must be based on facts, what information from the previous readings would you draw on to support the changes you are recommending?

    (d) What are your thoughts on decriminalizing psychoactive agents versus legalizing them? What would be the implications of either action?

2. (a) What are the greatest ethical challenges an addiction counsellor faces?

    (b) What ethical concerns do you have as you prepare to enter the field?

    (c) Are you more a teleological or a deontological ethical decision maker?

    (d) What actions did you take with Debbie, Violet, Mary, and John?

    (e) What self-care activities do you have in place for when you have to respond to a lose-lose ethical dilemma?

3. (a) Which of the technical and behavioural competencies are your strengths?

    (b) Which of the technical and behavioural competencies do you require more knowledge about?

    (c) Which of the technical and behavioural competencies do you require more practice experience to master?

4. (a) What fears do you have about not being an ethical, competent counsellor?

    (b) What would you suggest if a service user presented these concerns?

5. What is your level of cultural competency?

6. What steps do you need to take, if any, to exhibit cultural humility?

References

Aaron, M. (2012). The pathways of problematic sexual behavior: A literature review of factors affecting adult sexual behavior in survivors of childhood sexual abuse. *Sexual Addiction & Compulsivity, 19*(3), 199–218.

Abbott, A. (1994). A feminist approach to substance abuse treatment and service delivery. *Social Work in Health Care, 19*(3–4), 67–83.

Acker, C. (2002). *Creating the American junkie: Addiction research in the classic era of narcotic control.* Johns Hopkins University Press.

Adams, R. (1990). *Self-help, social work and empowerment.* British Association of Social Workers.

Addiction Studies Institute. (2010). *The stages of the Transtheoretical Model of Change.* www.utexas.edu/research/cswr/nida/rdpGraphics/rdpConceptArt1.gif

Adoni, H., & Mane, S. (1984). Media and the social construction of reality: Toward an integration of theory and research. *Communication Research, 11*(3), 323–340.

Ahmadi, K., Javadinia, S., Saadat, S., Ramezani, M., & Sedghijalal, H. (2017). Triangular relationship among risky sexual behavior, addiction, and aggression: A systematic review. *Electronic Physician, 9*(8), 5129–5137.

Ainsworth, M. (1973). The development of infant-mother attachment. In B. Cardwell & H. Ricciuti (Eds.), *Review of child development research* (pp. 1–94). University of Chicago Press.

Ainsworth, M. (1991). Attachments and other affectional bonds across the life cycle. In C. Parkes, J. Stevenson-Hinde, & P. Marris (Eds.), *Attachment across the life cycle* (pp. 33–51). Routledge.

Ainsworth, M., Blehar, M., Waters, E., & Wall, S. (1978). *Patterns of attachment: A psychological study of the strange situation.* Erlbaum.

Alaggia, R., & Csiernik, R. (2017). Coming home: Rediscovering the family in addiction treatment in Canada. In R. Csiernik & W. Rowe (Eds.), *Responding to the oppression of addiction: Canadian social work perspectives* (3rd ed., pp. 76–94). Canadian Scholars' Press.

Alam, S., Lang, J. J., Drucker, A. M., Gotay, C., Kozloff, N., Mate, K., Patten, S., Orphana, H., Afshin, A., & Cahill, L. E. (2019). Assessment of the burden of diseases and injuries attributable to risk factors in Canada from 1990 to 2016: An analysis of the Global Burden of Disease Study. *Canadian Medical Associaion Journal, 7*(1), E140.

Alberta Alcohol and Drug Abuse Commission. (2001). *Alberta Alcohol and Drug Addiction Commission policy on harm reduction.* AADAC.

Alberta Gaming and Liquor Commission. (2018). *BAC estimation charts.* http://protect.aglc.ca/siteuploads/document/BAC%20Estimation%20Charts_200806.pdf?v

Alberta Tobacco Reduction Strategy. (2003). *ATRS update.* AADAC.

Alcoholics Anonymous. (2001). *Alcoholics Anonymous* (4th ed.). AA World Services.

Alda, M. (2015). Lithium in the treatment of bipolar disorder: Pharmacology and pharmacogenetics. *Molecular psychiatry, 20*(6), 661–670.

Aldington, S., Harwood, M., Cox, B., Weatherall, M., Beckert, L., Hansell, A., ... Beasely, R. (2008). Cannabis use and risk of lung cancer: A case-control study. *European Respiratory Journal, 31*(2), 280–286.

Aldington, S., Williams, M., Nowitz, M., Weatherall, M., Pritchard, A., McNaughton, A., ... Beasley, R. (2007). The effects of cannabis on pulmonary structure, functions and symptoms. *Thorax, 62*(12), 1058–1063.

Alessi-Severini, S., Biscontri, R., Collins, D., Kozyrskyj, A., Sareen, J., & Enns M. (2008). Utilization and costs of antipsychotic agents: A Canadian population-based study, 1996–2006. *Psychiatric Services, 59*(5), 547–553.

Alexander, B. (1985). Drug use, dependence, and addiction at a British Columbia university: Good news and bad news. *Canadian Journal of Higher Education, 15*(1), 77–91.

Alexander, B. (1988). The disease and adaptive models of addiction: A framework evaluation. In Stanton Peele (Ed.), *Visions of addiction: Major contemporary perspectives on addictions and alcoholism.* Lexington Books.

Alexander, B., Beyerstein, B., Hadaway, P., & Coambs, R. (1981). Effects of early and later colony housing on oral ingestion of morphine in rats. *Psychopharmacology Biochemistry and Behavior, 58*(2), 175–179.

Alexander, C., Robinson, P., & Rainforth, M. (1994). Treating alcohol, nicotine and drug abuse through transcendental meditation: A review and statistical meta-analysis. *Alcoholism Treatment Quarterly, 11*(1–2), 11–84.

Alexander, M., & Stockton, G. (2000). Methylphenidate abuse and psychiatric side effects. *Journal of Clinical Psychiatry, 2*(5), 159–164.

Alexandrov, L., Ju, Y., Haase, K., Van Loo, P., Martincorena, I., Nik-Zainal, S., ... Campbell, P. (2016). Mutational signatures associated with tobacco smoking in human cancer. *Science, 354*(6312), 618–622.

Allen, C., & Ivester, J. (2017). Ketamine for pain management: Side effects & potential adverse events. *Pain Management Nursing, 18*(6), 372–377.

Allott, R., Paxton, R., & Leonard, R. (1999). Drug education: A review of British government policy and evidence on effectiveness. *Health Education Research Theory & Practice, 14*(4), 491–505.

Alper, K., Lotsof, H., Frenken, M., Luciano, D., & Bastiaans, J. (1999). Treatment of acute opioid withdrawal with ibogaine. *The American Journal on Addictions, 8*(3), 234–242.

Alper, K., Lotsof, H., & Kaplan, C. (2008). The ibogaine medical subculture. *Journal of Ethnopharmacology, 115*(1), 9–24.

Alwyn, T., John, B., Hodgson, R., & Phillips, C. (2004). The addition of a psychological intervention to a home detoxification programme. *Alcohol & Alcoholism, 39*(6), 536–541.

Amato, D., Canneva, F., Cumming, P., Maschauer, S., Groos, D., Dahlmanns, J., Grömer, T., Chiofalo, L., Dahlmanns, M., Zheng, F., Kornhuber, J., Prante, O., Alzheimer, C., von Hörsten, S., & Müller, C. (2018). A dopaminergic mechanism of antipsychotic drug efficacy, failure, and failure reversal: The role of the dopamine transporter. *Molecular Psychiatry, 25.* https://doi.org/10.1038/s41380-018-0114-5

American Association for the Advancement of Science. (2000). Proceedings of the American Association for the Advancement of Science Annual Meeting, "Science in an Uncertain Millennium," February 17–22. AAAS.

American Cancer Society. (2009). *Deadly in pink: Big tobacco steps up its targeting of women and girls.* Robert Wood Johnson Foundation.

American Psychiatric Association. (2000). *Diagnostic and statistical manual of mental disorders* (4th ed.). American Psychiatric Publishing.

American Psychiatric Association. (2013). *Diagnostic and statistical manual of mental disorders* (5th ed.). American Psychiatric Publishing.

American Psychiatric Association. (2017). *Practice guidelines for the pharmacological treatment of patients with alcohol use disorder.* American Psychiatric Publishing.

American Society of Addiction Medicine. (2019). *Definition of addiction.* https://www.asam.org/Quality-Science/definition-of-addiction

Ames, G., Duke, M., Moore, R., & Cunradi, C. (2008). The impact of occupational culture on drinking behavior of young adults in the U.S. navy. *Journal of Mixed Methods Research, 3*(2), 129–150.

Amos, C., Pinney, S., Li, Y., Kupert, E., Lee, J., de Andrade, M., ... Anderson, M. (2010). A susceptibility locus on chromosome 6q greatly increases lung cancer risk among light and never smokers. *Cancer Research, 70*(6), 2359–2367.

Anderson, G., & Brown, R. (1984). Real and laboratory gambling, sensation seeking and arousal: Toward a Pavlovian component in general theories of gambling and gambling addictions. *British Journal of Psychology, 75*(3), 401–411.

Andersson, H., Otterholt, E., & Gråwe, R. (2017). Patient satisfaction with treatments and outcomes in residential addiction institutions. *Nordic Studies on Alcohol and Drugs, 34*(5), 375–384.

Andreassen, C., Torsheim, T., Brunborg, G., & Pallesen, S. (2012). Development of a Facebook addiction scale. *Psychological Reports, 110*(2), 501–517.

Angell, M. (2008). Industry-sponsored clinical research: A broken system. *Journal of the American Medical Association, 300*(9), 1069–1071.

Angst, M., Lazzeroni, L., Nicholas, P., Drover, D., Tingle, M., Ray, A., ... Clark, J. (2012). Aversive and reinforcing opioid effects: A pharmacogenomic twin study. *Anesthesiology, 117*(1), 22–37.

Annis, H. (1984). Is inpatient rehabilitation of the alcoholic cost effective? Con position. *Advances in Alcohol and Substance Abuse, 5*(1–2), 175–190.

Antnowicz, J., Metzger, A., & Ramanujam, S. (2011). Paranoid psychosis induced by consumption of methylenedioxypyrovalerone: Two cases. *General Hospital Psychiatry, 33*(6), 640.e5–6.

Anton, R. (1994). Medications for treating alcoholism. *Alcohol, Health and Research World, 18*(4), 265–271.

Anton, R. (1999). What is a craving? Models and implications for treatment (alcohol craving). *Alcohol Research & Health, 23*(3), 165–173.

Arendt, M., Mortensen, P., Rosenberg, R., Pedersen, C., & Waltoft, B. (2008). Familial predisposition for psychiatric disorder: Comparison of subjects treated for cannabis-induced psychosis and schizophrenia. *Archives of General Psychiatry, 65*(11), 1269–1274.

Armed Conflict Location & Event Data Project. (2019). *Analysis by country: Philippines.* https://www.acleddata.com/tag/philippines/

Arminen, I., & Halonen, M. (2007). Laughing with and at patients: The roles of laughter in confrontations in addiction group therapy. *Qualitative Report, 12*(3), 484–513.

Armor, D., Polich, J., & Stambul, H. (1978). *Alcoholism and treatment.* New York: Wiley.

Asay, T., & Lambert, M. (1999). The empirical case for the common factors in therapy: Quantitative findings. In M. Hubble, B. Duncan, & S. Miller (Eds.), *The heart and soul of change: What works in therapy.* American Psychological Association.

Asbridge, M., Hayden, J., & Cartwright, J. (2012). Acute cannabis consumption and motor vehicle collision risk: Systematic review of observational studies and meta-analysis. *British Journal of Medicine, 344*, e536. https://doi.org/10.1136/bmj.e536

Ashton, H. (2002). The benzodiazepines: What they do in the body. *Benzodiazepines: How they work and how to withdraw* (Chapter 1). http://www.benzo.org.uk/manual/bzcha01.htm

Ashton, H. (2005). The diagnosis and management of benzodiazepine dependence. *Current Opinions in Psychiatry, 18*(2), 249–255.

Ashton, H. (2013). *Benzodiazepines: How they work and how to withdraw: The Ashton Manual supplement.* http://www.benzo.org.uk/ashsupp11.htm

Aslan, L. (2018). Doing time on a TC: How effective are drug-free therapeutic communities in prison? A review of the literature. *Therapeutic Communities: The International Journal of Therapeutic Communities, 39*(1), 26–34.

Atkinson, A., & Sumnall, H. (2016). "If I don't look good, it just doesn't go up": A qualitative study of young women's drinking cultures and practices on Social Network Sites. *International Journal of Drug Policy, 38*(Suppl. C), 50–62.

Atroszko, P., Andreassen, C., Griffiths, M., & Pallesen, S. (2015). Study addiction—a new area of psychological study: Conceptualization, assessment, and preliminary empirical findings. *Journal of Behavioral Addictions, 4*(2), 75–84.

Atroszko, P., Andreassen, C., Griffiths, M., & Pallesen, S. (2016a). Study addiction: A cross-cultural longitudinal study examining temporal stability and predictors of its changes. *Journal of Behavioral Addictions, 5*(2), 357–362.

Atroszko, P., Andreassen, C., Griffiths, M., & Pallesen, S. (2016b). The relationship between study addiction and work addiction: A cross-cultural longitudinal study. *Journal of Behavioral Addictions, 5*(4), 708–714.

Atroszko, P., Demetrovics, Z., & Griffiths, M. (2019). Beyond the myths about work addiction: Toward a consensus on definition and trajectories for future studies on problematic overworking: A response to the commentaries on: Ten myths about work addiction. *Journal of Behavioral Addictions, 8*(1), 7–15.

Aubin, H., Farley, A., Lycett, D., Lahmek, P., & Aveyard, P. (2012). Weight gain in smokers after quitting cigarettes: Meta-analysis. *British Medical Journal, 345*, e4439. https://doi.org/10.1136/bmj.e4439

Avants, B., Hurt, H., Giannetta, J., Epstein, C., Shera, D., Rao, H., ... Gee, J. (2007). Effects of heavy in utero cocaine exposure on adolescent caudate morphology. *Pediatric Neurology, 27*(4), 275–279.

Azodi, O., Orsini, N., Andrén-Sandberg, Å., & Wolk, A. (2011). Effect of type of alcoholic beverage in causing acute pancreatitis. *British Journal of Surgery, 98*(11), 1609–1616.

Azrin, N. (1976). Improvements in the community-reinforcement approach to alcoholism. *Behavioiur Research and Therapy, 14*(4), 339–348.

Azzopardi, C., & McNeill, T. (2016). From cultural competence to cultural consciousness: Transitioning to a critical approach to working across differences in social work. *Journal of Ethnic & Cultural Diversity in Social Work, 25*(4), 282–299.

Babor, T., Caetano, R., Casswell, S., Edwards, G., Giesbrecht, N., Graham, K., ... Rossow, I. (2003). *Alcohol: No ordinary commodity—research and public policy.* Oxford University Press.

Babor, T., & Del Boca, F. (2002). *Treatment matching in alcoholism.* National Institute on Alcohol Abuse and Alcoholism.

Babor, T., Higgins-Biddle, J., Saunders, J., & Monterra, M. (2001). *AUDIT—the alcohol use disorders identification test: Guidelines for use in primary care.* World Health Organization.

Back, S., Gentilin, S., & Brady, K. (2007). Cognitive-behavioral stress management for individuals with substance use disorders: A pilot study. *The Journal of Nervous and Mental Disease, 195*(8), 662–668.

Bador, K., & Kerekes, N. (2019). Evaluation of an integrated intensive cognitive behavioral therapy treatment within addiction care. *The Journal of Behavioral Health Services & Research, 47*, 102–112. https://doi.org/10.1007/s11414-019-09657-5

Bahr, S., & Hoffmann, J. (2010). Parenting style, religiosity, peers, and adolescent heavy drinking. *Journal of Studies on Alcohol and Drugs, 71*(4), 539–543.

Bahr, S., Hoffmann, J., & Yang, X. (2005). Parental and peer influences on the risk of adolescent drug use. *The Journal of Primary Prevention, 26*(6), 529–551.

Bailey, J., Epstein, M., Steeger, C., & Hill, K. (2018). Concurrent and prospective associations between substance-specific parenting practices and child cigarette, alcohol, and marijuana use. *Journal of Adolescent Health, 62*(6), 681–687.

Baker, P. (2006). Developing a blueprint for evidence-based drug prevention in England. *Drugs: Education, Prevention and Policy, 13*(1), 17–32.

Balakrishnan, J., & Griffiths, M. (2017). Social media addiction: What is the role of content in YouTube? *Journal of Behavioral Addictions, 6*(3), 364–377.

Balakrishnan, J., & Griffiths, M. (2018). An exploratory study of "selfitis" and the development of the Selfitis Behavior Scale. *International Journal of Mental Health and Addiction 16*(3), 722–736.

Bales, R. (1946). Cultural differences in rates of alcoholism. *Quarterly Journal of Studies on Alcohol, 35*, 1242–1255.

Balfour, D. (2004). The neurobiology of tobacco dependence: A preclinical perspective on the role of the dopamine projections to the nucleus accumbens. *Nicotine and Tobacco Research, 6*(6), 899–912.

Bandura, A. (1986). *Social foundations of thought and action*. Prentice Hall.

Barker, A., Smith, J., Hunter, A., Britton, J., & Murray, R. (2018). Quantifying tobacco and alcohol imagery in Netflix and Amazon Prime instant video original programming accessed from the UK: A content analysis. *BMJ Open 9*(2), e025807. https://doi.org/10.1136/bmjopen-2018-025807

Barnes, G. (1979). The alcoholic personality. *Journal of Studies on Alcohol, 40*(7), 571–634.

Barnes, K. (2011). *Problem solving in Canada's court rooms*. National Judiciary Institute.

Barnett, A., Hall, W., Fry, C., & Carter, A. (2018). Drug and alcohol treatment provider's views about the disease model of addiction and its impact on clinical practice: A systemic review. *Drug and Alcohol Review, 37*(6), 697–720.

Barnett, J. (2009). An examination of Western Missouri Correctional Center's therapeutic community. *Journal of Groups in Addiction and Recovery, 4*(1–2), 245–264.

Barnoya, J., & Glantz, S. (2005). Cardiovascular effects of second hand smoke nearly as large as smoking. *Circulation, 111*(20), 2684–2698.

Barrilleaux, J. (2016). Sexual addiction: Definitions and interventions. *Journal of Social Work Practice in the Addictions, 16*(4), 421–438.

Barry, C., Kennedy-Hendricks, A., Gollust, S., Niederdeppe, J., Bachhuber, M., Webster D., & McGinty, E. (2016). Understanding Americans' view on opioid pain reliever abuse. *Society for the Study of Addiction, 111*(1), 85–93.

Barry, H., III. (1988). Psychoanalytic theory of alcoholism. In C. Chaudron & D. Wilkinson (Eds.), *Theories on addiction* (pp. 103–141). Addiction Research Foundation.

Barth, R., & Kinder, B. (1987). The mislabeling of sexual impulsivity. *Journal of Sex and Marital Therapy, 13*(1), 15–23.

Bassin, A. (1975). Different strokes for different folks: A defence of confrontation tactics in psychotherapy. *The Counseling Psychologist, 5*(3), 128–130.

Baum, D. (2016). Legalize it all. *Harper's Magazine, 24*. https://harpers.org/archive/2016/04/legalize-it-all/

Bauman, K., Ennett, S., Foshee, V., Pemberton, M., King, T., & Koch, G. (2000). Influence of a family-directed program on adolescent cigarette and alcohol cessation. *Prevention Science, 1*(4), 227–237.

Bautista, T., James, D., & Amaro, H. (2019). Acceptability of mindfulness-based interventions for substance use disorder: A systematic review. *Complementary therapies in clinical practice, 35*(2), 201–207.

Beaulieu, J., Marion, S., Rodriguiz, R., Medvedev, I., Sotnikova, T., Ghisi, V., Wetsel, W., Lefkowitz, R., Gainetdinov, R., & Caron M. (2008). A beta-arrestin 2 signaling complex mediates lithium action on behavior. *Cell, 132*(1), 125–136.

Beayno, A., El Hayek, S., Noufi, P., Tarabay, Y., & Shamseddeen, W. (2019). The role of epigenetics in addiction: Clinical overview and recent updates. In F. Kobeissay (Ed.), *Psychiatric disorders: Methods and protocols, methods in molecular biology* (pp. 609–631). Springer Nature.

Becirevic, A., Reed, D., Amlung, M., Murphy, J. G., Stapleton, J., & Hillhouse, J. (2017). An initial study of behavioral addiction symptom severity and demand for indoor tanning. *Experimental and Clinical Psychopharmacology, 25*(5), 346–352.

Becker, A., Dörter, F., Eckhardt, K., Viniol, A., Baum, E., Kochen, ... Donner-Banzhoff, N. (2011). The association between a journal's source of revenue and the drug recommendations made in the articles it publishes. *Canadian Medical Journal, 183*(5), 544–548.

Becker, D., Hogue, A. & Liddle, H. (2002). Methods of engagement in family-based preventive intervention. *Child and Adolescent Social Work Journal, 19*(2), 163–179.

Becker, H. (1963). *Outsiders: Studies in the sociology of deviance.* Free Press.

Becoña, E. (2018). Brain disease or biopsychosocial model in addiction? Remembering the Vietnam Veteran Study. *Psicothema, 30*(3), 270–275.

Begum, F. (2019). Selfitis: A newer behavioural addiction—a review. *International Journal of Trend in Scientific Research and Development, 3*(5), 1572–1574.

Beier, J., Artel, G., & McClain, C. (2011). Advances in alcoholic liver disease. *Current Gastroenterology Reports, 13*(1), 56–64.

Beilfuss, S. (2019). Pharmaceutical opioid marketing and physician prescribing behavior. *Social Sciences Research Network.* http://dx.doi.org/10.2139/ssrn.3379855

Beirness, D., & Beasley, E. (2009). *Alcohol and drug use among drivers: British Columbia roadside survey 2008.* Canadian Centre on Substance Abuse.

Bell, S., Daskalopoulou, M., Rapsomaniki, E., George, J., Britton, A., Bobak, M., Casas, J., Dale, C., Denaxas, S., Shah, A., & Hemingway, H. (2017). Association between clinically recorded alcohol consumption and initial presentation of 12 cardiovascular diseases: Population based cohort study using linked health records. *BMJ, 356*, j909. https://doi.org/10.1136/bmj.j909

Bennett, G., Withers, J., Thomas, P., Higgins, D., Bailey, J., Parry, L., & Davies, E. (2005). A randomised trial of early warning signs relapse prevention training in the treatment of alcohol dependence. *Addictive Behaviors, 30*(6), 1111–1124.

Bennett, T., Holloway, K., & Farrington, D. (2008). The statistical association between drug misuse and crime: A meta-analysis. *Aggression and Violent Behavior: A Review Journal, 13*(2), 107–118.

Benson, A., & Eisenach, D. (2013). Stopping overshopping: An approach to the treatment of compulsive-buying disorder. *Journal of Groups in Addiction & Recovery, 8*(1), 3–24.

Bepko, C. (1991). *Feminism and addiction.* Haworth Press.

Beres, L. (2017). Narrative therapy ideas and practices for working with addiction. In R. Csiernik & W. Rowe (Eds.), *Responding to the oppression of addiction: Canadian social work perspectives* (3rd ed., pp. 134–151). Canadian Scholars' Press.

Berg, I., & Miller, S. (1992). *Working with the problem drinker: A solution-oriented approach.* Norton.

Berghmans, R., de Jong, J., Tibben, A., & Guido de Wert, T. (2009). On the biomedicalization of alcoholism. *Theoretical Medicine and Bioethics, 30* (4), 311–321.

Bergler, E. (1958). *The psychology of gambling.* Hill and Wang.

Bergman, P., Dudovitz, R., Dosanjh, K., & Wong, M. (2019). Engaging parents to prevent adolescent substance use: A randomized controlled trial. *American Journal of Public Health, 109*(10), 1455–1461.

Berrettini, W., & Lerman, C. (2005). Pharmacotherapy and pharmacogenetics of nicotine dependence. *American Journal of Psychiatry, 162*(8), 1441–1451.

Berridge, K., & Kringelbach, M. (2015). Pleasure systems in the brain. *Neuron, 86*(3), 646–664.

Berridge, V., & Edwards, G. (1981). *Opium and the people: Opiate use in nineteenth-century England.* St. Martin's Press.

Bershad, A., Mayo, L., Van Hedger, K., McGlone, F., Walker, S., & de Wit, H. (2019). Effects of MDMA on attention to positive social cues and pleasantness of affective touch. *Neuropsychopharmacology, 44*(10), 1698–1705.

Bertol, E., Fineschi, V., Karch, S., Mari, F., & Riezzo, I. (2004). *Nymphaea* cults in ancient Egypt and the New World: A lesson in empirical pharmacology. *Journal of the Royal Society of Medicine, 97*(2), 84–85.

Beutler, L., Harwood, T., Kimpara, S., Verdirame, D., & Blau, K. (2011). Adapting psychotherapy to the individual patient: Coping style. *Journal of Clinical Psychology, 67*(2), 176–183.

Bickel, A. (1995). *Family involvement: Strategies for comprehensive alcohol, tobacco, and other drug use prevention programs.* Northwest Regional Education Laboratory.

Bickel, W., Mellis, A., Snider, S., Athamneh, L., Stein, J., & Pope D. (2018). 21st century neurobehavioral theories of decision making in addiction: Review and evaluation. *Pharmacology, Biochemistry and Behavior, 164*(1), 4–21.

Bien, T., Miller, W., & Tonigan, J. (1993). Brief interventions for alcohol problems: A review. *Addiction, 88*(3), 315–336.

Bierut, L. (2011). Genetic vulnerability and susceptibility to substance dependence. *Neuron, 69*(4), 618–627.

Biglan, A., & Metzler, C. (1998). A public health perspective for research on family-focused interventions. In R. Ashery, E. Robertson, & K. Kumpfer (Eds.), *Drug abuse prevention through family interventions* (pp. 430–458). United States Department of Health and Human Services.

Bilevicius, E., Neufeld, D., Single, A., Foot, M., Ellery, M., Keough, M., & Johnson, E. (2019). Vulnerable narcissism and addiction: The mediating role of shame. *Addictive Behaviors, 92*, 115–121.

Billieux, J., Schimmenti, A., Khazaal, Y., Maurage, P., & Heeren, A. (2015). Are we overpathologizing everyday life? A tenable blueprint for behavioral addiction research. *Journal of Behavioral Addictions, 4*(3), 119–123.

Bischof, G., Richmond, C., & Case, A. (2003). Detoxification at home: A brief solution-oriented family system approach. *Contemporary Family Therapy: An International Journal, 25*(1), 17–39.

Black, D. (2014). Mindfulness-based interventions: An antidote to suffering in the context of substance use, misuse, and addiction. *Substance Use & Misuse, 49*(5), 487–491.

Blackwell, T. (2011, November 12). The selling of OxyContin. *National Post.* http://news.nationalpost.com/2011/11/12/the-selling-of-oxycontin/

Blake, S., Amaro, H., Schwartz, P., & Flinchbaugh, L. (2001). A review of substance abuse prevention interventions for young adolescent girls. *Journal of Early Adolescence, 21*(3), 294–324.

Blasco-Fontecilla, H., Fernández-Fernández, R., Colino, L., Fajardo, L., Perteguer-Barrio, R., & De Leon, J. (2016). The addictive model of self-harming (non-suicidal and suicidal) behavior. *Frontiers in Psychiatry, 7*, 8. https://doi.org/10.3389/fpsyt.2016.00008

Blaszczynski, A., & Nower, L. (2002). A pathways model of problem and pathological gambling. *Addiction, 97*(5), 487–499.

Blaszczynski, A., Winter, S., & McConaghy, N. (1986). Plasma endorphin levels in pathological gamblers. *Journal of Gambling Behavior, 2*(1), 3–14.

Blednov, Y., Cravatt, B., Boehm II, S., Walker, D., & Harris, R. (2007). Role of endocannabinoids in alcohol consumption and intoxication: Studies of mice lacking fatty acid Amide Hydrolase. *Neuropsychopharmacology, 32*(7), 1570–1582.

Blodgett, J., Maisel, N., Fuh, I., Wilbourne, P., & Finney, J. (2014). How effective is continuing care for substance use disorders? A meta-analytic review. *Journal of Substance Abuse Treatment, 46*(2), 87–97.

Boffetta, P., & Straif, K. (2009). Use of smokeless tobacco and risk of myocardial infarction and stroke: Systematic review and meta-analysis. *British Medical Journal, 339*, b3060. https://doi.org/http://dx.doi.org/10.1136/bmj.b3060

Boivin, J., Piscopo, D., & Wilbrecht, L. (2015). Brief cognitive training interventions in young adulthood promote long-term resilience to drug-seeking behaviour. *Neuropharmacology, 97*, 404–413.

Bolla, K., McCann, U., & Ricaurte, G. (1998). Memory impairment in abstinent MDMA users. *Neurology, 51*(6), 1532–1557.

Bolton, M., Chapman, B., & Van Marwijk, H. (2020). Low-dose naltrexone as a treatment for chronic fatigue syndrome. *BMJ Case Reports CP, 13*(1). http://dx.doi.org/10.1136/bcr-2019-232502

Bonaparte, M., Freud, A., & Kris, E. (1954). *The origins of psychoanalysis.* Harper Collins.

Boniface, S., Scannell, J. W., & Marlow, S. (2017). Evidence for the effectiveness of minimum pricing of alcohol: A systematic review and assessment using the Bradford Hill criteria for causality. *BMJ Open, 7*(5). https://bmjopen.bmj.com/content/7/5/e013497

Booth, M. (2005). *Cannabis: A history.* Picador.

Borchers, M., Wesselkamper, C., Curull, V., Ramirez-Sarmiento, A., Sánchez-Font, A., Garcia-Aymerich, J., … Orozco-Levi, M. (2009). Sustained CTL activation by murine pulmonary epithelial cells promotes the development of COPD-like disease. *The Journal of Clinical Investigation, 119*(3), 636–649.

Bornovalova, M., & Daughters, S. (2007). How does dialectical behavior therapy facilitate treatment retention among individuals with comorbid borderline personality disorder and substance use disorders? *Clinical Psychology Review, 27*(8), 923–943.

Bosworth, K. (1998). Assessment of drug abuse prevention curricula developed at the local level. *Journal of Drug Education, 28*(4), 307–325.

Botvin, G. (1990). Substance abuse prevention: Theory, practice and effectiveness. *Crime and Justice, 13*, 461–519.

Botvin, G. (2000). Preventing drug abuse in schools: Social and competence enhancement approaches targeting individual-level etiologic factors. *Addictive Behaviors, 25*(6), 887–897.

Botvin, G., & Griffin, K. (2004). Life skills training: Empirical findings and future directions. *The Journal of Primary Prevention, 25*(2), 211–232.

Boudreau, R. (1997). Addiction and the family. In S. Harrison & V. Carver (Eds.), *Alcohol and drug problems: A practical guide for counsellors* (2nd ed., pp. 407–418). Addiction Research Foundation.

Boumparis, N., Karyotaki, E., Schaub, M., Cuijpers, P., & Riper, H. (2017). Internet interventions for adult illicit substance users: A meta-analysis. *Addiction, 112*(9), 1521–1532.

Bourgeois, F., Kim, J., & Mandl, K. (2014). Premarket safety and efficacy studies for ADHD medications in children. *PLoS ONE, 9*(7), e102249. https://doi.org/10.1371/journal.pone.0102249

Bouziane, C., Filatova, O., Schrantee, A., Caan, M., Vos, F., & Reneman, L. (2019). White matter by diffusion MRI following methylphenidate treatment: A randomized control trial in males with attention-deficit/hyperactivity disorder. *Radiology, 293*(1), 186–192.

Bowen, S. (2011). Two serious and challenging medical complications associated with volatile substance misuse: Sudden sniffing death and fetal solvent syndrome. *Substance Use & Misuse, 46*(S1), 68–72.

Bowen, S., Chawla, N., & Marlatt, G. A. (2011). *Mindfulness-based relapse prevention for addictive behaviors: A clinician's guide.* Guilford Press.

Bowen, S., Witkiewitz, K., Dillworth, T., Chawla, N., Simpson, T., Ostafin, B., … Marlatt, G. (2006). Mindfulness meditation and substance use in an incarcerated population. *Psychology of Addictive Behaviors, 20*(3), 343–347.

Bowlby, J. (1958). The nature of the child's tie to his mother. *International Journal of Psychoanalysis, 39*(4), 350–371.

Bowlby, J. (1969). *Attachment: Attachment and loss* (Vol. 1). Basic Books.

Boyatzis, R. (2008). Competencies in the 21st century. *Journal of Management Development, 27*(1), 5–12.

Boyd, N. (1983). The dilemma of Canadian narcotics legislation: The social control of altered states of consciousness. *Contemporary Crises, 7*(3), 257–269.

Boyd, S., Fang, L., Medoff, D., Dixon, L., & Gorelick, D. (2012). Use of a "microecological technique" to study crime incidents around methadone maintenance treatment centers. *Addiction, 107*(9), 1632–1638.

Boyett, B. (2019). The individualized treatment of opioid use disorder. *Journal of Managed Care and Speciality Pharmacy, 25*(6), 634–636.

Bozarth, M., Murray, A., & Wise, R. (1989). Influence of housing conditions on the acquisition of intravenous heroin and cocaine self-administration in rats. *Pharmacology, Biochemistry, and Behavior, 33*(4), 903–907.

Brache, K., & Stockwell, T. (2011). Drinking patterns and risk behaviors associated with combined alcohol and energy drink consumption. *Addictive Behaviors, 36*(12), 1133–1140.

Brandon, T., Vidrine, J., & Litvin, E. (2007). Relapse and relapse prevention. *Annual Review of Clinical Psychology, 3*, 257–284.

Brault, M., & Lacourse, E. (2012). Prevalence of prescribed attention-deficit hyperactivity disorder medications and diagnoses among Canadian preschoolers and school-aged children: 1994–2007. *Canadian Journal of Psychiatry, 57*(2), 93–101.

Brautigam, E. (1977). Effects of the transcendental meditation program on drug abusers: A prospective study. In D. Orme-Johnson & J. Farrow (Eds.), *Scientific research on the transcendental meditation program: Collected papers* (Vol. 1, pp. 506–514). M.E.R.U. Press.

Breeding, J., & Baughman, F. (2003). Informed consent and the psychiatric drugging of children. *Journal of Humanistic Psychology, 43*(1), 50–64.

Brennan, R., & Van Hout, M. (2014). Gamma-Hydroxybutyrate (GHB): A scoping review of pharmacology, toxicology, motives for use, and user groups. *Journal of Psychoactive Drugs, 46*(3), 243–251.

Brett, E., Miller, M., Leavens, E., Lopez, S., Wagener, T., & Leffingwell, T. (2019). Electronic cigarette use and sleep health in young adults. *Journal of Sleep Research*, e12902. https://doi.org/10.1111/jsr.12902

Briones, A., Cumsille, F., Henao, A., & Pardo, B. (2013). *The drug problem in the Americas.* Organization of American States.

Britt, E., Hudson, S., & Blampied, N. (2004). Motivational interviewing in health settings: A review. *Patient Education and Counseling, 53*(2), 147–155.

Brooks, H., Kassam, S., Salvalaggio, G., & Hyshka, E. (2018). Implementing managed alcohol programs in hospital settings: A review of academic and grey literature. *Drug and alcohol review, 37*(1), S145–S155.

Brooks, J. (2006). Strengthening resilience in children and youths: Maximizing opportunities through the schools. *Children & Schools, 28*(2), 69–76.

Brorson, H., Arnevik, E., Rand-Hendriksen, K., & Duckert, F. (2013). Drop-out from addiction treatment: A systematic review of risk factors. *Clinical psychology review, 33*(8), 1010–1024.

Brounstein, P., & Zweig, J. (1999). *Understanding substance abuse prevention—Towards the 21st century: A primer on effective programs.* Substance Abuse and Mental Health Administration.

Brown, J. (2001). Youth, drugs and resilience education. *Journal of Drug Education, 31*(1), 83–122.

Brown, J., Beard, E., Kotz, D., Michie, S., & West, R. (2014). Real-world effectiveness of e-cigarettes when used to aid smoking cessation: A cross-sectional population study. *Addiction, 109*(9), 1531–1540.

Brown, V., Harris, M., & Fallot, R. (2013). Moving toward trauma-informed practice in addiction treatment: A collaborative model of agency assessment. *Journal of Psychoactive Drugs, 45*(5), 386–393.

Brownsberger, W. (2000). Race matters: Disproportionality of incarceration for drug dealings in Massachusetts. *Journal of Drug Issues, 30*(2), 345–374.

Brunette, M., Drake, R., Woods, M., & Harnett, T. (2001). A comparison of long-term and short-term residential treatment programs for dual diagnosis patients. *Psychiatric Services, 52*(4), 526–528.

Bruno, T., & Csiernik, R. (2018). An examination of universal drug education programming in Ontario, Canada's elementary school system. *International Journal of Mental Health and Addiction, 18*, 707–719. https://doi.org/10.1007/s11469-018-9977-6

Bruun, K., Edwards, G., Lummio, M., Makela, K., Pan, L., Popham, R., ... Osterberg, E. (1975). *Alcohol control policies in public health perspective.* Finish Foundation for Alcohol Studies.

Bry, B., Catalano, R., Kumpfer, K., Lochman, J., & Szapocznik, J. (1998). Scientific findings from family prevention intervention research. In R. Ashery, E. Robertson, & K. Kumpfer (Eds.), *Drug abuse prevention through family interventions* (pp. 103–129). Rockville: United States Department of Health and Human Services.

Buchman, D., Illes, J., & Reine, B. (2010). The paradox of addiction neuroscience. *Neuroethics, 4*(1), 65–77.

Budd, J., Hoffart, I., Smith, P., Weinrath, M., & Wilde, C. (2019). *Drug treatment court facts.* https://cadtc.org/dtc-facts/

Burnside, L., & Fuchs, D. (2013). Bound by the clock: The experiences of youth with FASD transitioning to adulthood from child welfare care. *First Peoples Child & Family Review, 8*(1), 40–61.

Buscemi, L., & Turchi, C. (2011). An overview of the genetic susceptibility to alcoholism. *Medicine, Science and the Law, 51*(4), S2–S6.

Busse, J., Craigie, S., Juurlink, D., Buckley, D., Wang, L., Couban, R., ... Guyatt, G. (2017). Guideline for opioid therapy and chronic noncancer pain. *Canadian Medical Association Journal, 189*(18), E659–E666.

Cade, B., & O'Hanlon, W. (1993). *A brief guide to brief therapy.* Norton.

Cadet, J., Bisagno, V., & Milroy, C. (2014). Neuropathology of substance use disorders. *Acta Neuropathology, 127*(1), 91–107.

Cairncross, Z., Herring, J., van Ingen, T., Smith, B., Leece, P., Schwartz, B., & Hohenadel, K. (2018). Relation between opioid-related harms and socioeconomic inequalities in Ontario: A population-based descriptive study. *Canadian Medical Association Journal Open, 6*(4), E478–E485. https://doi.org/10.9778/cmajo.20180084

Cakic, V., Potkonyak, J., & Marshall, A. (2010). Dimethyltryptamine (DMT): Subjective effects and patterns of use among Australian recreational users. *Drug and Alcohol Dependence, 111*(1), 30–37.

California Department of Health Services. (2005). New data show California military, Korean men and LGBT populations smoke much more than others in the state. http://www.applications.dhs.ca.gov/pressreleases/store/pressreleases/05-60.html

Callahan, J., & Swift, J. (2009). The impact of client treatment preferences on outcome: A meta-analysis. *Journal of Clinical Psychology, 65*(4), 368–381.

Callow, T., Donaldson, S., & De Ruiter, M. (2008). Effectiveness of home detoxification: A clinical audit. *British Journal of Nursing, 17*(11), 692–695.

Cameron, K., Kolanos, R., Solis Jr., E., Glennon, R., & Felice, L. (2013a). Bath salts components mephedrone and methylenedioxypyrovalerone (MDPV) act synergistically at the human dopamine transporter. *British Journal of Pharmacology, 168*(7), 1750–1757.

Cameron, K., Kolanos, R., Verkariva, R., Felice, L., & Glennon, R. (2013b). Mephedrone and methylenedioxypyrovalerone (MDPV), major constituents of "bath salts," produce opposite effects at the human dopamine transporter. *Psychopharmacology, 227*(3), 493–499.

Campbell, C., Hahn, R., Elder, R., Brewer, R., Chattopadhyay, S., Fielding, J., ... Middleton, J. (2009). The effectiveness of limiting alcohol outlet density as a means of reducing excessive alcohol consumption and alcohol-related harms. *American Journal of Preventive Medicine, 37*(6), 556–569.

Canadian Addiction Counsellors Certification Federation. (2019). *Canon of ethical principles.* https://caccf.ca/wp-content/uploads/2019/04/Membership-Handbook.pdf

Canadian Association of Drug Treatment Court Professionals. (n.d.). *DTC program.* https://cadtc.org/dtc-program-title/

Canadian Centre on Substance Abuse. (2005). *Methamphetamine fact sheet.* CCSA.

Canadian Centre on Substance Abuse. (2007). *Core competencies for Canada's substance abuse field (version 1).* CCSA.

Canadian Centre on Substance Abuse. (2008). *Common ground.* CCSA.

Canadian Centre on Substance Abuse (2010a). *Stronger together: Canadian standards for community-based youth substance abuse prevention.* CCSA.

Canadian Centre on Substance Abuse. (2010b). *Competencies for Canada's substance abuse workforce.* CCSA.

Canadian Centre on Substance Abuse. (2014a). *National treatment indicators report.* CCSA. http://www.academia.edu/6537731/National_Treatment_Indicators_Report_2011-2012_Data

Canadian Centre on Substance Abuse. (2014b). *Competencies for Canada's substance abuse workforce.* CCSA.

Canadian Centre on Substance Abuse. (2014c). *Trauma-informed care.* CCSA. https://www.ccsa.ca/trauma-informed-care-essentials-series

Canadian Centre on Substance Use and Addiction. (2017). *Addiction treatment in Canada: The national treatment indicators report.* Canadian Centre on Substance Use and Addiction.

Canadian Centre on Substance Use and Addiction. (2019). *Edible cannabis, cannabis extracts and cannabis topicals: A primer on the new cannabis products.* Canadian Centre on Substance Use and Addiction.

Canadian Institute for Health Information. (2016). *Hospitalizations and emergency department visits due to opioid poisoning in Canada.* Canada Institute for Health Information.

Canadian Institute for Health Information. (2019a). *Hospital morbidity database and Ontario mental health reporting system, 2017–2018.* CIHI.

Canadian Institute for Health Information. (2019b). *Hospital stays for harm caused by substance use, 2018–2019: Breakdown by substance and age.* CIHI.

Canadian Public Health Association. (2016). *The Opiate Crisis in Canada.* CPHA.

Canadian Society of Addiction Medicine. (2014). *Definition of addiction.* Retrieved from http://www.cpsa.ca/physician-health-monitoring-program-phmp/phmp-policies/definitions/

Canadian Substance Use Costs and Harms Scientific Working Group. (2018). *Canadian substance use costs and harms in provinces and territories (2007–2014).* Canadian Institute for Substance Use Research, University of Victoria, and the Canadian Centre on Substance Use and Addiction.

Canistro, D., Vivarelli, F., Cirillo, S., Marquillas, C., Buschini, A., Lazzaretti, M., ... Cipriani, C. (2017). E-cigarettes induce toxicological effects that can raise the cancer risk. *Scientific Reports, 7*(1), 2028.

Cantu, C., Arauz, A., Murillo-Bonilla, L., Lopez, M., & Barinagarrementeria, F. (2003). Stroke associated with sympathomimetics contained in over-the-counter cough and cold drugs. *Stroke, 34*(7), 1667–1672.

Canuso, C., Singh, J., Fedgchin, M., Alphs, L., Lane, R., Lim, P., Pinter, C., Hough, D., Sanacora, G., Manji, H., & Drevets, W. (2018). Efficacy and safety of intranasal esketamine for the rapid reduction of symptoms of depression and suicidality in patients at imminent risk for suicide: Results of a double-blind, randomized, placebo-controlled study. *American Journal of Psychiatry, 175*(7), 620–630.

Carbonaro, T., Bradstreet, M., Barrett, F., MacLean, K., Jesse, R., Johnson, M., & Griffiths, R. (2016). Survey study of challenging experiences after ingesting psilocybin mushrooms: Acute and enduring positive and negative consequences. *Journal of Psychopharmacology, 30*(12), 1268–1278.

Carhart-Harris, R., Bolstridge, M., Day, C., Rucker, J., Watts, R., Erritzoe, D., ... Rickard, J. (2018). Psilocybin with psychological support for treatment-resistant depression: Six-month follow-up. *Psychopharmacology, 235*(2), 399–408.

Carhart-Harris, R., Muthukumaraswamy, S., Roseman, L., Kaelen, M., Droog, W., Murphy, K., ... Leech, R. (2016). Neural correlates of the LSD experience revealed by multimodal neuroimaging. *Proceedings of the National Academy of Sciences, 113*(17), 4853–4858.

Carlton, P., & Goldstein, L. (1987). Physiological determinants of pathological gambling. In T. Galski (Ed.), *A handbook of pathological gambling* (pp. 111–122). Charles C. Thomas.

Carnes, P. (1996). Addiction or compulsion: Politics or illness? *Sexual Addiction and Compulsivity: The Journal of Treatment and Prevention, 3*(2), 127–150.

Carnes, P. (2001). *Out of the shadows: Understanding sexual addiction.* Hazelden.

Carnes, P., & Adams, K. (Eds.). (2019). *Clinical management of sex addiction.* Routledge.

Carr, A. (1998). Michael White's narrative therapy. *Contemporary Family Therapy, 20*(4), 485–503.

Carroll, K. (1996). Relapse prevention as a psychosocial treatment: A review of controlled clinical trials. *Experimental and Clinical Psychopharmacology, 4*(1), 46–54.

Carroll, K., & Onken, L. (2005). Behavioral therapies for drug abuse. *American Journal of Psychiatry, 162*(8), 1452–1460.

Carter, A., & Hall, W. (2018). From coerced to compulsory treatment of addiction in the patient's best interests. In C. Spivakovsky, K. Seear, & A. Carter (Eds.), *Critical perspectives on coercive interventions: Law, medicine and society* (pp. 15–29). Routledge.

Carvalho, F. (2003). The toxicological potential of khat. *Journal of Ethnopharmacology, 87*(1), 1–2.

Case, S., & Haines, K. (2003). Promoting prevention: Preventing youth drug use in Swansea, UK, by targeting risk and protective factors. *Journal of Substance Use, 8*(4), 243–251.

Cassidy, R., Jackson, K., Rohsenow, D., Tidey, J., Barnett, N., Monti, P., Miller, M., & Colby, S. (2018). Contingency management for college student smokers: The role of drinking as a moderator and mediator of smoking abstinence during treatment. *Addictive behaviors, 80*(1), 95–101.

Cassin, S., & von Ranson, K. (2007). Is binge eating experienced as an addiction? *Appetite, 49*(3), 687–690.

Catalano, R., Berglund, M., Ryan, J., Lonczak, H., & Hawkins, J. (2004). Positive youth development in the United States: Research findings on evaluations of positive youth development programs. *The Annals of the American Academy of Political Science, 591*(1), 98–124.

Catalano, R., Hawkins, J., Krenz, C., Gillmore, M., Morrison, D., Wells, E., & Abbott, R. (1993). Using research to guide culturally appropriate drug abuse prevention. *Journal of Consulting and Clinical Psychology, 61*(5), 804–811.

Caulkins, J., Pacula, R., Paddock, S., & Chiesa, J. (2002). *School-based drug prevention: What kind of drug use does it prevent?* RAND Corporation.

Caulkins, J., Pardo, B., & Kilmer, B. (2019). Supervised consumption sites: A nuanced assessment of the causal evidence. *Addiction, 114*(12), 2109–2115. doi.org/10.1111/add.14747

Center on Alcohol Marketing and Youth. (2012). *Youth exposure to alcohol advertising on television, 2001–2009.* Johns Hopkins University.

Centers for Disease Control and Prevention. (1999). Decline in cigarette consumption following implementation of a comprehensive tobacco prevention and education program—Oregon, 1996–1998. *Morbidity and Mortality Weekly Report, 48*(7), 140–143.

Centers for Disease Control and Prevention. (2007). Decline in smoking prevalence—New York City, 2002–2006. *Morbidity and Mortality Weekly Report, 56*(24), 604–608.

Centre for Addiction and Mental Health. (1999). *Addiction and drug prevention programs for youth: What works?* CAMH.

Chai, G., Governale, L., McMahon, A., Trinidad, J., Staffa, J., & Murphy, D. (2012). Trends of outpatient prescription drug utilization in US children, 2002–2010. *Pediatrics, 130*(1), 23–31.

Chaloupka, F., Grossman, M., & Saffer, H. (2002). *The effects of price on alcohol consumption and alcohol-related problems.* National Institute on Alcohol Abuse and Alcoholism.

Chambers, R., Sajdyk, T., Conroy, S., Lafuze, J., Fitz, S., & Shekhar, A. (2007). Neonatal amygdala lesions: Co-occurring impact on social/fear-related behavior and cocaine sensitization in adult rats. *Behavioral Neuroscience, 121*(6), 1316–1327.

Champion, K., Newton, N., Barrett, E., & Teesson, M. (2013). A systematic review of school-based alcohol and other drug prevention programs facilitated by computers or the internet. *Drug and Alcohol Review, 32*(2), 115–123.

Champion, K., Newton, N., Stapinski, L., & Teesson M. (2016). Effectiveness of a universal internet-based prevention program for ecstasy and new psychoactive substances: A cluster randomized controlled trial. *Addiction, 111*(8), 1396–1405.

Chan, B., Freeman, M., Kondo, K., Ayers, C., Montgomery, J., Paynter, R., & Kansagara, D. (2019). Pharmacotherapy for methamphetamine/amphetamine use disorder—a systematic review and meta-analysis. *Addiction, 114*(12), 2122–2136.

Chandler, L. (2003). Ethanol and brain plasticity: Receptors and molecular networks of the postsynaptic density as targets of ethanol. *Pharmacology & Therapeutics, 99*(3), 311–326.

Chappel, J., & DuPont, R. (1999). Twelve-step and mutual-help programs for addictive disorders. *The Psychiatric Clinics of North America, 22*(2), 425–446.

Chaudron, C., & Wilkinson, D. (1988). *Theories on addiction.* Addiction Research Foundation.

Chechak, D., & Csiernik, R. (2014). Workplace violence. In R. Csiernik (Ed.), *Workplace wellness: Issues and responses* (pp. 15–32). Canadian Scholars' Press.

Chen, H., Huang, X., Guo, X., Mailman, R., Park, Y., Kamel, F., ... Blair, A. (2010). Smoking duration, intensity, and risk of Parkinson disease. *Neurology, 74*(11), 878–884.

Chen, Y., Dales, R., & Lin, M. (2003). The epidemiology of chronic rhinosinusitis in Canadians. *The Laryngoscope, 113*(7), 1199–1205.

Chenier, N. (2001). *Substance abuse and public policy.* Government of Canada.

Cho, S., & Wang, W. (2009) Acupuncture for alcohol dependence: A systematic review. *Alcoholism: Clinical and Experimental, 33*(8), 305–1313.

Chorniy, A., & Kitashima, L. (2016). Sex, drugs, and ADHD: The effects of ADHD pharmacological treatment on teens' risky behaviors. *Labour Economics, 43*(1), 87–105.

Christensen, M., & Kohlmeier, K. (2014). Age-related changes in functional postsynaptic nicotinic acetylcholine receptor subunits in neurons of the laterodorsal tegmental nucleus, a nucleus important in drug addiction. *Addiction Biology, 21*(2), 267–281.

Cianci, R., & Gambrel, P. (2003). Maslow's hierarchy of needs: Does it apply in a collectivist culture? *Journal of Applied Management and Entrepreneurship, 8*(2), 143–161.

Cicchetti, D., Toth, C., & Lynch, M. (1995). Bowlby's dream comes full circle: The application of attachment theory to risk and psychopathology. *Advances in Clinical Child Psychology, 17*, 1–75.

Ciovacco, L., & Hughes, S. (2017). Sanity of addiction: Contemplative and humanistic reflections on the Surgeon General's Report on Drugs. *Journal of Humanistic Psychology.* https://doi.org/10.1177/0022167817740464

Ciraulo, D., & Oldham, M. (2014). Sedative hypnotics. In B. Madras and M. Kuhar (Eds.), *The effects of drug abuse on the human nervous system* (pp. 499–532). Elsevier.

Clark, C. (1995). Alcoholics Anonymous: Common misconceptions. *American Psychological Association Addiction Newsletter, 2*(3), 9–22.

Clark, H., Ringwalt, L., Hanley, S., Shablen, S., Flewelling, R., & Hano, M. (2010). Project SUCCESS' effects on the substance use of alternative high school students. *Addictive Behaviors, 35*(3), 209–217.

Clarke, D. (2006). Impulsivity as a mediator in the relationship between depression and problem gambling. *Personality and Individual Differences, 40*(1), 5–15.

Cloninger, C. (1987). Neurogenetic adaptive mechanisms in alcoholism. *Science, 236*(4), 410–416.

Coffin, P., & Sullivan S. (2013). Cost-effectiveness of distributing naloxone to heroin users for lay overdose reversal. *Annals of Internal Medicine, 158*(1), 1–9.

Cole, C., Jones, L., McVeigh, J., Kicman, A., Syed, Q., & Bellis, M. (2011). Adulterants in illicit drugs: A review of empirical evidence. *Drug Testing and Analysis, 3*(2), 89–96.

Coleman, E., Raymond, N., & McBean, A. (2003). Assessment and treatment of compulsive sexual behaviour. *Minnesota Medicine, 86*(1), 42–47.

Collin, C. (2006). *Substance abuse issues and public policy in Canada: Canada's federal drug strategy.* Parliamentary Information and Research Service.

Collins, B., Cuddy, K., & Martin, A. (2017). Assessing the effectiveness and cost-effectiveness of drug intervention programs: UK case study. *Journal of Addictive Diseases, 36*(1), 5–13.

Collins, L. (2002). Alcohol and drug addiction in women: Phenomenology and prevention. In M. Ballou & L. Brown (Eds.), *Rethinking mental health and disorder: Feminist perspectives.* (pp. 198–230). Guilford Press.

Collins, S., Clifasefi, S., Dana, E., Andrasik, M., Stahl, N., Kirouac, M., & Malone, D. (2012). Where harm reduction meets housing first: Exploring alcohol's role in a project-based housing first setting. *International Journal of Drug Policy, 23*(2), 111–119.

Colorado Department of Revenue. (2015). *Colorado marijuana tax data.* https://www.colorado.gov/pacific/revenue/colorado-marijuana-tax-data

Comings, D., Rosenthal, R., Lesieur, H., & Rugle, L. (1996). A study of the dopamine D2 receptor gene in pathological gambling. *Pharmacogenetics, 6*(3), 223–234.

Connor, J., Kypri, K., Bell, M., & Cousins, K. (2010). Alcohol outlet density, levels of drinking and alcohol-related harm in New Zealand: A national study. *Journal of Epidemiological and Community Health, 65*(10), 841–846.

Conrad, P. (2007). *The medicalization of society.* Johns Hopkins University Press.

Conrad, P., & Barker, K. (2010). The social construction of illness: Key insights and policy implications. *Journal of Health and Social Behavior, 51*(1), S67–S79.

Cook, C. (1988). The Minnesota model in the management of drug and alcohol dependency: Miracle, method or myth? The philosophy and the programme. *British Journal of Addiction, 83*(6), 625–634.

Copeland, J., Frewen, A., & Elkins, K. (2009). *Management of cannabis use disorder and related issues.* National Cannabis Prevention and Information Centre.

Coppel, A. (2015). *Drug consumption rooms: An overview of provision and evidence.* European Monitoring Centre for Drugs and Drug Addiction.

Cornelis, M., & El-Sohemy, A. (2007). Coffee, caffeine, and coronary heart disease. *Current Opinion in Lipidology, 18*(1), 13–19.

Corwin, R., & Grigson, P. (2009). Symposium overview—food addiction: Fact or fiction? *Journal of Nutrition, 139*(3), 617–619.

Cosgrove, L., & Krimsky, S. (2012). A comparison of *DSM*-IV and *DSM*-5 panel members' financial associations with industry: A pernicious problem persists. *PLoS Medicine, 9*(3). https://doi.org/10.1371/journal.pmed.1001190

Cosgrove, L., Krimsky, S., Vijayaraghavan, M., & Schneider L. (2006). Financial ties between DSM-IV panel members and the pharmaceutical industry. *Psychotherapy and Psychosomatics, 75*(2), 154–160.

Costa, S., Barberis, N., Griffiths, M., Benedetto, L., & Ingrassia, M. (2019). The love addiction inventory: Preliminary findings of the development process and psychometric characteristics. *International Journal of Mental Health and Addiction.* https://doi.org/10.1007/s11469-019-00097-y

Costello, M., Li, Y., Remers, S., MacKillop, J., Sousa, S., Ropp, C., Roth, D., Weiss, M., & Rush, B. (2019). Effects of 12-step mutual support and professional outpatient services on short-term substance use outcomes among adults who received inpatient treatment. *Addictive Behaviors, 98*, 106055.

Cousins, G., Boland, F., Courtney, B., Barry, J., Lyons, S., & Fahey, T. (2016). Risk of mortality on and off methadone substitution treatment in primary care: A national cohort study. *Addiction, 111*(1), 73–82.

Covington, S., Burke, C., Keaton, S., & Norcott, C. (2008). Evaluation of a trauma-informed and gender-responsive intervention for women in drug treatment. *Journal of Psychoactive Drugs, 40*(sup5), 387–398.

Cox, W. (1979). The alcoholic personality. In B. Maher (Ed.), *Progress in experimental personality research* (Vol. 9, pp. 89–148). Academic Press.

Cox, W. (1987). Research on the personality correlates of alcohol use. *Drugs and Society, 1*(4), 61–84.

Cox, W. (1988). Personality theory. In C. Chaudron & D. Wilkinson (Eds.), *Theories on addiction* (pp. 55–89). Addiction Research Foundation.

Cox, W., & Klinger, E. (1988). A motivational model of alcohol use. *Journal of Abnormal Psychology, 97*(2), 168–180.

Coyle, J. (2016, July 23). Canada tops list of developed countries for rate of impaired-driving fatalities. *The Star.* https://www.thestar.com/news/canada/2016/07/23/canada-tops-list-of-developed-countries-for-rate-of-impaired-driving-fatalities.html

Cozby, P., & Rawn, C. (2012). *Methods in behavioural research: Canadian edition.* McGraw-Hill Ryerson.

Crane, E. (1980). The first wheel of commerce: Newport, Rhode Island and the slave trade, 1760–1776. *Slavery & Abolition, 1*(2), 178–198.

Crean, R., Crane, N., & Mason, B. (2011). An evidence-based review of acute and long-term effects of cannabis use on executive cognitive functions. *Journal of Addiction Medicine, 5*(1), 1–8.

Crist, R., Reiner, B., & Berrettini, W. (2019). A review of opioid addiction genetics. *Current Opinion in Psychology, 27*(1), 31–35.

Crumbaugh, J., & Carr, G. (1979). Treatment of alcoholics with logotherapy. *The International Journal of the Addictions, 14*(6), 847–853.

Cruz, F., Rubio, F., & Hope, B. (2014). Using *c-fos* to study neuronal ensembles in corticostriatal circuitry of addiction. *Brain Research, 1628*, 157–173.

Cruz, M. (2011). Lurasidone HCl (Latuda), an oral, once-daily atypical antipsychotic agent for the treatment of patients with schizophrenia. *Pharmacy and Therapeutics, 36*(8), 489-492.

Cruz, S. (2011). The latest evidence in the neuroscience of solvent misuse. (2011). *Substance Use and Misuse, 46*(1), 62–67.

Csiernik, R. (2002). Determining the value of Alcoholics Anonymous. *Canadian Social Work, 4*(1), 14–22.

Csiernik, R. (2011). The glass is filling: An examination of Employee Assistance Program Evaluations in the first decade of the new millennium. *Journal of Workplace Behavioral Health, 26*(4), 344–355.

Csiernik, R. (2017). Maintaining the continuum of care: Arguing for community based residential addiction programs. In R. Csiernik & W. Rowe (Eds.), *Responding to the oppression of addiction: Canadian social work responses* (3rd ed., pp. 187–196). Canadian Scholars' Press.

Csiernik, R. (2019). *The essential guide to psychoactive drugs in Canada* (2nd ed.). Canadian Scholars' Press.

Csiernik, R., & Arundel, M. K. (2013). Does counselling format play a role in client retention? *Journal of Groups in Addiction and Recovery, 8*(4), 262–269.

Csiernik, R., Gorlick, C., & Antone, J. (2017). Addiction intervention, employability, and welfare. In R. Csiernik & W. Rowe (Eds.), *Responding to the oppression of addiction: Canadian social work perspectives* (3rd ed., pp. 415–432). Canadian Scholars' Press.

Csiernik, R., & Jordanov, B. (2017). Is Alcoholics Anonymous of value for social work practitioners? In R. Csiernik & W. Rowe (Eds.), *Responding to the oppression of addiction: Canadian social work perspectives* (3rd ed., pp. 178–186). Canadian Scholars' Press.

Csiernik, R., & Rowe, W. (2017). Creating a social work understanding of addiction. In R. Csiernik & W. Rowe (Eds.), *Responding to the oppression of addiction: Canadian social work responses* (3rd ed., pp. 7–26). Canadian Scholars' Press.

Csiernik, R., Rowe, W., & Watkin, J. (2017). Prevention as controversy: Harm reduction approaches. In R. Csiernik & W. Rowe (Eds.), *Responding to the oppression of addiction: Canadian social work responses* (3rd ed., pp. 28–37). Canadian Scholars' Press.

Csiernik, R., & Troller, J. (2002). Evaluating the effectiveness of a relapse prevention group. *Journal of Social Work Practice in the Addictions, 2*(2), 29–38.

Cui, C., Mrad, M., & Hogg, M. (2018). Brand addiction: Exploring the concept and its definition through an experiential lens. *Journal of Business Research, 87*, 118–127.

Cuijpers, P. (2002). Effective ingredients of school-based prevention programs: A systematic review. *Addictive Behaviors, 27*(6), 1009–1023.

Cuijpers, P. (2003). Three decades of drug prevention research. *Drugs: Education, Prevention and Policy, 10*(1), 7–20.

Cuijper, P., van Straten, A., Schuurmans, J., Oppen, P., Hoolon, S., & Andersson, G. (2010). Psychotherapy for chronic major depression and dysthymia: A meta-analysis. *Clinical Psychology Review, 30*(1), 51–62.

Cunningham, P., & Henggeler, S. (2001). Implementation of an empirically based drug and violence prevention and intervention program in public school settings. *Journal of Clinical Child Psychology, 30*(1), 221–232.

Curran, H., & Morgan, C. (2000). Cognitive, dissociative and psychotogenic effects of ketamine in recreational users on the night of drug use and 3 days later. *Addiction, 95*(4), 575–590.

Curto, J. (2011). Alcohol in the context of the Atlantic slave trade: The case of Benguela (Angola) and its hinterland. *Cahiers d'Études Africaines, 201*, 51–85.

Daling, J., Doody, D., Sun, X., Trabert, B., Weiss, N., Chen, C., … Schwartz, S. (2009). Association of marijuana use and the incidence of testicular germ cell tumors. *Cancer, 115*(6), 1215–1223.

Dallas, M. (2011, November 6). Alcohol, asthma and allergies don't mix. *Health.* http://news.health.com/2011/11/06/alcohol-asthma-and-allergies-dont-mix/

Darnell, K., & Csiernik, R. (2014). The hazards of being a counsellor for the hazardous workplace. In R. Csiernik (Ed.), *Workplace Wellness: Issues and Responses* (pp. 51–62). Canadian Scholars' Press.

Davies, L., Jones, A., Vamvakas, G., Dubourg, R., & Donmall, M. (2009). *The drug treatment outcomes research study: Cost-effecitvenss analysis.* Home Office.

Davis, C. (2018). Home detox–supporting patients to overcome alcohol addiction. *Australian Prescriber, 41*(6), 180–182.

Davis, J., Pedersen, E., Tucker, J., Dunbar, M., Seelam, R., Shih, R., & D'Amico, E. (2019). *Journal of Youth Adolescence, 48*, 1311. https://doi.org/10.1007/s10964-019-01024-z

Davis, S., Huebner, A., Piercy, F., Shettler, L., Meszaros, P., & Matheson, J. (2004). Female adolescent smoking: A depth study on best prevention practices. *Journal of Drug Education, 34*(3), 295–311.

Day, D., & Rudd, J. (2019). Alcohol use disorders and the heart. *Addiction, 114*(9), 1670–1678. https://doi.org/10.111/add.14703

de Andrade, D., Elphinston, R., Quinn, C., Allan, J., & Hides, L. (2019). The effectiveness of residential treatment services for individuals with substance use disorders: A systematic review. *Drug and Alcohol Dependence, 201*, 227–235.

de Bruijn, A., Tanghe, J., de Leeuw, R., Engels, R., Anderson, P., Beccaria, F., Bujalski, M., Celata, C., Gosselt, J., Schreckenberg, D., Stodownik, L., Wothge, I., & van Dalen, W. (2016). European longitudinal study on the relationship between adolescents' alcohol marketing exposure and alcohol use. *Addiction, 111*(10), 1774–1783.

de Haes, W., & Schuurman, J. (1975). Results of an evaluation study of three drug education methods. *International Journal of Health Education, 28*(4), S1–S16.

De Leon, G. (1988). Legal pressures in therapeutic communities. In C. Leukefeld & F. Tims (Eds.), *Compulsory treatment of drug abuse: Research and clinical practice* (NIDA Research Monograph, No. 86). United States Department of Health and Human Services.

De Leon, G. (1995). Therapeutic communities for addictions: A theoretical framework. *The International Journal of the Addictions, 30*(12), 1603–1645.

De Leon, G. (1997). *Community as method: Therapeutic communities for special populations and special settings.* Praeger.

De Leon, G., Melnick, G., & Cleland C. (2008). Client matching: A severity-treatment intensity paradigm. *Journal of Addictive Disorders, 27*(3), 99–113.

De Maeyer, J., Vanderplasschen, W., & Broekaert, E. (2010). Quality of life among opiate-dependent individuals: A review of the literature. *International Journal of Drug Policy, 21*(5), 364–380.

De Pirro, S., Lush, P., Parkinson, J., Duka, T., Critchley, H., & Badiani, A. (2019). Effect of alcohol on the sense of agency in healthy humans. *Addiction Biology, 20*, e12796. https://doi.org/10.1111/adb.12796

De Rick, A., Vanheule, S., & Verhaeghe, P. (2009). Alcohol addiction and the attachment system: An empirical study of attachment style, alexithymia, and psychiatric disorders in alcoholic inpatients. *Substance Use and Misuse, 44*(1), 99–114.

de Shazer, S., & Dolan, Y. (2007). *More than miracles: The state of the art in solution focused brief therapy.* Haworth Press.

De-Sola Gutiérrez, J., Rodríguez de Fonseca, F., & Rubio, G. (2016). Cell-phone addiction: A review. *Frontiers in Psychiatry, 7.* https://doi.org/10.3389/fpsyt.2016.00175

de Vocht, F., Sobala, W., Wilczynska, U., Kromhout, H., Szeszenia-Dabrowska, N., & Peplonska, B. (2009). Cancer mortality and occupational exposure to aromatic amines and inhalable aerosols in rubber tire manufacturing in Poland. *Cancer Epidemiology, 33*(2), 94–102.

de Vocht, F., Tilling, K., Pliakas, T., Angus, C., Egan, M., Brennan, A., Campbell, R., & Hickman, M. (2017). The intervention effect of local alcohol licensing policies on hospital admission and crime: A natural experiment using a novel Bayesian synthetictime-series method. *Journal of Epidemiology and Community Health, 71*(9), 912–918.

Dedert, E., McDuffie, J., Stein, R., McNiel, J., Kosinski, A., Freiermuth, C., Hemminger, A., & Williams, J. (2015). Electronic interventions for alcohol misuse and alcohol use disorders: A systematic review. *Annals of Internal Medicine, 163*(3), 205–214.

Degenhardt, L., Charlson, F., Ferrari, A., Santomauro, D., Erskine, H., Mantilla-Herrara, A., ... Rehm, J. (2018). The global burden of disease attributable to alcohol and drug use in 195 countries and territories, 1990–2016: A systematic analysis for the Global Burden of Disease Study 2016. *The Lancet Psychiatry, 5*(12), 987–1012.

Degenhardt, L., & Hall, W. (2012). Extent of illicit drug use and dependence, and their contribution to the global burden of disease. *The Lancet, 379*(9810), 55–70.

Dehghani-Arani, F., Rostami, R., & Nadali, H. (2013). Neurofeedback training for opiate addiction: Improvement of mental health and craving. *Applied Psychophysiology and Biofeedback, 38*(2), 133–141.

Delcher, C., Maldaono-Mollina, M., & Wagenaar, A. (2012). Effects of alcohol taxes on alcohol-related disease mortality in New York State from 1969 to 2006. *Addictive Behaviors, 37*(7), 783–789.

Deleuze, J., Long, J., Liu, T., Maurage, P., & Billieux, J. (2018). Passion or addiction? Correlates of healthy versus problematic use of videogames in a sample of French-speaking regular players. *Addictive Behaviors, 82*(1), 114–121.

Demontis D., Rajagopal, M., Thorgeirsson, T., Als, T., Grove, J., Pallessen, J., ... Borglu, A. (2019). Genome-wide association study implicates CHRNA2 in cannabis use disorder. *Nature Neuroscience, 22*(7), 1066–1074.

Denis-Lalonde, D., & Estefan, A. (2020). Emerging psychedelic-assisted therapies: Implications for nursing practice. *Journal of Mental Health and Addiction Nursing, 4*(1). https://doi.org/10.22374/jmhan.v4i1.40

Denson, T. F. (2011). A social neuroscience perspective on the neurobiological bases of aggression. In M. Mikulincer & P. R. Shaver (Eds.), *Human aggression and violence: Causes, manifestations, and consequences, Herzilya series on personality and social psychology* (pp. 105–120). American Psychological Association.

Denys, K., Rasmussen, C., & Henneveld, D. (2011). The effectiveness of a community-based intervention for parents with FASD. *Community Mental Health Journal, 47*(2), 209–219.

Derevensky, J., St. Pierre, R., & Csiernik, R. (2017). Problem gambling: Current knowledge and clinical perspectives. In R. Csiernik & W. Rowe (Eds.), *Responding to the oppression of addiction: Canadian social work perspectives* (3rd ed., pp. 434–462). Canadian Scholars' Press.

Derzon, J., Sale, E., Springer, J., & Brounstein, P. (2005). Estimating intervention effectiveness: Synthetic projection of field evaluation results. *The Journal of Primary Prevention, 26*(4), 321–343.

Dick, D., Aliev, F., Latendresse, S., Hickman, M., Heron, J., Macleod, J., Joinson, C., Maughan, B., Lewis, G., & Kendler, K. (2013). Adolescent alcohol use is predicted by childhood temperament factors before age 5, with mediation through personality and peers. *Alcoholism: Clinical and Experimental Research, 37*(12), 2108–2117.

Dickson-Gomez, J., Convey, M., Hilario, H., Corbett, A., & Weeks, M. (2007). Unofficial policy: Access to housing, housing information and social services among homeless drug users in Hartford, Connecticut. *Substance Abuse Treatment, Prevention, and Policy, 2*(1), 8. https://doi.org/10.1186/1747-597X-2-8

DiClemente, C. (2007). The Transtheoretical Model of intentional behaviour change. *Drugs and Alcohol Today, 7*(1), 29–33.

DiLeo, P. (2003). *A message from the Office of the Commissioner: A decent place to live ... a basic right ... an essential for recovery.* http://www.ct.gov/dmhas/cwp/view.asp?a=2905&q=334404

Dimeff, L., & Linehan, M. (2008). Dialetical behavior therapy for substance abusers. *Addiction Science and Clinical Practice, 4*(2), 39–47.

DiNicolantonio, J., O'Keefe, J., & Wilson, W. (2018). Sugar addiction: Is it real? A narrative review. *British Journal of Sports Medicine, 52*(14), 910–913.

Dionne, P., Vasiliadis, H., Latimer, E., Berbiche, D., & Preville, M. (2013). Economic impact of inappropriate benzodiazepine prescribing and related drug interactions among elderly persons. *Psychiatric Services, 64*(4), 331–338.

Dishion, T., & McMahon, R. (1998). Parental monitoring and the prevention of child and adolescent problem behavior: A conceptual and empirical formulation. *Clinical Child and Family Psychology Review, 1*(1), 61–75.

Dolan, S., Bechara, A., & Nathan, P. (2007). Executive dysfunction as a risk marker for substance abuse: The role of impulsive personality traits. *Behavioral Sciences and the Law, 26*(6), 799–822.

Dole, V., & Nyswander, M. (1965). A medical treatment for diacetylmorphine (heroin) addiction. *Journal of the American Medical Association, 193*(8), 646–650.

Dom, G., D'Haene, P., Hulstiin, W., & Sabbe, B. (2006). Impulsivity in abstinent early- and late-onset alcoholics: Differences in self-report measures and a discounting task. *Addiction, 101*(1), 50–59.

Domino, E., & Luby, E. (2012). Phencyclidine/schizophrenia: One view toward the past, the other to the future. *Schizophrenia Bulletin, 38*(5), 914–919.

Donaldson, S., Graham, J., Piccinin, A., & Hansen, W. (1995). Resistance-skills training and onset of alcohol use: Evidence for beneficial and potentially harmful effects in public schools and in private catholic schools. *Health Psychology, 14*(4), 291–300.

Donegan, N., Rodin, J., O'Brien, C., & Solomon, R. (1983). A learning theory approach to commonalities. In P. Levison, D. Gerstein, & D. Maloff (Eds.), *Commonalities in substance abuse and habitual behavior* (pp. 111–156). Lexington Books.

Donovan, D., & O'Leary, M. (1979). Control orientation among alcoholics: A cognitive social learning perspective. *American Journal of Drug and Alcohol Abuse, 6*(4), 487–499.

dos Santos, R. (2013). Safety and side effects of ayahuasca in humans—an overview focusing on developmental toxicology. *Journal of Psychoactive Drugs, 45*(1), 68–78.

Douaihy, A., Kelly, T., & Sullivan, C. (2013). Medications for substance use disorders. *Social Work in Public Health, 28*(3–4), 264–278.

Douville, J. (1990). *Active and passive smoking hazards in the workplace.* Van Nostrand Reinhold.

Dowsling, J. (1980). Sex therapy for recovering alcoholics: An essential part of family therapy. *International Journal of the Addictions, 15*(8), 1179–1189.

Doyle, N. (1987). *Involuntary smoking: Health risks for non-smokers.* Public Affairs.

Drabble, L., Jones, S., & Brown, V. (2013). Advancing trauma-informed systems change in a family drug treatment court context. *Journal of Social Work Practice in the Addictions, 13*(1), 91–113.

Dryden, W., & Branch, R. (2012). *The CBT handbook.* Sage.

Dubey, A. (1997). African plant now a drug in Canada. *The Journal, 26*(5), 3.

Duffy, A., Dawson, D., & Das Nair, R. (2016). Pornography addiction in adults: A systematic review of definitions and reported impact. *The Journal of Sexual Medicine, 13*(5), 760–777.

Dufur, M., Parcel, T., & McKune, B. (2013). Does capital at home matter more than capital at school? The case of adolescent alcohol and marijuana use. *Journal of Drug Issues, 43*(1), 85–102.

Duggal, M. (2016). Long may you run: Drug courts in the twenty-first century. *Berkeley Journal of Criminal Law, 21*(1), 126–186.

Dultz, L., & Frangos, S. (2013). The impact of alcohol in pedestrian trauma. *Trauma, 15*(1), 64–75.

Dumka, L., Roosa, M., Michaels, M., & Suh, K. (1995). Using research and theory to develop prevention programs for high risk families. *Family Relations, 44*(1), 78–86.

DuPont, R. (1994). The twelve step approach. In N. Miller (Ed.), *Treating coexisting psychiatric and addictive disorders: A practical guide* (pp. 177–197). Hazelden.

Durlak, J. (1998). Primary prevention mental health programs for children and adolescents are effective. *Journal of Mental Health, 7*(5), 463–469.

Dusenbury, L. (2000). Family-based drug abuse prevention programs: A review. *The Journal of Primary Prevention, 20*(4), 337–352.

Dusenbury, L., Brannigan, R., Falco, M., & Hansen, W. (2003). A review of research on fidelity of implementation: Implications for drug abuse prevention in school settings. *Health Education Research, 18*(2), 237–256.

Dutton-Douglas, M., & Walker, L. (Eds.). (1988). *Feminist psychotherapies: Integration of therapeutic and feminist systems.* Ablex.

Dyck, E., & Bradford, T. (2012). Peyote on the prairies: Religion, scientists, and Native-newcomer relations in Western Canada. *Journal of Canadian Studies, 46*(1), 28–52.

Dyer, C. (1994). New report criticises Upjohn over Halcion. *British Medical Journal, 3089*(12), 1321–1322.

Eckley, L., Harrison, R., Cochrane, M., Pendlebury, M., Sumnall, H., & Timpson, H. (2016). *Evaluation of four recovery communities across England: Interim report for the Give It Up project.* Centre for Public Health.

Edens, E., Kasprow, W., Tsai, J., & Rosenheck, R. (2011). Association of substance use and VA service-connected disability benefits with risk of homelessness among veterans. *The American Journal on Addictions, 20*(5), 412–419.

Edwards, G., Babor, T., Darke, S., Hall, W., Marsden, J., Miller, P., & West, R. (2009). Drug trafficking: Time to abolish the death penalty. *Addiction, 104*(8), 1267–1269.

Edwards, G., & Guthrie, S. (1966). A comparison of inpatient and outpatient treatment of alcohol dependence. *The Lancet, 1*(7435), 467–468.

Edwards, G., & Guthrie, S. (1967). A controlled trial of inpatient and outpatient treatment of alcohol dependency. *The Lancet, 1*(7489), 555–559.

Edwards, G., Orford, J., Egert, S., Guthrie, A., Hensman, C., Mitcheson, M., … Taylor, C. (1977). Alcoholism: A controlled trial of "treatment" and "advice." *Journal of Studies on Alcohol, 38*(5), 1004–1031.

Edwards, S. (2016). Reinforcement principles for addiction medicine; from recreational drug use to psychiatric disorder. *Progress in Brain Research, 223*(1), 63–76.

Eisner, M., Klein, J., Hammond, S., Koren, G., Lactao, C., & Iribarren, C. (2005). Directly measured second hand smoke exposure and asthma health outcomes. *Thorax, 60*(10), 814–821.

Ejik, J., Demirakca, T., Frischknecht, U., Hermann, D., Mann, K., & Ende, G. (2012). Rapid partial regeneration of brain volume during the first 14 days of abstinence from alcohol. *Alcoholism: Clinical and Experimental Research, 37*(1), 67–74.

Elkashef, A., Vocci, F., Hanson, G., White, J., Wickes, W., & Tiihonen, J. (2008). Pharmacotherapy of methamphetamine addiction: An update. *Substance Abuse, 29*(3), 31–49.

Elkins, R. (1975). Aversion therapy for alcoholism: Chemical, electrical or verbal imaginary? *The International Journal of the Addictions, 10*(2), 157–209.

Elliott, R., Bohart, A., Watson, J., & Murphy, D. (2018). Therapist empathy and client outcome: An updated meta-analysis. *Psychotherapy, 55*(4), 399–410.

Ellis, A. (1982). The treatment of alcohol and drug abuse: A rational emotive approach. *Rational Living, 17*(2), 15–24.

Ellis, A. (1985). *Overcoming resistance: Rational emotitve therapy with difficult clients.* Spring Publishing.

Ellis, A. (1995). Addictive behaviors and personality disorders. *American Psychological Association Addiction Newsletter, 2*(3), 10–11, 26.

Ends, E., & Page, C. (1957). A study of three types of group psychotherapy with hospitalized male inebriates. *Quarterly Journal of Studies on Alcohol, 18,* 263–277.

Enoch, M. (2011). The role of early life stress as a predictor for alcohol and drug dependence. *Psychopharmacology, 214*(1), 17–31.

Enoch, M. (2012). The influence of gene-environment interactions on the development of alcoholism and drug dependence. *Current Psychiatry Reports, 14*(2), 150–158.

Erickson, C., & White, W. (2009). The neurobiology of addiction recovery. *Alcoholism Treatment Quarterly, 27*(3), 338–345.

Ersche, K., Jones, P., Williams, G., Robbins, T., & Bullmore, E. (2013). Cocaine dependence: A fast-track for brain ageing? *Molecular Psychiatry, 18*(2), 134–135.

Etemad, L., Moshiri, M., & Moallem, S. (2012). Epilepsy drugs and effects on fetal development: Potential mechanisms. *Journal of Research in Medical Sciences: The Official Journal of Isfahan University of Medical Sciences, 17*(9), 876–881.

Ettensohn, M., Markey, S., & Levine, S. (2018). Considering ketamine for treatment of comorbid pain, depression, and substance use disorders. *Psychiatric Annals, 48*(4), 180–183.

Ettner, S., Huang, D., Evans, E., Ash, D., Hardy, M., Jourabchi, M., & Hser, Y. (2006). Benefit–cost in the California treatment outcome project: Does substance abuse treatment "pay for itself"? *Health Services Research, 41*(1), 192–213.

Ettore, E. (1992). *Women and substance abuse.* Rutgers University Press.

Etz, K., Robertson, E., & Ashery, R. (1998). Drug abuse prevention through family-based interventions: Future research. In R. Ashery, E. Robertson, & K. Kumpfer (Eds.), *Drug abuse prevention through family interventions* (pp. 1–11). United States Department of Health and Human Services.

Euromonitor International. (2014). *Global tobacco: Key findings Part 1—Tobacco overview, cigarettes and the future.* Euromonitor.

European Monitoring Centre for Drugs and Drug Addiction. (2008). *Monitoring the supply of cocaine to Europe.* Office for Official Publications of the European Communities.

European Monitoring Centre for Drugs and Drug Addiction. (2009a). *Preventing later substance use disorders in at-risk children and adolescents: A review of the theory and evidence base of indicated prevention.* Office for Official Publications of the European Communities.

European Monitoring Centre for Drugs and Drug Addiction. (2009b). *Understanding the "spice" phenomenon.* Office for Official Publications of the European Communities.

European Monitoring Centre for Drugs and Drug Addiction. (2015). *Barbiturates.* http://www.emcdda.europa.eu/publications/drug-profiles/barbiturates

European Monitoring Centre for Drugs and Drug Addiction. (2016). *How can contingency management support treatment for substance use disorders? A systematic review.* Publications Office of the European Union.

European Monitoring Centre for Drugs and Drug Addiction. (2017). *Carfentanil.* http://www.emcdda.europa.eu/system/files/publications/6502/2017.6256_EN_04-WEB.pdf

European Monitoring Centre for Drugs and Addiction. (2019). *Drug prevention: Exploring a systems perspective.* Publications Office of the European Union.

Everitt, B. (2018). Drug cues, conditioned reinforcement, and drug seeking: The sequelae of a collaborative venture with Athina Markou. *Biological Psychiatry, 83*(11), 924–931.

Everitt, B., & Robbins, T. (2005). Neural systems of reinforcement for drug addiction: From actions to habits to compulsion. *Nature Neuroscience, 8*(10), 1481–1489.

Faggiano, F., Vigna-Taglianti, F., Versino, E., Zambon, A., Borraccino, A., & Lemma, P. (2006). School-based prevention for illicit drugs' use. *Cochrane Database of Systematic Reviews,* Issue 2, Art. No. CD003020. https://doi.org/10.1002/14651858.CD003020.pub2

Fairbairn, N., Kerr, T., Buxton, J., Li, K., Montaner, J., & Wood, E. (2007). Increasing use and associated harms of crystal methamphetamine injection in a Canadian setting. *Drug & Alcohol Dependence, 88*(2–3), 131–136.

Falco, M. (1976). Methaqualone misuse: Foreign experience and United States drug control policy. *The International Journal of the Addictions, 11*(4), 597–610.

Fallot, R., & Harris, M. (2009). *Creating cultures of trauma-informed care (CCTIC): A self-assessment and planning protocol.* Community Connections. https://www.healthcare.uiowa.edu/icmh/documents/CCTICSelf-AssessmentandPlanningProtocol0709.pdf

Fals-Stewart, W., & Lam, W. (2010). Computer-assisted cognitive rehabilitation for the treatment of patients with substance use disorders: A randomized clinical trial. *Experimental and Clinical Psychopharmacology, 18*(1), 87–98.

Fals-Stewart, W., & O'Farrell, T. (2003). Behavioral family counseling and naltrexone for male opioid-dependent patients. *Journal of Consulting and Clinical Psychology, 71*(3), 432–442.

Farah, M., Betancourt, L., Shera, D., Savage, J., Giannetta, J., Brodsky, N., … Hurt, H. (2008). Environmental stimulation, parental nurturance and cognitive development in humans. *Developmental Science, 11*(5), 793–801.

Faraone, S., Biederman, J., Morley, C., & Spencer, T. (2008). Effects of stimulants on height and weight: A review of the literature. *Journal of the American Academy of Child and Adolescent Psychiatry, 47*(9), 994–1009.

Farber, B., & Doolin, E. (2011). Evidence-based psychotherapy relationships: Positive regard. *Psychotherapy, 48*(1), 58–64.

Fareed, A., Vayalapalli, S., Casarella, J., & Drexler, K. (2012). Effect of buprenorphine dose on treatment outcome. *Journal of Addictive Diseases, 31*(1), 8–18.

Farhoudian, R., Jafarpour, H., Barimani, A., Farhoudian, R., & Rezaei, R. (2019). The effectiveness of stress management training on mental health status of addicts referred to addiction treatment clinic. *Chronic Diseases Journal, 7*(3), 186–194.

Feduccia, A., & Mithoefer, M. (2018). MDMA-assisted psychotherapy for PTSD: Are memory reconsolidation and fear extinction underlying mechanisms? *Progress in Neuro-Psychopharmacology and Biological Psychiatry, 84*(A), 221–228.

Fehrman, E., Egan, V., Gorban, A., Levesley, J., Mirkes, E., & Muhammad, A. (2019). *Personality traits and drug consumption: A story told by data.* Springer Nature Switzerland.

Ferguson, C., & Colwell, J. (2019). Lack of consensus among scholars on the issue of video game "addiction." *Psychology of Popular Media Culture, 9*(3), 359–366. https://doi.org/10.1037/ppm0000243

Ferguson, D., & Boden, J. (2008). Cannabis use and later life outcome. *Addiction, 103*(6), 969–976.

Ferrari, P., Jenab, M., Norat, T., Moskal, A., Slimani, N., Olsen, A., … Jensen, M. (2007). Lifetime and baseline alcohol intake and risk of colon and rectal cancers in the European prospective investigation into cancer and nutrition (EPIC). *International Journal of Cancer, 121*(9), 2065–2072.

Ferrari, V., Smeraldi, E., Bottero, G., & Politi, E. (2014). Addiction and empathy: A preliminary analysis. *Neurological Sciences, 35*(6), 855–859.

Ferri, M., Davoli, M., & Perucci, C. (2011). Heroin maintenance for chronic heroin-dependent individuals. *Cochrane Database of Systematic Reviews*, Issue 12, Art. No. CD003410. https://doi.org/10.1002/14651858.CD003410.pub4

Festinger, L. (1957). *A theory of cognitive dissonance.* Stanford University Press.

Fichter, M., & Quadflieg, N. (2016). Mortality in eating disorders—results of a large prospective clinical longitudinal study. *International Journal of Eating Disorders, 49*(4), 391–401.

Fillmore, K., Hartka, E., Johnstone, B., Speiglman, R., & Temple, M. (1988). *Spontaneous remission from alcohol problems: A critical review.* United States Institute of Medicine.

Finckh, A., Dehler, S., Costenbader, K., & Gabay, C. (2007). Cigarette smoking and radiographic progression in rheumatoid arthritis. *Annals of the Rheumatic Diseases, 66*(8), 1066–1071.

Fingarette, H. (1988). *Heavy drinking: The myth of alcoholism as a disease.* University of California Press.

Fingarette, H. (1989). The perils of Powell: In search of a factual foundation for the "disease concept of alcoholism." *Drugs and Society, 3*(3–4), 1–27.

Fisher, G., & Harrison, T. (1977). *Substance abuse: Information for school counsellors, social workers, therapists and counsellors.* Allyn & Bacon.

Fisher, S. (1995). Group therapy protocols for persons with personality disorders who abuse substances: Effective treatment alternatives. *Social Work with Groups, 18*(4), 71–89.

Flammer, E., & Bongartz, W. (2003). On the efficacy of hypnosis: A meta-analytic study. *Contemporary Hypnosis, 20*(2), 179–197.

Floraa, M., Mascie-Taylorb, C., & Rahmanc, M. (2012). Betel quid chewing and its risk factors in Bangladeshi adults. *South-East Asia Journal of Public Health, 1*(2), 169–181.

Flores, P. (1983). *Group therapy for alcoholics*. Haworth Press.

Flores, P. (2001). Addiction as an attachment disorder: Implications for group therapy. *International Journal of Group Psychotherapy, 51*(1), 63–81.

Flores, P. (2006). Conflict and repair in addiction treatment: An attachment disorder perspective. *Journal of Groups in Addiction and Recovery, 1*(1), 5–26.

Floresta, G., Dichiara, M., Gentile, D., Prezzavento, O., Marrazzo, A., Rescifina, A., & Amata, E. (2019). Morphing of ibogaine: A successful attempt into the search for sigma-2 receptor ligands. *International Journal of Molecular Sciences, 20*(3), 488.

Flückiger, C., Del Re, A., Wampold, B., & Horvath, A. (2018). The alliance in adult psychotherapy: A meta-analytic synthesis. *Psychotherapy, 55*(4), 316–340.

Foronda, C., Baptiste, D., Reinholdt, M., & Ousman, K. (2016). Cultural humility: A concept analysis. *Journal of Transcultural Nursing, 27*(3), 210–217.

Forster, M., Grigsby, T., Rogers, C., & Benjamin, S. (2018). The relationship between family-based adverse childhood experiences and substance use behaviors among a diverse sample of college students. *Addictive Behaviors, 76*(3), 298–304.

Foster, K., Hicks, B., & Zucker, R. (2018). Positive and negative effects of internalizing on alcohol use problems from childhood to young adulthood: The mediating and suppressing role of externalizing. *Journal of Abnormal Psychology, 127*(4), 394–403.

Fothergill, K., Ensminger, M., Doherty, E., Juon, H., & Green, K. (2016). Pathways from early childhood adversity to later adult drug use and psychological distress: A prospective study of a cohort of African Americans. *Journal of Health and Social Behavior, 57*(2), 223–239.

Foucault, M. (1965). *Madness and civilization: A history of insanity in the age of reason*. Random House.

Fowler, T., Lifford, K., Shelton, K., Rice, F., Thapar, A., Neale, M., … van den Bree, M. (2007). Exploring the relationship between genetic and environmental influences on initiation and progression of substance use. *Addiction, 102*(3), 413–422.

Foxcroft, D., Ireland, D., Lister-Sharp, D., Lowe, G., & Breen, R. (2002). Long-term primary prevention for alcohol misuse in young people: A systematic review. *Addiction, 98*(4), 397–411.

Foxcroft, D., Ireland, D., Lowe, G., & Breen, R. (2006). *Primary prevention for alcohol misuse in young people*. Cochrane Database Systematic Reviews, Issue 3, Art. No. CD003024. https://doi.org/10.1002/14651858.CD003024

Foxcroft, D., Lister-Sharp, D., & Lowe, G. (1997). Alcohol misuse prevention for young people: A systematic review reveals methodological concerns and lack of reliable evidence of effectiveness. *Addiction, 92*(5), 531–537.

Frank, L., & Nagel, S. (2017). Addiction and moralization: The role of the underlying model of addiction. *Neuroethics, 10*(1), 129–139.

Fraser Health. (2018). *Riverstone home/mobile detox/daytox program*. https://www.fraserhealth.ca/Service-Directory/Services/mental-health-and-substance-use/substance-use/riverstone-home-mobile-detox-daytox-program#.X4ppluaSmUk

Freedman, N., Abnet, C., Leitzmann, M., Mouw, T., Subar, A., Hollenbeck, A., & Schatzkin, A. (2007). A prospective study of tobacco, alcohol, and the risk of esophageal and gastric cancer subtypes. *American Journal of Epidemiology, 165*(12), 1424–1433.

Freeman, S., & Alder J. (2002). Arylethylamine psychotropic recreational drugs: A chemical perspective. *European Journal of Medicinal Chemistry, 37*(7), 527–539.

Freud, S. (1905). Three essays on the theory of sexuality. In J. Strachey (Ed.), *The complete psychological works* (pp. 123–246). W. W. Norton.

Friedlander, M., Escudero, V., Heatherington, L., & Diamond, G. (2011). Alliance in couple and family therapy. *Psychotherapy, 48*(1), 25–33.

Friesen, C., Roscher, M., Alt, A., & Miltner, E. (2008). Methadone, commonly used as maintenance medication for outpatient treatment of opioid dependence, kills leukemia cells and overcomes chemoresistance. *Cancer Research, 68*(15), 6059–6064.

Fulton, H., Barrett, S., Stewart, S., & MacIsaac, C. (2012). Prescription opioid misuse: Characteristics of earliest and most recent memory of hydromorphone use. *Journal of Addiction Medicine, 6*(2), 137–144.

Fusar-Poli, P., Rubia, K., Rossi, G., Sartori, G., & Balottin, U. (2012). Striatal dopamine transporter alterations in ADHD: Pathophysiology or adaptation to psychostimulants? A meta-analysis. *American Journal of Psychiatry, 169*(3), 264–227.

Gable, R. (2006). Risk assessment of ritual use of oral dimethyltryptamine (DMT) and harmala alkaloids. *Addiction, 102*(1), 24–34.

Gabour, P., & Ing, C. (1991). Stop and think: The application of cognitive-behavioural approaches in work with young people. *Journal of Child and Youth Care, 6*(1), 43–53.

Gainsbury, S., & Blaszcynski, A. (2011). A systematic review of Internet-based therapy for the treatment of addictions. *Clinical Psychology Review, 31*(3), 490–498.

Galistu, A., & Paolo, S. D. (2012). Effect of the dopamine D1-like receptor antagonist SCH 23390 on the microstructure of ingestive behaviour in water-deprived rats licking for water and NaCl solutions. *Physiology & Behavior, 105*(2), 230–233.

Garbutt, J. (2009). The state of pharmacotherapy for the treatment of alcohol dependence. *Journal of Substance Abuse Treatment, 36*(1), S15–23.

Gardner, E. (2011). Addiction and brain reward and anti-reward pathways. *Advances in Psychosomatic Medicine, 30*(1), 22–60.

Gardner, P., & Poole, J. (2009). One story at a time: Narrative therapy, older adults, and addictions. *Journal of Applied Gerontology, 28*(5), 600–620.

Garland, E. (2013). *Mindfulness-oriented recovery enhancement for addiction, stress, and pain.* NASW Press.

Garland, E., & Howard, M. (2018). Mindfulness-based treatment of addiction: Current state of the field and envisioning the next wave of research. *Addiction Science & Clinical Practice, 13*(1), 14.

Garnier, H., & Stein, J. (2002). An 18 year model of family and peer effects on adolescent drug use and delinquency. *Journal of Youth and Adolescence, 31*(1), 45–56.

Garte-Wolf, S. (2011). Narrative therapy group work for chemically dependent clients with HIV/AIDS. *Social Work with Groups: A Journal of Community and Clinical Practice, 34*(3–4), 330–338.

Gartner, A., & Riessman, F. (1977). *Self-help in the human services.* Jossey-Bass.

Gastfriend, D. (2014). A pharmaceutical industry perspective on the economics of treatments for alcohol and opioid use disorders. *Annals of the New York Academy of Sciences, 1327*(1), 112–130.

Gately, I. (2001). *Tobacco: A cultural history of how an exotic plant seduced civilization.* Grove Press.

Gaume, J., Gmel, G., Faouzim, M., & Daeppen, J. (2009). Counselor skill influences outcomes of brief motivational interventions. *Journal of Substance Abuse Treatment, 37*(2), 151–159.

Gehrke, R. (2011, August 1). Utah tobacco sales drop nearly 10 million packs. *The Salt Lake Tribune.* http://www.sltrib.com/sltrib/politics/52273720-90/tax-sales-million-tobacco.html.csp

Geller, L. (1982). The failure of self-actualization theory: A critique of Carl Rogers and Abraham Maslow. *Journal of Humanistic Psychology, 22*(2), 56–73.

Gevirtz, C., Frost, E., & Kaye, A. (2011). Ultra-rapid opiate detoxification. In R. Urman, W. Gross, & B. Philip (Eds.), *Anesthesia outside of the operating room* (pp. 309–315). Oxford University Press.

Ghosh, A., Coakley, R., Ghio, A., Muhlebach, M., Esther Jr., C., Alexis, N., & Tarran, R. (2019). Chronic e-cigarette use increases neutrophil elastase and matrix metalloprotease levels in the lungs. *American Journal of Respiratory and Critical Care Medicine, 200*(11). https://doi.org/10.1164/rccm.201903-0615OC

Gifford, E., & Humphreys, K. (2007). The psychological science of addiction. *Addiction, 102*(3), 352–361.

Gilligan, C., Kypri, K., & Lubman, D. (2012). Changing parental behaviour to reduce risky drinking among adolescents: Current evidence and future directions. *Alcohol and Alcoholism, 47*(3), 349–354.

Gilligan, C., Wolfenden, L., Foxcroft, D., Williams, A., Kingsland, M., Hodder, R., Stockings, E., McFadyen, T., Tindall, J., Sherker, S., Rae, J., & Wiggers, J. (2019). Family-based prevention programmes for alcohol use in young people. *Cochrane Database of Systematic Reviews,* Issue 3, Art. No. CD012287.

Girelli, G. (2019). *The death penalty for drug offences: Global overview, 2018.* Harm Reduction International.

Glasner, S., Mooney, L., Ang, A., Garneau, H., Hartwell, E., Brecht, M., & Rawson, R. (2017). Mindfulness-based relapse prevention for stimulant dependent adults: A pilot randomized clinical trial. *Mindfulness, 8*(1), 126–135.

Glatt, M. (1958). Group therapy in alcoholism. *British Journal of Addiction, 54*(2), 133–148.

Glatt, M. (1980). The alcoholic: Controlled drinking. *British Journal of Alcohol and Alcoholism, 15*(2), 48–55.

Global Burden of Disease Collaborative Network. (2017). *Global burden of disease study 2016 results.* Institute for Health Metrics and Evaluation.

Glover, E. (1928). The aetiology of alcoholism. *Journal of the Royal Society of Medicine, 21,* 1351–1355.

Gold, A., Stathopoulou, G., & Otto, M. (2020). Emotion regulation and motives for illicit drug use in opioid-dependent patients. *Cognitive Behaviour Therapy, 49*(1), 74–80.

Golden, S., & Shaham, Y. (2018). Aggression addiction and relapse: A new frontier in psychiatry. *Neuropsychopharmacology, 43*(1), 224–225.

Goldstein, A. (1979). Heroin maintenance: A medical view. A conversation between a physician and a politician. *Journal of Drug Issues, 9*(4), 341–347.

González-Maeso, J., Weisstaub, N., Zhou, M., Chan, P., Ivic, L., Ang, R., … Bradley, M. (2007). Hallucinogens recruit specific cortical 5-HT$_{2A}$ receptor-mediated signalling pathways to affect behavior. *Neuron, 53*(3), 439–452.

González-Pinto, A., Vega, P., Ibáñez, B., Mosquera, F., Barbeito, S., Gutiérrez, M., … Vieta, E. (2008). Impact of cannabis and other drugs on age at onset of psychosis. *Journal of Clinical Psychiatry, 69*(8), 1210–1216.

Goodchild, M., Nargis, N., & d'Espaignet, E. (2018). Global economic cost of smoking-attributable diseases. *Tobacco Control, 27*(1), 58–64.

Goode, E., & Ben-Yehuda, N. (1994). Moral panics: Culture politics, and social constructions. *Annual Review of Sociology, 20*(1), 149–171.

Goodman, A. (1990). Addiction: Definition and implications. *British Journal of Addictions, 85*(11), 1403–1408.

Goodman, A (2001). What's in a name? Terminology for designating a syndrome of driven sexual behavior. *Sexual Addiction & Compulsivity, 8*(2), 191–213.

Goodman, D. (2013). Opioid dose and risk of road trauma in Canada: A population-based study. *Journal of the American Medical Association, 173*(3), 196–201.

Goodman, R. (2017). Contemporary trauma theory and trauma-informed care in substance use disorders: A conceptual model for integrating coping and resilience. *Advances in Social Work, 18*(1), 186–201.

Goodwin, D., Schulsinger, E., Hermansen, L., Guze, S., & Winokur, G. (1973). Alcohol problems in adoptees raised apart from biological parents. *Archives of General Psychiatry, 28*(2), 238–243.

Goodwin, G., Haddad, P., Ferrier, I., Aronson, J., Barnes, T., Cipriani, A., Coghill, D., Fazel, S., Geddes, J., Grunze, H., Holmes, E., Howes, O., Hudson, S., Hunt, N., Jones, I., Macmillan, I., McAllister-Williams, H., Miklowitz, D., Morriss, R., … Young, A. (2016). Evidence-based guidelines for treating bipolar disorder: Revised third edition recommendations from the British Association for Psychopharmacology. *Journal of Psychopharmacology, 30*(6), 495–553.

Gordis, E. (1987). Accessible and affordable health care for alcoholism and related problems: Strategy for cost containment. *Journal of Studies on Alcohol, 48*(6), 579–585.

Gorji, M. (2019). The effect of Mandala art therapy on reducing anxiety in women with substance abuse. *Research on Addiction, 13*(53), 269–284.

Gorman, D. (1997). The failure of drug education. *Public Interest, 129*(Fall), 50–60.

Gorman, D. (2002). Defining and operationalizing "research-based" prevention: A critique (with case studies) of the US Department of Education's safe, disciplined and drug-free schools exemplary programs. *Evaluation and Program Planning, 25*(3), 295–302.

Gorman, D. (2003). The best of practices, the worst of practices: The making of science-based primary prevention programs. *Psychiatric Services, 54*(8), 1087–1089.

Gottfredson, D., & Wilson, D. (2003). Characteristics of effective school-based substance abuse prevention. *Prevention Science, 4*(1), 27–38.

Gottheil, E., Thornton, C., & Weinstein, S. (2002). Effectiveness of high versus low structure individual counseling for substance abuse. *American Journal on Addictions, 11*(4), 279–290.

Government of Canada. (2015). *Controlled drugs and substances act* [S. C. 1996, c. 19]. http://laws-lois.justice.gc.ca/eng/acts/c-38.8/

Government of Canada. (2019a). *National report: Apparent opioid-related deaths in Canada.* https://health-infobase.canada.ca/datalab/national-surveillance-opioid-mortality.html#AORD

Government of Canada. (2019b). *Vaping product regulation.* https://www.canada.ca/en/health-canada/services/smoking-tobacco/vaping/product-safety-regulation.html

Government of Canada. (2019c). *Cannabis crime statistics in Canada, 2017.* https://www.justice.gc.ca/eng/rp-pr/jr/jf-pf/2019/mar03.html

Government of Canada. (2019d). *Impaired driving investigations.* http://www.rcmp-grc.gc.ca/ts-sr/aldr-id-cfa-aldr-eng.htm

Government of Canada. (2019e). *Cannabis legalization and regulation.* https://www.justice.gc.ca/eng/cj-jp/cannabis/

Graham, A., & Adams, J. (2014). Alcohol marketing in televised English professional football: A frequency analysis. *Alcohol and Alcoholism, 49*(3), 343–348.

Grant, J. (2009). Profile of substance abuse, gender, crime, and drug policy in the United States and Canada. *Journal of Offender Rehabilitation, 48*(8), 654–668.

Grant, J., Schreiber, L., & Odlaug, B. (2013). Phenomenology and treatment of behavioural addictions. *The Canadian Journal of Psychiatry, 58*(5), 252–259.

Grape, S., Schug, B., & Schug, S. (2010). Formulations of fentanyl for the management of pain. *Drugs, 70*(1), 57–72.

Grassi, G., Makris, N., & Pallanti, S. (2019). Addicted to compulsion: Assessing three core dimensions of addiction across obsessive-compulsive disorder and gambling disorder. *CNS Spectrums, 25*(3), 392–401. https://doi.org/10.1017/S1092852919000993

Graveland, B. (2018, October 28). Authorities warn of crystal meth "epidemic" in Prairie provinces. *CTV News.* https://www.ctvnews.ca/canada/authorities-warn-of-crystal-meth-epidemic-in-prairie-provinces-1.4152749

Green, J., Lynn, S., & Montgomery, G. (2006). A meta-analysis of gender, smoking cessation, and hypnosis: A brief communication. *International Journal of Clinical and Experimental Hypnosis, 54*(2), 224–233.

Green, M. (1980). *Components of the treatment system for clients with drug and/or alcohol problems.* Addiction Research Foundation.

Greenberg, G. (2010). *Manufacturing depression: The secret history of modern disease.* Simon & Schuster.

Greenberg, M., Domitrovich, C., & Bumbarger, B. (2000). *Preventing mental disorders in school-aged children: A review of the effectiveness of prevention programs.* Substance Abuse Mental Health Services Administration.

Grella, C., & Lovinger, K. (2011). 30-year trajectories of heroin and other drug use among men and women sampled from methadone treatment in California. *Drug and Alcohol Dependency, 118*(2–3), 251–258.

Griffin, K. (2004). *One breath at a time: Buddhism and the twelve steps.* Rodale.

Griffin, K., Botvin, G., Scheier, L., Diaz, T., & Miller, N. (2000). Parenting practices of predictors of substance use, delinquency, and aggression among urban minority youth: Moderating effects of family structure and gender. *Psychology of Addictive Behaviors, 14*(2), 174–184.

Griffin, T., & Svendsen, R. (1992). *Promising prevention strategies for the 90s.* Center of Alcohol Studies.

Griswold, M., Fullman, N., Hawley, C., Arian, N., Zimsen, S., Tymeson, H., ... Abate, K. (2018). Alcohol use and burden for 195 countries and territories, 1990–2016: A systematic analysis for the Global Burden of Disease Study 2016. *The Lancet, 392*(10152), 1015–1035.

Grizenko, N., Cai, E., Jolicoeur, C., & Ter-Stepanian, M. (2013). Effects of methylphenidate on acute math performance in children with attention-deficit hyperactivity disorder. *Canadian Journal of Psychiatry, 58*(11), 632–639.

Grob, C., Danforth, A., Chopra, G., Hagerty, M., McKay, C., Halberstadt, A., & Greer, G. (2011). Pilot study of psilocybin treatment for anxiety in patients with advanced-stage cancer. *Archives of General Psychiatry, 68*(1), 71–78.

Grof, C. (2018). Cannabis, from plant to pill. *British Journal of Clinical Pharmacology, 84*(11), 2463–2467.

Groves, P. (2014). Buddhist approaches to addiction recovery. *Religions, 5*(4), 985–1000.

Guenzel, N., & McChargue, D. (2019). Addiction relapse prevention. *StatPearls.* https://www.ncbi.nlm.nih.gov/books/NBK551500/

Guerino, P., Harrison, P., & Sabol, W. (2010). *Prisoners in 2010* (Rev. ed.). United States Bureau of Justice Statistics.

Guerra-Doce, E. (2015). Psychoactive substances in prehistoric times: Examining the archaeological evidence. *Time and Mind, 8*(1), 91–112.

Gupta, B., & Gupta, U. (1999). *Caffeine and behavior: Current views and research trends.* CRC Press.

Gupta, P., & Ray, C. (2004). Epidemiology of betel quid usage. *Annals of the Academy of Medicine, Singapore, 33*(S), 31S–36S.

Guthrie, B., & Flinchbaugh, L. (2001). Gender-specific substance prevention programming: Going beyond just focusing on girls. *Journal of Early Adolescence, 21*(3), 354–372.

Ha, T., & Vaughn, J. (2017, November 12). Cold turkey at Vietnam's compulsory drug rehab centres. *France 24.* https://www.france24.com/en/20171211-cold-turkey-vietnams-compulsory-drug-rehab-centres

Hackshaw, A., Rodeck, C., & Boniface, S. (2011). Maternal smoking in pregnancy and birth defects: A systematic review based on 173 687 malformed cases and 11.7 million controls. *Human Reproduction Update, 15*(5), 589–604.

Hafez, N., & Ling, P. (2005). How Philip Morris built Marlboro into a global brand for young adults: Implications for international tobacco control. *Tobacco Control, 14*(2), 262–271.

Hagan, G. (1999). *HIV/AIDS and the drug culture*. Haworth Press.

Hagele, C., Friedel, E., Kienast, T., & Kiefer, F. (2014). How do we "learn" addiction? Risk factors and mechanisms getting addicted to alcohol. *Neuropsychobiology, 70*(1), 67–70.

Haggard, H. (1944). Critique of the concept of the allergic nature of alcohol addiction. *Quarterly Journal of Studies on Alcohol, 5*, 233–241.

Hajek, P., Phillips-Waller, A., Przulj, D., Pesola, F., Myers Smith, K., Bisal, N., Li, J., Parrott, S., Sasieni, P., Dawkins, L., Ross., L., Goniewica, M., Wu, Q., & McRobbie, H. (2019). A randomized trial of e-cigarettes versus nicotine-replacement therapy. *New England Journal of Medicine, 380*(7), 629–637.

Hall, K., Gibbie, T., & Lubman, D. I. (2012). Motivational interviewing techniques: Facilitating behaviour change in the general practice setting. *Australian Family Physician, 41*(9), 660–667.

Hall, M., & Vander Bilt, J. (2000). Facing the odds: The mathematics of gambling and other risks. Harvard University Press.

Hall, P. (2014). Sex addiction—an extraordinarily contentious problem. *Sexual and Relationship Therapy, 29*(1), 68–75.

Hallfors, D., & Godette, D. (2002). Will the "Principles of Effectiveness" improve prevention practice? Early findings from a diffusion study. *Health Education Research, 17*(4), 461–470.

Halpern, J., Sherwood, A., Hudson, J., Yurgelun-Todd, D., & Pope Jr, H. (2005). Psychological and cognitive effects of long-term peyote use among Native Americans. *Biological Psychiatry, 58*(8), 624–631.

Hamilton, R., Olmedo, R., Shah, S., Hung, O., Howland, M., Perrone, J., ... Hoffman, R. (2002). Complications of ultrarapid opioid detoxification with subcutaneous naltexone pellets. *Academic Emergency Medicine, 9*(1), 63–68.

Hancock, S., & McKim, W. (2018). *Drugs and behaviour: An introduction to behavioral pharmacology* (8th ed.). Pearson.

Handford, C., Kahan, M., Srivastava, A., Cirone, S., Sanhera, S., & Palda, V. (2011). *Buprenorphine/Naloxone for opioid dependence*. Centre for Addiction and Mental Health.

Hankins, C. (1998). Syringe exchange in Canada: Good but not enough to stem the HIV tide. *Substance Use and Misuse, 33*(5), 1129–1146.

Hans, M. (2010). Chemistry, pharmacology, and metabolism of emerging drugs of abuse. *Therapeutic Drug Monitoring, 32*(5), 544–549.

Harding, S., (1987). *Feminism and methodology*. University of Indiana Press.

Harkin, A., Connor, T., Mulrooney, J., Kelly, J., & Leonard, B. (2001). Prior exposure to methylenedioxyamphetamine (MDA) induces serotonergic loss and changes in spontaneous exploratory and amphetamine-induced behaviors in rats. *Life Sciences, 68*(12), 1367–1382.

Harm Reduction International. (2020). *The death penalty for drug offences: Global overview 2019.* https://www.hri.global/death-penalty-drugs-2019

Harris, M., & Fallot, R. (2001a). *Creating cultures of trauma-informed care (CCTIC): A self-assessment and planning protocol.* Community Connections.

Harris, M., & Fallot, R. (2001b). Designing trauma-informed addictions services. *New Directions for Mental Health Services, 2001*(89), 57–73.

Harrow, M., Jobe, T., & Faull, R. (2012). Do all schizophrenia patients need antipsychotic treatment continuously throughout their lifetime? A 20-year longitudinal study. *Psychological Medicine, 42*(10), 1–11.

Hart, K., & Singh, T. (2009). An existential model of flourishing subsequent to treatment for addiction: The importance of living a meaningful and spiritual life. *Illness, Crisis, and Loss, 17*(2), 125–147.

Hartmann-Boyce, J., McRobbie, H., Bullen, C., Begh, R., Stead, L. F., & Hajek, P. (2016). Electronic cigarettes for smoking cessation. *Cochrane Database of Systematic Reviews*, Issue 9, Art. No. CD010216.

Harwin, J., Alrouh, B., Ryan, M., McQuarrie, T., Golding, L., Broadhurst, K., Tunnard, J., & Swift, S. (2016). *After FDAC: Outcomes 5 years later, final report.* Lancaster University.

Hasler, B., Smith, L., Cousins, J., & Bootzins, R. (2012). Circadian rhythms, sleep, and substance abuse. *Sleep Medicine Reviews, 16*(1), 67–81.

Hauck, C., Cook, B., & Ellrott, T. (2019). Food addiction, eating addiction and eating disorders. *Proceedings of the Nutrition Society*, 1–10. https://doi.org/10.1017/S0029665119001162

Hawkins, E., Cummins, L., & Marlatt, G. (2004). Preventing substance abuse in American Indian and Alaska native youth: Promising strategies for healthier communities. *Psychological Bulletin, 130*(2), 304–323.

Hawthorne, G. (2001). Drug education: Myth and reality. *Drug and Alcohol Review, 20*(1), 111–119.

Hayashida, M. (1998). An overview of outpatient and inpatient detoxification. *Alcohol Health and Research World, 22*(1), 44–46.

Hayashida, M., Alterman, A., McLellan, A., O'Brien, C., Purtill, J., Volpicelli, J., … Hall, C. (1989). Comparative effectiveness and costs of inpatient and outpatient detoxification of patients with mild-to-moderate alcohol withdrawal syndrome. *New England Journal of Medicine, 320*(6), 358–364.

Hayen, B., Canuel, N., & Shanse, J. (2013). What was brewing in the Natufian? An archaeological assessment of brewing technology in the Epipaleolithic. *Journal of Archaeological Method and Theory, 20*(1), 102–150.

Hayes, S., Masuda, A., Bissett, R., Luoma, J., & Guerrero, L. (2004). DBT, FAP, and ACT: How empirically oriented are the new behavior therapy technologies? *Journal of Behavior Therapy, 35*(1), 35–54.

Hayes, S., Strosahl, K., & Wilson, K. (2009). *Acceptance and commitment therapy.* American Psychological Association.

Hays, S., Hays, C., & Mulhall, P. (2003). Community risk and protective factors and adolescent substance use. *The Journal of Primary Prevention, 24*(2), 125–142.

Hayward, B., Cook, R., & Thorne, J. (1994). *Community-based prevention services for high risk youth: A study of the Governor's DFSCA program.* Research Triangle Institute.

Hazan, C., & Shaver, P. (1987). Romantic love conceptualized as an attachment process. *Journal of Personality and Social Psychology, 52*(6), 511–524.

Health Canada. (2001). *Reducing the harm associated with injection drug use in Canada.* Ottawa: Health Canada.

Health Canada. (2008). *Methadone maintenance treatment.* http://www.hc-sc.gc.ca/hc-ps/pubs/adp-apd/methadone-treatment-traitement/index-eng.php#fnb20

Health Canada. (2009). *Straight facts about drugs and drug abuse.* Health Canada.

Health Canada. (2013). Health Canada's review recommends codeine only be used in patients aged 12 and over. http://healthycanadians.gc.ca/recall-alert-rappel-avis/hc-sc/2013/33915a-eng.php

Health Canada. (2015). Summary safety review—ABILIFY and ABILIFY MAINTENA (aripiprazole)—Evaluating the risk of certain impulse control behaviours. https://www.canada.ca/en/health-canada/services/drugs-health-products/medeffect-canada/safety-reviews/summary-safety-review-abilify-abilify-maintena-aripiprazole-evaluating-risk-certain-impulse-control-behaviours.html

Health Canada. (2018). *Canadian tobacco, alcohol and drugs survey (CTADS): Summary of results for 2017.* Health Canada.

Health Canada. (2019). *The Canadian student tobacco, alcohol and drugs survey 2018–2019.* Health Canada.

Healy, B., Ali, E., Guttmann, C., Chitnis, T., Glanz, B., Buckle, G., … Ascherio, A. (2009). Smoking and disease progression in Multiple Sclerosis. *Archives of Neurology, 66*(7), 858–864.

Heath, A., Jardine, R., & Martin, N. (1989). Interactive effects of genotype and social environment on alcohol consumption and female twins. *Journal of Studies on Alcohol, 50*(1), 38–48.

Heather, N., Hönekopp, J., & Smailes, D. (2009). Progressive stage transition does mean getting better: A further test of the Transtheoretical Model in recovery from alcohol problems. *Addiction, 104*(6), 949–958.

Hecht, M., & Raup-Krieger, J. (2006). The principle of cultural grounding in school-based substance abuse programs: The drug resistance strategies project. *Journal of Language and Social Psychology, 25*(3), 301–319.

Hedegaard, H., Miniño, A., & Warner, M. (2020). Drug overdose deaths in the United States, 1999–2018. National Centre for Health Statistics.

Heinen, M., Verhage, B., Ambergen, T., Goldbohm, R., & van den Brandt, P. (2009). Alcohol consumption and risk of pancreatic cancer in the Netherlands cohort study. *American Journal of Epidemiology, 169*(10), 1233–1242.

Heinz, A., Daedelow, L., Wackerhagen, C., & Di Chiara, G. (2019). Addiction theory matters—why there is no dependence on caffeine or antidepressant medication. *Addiction Biology 25*(2), e12735. https://doi.org/10.1111/adb.12735

Heller, T. (2003). *Eating disorders: A handbook for teens, families, and teachers.* McFarland & Company.

Hellman, M., Schoenmakers, T., Nordstrom, B., & Van Holst, R. (2013). *Addiction Research and Theory, 21*(2), 102–112.

Hendershot, C., Witkiewitz, K., George, W., & Marlatt, G. (2011). Relapse prevention for addictive behaviors. *Substance Abuse Treatment, Prevention, and Policy, 6*(1), 17.

Henwood, B. (2015). Commentary on Somers et al. (2015): Housing First—a platform for recovery? *Addiction, 110*(10), 1615–1616.

Hepworth, D., & Larson, J. (2012). *Direct social work practice* (9th ed.). American Psychiatric Publishing Company.

Herbert, J., & Foreman, E. (2011). Acceptance and mindfulness in cognitive behavior therapy. In J. Herbert & E. Foreman (Eds.), *The evolution of cognitive behavior therapy* (pp. 3–25). John Wiley and Sons.

Hermanns-Clausen, M., Kneisel, S., Szabo, B., & Auwärter, V. (2013). Acute toxicity due to the confirmed consumption of synthetic cannabinoids: Clinical and laboratory findings. *Addiction, 108*(3), 534–544.

Hesselbrock, M., Hesselbrock, V., & Chartier, K. (2013). Genetics of alcohol dependence and social work research: Do they mix? *Social Work in Public Health, 28*(3–4), 178–193.

Hester, R., Nirenberg, T., & Begin, A. (1990). Behavioral treatment of alcohol and drug abuse. In M. Galanter (Ed.), *Recent developments in alcoholism* (Vol. 8, pp. 305–327). Plenum Press.

Hickert, A., & Taylor, M. (2011). Supportive housing for addicted, incarcerated homeless adults. *Journal of Social Service Research, 37*(2), 136–151.

Hickman, M., Steer, C., Tilling, K., Lim, A., Marsden, J., Millar, T., Strang, J., Tefler, M., Vicerman, P., & Macleod, J. (2018). The impact of buprenorphine and methadone on mortality: A primary care cohort study in the United Kingdom. *Addiction, 113*(8), 1461–1476.

Hiebert-Murphy, D., & Woytkiw, L. (2017). A model for working with women dealing with child sexual abuse and addiction: The Laurel Centre, Winnipeg, Manitoba. In R. Csiernik & W. Rowe (Eds.), *Responding to the oppression of addiction: Canadian social work perspectives* (3rd ed., pp. 120–133). Canadian Scholars' Press.

Hill, D. (2016). Heroin-assisted treatment. In S. Boslaugh (Ed.), *The SAGE encyclopedia of pharmacology and society* (Vol. 4, pp. 694–696). SAGE Publications.

Hill, K. (1983). *Helping you helps me.* Canadian Council on Social Development.

Hillhouse, T., & Porter, J. (2015). A brief history of the development of antidepressant drugs: From monoamines to glutamate. *Experimental and Clinical Psychopharmacology, 23*(1), 1–21.

Hirayama, T. (1981). Non-smoking wives of heavy smokers have a higher risk of lung cancer: A study from Japan. *British Medical Journal, 282*(6259), 183–185.

Hiroi, N., & Agatsuma, S. (2005). Genetic susceptibility to substance dependence. *Molecular Psychiatry, 10*(4), 336–344.

Ho, J. (2019). The contemporary American drug overdose epidemic in international perspective. *Population and Development Review, 45*(1), 7–40.

Hoehne, D. (1988). Self-help and social change. *Social movements/social change.* Between the Lines.

Hofstede, G. (1984). The cultural relativity of the quality of life concept. *Academy of Management Review, 9*(3), 389–398.

Hofstee, W., De Raad, B., & Goldberg, L. (1992). Integration of the big five and circumplex approaches to trait structures. *Journal of Personality and Social Psychology, 63*(1), 146–163.

Hogue, A., Liddle, H., Becker, D., & Johnson-Leckrone, J. (2002). Family-based prevention counseling for high-risk young adolescents: Immediate outcome. *Journal of Community Psychology, 30*(1), 1–22.

Holder, J., & Shriner, B. (2012). Subluxation based chiropractic care in the management of cocaine addiction: A case report. *Annals of Vertebral Subluxation Research, 14*(1), 8–17.

Holmes, A., Fitzgerald, P., De Brouse, L., Colacicco, G., Flynn, S., Masneuf, S., … Camp, M. (2012). *Nature Neuroscience, 15*(10), 1359–1361.

Holmes, C., Barton, A., MacKillop, J., Galván, A., Owens, M., McCormick, M., Yu, T., Beach, S., Brody, G., & Sweet, L. (2018). Parenting and salience network connectivity among African Americans: A protective pathway for health risk behaviors. *Biological Psychiatry, 84*(5), 365–371.

Holroyd, J., & Luca, M. (2019). Psychotherapy with clients with addiction(s): A grounded theory study of effective therapeutic approaches. *Journal of Psychological Therapies, 4*(2), 131–154.

Holt, E., & Kaiser, D. (2009). The first step series: Art therapy for early substance abuse treatment. *The Arts in Psychotherapy, 36*(4), 245–250.

Holzbach, R., Stammen, G., Kirchhof, U., & Scherbaum, N. (2019). The prescription of anticraving medication and its economic consequences. *European Addiction Research, 25*(5), 224–228.

Hoogman, M., Bralten, J., Hibar, D., Mennes, M., Zwiers, M., Schweren, L., … de Zeeuw, P. (2017). Subcortical brain volume differences in participants with attention deficit hyperactivity disorder in children and adults: A cross-sectional mega-analysis. *The Lancet Psychiatry, 4*(4), 310–319.

Horton, D. (1943). The functions of alcohol in primitive societies: A cross cultural study. *Quarterly Journal of Studies on Alcohol, 4*, 199–320.

Hubble, M., Duncan, B., Miller, S., & Wampold, B. (2010). Introduction. In B. Duncan, S. Miller, B. Wampold, & M. Hubble (Eds.), *The heart and soul of change: Delivering what works in therapy* (2nd ed., pp. 23–46). American Psychological Association.

Huestis, M., & Smith, M. (2016). Cannabinoids pharmacology, abuse, and addiction. In D. Pfaff & N. Volkow (Eds.), *Neuroscience in the 21st century* (pp. 1–27). Springer.

Human Rights Watch. (2010). *Cambodia: Skin on the cable.* Human Rights Watch.

Humphreys, K., Blodgett, J., & Wagner, T. H. (2014). Estimating the efficacy of Alcoholics Anonymous without self-selection bias: An instrumental variables re-analysis of randomized clinical trials. *Alcoholism: Clinical and Experimental Research, 38*(11), 2688–2694.

Humphreys, K., & Saitz, R. (2019). Should physicians recommend replacing opioids with cannabis? *Journal of the American Medical Association, 321*(7), 639–640.

Huncar, A. (2018, March 10). Meth supply, organized crime focus of Pan-Canadian group tackling rural crime. *CBC News.* https://www.cbc.ca/news/canada/edmonton/rural-crime-alberta-schweitzer-ottawa-working-group-1.5491780

Hunt, G., & Azrin, N. (1973). A community-reinforcement approach to alcoholism. *Behaviour Research and Therapy, 11*(1), 91–104.

Hunt, J., van der Hel, O., McMillan, G., Boffetta, P., & Brennan, P. (2005). Renal cell carcinoma in relation to cigarette smoking: Meta-analysis of 24 studies. *International Journal of Cancer, 114*(1), 101–108.

Hurt, H., Brodsky, N., Roth, H., Malmud, E., & Giannetta, J. (2005). School performance of children with gestational cocaine exposure. *Neurotoxiology and Teratology, 27*(2), 203–211.

Hurt, H., Giannetta, J., Korczkowski, M., Hoang, A., Tang, K., Beancourt, L., … Detre, J. (2008). Functional magnetic resonance imaging and working memory in adolescents with gestational cocaine exposure. *The Journal of Pediatrics, 152*(3), 371–377.

Hurt, H., Malmud, E., Betancourt, L., Braitman, L., Brodsky, N., & Giannetta, J. (1997). Children with in utero cocaine exposure do not differ from control subjects on intelligence testing. *Achieves of Pediatric Adolescent Medicine, 151*(12), 1237–1241.

Hurt, H., Malmud, E., Betancourt, L., Brodsky, N., & Giannetta, J. (2001). A prospective comparison of developmental outcome of children with in utero cocaine exposure and controls using the Battelle Developmental Inventory. *Journal of Developmental & Behavioral Pediatrics, 22*(1), 27–34.

Hyshka, E., Strathdee, S., Wood, E., & Kerr, T. (2012). Needle exchange and the HIV epidemic in Vancouver: Lessons learned from 15 years of research. *International Journal of Drug Policy, 23*(4), 261–270.

Iadarola, N., Niciu, M., Richards, E., Vande Voort, J., Ballard, E., Lundin, N., Nugent, A., Machado-Vieira, R., & Zarate, C. (2015). Ketamine and other N-methyl-D-aspartate receptor antagonists in the treatment of depression: A perspective review. *Therapeutic Advances in Chronic Disease, 6*(3), 97–114.

Ii, T., Sato, H., Watanabe, N., Kondo, M., Masuda, A., Hayes, S. C., & Akechi, T. (2019). Psychological flexibility-based interventions versus first-line psychosocial interventions for substance use disorders: Systematic review and meta-analyses of randomized controlled trials. *Journal of Contextual Behavioral Science, 13*, 109–120. https://doi.org/10.1016/j.jcbs.2019.07.003

Ilgen, M., & Moos, R. (2005). Deterioration following alcohol use disorder treatment in Project Match. *Journal of Studies in Alcohol, 66*(4), 517–525.

Imel, Z., Wampold, B., Miller, S., & Fleming, R. (2008). Distinctions with a difference: Direct comparisons of psychotherapies for alcohol use disorders. *Psychology of Addictive Behaviors, 22*(4), 533–543.

Inaba, D., & Cohen, W. (2011). *Uppers, downers, all arounders.* CNS Productions.

Inner City Health. (2010). *Programs and services.* http://ottawainnercityhealth.ca/FCKeditor/editor/fileCabinet/OICH_Alcohol_FAQ_Read_More_Document1.pdf

Institute of Alcohol Studies. (2017). *Splitting the bill: Alcohol's impact on the economy.* Institute of Alcohol Studies.

International Drug Policy Consortium. (2010). *Drug policy guide.* International Drug Policy Consortium.

International Drug Policy Consortium. (2012). *Drug policy guide* (2nd ed.). International Drug Policy Consortium.

International Narcotics Control Board. (2014). *Report of the International Narcotics Control Board, 2013.* United Nations.

International Narcotics Control Board. (2019). *Report of the International Narcotics Control Board, 2018.* United Nations.

International Transportation Forum. (2018). *Alcohol-related road casualties in official crash statistics.* International Transportation Forum.

Ishaq, G., Rafique, R., & Asif, M. (2017). Personality traits and news addiction: Mediating role of self-control. *Journal of the Dow University of Health Sciences, 11*(2), 48–53.

Isir, A., Nacak, M., Balci, S., Aynacioglu, A., & Pehlivan, S. (2016). Genetic contributing factors to substance abuse: An association study between eNOS gene polymorphisms and cannabis addiction in a Turkish population. *Australian Journal of Forensic Sciences, 48*(6), 676–683.

Jabbar, S., & Hanly, M. (2013). Fatal caffeine overdose: A case report and review of literature. *American Journal of Forensic Medicine & Pathology, 34*(4), 321–324.

Jackson, L. (2017). A novel bioinformatic approach to understanding addiction. *Journal of Family Strengths, 17*(1), Article 4.

Jackson, T., & Smith, J. (1978). A comparison of two aversion treatment methods for alcoholism. *Journal of Studies on Alcohol, 39*(1), 187–191.

Jafri, H. (2015). A study on Facebook addiction and its relationship with emotional experience and coping strategies. *The International Journal of Indian Psychology, 2*(4), 6–14.

Jansen, K. (2000). A review of the nonmedical use of ketamine: Use, users and consequences. *Journal of Psychoactive Drugs, 32*(4), 419–432.

Jansson, L., & Velez, M. (2012). Neonatal abstinence syndrome. *Current Opinion in Pediatrics, 24*(2), 252–258.

Jarvik, S. (1967). Psychopharmacological revolution. *Psychology Today, 59*(1), 18–24.

Järvinen, M. (2012). A will to health? Drinking, risk and social class. *Health, Risk & Society, 14*(3), 241–256.

Jauk, E., & Dieterich, R. (2019). Addiction and the dark triad of personality. *Frontiers of Psychiatry, 10.* https://doi.org/10.3389/fpsyt.2019.00662

Jee, Y. (2016). Exercise addiction and rehabilitation. *Journal of Exercise Rehabilitation, 12*(2), 67–68.

Jellinek, E. (1952). Phases of alcohol addiction. *Quarterly Journal of Studies on Alcohol, 13*(4), 673–684.

Jellinek, E. (1960). *The disease concept of alcoholism.* Hillhouse Press.

Jensen, C., Cushing, C., Aylward, B., Craig, J., Sorell, D., & Steele, R. (2011). Effectiveness of motivational interviewing interventions for adolescent substance use behavior change: A meta-analytic review. *Journal of Consulting and Clinical Psychology, 79*(4), 433–440.

Jernigan, D. (2009). The global alcohol industry: An overview. *Addiction, 104*(1), 6–12.

Jerome, L., Schuster, S., & Yazar-Klosinski, B. (2013). Can MDMA play a role in the treatment of substance abuse? *Current Drug Abuse Reviews, 6*(1), 54–62.

Jia, D., Jiang, Z., Zhang, Y., Wang, J., Zhou, Y., Ma, L., & Guo, S. (2019). The development trends in drug rehabilitation in China's Judicial Administration Department. *Beijing Law Review, 10,* 239–245.

Jit, M., Aveyard, P., Barton, P., & Meads, C. (2010). Predicting the life-time benefit of school-based smoking prevention programmes. *Addiction, 105*(6), 1109–1116.

Johnson, B. (2018). Engineering neurobiological systems: Addiction. *Psychiatric Clinics, 41*(2), 331–339.

Johnson, V. (1973). *I'll quit tomorrow.* Harper & Row.

Johnston Counsulting. (2014). *Clients' outcome report: Addiction supportive housing review (phase two).* Addictions & Mental Health Ontario.

Jones-Smith, E. (2012). *Theories of counselling and psychotherapry.* Sage.

Julig, J. (2019). Colorado surpasses $1 billion in marijuana tax revenue. *Denver Post.* https://www.denverpost.com/2019/06/12/colorado-marijuana-revenue-one-billion/

Jung, J. (1994). *Under the influence: Alcohol and human behavior.* Brooks/Cole Publishing.

Just-Østergaard, E., Mortensen, E., & Flensborg-Madsen, T. (2018). Major life events and risk of alcohol use disorders: A prospective cohort study. *Addiction, 113*(1), 25–33.

Kabat-Zinn, J. (1982). An outpatient program in behavioral medicine for chronic pain patients based on the practice of mindfulness meditation: Theoretical considerations and preliminary results. *General Hospital Psychiatry, 4*(1), 33–47.

Kabat-Zinn, J. (1990). *Full catastrophe living: Using the wisdom of your body and mind to face stress, pain, and illness.* Delta.

Kadimisetty, K., Malla, S., & Rusling, J. (2017). Automated 3-D printed arrays to evaluate genotoxic chemistry: E-cigarettes and water samples. *ACS Sensors, 2*(5), 670–678.

Kahan, M., Srivastava, A., Ordean, A., & Cirone, S. (2011). Buprenorphine: New treatment of opioid addiction in primary care. *Canadian Family Physician, 57*(3), 281–289.

Kalant, H. (2009). What neurobiology cannot tell us about addiction. *Addiction, 105*(5), 780–789.

Kalant, H. (2015). Neurobiological research on addiction: What value has it added to the concept? *The International Journal of Alcohol and Drug Research, 4*(1), 53–59.

Kalkhoran, S., & Glantz, S. (2016). E-cigarettes and smoking cessation in real-world and clinical settings: A systematic review and meta-analysis. *The Lancet Respiratory Medicine, 4*(2), 116–128.

Kalsched, D. (2014). *The inner world of trauma: Archetypal defences of the personal spirit.* Routledge.

Kampman, K., Lynch, K., Pettinati, H., Spratt, K., Wierzbicki, M., Dackis, C., & O'Brien, C. (2015). A double blind, placebo controlled trial of modafinil for the treatment of cocaine dependence without co-morbid alcohol dependence. *Drug and Alcohol Dependence, 155*(1), 105–110.

Karyadi, K., VanderVeen, J., & Cyders, M. (2014). A meta-analysis of the relationship between trait mindfulness and substance use behaviors. *Drug and Alcohol Dependence, 143,* 1–10.

Kaskutas, L. (1989). Women for sobriety: A qualitative analysis. *Contemporary Drug Problems,* (Summer), 177–199.

Katikireddi, S., Whitley, E., Lewsey, J., Gray, L., & Leyland, A. (2017). Socioeconomic status as an effect modifier of alcohol consumption and harm: Analysis of linked cohort data. *The Lancet Public Health, 2*(6), e267–e276.

Katz, A., & Bender, E. (1976). *The strength in us.* New Viewpoints.

Keefer, P., Loayza, N., & Soares, R. (2008). The development impact of the illegality of drug trade. *World Bank Policy Research Working Paper 4543.* World Bank.

Kelly, A. (2004). Memory and addiction: Shared neural circuitry and molecular mechanisms. *Neuron, 44*(1), 161–179.

Kelly, J., & Westerhoff, C. (2010). Does it matter how we refer to individuals with substance-related conditions? A randomized study of two commonly used terms. *International Journal of Drug Policy 21*(3), 202–207.

Kemp, R. (2019). Addiction and addiction recovery: A qualitative research viewpoint. *Journal of Psychological Therapies, 4*(2), 167–179.

Kempf-Leonard, K., Tracy, P., & Howell, J. (2001). Serious, violent, and chronic juvenile offenders: The relationship of delinquency career types to adult criminality. *Justice Quarterly, 18*(3), 449–478.

Kendler, K., Heath, A., Neale, M., Kessler, R., & Eaves, L. (1992). A population-based twin study of alcoholism in women. *Journal of the American Medical Association, 268*(14), 1877–1882.

Kendler, K., Sundquist, K., Ohlsson, H., Palmér, K., Maes, H., Winkleby, M., & Sundquist, J. (2012). Genetic and familial environmental influences on the risk for drug abuse: A national Swedish adoption study. *Archives of General Psychiatry, 69*(7), 690–697.

Kennedy, M., Hayashi, K., Milloy, M., Wood, E., & Kerr, T. (2019). Supervised injection facility use and all-cause mortality among people who inject drugs in Vancouver, Canada: A cohort study. *PLoS Med 16*(11), e1002964. https://doi.org/10.1371/journal.pmed.1002964

Kent, H. (2002). New "daytox" centre opens for subgroup of Vancouver drug/alcohol addicts. *Canadian Medical Association Journal, 166*(5), 643.

Kerr, T., Small, W., Hyshkal, E., Maher, L., & Shannon, K. (2013). "It's more about the heroin": Injection drug users' response to an overdose warning campaign in a Canadian setting. *Addiction, 108*(7), 1270–1276.

Kerrigan, S., & Lindsey, T. (2005). Fatal caffeine overdose: Two case studies. *Forensic Science International, 153*(1), 67–69.

Kesselheim, A. (2011). Covert pharmaceutical promotion in free medical journals. *Canadian Medical Journal, 183*(5), 534–535.

Khantzian, E. (2003). Understanding addictive vulnerability: An evolving psychodynamic perspective. *Neuro-Psychoanalysis, 5*(1), 5–21.

Khatib, M., Jarrar, Z., Bizrah, M., & Checinski, K. (2013). Khat: Social habit or cultural burden? A survey and review. *Journal of Ethnicity in Substance Abuse, 12*(2), 140–153.

Kiang, M., Humphreys, K., Cullen, M., & Basu, S. (2020). Opioid prescribing patterns among medical providers in the United States, 2003–17: Retrospective, observational study. *British Medical Journal, 368.* https://doi.org/10.1136/bmj.l6968

Kimberly, M., & Osmond, M. (2017). Concurrent disorders and social work intervention. In R. Csiernik & W. Rowe (Eds.), *Responding to the oppression of addiction: Canadian social work responses* (3rd ed., pp. 363–394). Canadian Scholars' Press.

Kimura, M., & Higuchi, S. (2011). Genetics of alcohol dependence. *Psychiatry and Clinical Neurosciences, 65*(3), 213–225.

King, A., de Wit, H., McNamara, P., & Cao, D. (2011). Stimulant, and sedative alcohol responses and relationship to future binge drinking. *Archives of General Psychiatry, 68*(4), 389–399.

Kinnard, E., Howe, C., Kerr, T., Hass, V., & Marshall, B. (2014). Self-reported changes in drug use behaviors and syringe disposal methods following the opening of a supervised injecting facility in Copenhagen, Denmark. *Harm Reduction Journal, 11*(1), 29.

Kirby, K., Benishek, L., & Tabit, M. (2016). Contingency management works, clients like it, and it is cost-effective. *The American Journal of Drug and Alcohol Abuse, 42*(3), 250–253.

Kirby, M. (2004). *Mental health, mental illness and addiction: Overview of policies and programs in Canada.* Senate Standing Committee on Social Affairs, Science and Technology.

Kirchmayer, U., Davoli, M., & Verster, A. (2003). Naltrexone maintenance treatment for opioid dependence. *Cochrane Database of Systematic Reviews*, Issue 4, Art. No. CD001333. https://doi.org/10.1002/14651858.CD001333

Kirst, M., Zerger, S., Misir, V., Hwang, S., & Stergiopoulos, V. (2015). The impact of a Housing First randomized controlled trial on substance use problems among homeless individuals with mental illness. *Drug and Alcohol Dependence, 146*(1), 24–29.

Kishline, A. (1994). *Moderate drinking: The new option for problem drinkers.* See Sharp Press.

Kitchener, K. (1984). Intuition, critical evaluation and ethical principles: The foundations for ethical decisions in counseling psychology. *Counseling Psychologist, 12*(1), 43–56.

Kliem, S., Kröger, C., & Kossfelder, J. (2010). Dialectical behavior therapy for borderline personality disorder: A meta-analysis using mixed-effects modeling. *Journal of Consulting and Clinical Psychology, 78*(6), 936–951.

Klostermann, K., Kelley, M. L., Mignone, T., Pusateri, L., & Wills, K. (2011). Behavioral couples therapy for substance abusers: Where do we go from here? *Substance Use & Misuse, 46*(12), 1502–1509.

Koehn, C., O'Neill, L., & Sherry, J. (2012). Hope-focused interventions in substance abuse counselling. *International Journal of Mental Health and Addiction, 10*(4), 441–452.

Koffarnus, M., & Kaplan, B. (2018). Clinical models of decision making in addiction. *Pharmacology, Biochemistry, and Behavior, 164*(1), 71–83.

Kolden, G., Klein, M., Wang, C., & Austin, S. (2011). *Psychotherapy, 48*(1), 65–71.

Koltko-Rivera, M. (2006). Rediscovering the later version of Maslow's hierarchy of needs: Self-transcendence and opportunities for theory, research, and unification. *Review of General Psychology, 10*(4), 302–317.

Komro, K., Maldonado-Molina, M., Tobler, A., Bonds, J., & Muller, K. (2007). Effects of home access and availability of alcohol on young adolescents' alcohol use. *Addiction, 102*(10), 1597–1608.

Koning, I., Maric, M., MacKinnon, D., & Vollebergh, W. (2015). Effects of a combined parent–student alcohol prevention program on intermediate factors and adolescents' drinking behavior: A sequential mediation model. *Journal of Consulting and Clinical Psychology, 83*(4), 719–727.

Konkolÿ Thege, B., Woodin, E., Hodgins, D., & Williams, R. (2015a). Natural course of behavioral addictions: A 5-year longitudinal study. *BMC Psychiatry, 15*(1), 4.

Konkolÿ Thege, B., Colman, I., El-Guebaly, N., Hodgins, D., Patten, S., Schopflocher, D., Wolfe, J., & Wild, T. C. (2015b). Substance-related and behavioural addiction problems: Two surveys of Canadian adults. *Addiction Research & Theory, 23*(1), 34–42.

Konova, A., Moeller, S., Tomasi, D., Volkow, N., & Goldstein, R. (2013). Effects of methylphenidate on resting-state functional connectivity of the mesocorticolimbic dopamine pathways in cocaine addiction. *JAMA Psychiatry, 70*(8), 857–868.

Konova, A., Parvaz, M., Bernstein, V., Zilverstand, A., Moeller, S., Delgado, M., Alia-Klein, N., & Goldstein, R. (2019). Neural mechanisms of extinguishing drug and pleasant cue associations in human addiction: Role of the VMPFC. *Addiction Biology, 24*(1), 88–99.

Koob, G. (2008). Neurobiology of addiction. In M. Galanter & H. Kleber (Eds.), *Textbook of substance abuse treatment* (pp. 3–16). American Psychiatric Publishing.

Koob, G., & LeMoal, M. (1999). Brain reward circuits in alcoholism. *CNS Spectrums, 4*(1), 23–38.

Koob, G., & Volkow, N. (2016). Neurobiology of addiction: A neurocircuitry analysis. *The Lancet: Psychiatry, 3*(8), 760-773.

Korolenko, T. (2019). Psychodynamic psychiatry and psychodynamic therapy versus traditional approaches. *EC Psychology and Psychiatry, 8*(10), 1098–1102.

Koski, A., Sirén, R., Vuori, E., & Poikolainen, K. (2007). Alcohol tax cuts and increase in alcohol-positive sudden deaths—a time-series intervention analysis. *Addiction, 102*(3), 362–368.

Kottler, J., & Montgomery, M. (2010). *Theories of counselling and therapy.* Sage.

Kougiali, Z., Fasulo, A., Needs, A., & Van Laar, D. (2017). Planting the seeds of change: Directionality in the narrative construction of recovery from addiction. *Psychology & Health, 32*(6), 639–664.

Koukouli, F., Rooy, M., Tziotis, D., Sailor, K., O'Neill, H., Levenga, J., ... Stitzel, J. (2017). Nicotine reverses hypofrontality in animal models of addiction and schizophrenia. *Nature Medicine, 23*(3), 347.

Koval, R., Willett, J., & Briggs, J. (2018). Potential benefits and risks of high-nicotine e-cigarettes. *Journal of the American Medical Association, 320*(14), 1429–1430.

Kozlowski, L., Wilkinson, A., Skinner, W., Kent, C., Franklin, T., & Pope, M. (1989). Comparing tobacco cigarette dependence with other drug dependencies greater or equal "difficulty quitting" and "urges to use," but less "pleasure" from cigarettes. *Journal of the American Medical Association, 261*(6), 898–901.

Kozor, R., Grieve, S., Buchholz, S., Kaye, S., Darke, S., Bhindi, R., & Figtree, G. (2014). Regular cocaine use is associated with increased systolic blood pressure, aortic stiffness and left ventricular mass in young otherwise healthy individuals. *PLoS One, 9*(4), e89710. https://doi.org/10.1371/journal.pone.0089710

Krabbe, P., Koning, J., Heinen, N., Laheij, R., Van Cauter, R., & De Jong, C. (2003). Rapid detoxification from opioid dependence under general anaesthesia versus standard methadone tapering: Abstinence rates and withdrawal distress experiences. *Addiction Biology, 8*(3), 351–358.

Kraft, W., Adeniyi-Jones, S., Chervoneva, I., Greenspan, J., Abatemarco, D., Kaltenbach, K., & Erlich, M. (2017). Buprenorphine for the treatment of the Neonatal Abstinence Syndrome. *New England Journal of Medicine, 376*(24), 2341–2348.

Kraus, D., Castonguay, L., Boswell, J., Nordberg, S., & Hayes, J. (2011). Therapist effectiveness: Implications for accountability and patient care. *Psychotherapy Research, 21*(3), 267–276.

Kraus, S., Voon, V., & Potenza, M. (2016). Should compulsive sexual behavior be considered an addiction? *Addiction, 111*(12), 2097–2106.

Krebs, T., & Johansen, P. (2012). Lysergic acid diethylamide (LSD) for alcoholism: Metaanalysis. *Journal of Psychopharmacology, 26*(7), 994–1002.

Kristjansson, A., Mann, M., Sigfusson, J., Thorisdottir, I., Allegrante, J., & Sigfusdottir, I. (2019). Development and guiding principles of the Icelandic Model for Preventing Adolescent Substance Use. *Health Promotion Practice, 21*(1). https://doi.org/10.1177/1524839919849032

Kristjansson, A., Sigfusdottir, I., Thorlindsson, T., Mann, M., Sigfusson, J., & Allegrante, J. (2016). Population trends in smoking, alcohol use, and primary prevention variables among adolescents in Iceland, 1997–2014. *Addiction, 111*(4), 645–652.

Krystal, J., Cramer, J., Krol, W., Kirk, G., & Rosenheck, R. (2001). Naltrexone in the treatment of alcohol dependence. *New England Journal of Medicine, 345*(24), 1734–1739.

Ksaanetz, F., Deroche-Gamonet, V., Beerson, N., Balado, E., Lafourcade, M., Manzoni, O., & Piazza, P. (2010). Transition to addiction is associated with a persistent impairment in synaptic plasticity. *Science, 328*(5986), 1709–1712.

Kubiliene, A., Marksiene, R., Kazlauskas, S., Sadauskiene, I., Razukas, A., & Ivanov, L. (2008). Acute toxicity of ibogaine and noribogaine. *Medicina, 44*(12), 984–988.

Kuhar, M. (2002). Social rank and vulnerability to drug abuse. *Nature Neuroscience, 5*(2), 169–180.

Kulis, S., Marsiglia, F., Elek, E., Dustman, P., Wagstaff, D., & Hecht, M. (2005). Mexican/Mexican-American adolescents and keepin' it REAL: An evidence-based substance use prevention program. *Children and Schools, 27*(3), 133–145.

Kully-Martens, K., Treit, S., Pei, J., & Rasmussen, C. (2013). Affective decision-making on the Iowa Gambling Task in children and adolescents with fetal alcohol spectrum disorders. *Journal of the International Neuropsychological Society, 19*(2), 137–144.

Kumpfer, K., Alexander, J., McDonald, L., & Olds, D. (1998). Family-focused substance abuse prevention: What has been learned from other fields. In R. Ashery, E. Robertson, & K. Kumpfer (Eds.), *Drug abuse prevention through family interventions* (pp. 78–102). United States Department of Health and Human Services.

Kumpfer, K., & Alvarado, R. (1998). *Effective family strengthening interventions.* United States Department of Justice.

Kumpfer, K., & Alvarado, R. (2003). Family-strengthening approaches for the prevention of youth problem behaviors. *American Psychologist, 58*(6), 457–465.

Kumpfer, K., & Kaftarian, S. (2000). Bridging the gaps between family-focused research and substance abuse prevention practice: Preface. *Journal of Primary Prevention, 21*(2), 169–183.

Kung, E., & Farrell, A. (2000). The roles of parents and peers in early adolescent substance use: An examination of mediating and moderating effects. *Journal of Child and Family Studies, 9*(4), 509–528.

Kurtz, L., & Powell, T. (1987). Three approaches to understanding self-help groups. *Social Work with Groups, 10*(3), 69–80.

Kuss, D., & Griffiths, M. (2012). Internet gaming addiction: A systematic review of empirical research. *International Journal of Mental Health and Addiction, 10*(2), 278–296.

Kuypers, K., Dolder, P., Ramaekers, J., & Liechti, M. (2017). Multifaceted empathy of healthy volunteers after single doses of MDMA: A pooled sample of placebo-controlled studies. *Journal of Psychopharmacology, 31*(5), 589–598.

Kyle, P., Iverson, R., Gajaogowni, R., & Spencer, L. (2011). Illicit bath salts: Not for bathing. *Journal of the Mississippi State Medical Association, 52*(12), 375–377.

Kypri, K., Dean, J., & Stojanovski, E. (2007). Parent attitudes on the supply of alcohol to minors. *Drug and Alcohol Review, 26*(1), 41–47.

Kypri, K., Vater, T., Bowe, S., Saunders, J., Cunningham, J., Horton, N., & McCambridge, J. (2014). Web-based alcohol screening and brief intervention for university students: A randomized trial. *JAMA, 311*(12), 1218-1224.

Kypri, K., Voas, R., Langley, J., Stephenson, S., Begg, D., Tippets, A., & Davie, G. (2006). Minimum purchasing age for alcohol and traffic crash injuries among 15- to 19-year-olds in New Zealand. *American Journal of Public Health, 96*(1), 126–131.

LaBrie, J., Hummer, J., & Pedersen, E. (2007). Reasons for drinking in the college student context: The differential role and risk of the social motivator. *Journal of Studies on Alcohol and Drugs, 68*(3), 393–398.

Lachenmeier, D., Kanterers, F., & Rehm, J. (2009). Carcinogenicity of acetaldehyde in alcoholic beverages: Risk assessment outside ethanol metabolism. *Addiction, 104*(4), 533–550.

Lacsán, K., Arany, Z., & Farkas, A. (2017). The role of leisure in prevention and treatment of addiction. In Z. Benkő, I. Modi, & K. Tarkó (Eds.), *Leisure, Health and Well-Being: A Holistic Approach* (pp. 115–120). Palgrave Macmillan.

Ladouceur, R., & Walker, M. (1996). A cognitive perspective on gambling. In P. Salkovskies, (Ed.), *Trends in cognitive and behavioural therapies* (pp. 89–120). John Wiley and Sons.

Lalazaryan, A., & Zare-Farashbandi, F. (2014). A review of models and theories of health information seeking behavior. *International Journal of Health System & Disaster Management, 2*(4), 193–203.

Lamars, M. (2019, September 25). Canada "falling woefully short" of displacing illicit cannabis market, researcher says. *Marijuana Business Daily.* https://mjbizdaily.com/canada-falling-woefully-short-of-displacing-illicit-cannabis-market-researcher-says/

Lamberti, M., Siracusano, R., Italiano, D., Alosi, N., Cucinotta, F., Di Rosa, G., Germanò, E., Spina, E., & Gagliano, A. (2016). Head-to-head comparison of Aripiprazole and Risperidone in the treatment of ADHD symptoms in children with Autistic Spectrum Disorder and ADHD: A pilot, open-label, randomized controlled study. *Paediatric Drugs, 18*(4), 319–329.

Land, T., Keithly, L., Kane, K., Chen, L., Paskowsky, M., Cullen, D., … Li, W. (2014). Recent increases in efficiency in cigarette nicotine delivery: Implications for tobacco control. *Nicotine & Tobacco Research, 16*(6), 753–758.

Lander, L., Howsare, J., & Byrne, M. (2013). The impact of substance use disorders on families and children: From theory to practice. *Social Work in Public Health, 28*(3–4), 194–205.

Landolfi, E. (2013). Exercise addiction. *Sports Medicine, 43*(2), 111–119.

Larimer, M. (2012). *From controlled drinking to housing first: Marlatt's impact on harm reduction research and practice.* Presented at the 120th American Psychological Association Annual Convention, Orlando, Florida, August 2–5.

Larimer, M., Malone, D., Garner, M., Atkins, D., Burlingham, B., Lonczak, H., … Marlatt, G. (2009). Health care and public service use and costs before and after provision of housing for chronically homeless persons with severe alcohol problems. *Journal of the American Medical Association, 301*(13), 1349–1357.

Latino-Martel, P., Chan, D., Druesne-Pecollo, N., Barrandon, E., Hercbert, S., & Norat, T. (2010). Maternal alcohol consumption during pregnancy and risk of childhood leukemia: Systematic review and meta-analysis. *Cancer Epidemiology Biomarkers and Prevention, 19*(5), 1238–1260.

Lauritsen, K., & Rosenberg, H. (2016). Comparison of outcome expectancies for synthetic cannabinoids and botanical marijuana. *American Journal of Drug and Alcohol Abuse, 42*(4), 377–384.

Lawrence, A., Luty, J., Bogdan, N., Sahakian, B., & Clark, L. (2009). Impulsivity and response inhibition in alcohol dependence and problem gambling. *Psychopharmacology, 207*(1), 163–172.

Lawson, G. (1992). Twelve-step programs and the treatment of adolescent substance abusers. In G. Lawson & A. Lawson (Eds.), *Adolescent substance abuse: Etiology, treatment and prevention* (pp. 165–186). Aspen Publications.

Lawson, G., Peterson, J., & Lawson, A. (1983). *Alcoholism and the family: A guide to treatment and prevention.* Aspen Publications.

Lawson, P. (2005). Intervention in the workplace. In R. Csiernik (Ed.), *Wellness and work: Employee assistance programming in Canada* (pp. 203–208). Canadian Scholars' Press.

Lebowitz, M., & Appelbaum, P. (2017). Beneficial and detrimental effects of genetic explanations for addiction. *International Journal of Social Psychiatry, 63*(8), 717–723.

Le Dain Commission. (1973). *Final report of the Commission of Inquiry into the Non-Medical Use of Drugs*. Information Canada.

Ledermann, S. (1956). *Alcohol, alcoholisme, alcoholisation* (Vol. 1). Presses Universitaires de France.

Lee, J., Nunes Jr., E., Novo, P., Bachrach, K., Bailey, G., Bhatt, S., … Rotrosen, J. (2018). Comparative effectiveness of extended-release naltrexone versus buprenorphine-naloxone for opioid relapse prevention (X:BOT): A multicentre, open-label, randomised controlled trial. *Lancet, 391*(10118), 309–318.

Lee, S., Humphreys, K., Flory, K., Liu, R., & Glass, K. (2011). Prospective association of childhood attention-deficit/hyperactivity disorder (ADHD) and substance use and abuse/dependence: A meta-analytic review. *Clinical Psychology Review, 31*(3), 328–341.

Lembke, A., Papac, J., & Humphreys, K. (2018). Our other prescription drug problem. *New England Journal of Medicine, 378*(8), 693–695.

Leonardi-Bee, J., Britton, J., & Venn, A. (2011). Second hand smoke and adverse fetal outcomes in non-smoking pregnant women: A meta-analysis. *Pediatrics, 127*(4), 734–741.

Leshner, A. (1997). Addiction is a brain disease, and it matters. *Science, 278*(5335), 45–47.

Leshner, A. (2010). NIDA in the 90s. *Drug and Alcohol Dependency, 107*(1), 99–101.

Lesieur, H., & Rosenthal, R. (1991). Pathological gambling: A review of the literature. *Journal of Gambling Studies, 7*(1), 5–39.

LeTendre, M., & Reed, B. (2017). The effect of adverse childhood experience on clinical diagnosis of a substance use disorder: Results of a nationally representative study. *Substance Use & Misuse, 52*(6), 689–697.

Lethem, J. (2002). Brief solution focused therapy. *Child and Adolescent Mental Health, 7*(4), 189–192.

Leung, P., Macdonald, E., Stanbrook, M., Dhalla, I., & Juurlink, D. (2017). A 1980 letter on the risk of opioid addiction. *New England Journal of Medicine, 376*, 2194–2195.

Lev-Rana, S., Le Foll, B., McKenzie, K., George, T., & Rehme, J. (2013). Cannabis use and cannabis use disorders among individuals with mental illness. *Comprehensive Psychiatry, 54*(6), 589–598.

Lev-Rana, S., Le Foll, B., McKenzie, K., & Rehme, J. (2012). Cannabis use and mental health-related quality of life among individuals with anxiety disorders. *Journal of Anxiety Disorders, 26*(8), 799–810.

Levenson, J. (2017). Trauma-informed social work practice. *Social Work, 62*(2), 105–113.

Levinthal, C. (2012). *Drugs, behavior, and modern society* (7th ed.). Allyn and Bacon.

Levy, D., Borland, R., Lindblom, E., Goniewicz, M., Meza, R., Holford, T., Zhe, Y., Lua, Y., O'Connor, R., Niaura, R., & Abrams, D. (2018). Potential deaths averted in USA by replacing cigarettes with e-cigarettes. *Tobacco Control, 27*(1), 18–25.

Lewis, B., Kirchner, H., Short, E., Minnes, S., Weishampel, P., Satayathum, S., & Singer, L. (2007). Prenatal cocaine and tobacco effects on children's language trajectories. *Pediatrics, 120*(1), e78–e85.

Lewis, J., Dana, R., & Belevins, G. (1988). *Substance abuse counselling: An individualized approach.* Brooks/Cole Publishing.

Lewis, M. (2017). Addiction and the brain: Development, not disease. *Neuroethics 10*(1), 7–18.

Lewis, M., & Lockmuller, J. (1990). Alcohol reinforcement. *Alcohol Health and Research World, 14*(2), 98–103.

Li, H., Lu, Q., Xiao, E., Li, Q., He, Z., & Mei, X. (2014). Methamphetamine enhances the development of schizophrenia in first-degree relatives of patients with schizophrenia. *Canadian Journal of Psychiatry, 59*(2), 107–113.

Li, X., & Wolf, M. (2015). Multiple faces of BDNF in cocaine addiction. *Behavioural Brain Research, 279*(3), 240–254.

Liddle, H., & Hogue, A. (2000). A family-based development-ecological preventive intervention for high-risk adolescents. *Journal of Marital and Family Therapy, 26*(3), 265–279.

Lilienfield, S. O., Lynn, S. J., Namy, L. L., & Woolf, N. J. (2011). *Psychology: From inquiry to understanding* (2nd ed.). Pearson Education.

Lilienfield, S., & Satel, S. (2019). Is addiction a brain disease? In A. Raz and R. Thibault (Eds.), *Casting light on the dark side of brain imaging* (pp. 13–17). Academic Press.

Lin, W., Jiang, R., Wu, H., Chen, F., & Liu, S. (2011). Smoking, alcohol, and betel quid and oral cancer: A prospective cohort study. *Journal of Oncology.* https://doi.org/10.1155/2011/525976

Linehan, M. (1993). *Cognitive behavioral treatment of borderline personality disorder.* Guilford Press.

Linehan, M. (2015). *DBT skills training manual* (2nd ed.). Guilford Press.

Linehan, M., Armstrong, H., Suarez, A., Allmon, D., & Heard, H. (1991). Cognitive-behavioral treatment of chronically parasuicidal borderline patients. *Archives of General Psychiatry, 48*(12), 1060–1064.

Linehan, M., Heard, H., & Armstrong, H. (1993). Naturalistic follow-up of a behavioral treatment of chronically parasuicidal borderline patients. *Archives of General Psychiatry, 50*(12), 971–974.

Lines, R. (2007). *The death penalty for drug offences: A violation of international human rights law.* International Harm Reduction Association.

Linke, S., & Ussher, M. (2015). Exercise-based treatments for substance use disorders: Evidence, theory, and practicality. *American Journal of Drug and Alcohol Abuse, 41*(1), 7–15.

Linley, J., & Warren, K. (2019). The alumni club: Interpersonal contact and the exchange of recovery oriented helping in a sample of former residents of a therapeutic community for women. *Therapeutic Communities: The International Journal of Therapeutic Communities, 40*(1), 42–50.

Linn, E. (1975). Clinical manifestation of psychiatric disorders. In A. Freedman, H. Kaplan, & B. Sadock (Eds.), *Comprehensive textbook of psychiatry* (pp. 990–1034). Williams & Wilkins.

Lipton, D. (1995). *The effectiveness of treatment for drug abusers under criminal justice supervision.* United States Department of Justice.

Litten, R., & Allen, J. (1998). Advances in the development of medications for alcoholism treatment. *Psychopharmacology, 139*(1–2), 20–33.

Liu, G., Wasserman, E., Kong, L., & Foulds, J. (2017). A comparison of nicotine dependence among exclusive e-cigarette and cigarette users in the PATH study. *Preventive Medicine, 104*(1), 86–91.

Llamas, M. (2019, July 20). E-cig lawsuits mount over exploding devices. *Drugwatch.* https://www.drugwatch.com/news/2016/07/20/exploding-e-cig-lawsuits-on-rise/

Llewellyn, D., Lang, I., Langa, K., Naughton, F., & Matthews, F. (2009). Exposure to second hand smoke and cognitive impairment in non-smokers: National cross sectional study with cotinine measurement. *British Medical Journal, 338,* b462.

Lo, C., Lossie, A., Liang, T., Liu, Y., Xuei, X., Lumeng, L., Zhou, F., & Muir, W. (2016). High resolution genomic scans reveal genetic architecture controlling alcohol preference in bidirectionally selected rat model. *PLoS Genetics, 12*(8), e1006178.

Lochman, J., & van den Steenhoven, A. (2002). Family-based approaches to substance abuse prevention. *The Journal of Primary Prevention, 23*(1), 49–114.

Lo Coco, G., Melchiori, F., Oieni, V., Infurna, M., Strauss, B., Schwartze, D., Rosendahl, J., & Gullo, S. (2019). Group treatment for substance use disorder in adults: A systematic review and meta-analysis of randomized-controlled trials. *Journal of Substance Abuse Treatment, 99*(1), 104–116.

Loewenberg, F., & Dolgoff, R. (2008). *Ethical decision making for social work practice.* F.E. Peacock Publishers.

Logrip, M., Barak, S., Warnault, V., & Ron, D. (2015). Corticostriatal BDNF and alcohol addiction. *Brain research, 1628*(Pt A), 60–67.

London School of Economics. (2014). *Ending the drug wars.* LSE Expert Group on Economics of Drug Policy.

Longabaugh, R., & Morgenstern, J. (1999). Cognitive-behavioral coping-skills therapy for alcohol dependence: Current status and future directions. *Alcohol Research and Health, 23*(1), 78–85.

Lopez, G. (2014, September 10). The White House's plan to reform the war on drugs. *Vox Media.* http://www.vox.com/2014/9/10/6126541/the-white-houses-plan-to-reform-the-war-on-drugs

López-Muñoz, F., Ucha-Udabe, R., & Alamo, C. (2005). The history of barbiturates a century after their clinical introduction. *Journal of Neuropsychiatric Disease and Treatment, 1*(4), 329–343.

Loughran, H. (2009). Group work in the context of alcohol treatment. *Journal of Teaching in the Addictions, 9*(1–2), 125–141.

Love, T., Laier, C., Brand, M., Hatch, L., & Hajela, R. (2015). Neuroscience of Internet pornography addiction: A review and update. *Behavioral Sciences, 5*(3), 388–433.

Loy, H., Merry, S., Hetrick, S., & Stasiak, K. (2012). Atypical antipsychotics for disruptive behaviour disorders in children and youths. *Cochrane Database of Systematic Reviews,* Issue 9, Art. No. CD008559. https://doi.org/10.1002/14651858.CD008559.pub2

Lu, L., Liu, Y., Zhu, W., Shi, J., Liu, Y., Ling, W., & Kosten, T. (2009). Traditional medicine in the treatment of drug addiction. *American Journal of Drug and Alcohol Abuse, 35*(1), 1–11.

Ludwig, A. (1975). The psychiatrist as physician. *Journal of the American Medical Association, 234*(6), 603–604.

Luisetto, M., Almukhtar, N., Mashori, G., Ahmadabadi, B., & Sahu, R. (2019). Addiction and evolutionary process: Common aspects in physio-pathologic pathways useful in pharmacotoxicological approach. *Online Journal of Neurology and Brain Disorders, 2*(3), 134–144.

Lum, K., Polansky, J., Jackler, R., & Glantz, S. (2008). Signed, sealed and delivered: "Big tobacco" in Hollywood, 1927–1995. *Tobacco Control, 17*(4), 313–323.

Lundahl, B., Kunz, C., Brownell, C., Tollefson, D., & Burke, B. (2010). A meta-analysis of motivational interviewing: Twenty-five years of empirical studies. *Research on Social Work Practice, 20*(2), 137–160.

Lundborg, P. (2007). Parents' willingness to provide alcohol and adolescents' alcohol use: Evidence from Swedish data. *Vulnerable Children and Youth Studies, 2*(1), 60–70.

Lurie, Y., Gopher, A., Lavon, O., Almog, S., Sulimani, L., & Bentur, Y. (2012). Severe paramethoxymethamphetamine (PMMA) and paramethoxyamphetamine (PMA) outbreak in Israel. *Clinical Toxicology, 50*(1), 39–43.

Lynam, D., Milich, R., Zimmerman, R., Novak, S., Logan, T., Martin, C., ... Clayton, R. (1999). Project DARE: No effects at 10-year follow up. *Journal of Consulting and Clinical Psychology, 67*(4), 590–593.

Ma, G., & Thompson, B. (1999). Needs for youth substance abuse and violence prevention in schools and communities. *Journal of Primary Prevention, 20*(2), 93–105.

Maan, J., & Saadabadi, A. (2018). *Carbamazepine*. StatPearls Publishing.

Maas, U., & Strubelt, S. (2006). Fatalities after taking ibogaine in addiction treatment could be related to sudden cardiac death caused by autonomic dysfunction. *Medical Hypotheses, 67*(4), 960–964.

Macgregor, S., & Herring, R. (2010). *The Alcohol Concern SMART Recovery pilot project final evaluation report*. Middlesex University.

MacKinnon, D., & Lockwood, C. (2003). Advances in statistical methods for substance abuse prevention research. *Prevention Science, 4*(3), 155–171.

MacMaster, S. (2004). Harm reduction: A new perspective on substance abuse services. *Journal of Social Work, 49*(3), 356–363.

MacPherson, D., & Rowley, M. (2001). *A framework for action: A four-pillar approach to drug problems in Vancouver*. City of Vancouver.

Maertens, R., White, P., Rickert, W., Levasseur, G., Douglas, G., Bellier, P., ... Desjardins, S. (2009). The genotoxicity of mainstream and sidestream marijuana and tobacco smoke condensates. *Chemical Research in Toxicology, 22*(8), 1406–1414.

Magill, M. (2015). Branding addiction therapies and reified specific factors. *Addiction, 110*(3), 415–416.

Magill, M., & Ray, L. A. (2009). Cognitive-behavioral treatment with adult alcohol and illicit drug users: A meta-analysis of randomized controlled trials. *Journal of Studies on Alcohol and Drugs, 70*(4), 516–527.

Mahabee-Gittens, E., Xiao, Y., Gordon, J., & Khoury, J. (2013). The dynamic role of parental influences in preventing adolescent smoking initiation. *Addictive Behaviors, 38*(4), 1905–1911.

Main, M., & Solomon, J. (1986). Discovery of an insecure-disorganized/disoriented attachment pattern: Procedures, findings and implications for the classification of behavior. In T.Brazelton & M. Yogman (Eds.), *Affective development in infancy* (pp. 95–124). Ablex.

Main, T. (1946). The hospital as a therapeutic institution. *Bulletin of the Menninger Clinic, 10*(1), 66–70.

Maisto, S., Galizio, M., & Connors, G. (1995). *Drug use and abuse.* Harcourt Press.

Malhi, G., Tanious, M., Das, P., Coulston, C., & Berk, M. (2013). Potential mechanisms of action of lithium in bipolar disorder. *CNS Drugs, 27*(2), 135–153.

Malik, P., Gasser, R., Kemmler, G., Moncayo, R., Finkenstedt, G., Kurz, M., & Fleischhacker, W. (2008). Low bone mineral density and impaired bone metabolism in young alcoholic patients without liver cirrhosis: A cross-sectional study. *Alcoholism: Clinical and Experimental Research, 33*(2), 375–381.

Malivert, M., Fatséas, M., Denis, C., Langlois, E., & Auriacombe, M. (2012). Effectiveness of therapeutic communities: A systematic review. *European Addiction Research, 18*(1), 1–11.

Malyshevskaya, O., Aritake, K., Kaushik, M., Uchiyama, N., Cherasse, Y., Kikura-Hanajiri, R., & Urade, Y. (2017). Natural (Δ^9-THC) and synthetic (JWH-018) cannabinoids induce seizures by acting through the cannabinoid CB_1 receptor. *Scientific Reports, 7*(1), 10516.

Manchiraju, S., Sadachar, A., & Ridgway, J. (2017). The compulsive online shopping scale (COSS): Development and validation using panel data. *International Journal of Mental Health and Addiction, 15*(1), 209–223.

Mandell, W., Olden, M., Wenzel, S., Dahl, J., & Ebener, P. (2008). Do dimensions of TC treatment predict retention and outcomes? *Journal of Substance Abuse Treatment, 35*(3), 223–231.

Manning, N. (1989). *The therapeutic community movement: Charisma and routinization.* Routledge.

Manning, V., Garfield, J., Lam, T., Allsop, S., Berends, L., Best, D., Buykx, P., Room, R., & Lubman, D. (2019). Improved quality of life following addiction treatment is associated with reductions in substance use. *Journal of Clinical Medicine, 8*(9), 1407.

Mantsch, J., & Gasser, P. (2015). Glucocorticoid involvement in drug abuse and addiction. In J. Russell & M. Shipston (Eds.), *Neuroendocrinology of Stress.* John Wiley and Sons.

Manzoli, L., Flacco, M., Ferrante, M., La Vecchia, C., Siliquini, R., Ricciardi, W., Marzuillo, C., Villari, P., & Fiore, M. (2017). Cohort study of electronic cigarette use: Effectiveness and safety at 24 months. *Tobacco Control, 26*(3), 284–292.

Marcellus, L. (2014). Supporting women with substance use issues: Trauma-informed care as a foundation for practice in the NICU. *Neonatal Network, 33*(6), 307–314.

Markoff, L., Fallot, R., Reed, B., Elliott, D., & Bjelajac, P. (2005). Implementing trauma-informed alcohol and other drug and mental health services for women: Lessons learned in a multisite demonstration project. *American Journal of Orthopsychiatry, 75*(4), 525–539.

Marks, I. (1990). Behavioural (non-chemical) addictions. *British Journal of Addiction, 85*(11), 1389–1394.

Marlatt, G. (1973). A comparison of aversive conditioning procedures in the treatment of alcoholism. Western Psychological Association.

Marlatt, G. (1985). Relapse prevention: Theoretical rationale and overview of the model. In G. Marlatt & J. Gordon (Eds.), *Relapse prevention* (pp. 3–70). Guilford Press.

Marlatt, G., & George, W. (1984). Relapse prevention: Introduction and overview of the model. *British Journal of Addiction, 79*(3), 261–273.

Marlatt, G., & Gordon, J. (Eds.). (1985). *Relapse prevention*. Guilford Press.

Marlatt, G. & Witkiewitz, K. (2005). Relapse prevention for alcohol and drug problems. In G. Marlatt & D. Donovan (Eds.), *Relapse prevention: Maintenance strategies in the treatment of addictive behaviors* (pp. 1–44). Guilford Press.

Marovino, T. (1994). Laser auriculotherapy as part of the nicotine detoxification process: Evaluation of 1280 subjects and theoretical considerations of a developing model. *American Journal of Acupuncture, 22*(2), 129–135.

Marrelli, A. (2001). *Introduction to competency modeling*. American Express.

Marshall, S., Albery, I., & Frings, D., (2018). Who stays in addiction treatment groups? Anxiety and avoidant attachment styles predict treatment retention and relapse. *Clinical Psychology & Psychotherapy, 25*(4), 525–531.

Marsiglia, F., Holleran, L., & Jackson, K. (2000). Assessing the effects of external resources on school-based substance abuse prevention programs. *Social Work in Education, 22*(3), 145–161.

Martin, W., Minatrea, N., & Watson, J. (2009). Animal-assisted therapy in the treatment of substance dependence. *Anthrozoos: A Multidisciplinary Journal of the Interactions of People and Animals, 22*(2), 137–148.

Martins, S., & Alexandre, P. (2009). The association of ecstasy use and academic achievement among adolescents in two U.S. national surveys. *Addictive Behaviors, 34*(1), 1–124.

Marx, K. (2004). *Capital: A critique of political economy* (Vol. 1). Penguin Books.

Maslow, A. (1970). *Motivation and personality*. Harper & Row.

Matt, G., Quintana, P., Zakarina, J., Fortmann, A., Chatfield, D., Hoh, E., ... Hovell, M. (2011). When smokers move out and non-smokers move in: Residential thirdhand smoke pollution and exposure. *Tobacco Control, 20*(1), e1. https://doi.org/10.1136/tc.2010.037382

Maurel, D., Boisseau, N., Benhamou, C., & Jaffe, C. (2011). Alcohol and bone: Review of dose effects and mechanisms. *Osteoporosis International, 13*(1), 56–64.

Maust, D., Lin, L., Blow, F., & Marcus, S. (2018). County and physician variation in benzodiazepine prescribing to Medicare beneficiaries by primary care physicians in the USA. *Journal of General Internal Medicine, 33*(12), 2180–2188.

May, C. (1997). Habitual drunkards and the invention of alcoholism: Susceptibility and culpability in nineteenth century medicine. *Addiction Research, 5*(2), 169–187.

May, C. (2001). Pathology, identity and the social construction of alcohol dependence. *Sociology, 35*(2), 385–401.

Mayes, L., & Truman, S. (2002) Substance abuse and parenting. In M. Bornstein (Ed.), *Handbook of parenting: Social conditions and applied parenting* (pp. 328–359). Lawrence Erlbaum Publishers.

McCabe, S., Cranford, J., & Boyd, C. (2016). Stressful events and other predictors of remission from drug dependence in the United States: Longitudinal results from a national survey. *Journal of Substance Abuse Treatment, 71*(1), 41–47.

McCarthy, D., Mycyk, M., & DesLauriers, C. (2006). Hospitalization for caffeine abuse is associated with concomitant abuse of other pharmaceutical products. *Annals of Emergency Medicine, 48*(4), 101.

McCarty, D. (2008). *Substance abuse treatment benefits and costs knowledge asset.* Robert Wood Johnson Foundation's Substance Abuse Policy Research Program. http://saprp.org/knowledgeassets/knowledge_detail.cfm?KAID=1

McClelland, D., Davis, W., Kalin, R., & Wanner, E. (1972). *The drinking man.* Free Press.

McCollister, K., & French, M. (2003). The relative contribution of outcome domains in the total economic benefit of addiction interventions: A review of first findings. *Addiction, 98*(12), 1647–1659.

McConaghy, N., Armstrong, M., Blaszczynski, A., & Allcock, C. (1983). Controlled comparison of aversive therapy and imaginal desensitisation in compulsive gambling. *British Journal of Psychiatry, 142*(4), 366–372.

McConnell, H. (1989). Sick behaviours. *The Journal, 16*(1), 14.

McCoy, A. (2003). *The politics of heroin: CIA complicity in the global drug trade, Afghanistan, Southeast Asia, Central America.* Lawrence Hill.

McCrady, B., Epstein, E., Cook, S., Jensen, N., & Hildebrandt, T. (2009). A randomized trial of individual and couple behavioral alcohol treatment for women. *Journal of Consulting and Clinical Psychology, 77*(2), 243–256.

McCusker, J. (1970). The rum trade and the balance of payments of the thirteen continental colonies, 1650–1775. *Journal of Economic History, 30*(1), 244–247.

McDonald, R., & Strang, J. (2016). Are take-home naloxone programmes effective? Systematic review utilizing application of the Bradford Hill criteria. *Addiction, 111*(7), 1177–1187.

McElrath, D. (1997). The Minnesota model. *Journal of Psychoactive Drugs, 29*(2), 141–144.

McElroy, S., Keck, P., Pope, H., Smith, J., & Strakowski, S. (1994). Compulsive buying: A report of 20 cases. *Journal of Clinical Psychiatry, 55*(6), 242–248.

McGovern, R., Gilvarry, E., Addison, M., Alderson, H., Carr, L., Geijer-Simpson, E., Hrisos, N., Lingam, R., Minos, D., Smart, D., & Kaner, E. (2018). *Addressing the impact of non-dependent parental substance misuse upon children.* Public Health England.

McGregor, C., Ali, R., White, J., Thomas, P., & Gowing, L. (2002). A comparison of antagonist-precipitated withdrawal under anesthesia to standard inpatient withdrawal as a precursor to maintenance naltrexone treatment in heroin users: Outcomes at 6 and 12 months. *Drug and Alcohol Dependence, 68*(1), 5–14.

McGue, M., Iacono, W., & Krueger, R. (2006). The association of early adolescent problem behavior and adult psychopathology: A multivariate behavioral genetic perspective. *Behavior Genetics, 36*(4), 591–602.

McKay, J., Van Horn, D., Oslin, D., Ivey, M., Drapkin, M., Coviello, D., … Lynch, K. (2011). Extended telephone-based continuing care for alcohol dependence: 24-month outcomes and subgroup analyses. *Addiction, 106*(10), 1760–1769.

McKeganey, N., Russell, C., & Haseen, F. (2019). Vaping and the number of cigarettes not now smoked: An additional means of assessing the public health impact of e-cigarettes. *Journal of Pulmonary and Respiratory Medicine, 3*, 104. https://doi.org/10.29011/PROA-104.100004

McLellan, A., Arndt, I., Metzger, D., Woody, G., & O'Brien, C. (1993). The effects of psychosocial services in substance abuse treatment. *Journal of the American Medical Association, 269*(15), 1953–1959.

McLellan, A., Hagan, T., Levine, M., Gould, F., Meyers, K., Bencivengo, M., & Durell, J. (1998). Supplemental social services improve outcomes in public addiction treatment. *Addiction, 93*(10), 1489–1499.

McLellan, A., Luborsky, L., Woody, G., O'Brien, C., & Druley, K. (1983). Increased effectiveness of substance abuse treatment: A prospective study of patient-treatment "matching." *Journal of Nervous and Mental Disorders, 171*(10), 597–605.

McLellan, A., Weinstein, R., Shen, Q., Kendig, C., & Levine, M. (2005). Improving continuity of care in a public addiction treatment system with clinical case management. *American Journal on Addictions, 14*(5), 426–440.

McMaster Health Forum. (2019). *Determining the features of Managed Alcohol Programs.* McMaster University.

McMorris, B., Catalano, R., Kim, M., Toumbourou, J., & Hemphill, S. (2011). Influence of family factors and supervised alcohol use on adolescent alcohol use and harms: Similarities between youth in different alcohol policy contexts. *Journal of Studies on Alcohol and Drugs, 72*(3), 418–428.

McPherson, C., & Boyne, H. (2017). Access to substance use disorder treatment services in Canada. *Journal of Alcoholism and Drug Dependency, 5*(4). https://doi.org/10.4172/2329-6488.1000277

McPherson, C., Boyne, H., & Waseem, R. (2017). Understanding the factors that impact relapse post-residential addiction treatment, a six month follow-up from a Canadian treatment centre. *Journal of Alcoholism and Drug Dependency, 5*(3). https://doi.org/10.4172/2329-6488.10000268

Mehra, R., Moore, B., Crothers, K., Tetrault, J., & Fiellin, D. (2006). The association between marijuana smoking and lung cancer. *Achieves of Internal Medicine, 166*(13), 1359–1367.

Meichenbaum, D., Carlson, J., & Kjos, D. (2007). *Cognitive-behavioral therapy.* American Psychological Association.

Meier, P. (2008). *Independent review of the effects of alcohol pricing and promotion.* University of Sheffield.

Meissner, W., Schmidt, U., Hartmann, M., Kah, R., & Reinhart, K. (2000). Oral naloxone reverses opioid-associated constipation. *Pain, 84*(1), 105–109.

Merikle, P. (1988). Subliminal auditory messages: An evaluation. *Psychology and Marketing, 5*(4), 355–372.

Merlin, M. (2003). Archaeological evidence for the tradition of psychoactive plant use in the old world. *Economic Botany, 57*(3), 295–323.

Messinis, L., Kyprianidou, A., Malefaki, S., & Papathanasopoulos, P. (2006). Neuropsychological deficits in long-term frequent cannabis users. *Neurology, 66*(5), 737–739.

Methadone Strategy Working Group. (2001). *Countering the crisis: Ontario's prescription for opioid dependence.* Methadone Strategy Working Group.

Meyer, R. (1989). Prospects for a rational pharmacotherapy of alcoholism. *Journal of Clinical Psychiatry, 50*(11), 403–412.

Meyers, R., Roozen, H., & Smith, J. (2011). The community reinforcement approach: An update of the evidence. *Alcohol Research and Health, 33*(4), 380–388.

Middlemiss, P. (2002). Home detox gains support. *GP: General Practitioner, 32.* http://www.accessmylibrary.com/article-1G1-87784108/gp-business-home-detox.html

Midford, R., Cahill, H., Lester, L., Ramsden, R., Foxcroft, D., & Venning, L. (2017). Alcohol prevention for school students: Results from a 1-year follow up of a cluster-randomised controlled trial of harm minimisation school drug education. *Drugs, Education, Prevention and Policy, 25*(1), 88–96.

Midford, R., Munro, G., McBride, N., Snow, P., & Ladzinski, U. (2002). Principles that underpin effective school-based drug education. *Journal of Drug Education, 32*(4), 363–386.

Midgette, G., Davenport, S., Caulkins, J., & Kilmer, B. (2019). *What America's users spend on illegal drugs, 2006–2016.* Rand Corporation.

Millati Islami World Services. (2010a). *12 steps.* https://sites.google.com/site/aspiritualrecovery/12-steps-group-versions/millati-islami

Millati Islami World Services. (2010b). *12 traditions.* https://sites.google.com/a/millatiislami.org/www/Welcome/12-traditions

Miller, M., Swanson, S., Azrael, D., Pate, V., & Stürmer, T. (2014). Antidepressant dose, age, and the risk of deliberate self-harm. *JAMA Internal Medicine, 174*(6), 899–909.

Miller, N. (1999). Mortality risks in alcoholism and effects of abstinence and addiction treatment. *Addictive Disorders, 22*(2), 371–383.

Miller, N., & Gold, M. (1990). The disease and adaptive models of addiction: A re-evaluation. *Journal of Drug Issues, 20*(1), 29–35.

Miller, P., Book, S., & Stewart, S. (2011). Medical treatment of alcohol dependence: A systematic review. *The International Journal of Psychiatry in Medicine, 42*(3), 227–266.

Miller, S., & Berg, I. (1995). *The miracle method: A radically new approach to problem drinking.* New York: W.W. Norton.

Miller, W. (1983a). Controlled drinking: A history and a critical review. *Journal of Studies on Alcohol, 44*(1), 68–82.

Miller, W. (1983b). Motivational interviewing with problem drinkers. *Behavioural Psychotherapy, 11*(2), 147–172.

Miller, W. (2015). Retire the concept of "relapse." *Substance Use & Misuse, 50*(8–9), 976–977.

Miller, W., Forcehimes, A., & Zweben, A. (2011). *Treating addiction: A guide for professionals.* Guilford Press.

Miller, W., & Hester, R. (1986a). The effectiveness of alcoholism treatment: What research reveals. In W. Miller & N. Heather (Eds.), *Treating addictive behaviors: Processes of change* (pp. 121–174). Plenaum Press.

Miller, W., & Hester, R. (1986b). Inpatient alcoholism treatment: Who benefits? *American Psychologist, 41*(7), 794–805.

Miller, W., & Moyers, T. (2015). The forest and the trees: Relational and specific factors in addiction treatment. *Addiction, 110*(3), 401–413.

Miller, W., & Rollnick, S. (1991). *Motivational interviewing: Preparing people to change addictive behaviour.* Guilford Press.

Miller, W., & Rollnick, S. (2002). *Motivational interviewing: Preparing people for change.* Guilford Press.

Miller, W., & Rollnick, S. (2004). Talking oneself into change: Motivational interviewing, stages of change, and therapeutic process. *Journal of Cognitive Psychotherapy, 18*(4), 299–308.

Miller, W., & Rollnick, S. (2009). Ten things that motivational interviewing is not. *Behavioural and Cognitive Psychotherapy, 37*(2), 129–140.

Miller, W., & Rollnick, S. (2012). *Motivational interviewing: Helping people change.* Guilford Press.

Miller, W., & Rose, G. (2009). Toward a theory of motivational interviewing. *American Psychologist, 64*(6), 527–537.

Miller-Day, M. (2002). Parent-adolescent communication about alcohol, tobacco, and other drug use. *Journal of Adolescent Research, 17*(6), 604–616.

Mills, K. (2015). The importance of providing trauma-informed care in alcohol and other drug services. *Drug and Alcohol Review, 34*(3), 231.

Mills, K., & Teeson, M. (2019). Trauma-informed care in the context of alcohol and other drug use disorders. In R. Benjamin, J. Haliburn, & S. King (Eds.), *Humanising mental health care in Australia: A guide to trauma-informed approaches* (pp. 181–194). Routledge.

Minkoff, K., Zweben, J., Rosenthal, R., & Ries, R. (2004). Development of service intensity criteria and program categories for individuals with co-occurring disorders. *Journal of Addictive Diseases, 22*(S1), 113–129.

Minnesota Department of Education. (1992). *Promising prevention strategies: A look at what works.* Minnesota Department of Education.

Mirabile, R. (1997). Everything you wanted to know about competency modeling. *Training and Development, 51*(8), 73–78.

Mirin, S. (1984). Behavioral factors in drug dependency and withdrawal: A discussion. In G. Serban (Ed.), *The social and medical aspects of drug abuse* (pp. 205–213). Spectrum Publishing.

Miron, J. (1999). Violence and the U.S. prohibitions of drugs and alcohol. *American Law and Economics Review, 1*(1), 78–114.

Miron, J. (2005). *The budgetary implications of marijuana prohibition.* http://chanvreinfo. ch/info/en/IMG/pdf/The_Budgetary_Implications_of_Marijuana_Prohibition_ MironReport_2005.pdf

Miron, J. (2008). *The budgetary implications of drug prohibition.* http://leap.cc/dia/miron-economic-report.pdf

Miron, J. (2018). The budgetary effects of ending drug prohibition. *Tax and Budget Bulletin, 83.* https://www.cato.org/publications/tax-budget-bulletin/budgetary-effects-ending-drug-prohibition

Miron, J., & Waldock, K. (2010). *The budgetary impact of ending drug prohibition.* Cato Institute.

Mitchell, O., Wilson, D., Eggers, A., & MacKenzie, D. (2012). Assessing the effectiveness of drug courts on recidivism: A meta-analytic review of traditional and non-traditional drug courts. *Journal of Criminal Justice, 40*(1), 60–71.

Mithoefer, M., Mithoefer, A., Feduccia, A., Jerome, L., Wagner, M., Wymer, J., Holland, J., Hamilton, S., Yazar-Klosinski, B., Emerson, A., & Doblin, R. (2018). 3,4-methylenedioxymethamphetamine (MDMA)-assisted psychotherapy for post-traumatic stress disorder in military veterans, firefighters, and police officers: A randomised, double-blind, dose-response, phase 2 clinical trial. *Lancet Psychiatry, 5*(6), 486–497.

Moderation Management. (2014). *What is moderation management?* http://www.moderation.org/whatisMM.shtml

Mohai, C. (1991). *Are school-based drug prevention programs working?* http://eric.ed.gov/?q=Mohai%2c+&id=ED341886

Mohan, M., Yadukul, S., & Satish, K. (2018). Socio-demographic profile of pattern of solvent abuse among street children in Bengaluru. *Indian Journal of Forensic Medicine & Toxicology, 12*(2), 1–5.

Monahan, R. (1977). Secondary prevention of drug dependence through the transcendental meditation program in metropolitan Philadelphia. *International Journal of the Addictions, 12*(6), 729–754.

Montgomery, S., & Ekbom, A. (2002). Smoking during pregnancy and children's risk of diabetes. *British Medical Journal, 324*(7328), 26–27.

Montoya, I., Atkinson, J., & McFaden, W. (2003). Best characteristics of adolescent gateway drug prevention programs. *Journal of Addictions Nursing, 14*(2), 75–83.

Moos, R. (2005). Iatrogenic effects of psychosocial interventions for substance use disorders: Prevalence, predictors, prevention. *Addiction, 100*(5), 595–604.

Moran, M., Villanti, A., Johnson, A., & Rath, J. (2019). Patterns of alcohol, tobacco, and substance use among young adult peer crowds. *American Journal of Preventive Medicine, 56*(6), e185–e193. https://doi.org/10.1016/j.amepre.2019.02.010

Moreau, G. (2019). *Police-reported crime statistics in Canada, 2018.* Statistics Canada.

Morgan, C., Muetzelfeldt, L., & Curran, H. (2008). Ketamine use, cognition and psychological wellbeing: A comparison of frequent, infrequent and ex-users with polydrug and non-using controls. *Addiction, 104*(1), 77–87.

Morgan, N., & Mall, S. (2019). Pathways between urbanization and harmful substance use. *Current Opinion in Psychiatry, 32*(3), 218–223.

Morse, E. (2018). Addiction is a chronic medical illness. *North Carloina Medical Journal, 79*(3), 163–165.

Morton, C. (2019). Community social deprivation and availability of substance use treatment and mutual aid recovery groups. *Substance Abuse Treatment, Prevention, and Policy, 14*(1), 33.

Morzorati, L., Ramchandani, V., Fleury, L., Li, T., & O'Connor, S. (2002). Self-reported subjective perception of intoxication reflects family history of alcoholism when breath alcohol levels are constant. *Alcoholism, Clinical and Experimental Research, 26*(8), 1299–1306.

Motiuk, L., & Vuong, B. (2002). *Homicide, sex, robbery and drug offenders in federal corrections: An end-of-2001 review.* Correctional Service of Canada Research Branch.

Moussas, G., Christodoulou, C., & Douzenis, A. (2009). A short review on the aetiology and pathophysiology of alcoholism. *Annals of General Psychiatry, 8*(1). https://doi.org/10.1186/1744-859X-8-10

Moyers, T., Martin, T., Manuel, J., Hendrickson, S., & Miller, W. (2005). Assessing competence in the use of motivational interviewing. *Journal of Substance Abuse Treatment, 28*(1), 19–26.

Mrad, M., & Cui, C. (2017). Brand addiction: Conceptualization and scale development. *European Journal of Marketing, 51*(11/12), 1938–1960.

Mukamal, K. (2012). Understanding the mechanisms that link alcohol and lower risk of coronary heart disease. *Clinical Chemistry, 58*(4), 664–666.

Muller, A., & Clausen, T. (2014). Group exercise to improve quality of life among substance use disorder patients. *Scandinavian Journal of Public Health, 43*(2). https://doi.org/10.1177/1403494814561819

Munk-Olsen, T., Liu, X., Viktorin, A., Brown, H., Di Florio, A., D'Onofrio, B., Gomes, T., Howard, L., Khalifeh, H., Krohn, H., Larsson, H., Lichtenstein, P., Taylor, C., Van Kamp, I., Wesseloo, R., Meltzer-Brody, S., Vigod, S., & Bergink, V. (2018). Maternal and infant outcomes associated with lithium use in pregnancy. An international collaboration combining data from 6 cohort studies using meta-analysis covering 727 lithium exposed pregnancies and 21,397 bipolar or major depressive disorder reference pregnancies. *Lancet Psychiatry, 5*(8), 644–652.

Muralidharan, K., Ali, M., Silveira, L., Bond, D., Fountoulakis, K., Lam, R., & Yatham, L. (2013). Efficacy of second-generation antipsychotics in treating acute mixed episodes in bipolar disorder: A meta-analysis of placebo-controlled trials. *Journal of Affective Disorders, 150*(2), 408–414.

Murch, W., & Clark, L. (2016). Games in the brain: Neural substrates of gambling addiction. *The Neuroscientist, 22*(5), 534–545.

Murphy, E. (1922). *The black candle.* Thomas Allen.

Myers, R., & Miller, W. (2001). *A community reinforcement approach to addiction treatment.* Cambridge University Press.

Myers, R., Villanueva, M., & Smith, J. (2005). The community reinforcement approach: History and new directions. *Journal of Cognitive Psychotherapy, 19*(3), 251–264.

Nadler, A., Holder, J., & Talsky, M. (1998). Torque release technique: A technique model for chiropractic's second century. *Canadian Chiropractor, 3*(1), 1–6.

Nair, U., Bartsch, H., & Nair, J. (2004). Alert for an epidemic of oral cancer due to use of the betel quid substitutes gutkha and pan masala: A review of agents and causative mechanisms. *Mutagenesi, 19*(9), 251–262.

Naish, K., MacKillop, J., & Balodis, I. (2018). The concept of food addiction: A review of the current evidence. *Current Behavioral Neuroscience Reports, 5*(4), 281–294.

Nakken, C. (1996). *The addictive personality: Understanding the addictive process and compulsive behavior.* Hazelden.

Nance, E. (1992). Inpatient treatment of alcoholism: A necessary part of the therapeutic armamentarium. *Psychiatric Hospital, 21*(1), 9–12.

Naqvi, N., Rudrauf, D., Damasio, H., & Antoine Bechara, A. (2007). Damage to the insula disrupts addiction to cigarette smoking. *Science, 315*(5811), 531–534.

Narcotics Anonymous. (1987). *Narcotics Anonymous* (4th ed.). Narcotics Anonymous World Services.

Nasrulla, A. (2000). Khat: Harmless stimulant or addictive drug? *Journal of Addiction and Mental Health, 3*(3), 5–7.

Nation, J., Cardon, A., Heard, H., Valles, R., & Bratton, G. (2003). Perinatal lead exposure and relapse to drug-seeking behavior in the rat: A cocaine reinstatement study. *Psychopharmacology, 168*(1–2), 236–243.

Nation, J., Livermore, C., & Bratton, G. (1995). Cadmium exposure attenuates the initiation of behavioral sensitization to cocaine. *Brain Research, 70*(1–2), 223–232.

Nation, M., Crusto, C., Wandersman, A., Kumpfer, K., Seybolt, D., Morrissey-Kane, E., & Davino, K. (2003). What works in prevention: Principles of effective prevention programs. *American Psychologist, 58*(6), 449–456.

National Alcohol Strategy Advisory Committee. (2015). *Social reference prices for alcohol: A tool for Canadian governments to promote a culture of moderation.* Canadian Centre on Substance Abuse.

National Center on Addiction and Substance Abuse. (2009). *The importance of family dinners V.* Colombia University.

National Center on Addiction and Substance Abuse. (2012). *The importance of family dinners VIII.* Colombia University.

National Institute on Alcohol Abuse and Alcoholism. (1988). *A cognitive approach: Treating cocaine addiction.* United States Department of Health and Human Services, National Institutes of Health.

National Institute on Alcohol Abuse and Alcoholism. (1996). *How to cut down on your drinking.* United States Department of Health and Human Services, National Institutes of Health.

National Institute on Alcohol Abuse and Alcoholism. (2000). *Alcohol alert 48.* United States Department of Health and Human Services, National Institutes of Health.

National Institute on Alcohol Abuse and Alcoholism. (2005). *Helping patients who drink too much: A clinician's guide* (NIH Publication No. 07-3769). United States Department of Health and Human Services, National Institutes of Health. http://pubs.niaaa.nih.gov/publications/Practitioner/CliniciansGuide2005/guide.pdf

National Institute on Drug Abuse. (2012). *The science of drug abuse and addiction.* http://www.drugabuse.gov/publications/media-guide/science-drug-abuse-addiction

National Institute on Drug Abuse. (2019). *Methamphetamine.* http://www.drugabuse.gov/publications/research-reports/methamphetamine

National Institute on Drug Abuse. (2020). Inhalants DrugFacts. https://www.drugabuse.gov/publications/drugfacts/inhalants

National Treatment Agency. (2012). *Estimating the crime reduction benefits of drug treatment and recovery.* National Health Service.

National Treatment Strategy Working Group. (2008). *A systemic approach to substance use in Canada.* National Framework for Action to Reduce the Harms Associated with Alcohol and Other Drugs and Substances in Canada.

Navone, S., & Carollo, G. (2016). Extremely fragile: Playing with care! A study on music therapy's application with young patients suffering from drug addiction. *Nordic Journal of Music Therapy, 25*(sup1), 52–53.

Neale, J., Tompkins, C., Marshall, A., Treloar, C., & Strang, J. (2018). Do women with complex alcohol and other drug use histories want women-only residential treatment? *Addiction, 113*(6), 989–997.

Neher, A. (1991). Maslow's theory of motivation: A critique. *Journal of Humanistic Psychology, 31*(3), 89–112.

Nestler, E. (2005). The neurobiology of cocaine addiction. *Science and Practice Perspectives, 3*(1), 3–4.

Nestler, E., & Luscher, C. (2019). The molecular basis of drug addiction: Linking epigenetic to synaptic and circuit mechanisms. *Neuron, 102*(1), 48–59.

Neuberger, K. (2012). The status of horticultural therapy around the world: Practice, research, education. *Acta Horticulture, 954*(2), 187–189.

Newman, C. (2019). Cognitive-behavioral therapy for alcohol and other substance use disorders: The Beck model in action. *International Journal of Cognitive Therapy, 12*(4), 307–326.

Nguyen, T., Bradford, W., & Simon, K. (2019). Pharmaceutical payments to physicians may increase prescribing for opioids. *Addiction, 114*(6), 1051–1059.

Niccols, A., Milligan, K., Sword, W., Thabane, L., Henderson, J., Smith, A., Liu, J., & Jack, S. (2010). Maternal mental health and integrated programs for mothers with substance abuse issues. *Psychology of Addictive Behaviors, 24*(3), 466–474.

Nidecker, M., DiClemente, C., Bennett, M., & Bellack, A. (2008). Application of the Transtheoretical Model of Change: Psychometric properties of leading measures in patients with co-occurring drug abuse and severe mental illness. *Addictive Behaviors, 33*(8), 1021–1030.

Nilsen, P. (2010). Brief alcohol intervention—where to from here? Challenges remain for research and practice. *Addiction, 105*(6), 954–959.

Nixon, S., Tivis, R., & Parsons, O. (1992). Interpersonal problem-solving in male and female alcoholics. *Alcoholism: Clinical and Experimental Research, 16*(4), 684–687.

Noll, R. (2007). *The encylopedia of schizophrenia and other psychotic disorders* (3rd ed.). Facts on File.

Noone, M., Dua, J., & Markham, R. (1999). Stress, cognitive factors, and coping resources as predictors of relapse in alcoholics. *Addictive Behaviors, 24*(5), 687–693.

Norcross, J., & Lambert, M. (2018). Psychotherapy relationships that work III. *Psychotherapy, 55*(4), 303–315.

Norström, T., & Pape, H. (2012). Associations between adolescent heavy drinking and problem drinking in early adulthood: Implications for prevention. *Journal of Studies on Alcohol and Drugs, 73*(4), 542–548.

Nosyk, B., Geller, J., Guh, D., Oviedo-Joekes, E., Brissette, S., Marsh, D., ... Anis, A. (2010). The effect of motivational status on treatment outcome in the North American Opiate Medication Initiative (NAOMI) study. *Drug and Alcohol Dependence, 111*(1–2), 161–165.

Nosyk, B., Marshall, B., Fischer, B., Montaner, J., Wood, E., & Kerr, T. (2012). Increases in the availability of prescribed opioids in a Canadian setting. *Drug and Alcohol Dependence, 126*(1), 7–12.

Nutt, D., King, L., Saulbury, W., & Blakemore, C. (2007). Development of a rational scale to assess the harm of drugs of potential misuse. *The Lancet, 369*(9566), 1047–1053.

Ocean, G., & Smith, G. (1993). Social reward, conflict and commitment: A theoretical model of gambling behavior. *Journal of Gambling Studies, 9*(4), 321–339.

O'Connell, D. (2002). Managing psychiatric comorbidity in inpatient addictions treatment. In D. O'Connell & E. Beyer (Eds.), *Managing the dually diagnosed patient: Current issues and clinical approaches* (pp. 3–28). Haworth Press.

O'Connell, M., Kasprow, W., & Rosenheck, R. (2013). The impact of current alcohol and drug use on outcomes among homeless veterans entering supported housing. *Psychological Services, 10*(2), 241–249.

Odjers, C., Caspi, A., Nagin, D., Piquero, A., Slutske, W., Milne, B., ... Moffitt, T. (2008). Is it important to prevent early exposure to drugs and alcohol among adolescents? *Psychological Science, 19*(10), 1037–1044.

Office of the Auditor General of Ontario. (2008). *2008 Annual Report.* Queen's Printer for Ontario.

Office of the Surgeon General. (2016). *Facing addiction in America: The Surgeon General's report on alcohol, drugs, and health.* United States Department of Health and Human Services.

Ogborne, A., Annis, H., & Sanchez-Craig, M. (1978). *Report of the task force on halfway houses.* Addiction Research Foundation.

Ogborne, A., & Graves, G. (2005). Optimizing Canada's addiction treatment workforce: Results of a national survey of service providers. Canadian Centre on Substance Abuse.

O'Hanlon, W., & Weiner-Davis, M. (1989). *In search of solutions: A new direction in psychotherapy.* W. W. Norton.

O'Hare, T. (2005). *Evidence-based practices for social workers.* Lyceum.

Ohlendorf-Moffat, P. (1993). Addictions as allergies. *Pathways, 2*(1), 6–8.

Oksanen, A. (2013). Deleuze and the theory of addiction. *Journal of Psychoactive Drugs, 45*(1), 57–67.

Oluwoye, O., Kriegel, L., Alcover, K., McPherson, S., McDonell, M., & Roll, J. M. (2019). The dissemination and implementation of contingency management for substance use disorders: A systematic review. *Psychology of Addictive Behaviors, 34*(1), 99–110. https://doi.org/10.1037/adb0000487

O'Neill, D., Britton, A., Brunner, E., & Bell, S. (2017). Twenty-five-year alcohol consumption trajectories and their association with arterial aging: A prospective cohort study. *Journal of the American Heart Association, 6*(2), e005288. https://doi.org/10.1161/JAHA.116.005288

Ontario Ministry of Health and Long Term Care. (2010). *Methylphenidate extended release.* Province of Ontario.

Orford, J., Velleman, R., Natera, G., Templeton, L., & Copello, A. (2013). Addiction in the family is a major but neglected contributor to the global burden of adult ill-health. *Social Science and Medicine, 78*(1), 70–77.

Orman, J., & Keating, G. (2009). Spotlight on buprenorphine/naloxone in the treatment of opioid dependence. *CNS Drugs, 23*(10), 899–902.

Orosz, G., Dombi, E., Andreassen, C., Griffiths, M., & Demetrovics, Z. (2016). Analyzing models of work addiction: Single factor and bi-factor models of the Bergen Work Addiction Scale. *International Journal of Mental Health and Addiction*, *14*(5), 662–671.

Osmond, M., & Kimberley, M. (2017). Patterns of intimacy and sexual expression in interaction with addictions. In R. Csiernik & W. Rowe (Eds.), *Responding to the oppression of addiction: Canadian social work responses* (3rd ed., pp. 198–217). Canadian Scholars' Press.

Öst, L. (2014). The efficacy of acceptance and commitment therapy: An updated systematic review and meta-analysis. *Behaviour research and therapy*, *61*, 105–121.

Oster, R. (1983). Peer counseling: Drug and alcohol abuse prevention. *Journal of Primary Prevention*, *3*(3), 188–199.

Ota, A., Akimaru, K., Suzuki, S., & Ono, Y. (2008). Depictions of smoking in recent high-grossing Japanese movies. *Tobacco Control*, *17*(2), 143–144.

Ot'alora, G., Grigsby, J., Poulter, B., Van Derveer, J., Giron, S., Jerome, L., Feduccia, A., Hamilton, S., Yazar-Klosinski, B., Emerson, A., Mithoefer, M., & Doblin, R. (2018). 3,4-Methylenedioxymethamphetamine-assisted psychotherapy for treatment of chronic posttraumatic stress disorder: A randomized phase 2 controlled trial. *Journal of Psychopharmacology*, *32*(12), 1295–1307.

Otis, J. (2014). *The FARC and Colombia's Illegal Drug Trade*. Wilson Centre.

Overstreet, D., Miller, C., Janowksy, D., & Russell, R. (1996). Potential animal model of multiple chemical sensitivity with cholinergic supersensitivity. *Toxicology*, *111*(1–3), 119–134.

Paglia, A., & Room, R. (1999). Preventing substance use problems among youth: A literature review and recommendations. *The Journal of Primary Prevention*, *20*(1), 3–50.

Pai, N. (2016). Promoting concept of food addiction: Are we there yet? *Indian Journal of Social Psychiatry*, *32*(4), 407–407.

Palamar, J., Griffin-Tomas, M., & Ompad, D.C. (2015). Illicit drug use among rave attendees in a nationally representative sample of US high school seniors. *Drug Alcohol Dependence*, *152*(1), 24–31.

Pandey, G., Fawcett, J., Gibbons, R., Clark, C., & Davis, J. (1988). Platelet monoamine oxidase in alcoholism. *Biological Psychiatry*, *24*(1), 15–24.

Panova, T., & Carbonell, X. (2018). Is smartphone addiction really an addiction? *Journal of Behavioral Addictions*, *7*(2), 252–259.

Papaseit, E., Torrens, M., Pérez-Mañá, C., Muga, R., & Farré, M. (2018). Key interindividual determinants in MDMA pharmacodynamics. *Expert Opinion on Drug Metabolism & Toxicology*, *14*(2), 183–195.

Pape, B. (1990). *Self-help/mutual aid*. Canadian Mental Health Association.

Parolin, M., & Simonelli, A. (2016). Attachment theory and maternal drug addiction: The contribution to parenting interventions. *Frontiers in Psychiatry*, *7*, 152.

Parrott, A. (2014). The potential dangers of using MDMA for psychotherapy. *Journal of Psychoactive Drugs*, *46*(1), 37–43.

Patra, J., Giesbrecht, N., Rehm, J., & Bekmuradov, D. (2012). Are alcohol prices and taxes an evidence-based approach to reducing alcohol-related harm and promoting public health and safety: A literature review. *Contemporary Drug Problems, 39*(1), 7–48.

Pattison, E., Sobell, M., & Sobell, L. (1977). *Emerging concepts of alcohol dependence.* Springer.

Paul, S. (2006). Alcohol-sensitive GABA receptors and alcohol antagonists. *Proceedings of the National Academy of Science, 103*(22), 8307–8308.

Pauly, B., Reist, D., Belle-Isle, L., & Schactman, C. (2013). Housing and harm reduction: What is the role of harm reduction in addressing homelessness? *International Journal of Drug Policy, 24*(4), 284–290.

Peacock, A., Leung, J., Larney, S., Colledge, S., Hickman, M., Rehm, J., ... Ali, R. (2018). Global statistics on alcohol, tobacco and illicit drug use: 2017 status report. *Addiction, 113*(10), 1905–1926.

Peart, R. (1999). *Minutes of evidence.* Memorandum by Dr. R. Peart. Select Committee on Health, House of Commons, UK Parliament. https://publications.parliament.uk/pa/cm199899/cmselect/cmhealth/549/99072723.htm

Peele, S. (1983). *The science of experience.* Lexington Books.

Peele, S. (1985). What treatment for addiction can do and what it can't; what treatment for addiction should do and what it shouldn't. *Journal of Substance Abuse Treatment, 2*(3), 225–228.

Peele, S. (1989). Ain't misbehavin'—addiction has become an all-purpose excuse. *The Sciences,* (July/August), 1–10.

Peele, S. (2000). What addiction is and is not: The impact of mistaken notions of addiction. *Addiction Research, 8*(6), 599–607.

Peele, S. (2016). People control their addictions: No matter how much the "chronic" brain disease model of addiction indicates otherwise, we know that people can quit addictions—with special reference to harm reduction and mindfulness. *Addictive Behaviors Reports, 4,* 97–101.

Peele, S., & Brodsky, A. (1992). *Truth about addiction and recovery.* Simon & Schuster.

Peluso, P., & Freund, R. (2018). Therapist and client emotional expression and psychotherapy outcomes: A meta-analysis. *Psychotherapy, 55*(4), 461–472.

Pembleton, M. (2018). *Containing addiction: The Federal Bureau of Narcotics and the origins of America's global drug war.* University of Massachusetts Press.

Pendery, M., Maltzman, I., & West, L. (1982). Controlled drinking by alcoholics? New findings and a re-evaluation of a major affirmative study. *Science, 217*(4555), 169–175.

Peralta, R., & Steele, J. (2010). Nonmedical prescription drug use among US college students at a midwest university: A partial test of social learning theory. *Substance Use and Misuse, 45*(6), 865–887.

Pereira, J., Lawlor, P., Vigano, A., Dorgan, M., & Bruera, E. (2001). Equianalgesic dose ratios for opioids: A critical review and proposals for long-term dosing. *Journal of Pain Symptom Management, 22*(2), 672–687.

Perkins, A., Aggen, A., Sollie, R., Meredith, M., & Saville, G. (2019). Which medications for pain have the lowest propensity for addiction? *Evidence-Based Practice, 22*(2), 7.

Pernell-Arnold, A., & Finley, L. (2012). Training mental health providers in cultural competence: A transformative learning process. *Journal of Psychiatric Rehabilitation, 15*(4), 334–356.

Perrino, T., Coatsworth, J., Briones, I., Pantin, H., & Szapocznic, J. (2001). Initial engagement in parent-centered preventive interventions: A family systems perspective. *The Journal of Primary Prevention, 22*(1), 21–44.

Perry, C., Komro, K., Veblen-Mortenson, S., Bosma, L., Farbakhsh, K., Munson, K., … Lytle, L. (2003). A randomized controlled trial of middle and junior high school D.A.R.E. and D.A.R.E. plus programs. *Archives of Pediatric Medicine, 157*(2), 178–184.

Pescosolido, B., Martin, J., Long, S., Medina, T., Phelan, J., & Link, B. (2010). "A disease like any other"? A decade of change in public reactions to schizophrenia, depression, and alcohol dependence. *American Journal of Psychiatry, 167*(11), 1321–1330.

Petersen, K. (1987). *Company town: Potlatch, Idaho and the Potlatch Lumber Company.* Washington State University Press.

Petroff, O. (2002). GABA and glutamate in the human brain. *Neuroscientist, 8*(6), 562–573.

Petry, N. (2012). *Contingency management for substance abuse treatment: A guide to implementing this evidence-based practice.* Taylor & Francis.

Pettit, B. (2012). *Invisible men: Mass incarceration and the myth of black progress.* Russell Sage Foundation.

Pickard, H. (2012). The purpose in chronic addiction. *American Journal of Behavioral Neuroscience, 3*(2), 40–49.

Pietkiewicz, I., Nęcki, S., Bańbura, A., & Tomalski, R. (2018). Maladaptive daydreaming as a new form of behavioral addiction. *Journal of Behavioral Addictions, 7*(3), 838–843.

Pilarinos, A., Barker, B., Nosova, E., Milloy, M., Hayashi, K., Wood, E., Kerr, T. & DeBeck, K. (2020). Coercion into addiction treatment and subsequent substance use patterns among people who use illicit drugs in Vancouver, Canada. *Addiction, 115*(1), 97–106.

Pilz, R., Hartleb, R., Konrad, G., Reininghaus, E., & Unterrainer, H. (2017). The role of eye movement desensitization and reprocessing (EMDR) in substance use disorders: A systematic review. *Fortschritte der Neurologie-Psychiatrie, 85*(10), 584–591.

Piper, D., Moberg, D., & King, M. (2000). The Healthy for Life project: Behavioral outcomes. *The Journal of Primary Prevention, 21*(1), 47–73.

Podymow, T., Turnbull, J., Coyle, D., Yetisir, E., & Wells, G. (2006). Shelter-based managed alcohol administration to chronically homeless people addicted to alcohol. *Canadian Medical Association Journal, 174*(1), 45–49.

Polcin, D. (2009). Communal-living settings for adults recovering from substance abuse. *Journal of Groups in Addiction and Recovery, 4*(1–2), 7–22.

Polcin, D., Mericle, A., Howell, J., Sheridan, D., & Christensen, J. (2014). Maximizing social model principles in residential recovery settings. *Journal of Psychoactive Drugs, 46*(5), 436–443.

Pollack, M., Penava, S., Bolton, E., Worthington, J., Allen, G., Farach, F., & Otto, M. (2002). A novel cognitive-behavioral approach for treatment-resistant drug dependence. *Journal of Substance Abuse Treatment, 23*(2), 133–142.

Polo, O., Pesonen, P., & Tuominen, E. (2019). Low-dose naltrexone in the treatment of myalgic encephalomyelitis/chronic fatigue syndrome (ME/CFS). *Fatigue: Biomedicine, Health & Behavior, 7*(4), 207–217. https://doi.org/10.1080/21641846.2019.1692770

Popova, S., Lange, S., Burd, L., & Rehm, J. (2015). *The burden and economic effect of fetal alcohol spectrum disorder in Canada.* Centre on Addiction and Mental Health.

Popova, S., Mohapatra, S., Patra, J., Duhig, A., & Rehm, J. (2011). A literature review of cost-benefit analyses for the treatment of alcohol dependence. *International Journal of Environmental Research and Public Health, 8*(8), 3351–3364.

Porath-Waller, A. (2016). *Clearing the smoke on cannabis: Maternal cannabis use during pregnancy— an update.* Canadian Centre on Substance Abuse.

Pottie, K., Thompson, W., Davies, S., Grenier, J., Sadowski, C., Welch, V., Holbrook, A., Boyd, C., Swenson, R., Ma, A., & Farrell, B. (2018). Deprescribing benzodiazepine receptor agonists: Evidence-based clinical practice guideline. *Canadian Family Physician, 64*(5), 339–351.

Poulin, C., & Nicholson, J. (2005). Should harm minimization as an approach to adolescent substance use be embraced by junior and senior high schools? *International Journal of Drug Policy, 16*(6), 403–414.

Pratt, O., Rooprai, H., Shaw, G., & Thomson, A. (1990). The genesis of alcoholic brain tissue injury. *Alcohol and Alcoholism, 25*(2–3), 217–230.

Prest, L., & Protinsky, H. (1993). Family systems theory: A unifying framework for codependence. *American Journal of Family Therapy, 21*(4), 352–360.

Price, R., Hilchey, C., Darredeau, C., Fulton, H., & Barrett, S. (2010). Brief communication: Energy drink co-administration is associated with increased reported alcohol ingestion. *Drug & Alcohol Review, 29*(3), 331–333.

Price, R., Nock, M., Charney, D., & Mathew, S. (2009). Effects of intravenous ketamine on explicit and implicit measures of suicidality in treatment-resistant depression. *Biological Psychiatry, 66*(5), 522–526.

Primack, B., Douglas, E., & Kraemer, K. (2009). Exposure to cannabis in popular music and cannabis use among adolescents. *Addiction, 105*(3), 515–523.

Pringsheim, T., Lam, D., & Patten, S. (2011). The pharmacoepidemiology of antipsychotic medications for Canadian children and adolescents: 2005–2009. *Journal of Child and Adolescent Psychopharmacology, 21*(6), 537–543.

Prior, V., & Glaser, D. (2006). *Understanding attachment and attachment disorders: Theory, evidence and practice.* Jessica Kingsley Publishers.

Prochaska, J. (2008). Decision making in the Transtheoretical Model of behavior change. *Medical Decision Making, 28*(6), 845–849.

Prochaska, J., & DiClimente, C. (1982). Stages and process of self-change in smoking: Towards an integrative model of change. *Psychotherapy, 20*(2), 161–173.

Prochaska, J., DiClimente, C., & Norcross, J. (1992). In search of how people change: Applications to addictive behaviors. *American Psychologist, 47*(9), 1102–1114.

Prochaska, J., Norcross, J., & DiClimente, C. (1994). *Changing for good.* William Morrow.

Prochaska, J., & Velicer, W. (1997). The Transtheoretical Model of health behavior change. *American Journal of Health Promotion, 12*(1), 38–48.

Procyshyn, R., Bezchlibnyk-Butler, K., & Jeffries, J. (2017). *Clinical handbook of psychotropic drugs* (22nd ed.). Hogrefe & Huber Publishers.

Psychoyos, D., & Vinod, K. (2013). Marijuana, spice "herbal high," and early neural development: Implications for rescheduling and legalization. *Drug Test Analysis, 5*(1), 27–45.

Ptaszik, A. (2007). The courage to laugh: Comedy programs fights stigma, boosts self-esteem. *Crosscurrents, 10*(3), 4–5.

Public Health England. (2016). *The public health burden of alcohol and the effectiveness and cost-effectiveness of alcohol control policies.* Public Health England.

Pugh, A. (2004). Harnessing the benefits of animal assisted therapy. *Crosscurrents, 8*(2), 5.

Purdue Pharma. (2004). *Palladone.* Pudue Pharma.

Quadland, M. (1985). Compulsive sexual behavior: Definition of a problem and an approach to treatment. *Journal of Sex and Marital Therapy 11*(2), 121–132.

Quirion, B. (2014). Modalités et enjeux du traitement sous contrainte auprès des toxicomanes. *Santé mentale au Québec, 39*(2), 39–56.

Rabasseda, X. (2011). A report from the 2011 annual meeting of the American Academy of Allergy, Asthma and Immunology (March 18–22, 2011, San Francisco). *Drugs of Today, 47*(4), 313–323.

Rahula, W. (2006). *What the Buddha taught.* Buddhist Cultural Centre.

Raketic, D., Barisic, J., Svetozarevic, S., Gazibara, T., Tepavcevic, D., & Milovanovic, S. (2016). Five-factor model of personality profiles: The differences between alcohol and opiate addiction among females. *Psychiatria Danuba, 29*(1), 74–80.

Raman-Wilms, L. (2014). *Canadian Pharmacists Association guide to drugs in Canada* (4th ed.). Dorling Kindersley.

Ramchandani, V., Umhau, J., Pavon, F., Ruiz-Velasco, V., Margas, W., Sun, H., … Heilig, M. (2011). A genetic determinant of the striatal dopamine response to alcohol in men. *Molecular Psychiatry, 16*(6), 809–817.

Ramoz, N., & Gorwood, P. (2015). A genetic view of addiction. *Medical Science, 31*(4), 432–438.

Rampino, A., Marakhovskaia, A., Beaulieu, J., & Silva, T. (2019). Antipsychotic drug responsiveness and dopamine receptor signaling; old players and new prospects. *Frontiers of Psychiatry, 9.* https://doi.org/10.3389/fpsyt.2018.00702

Randolph, T. (1956). The descriptive features of food addiction: Addictive eating and drinking. *Quarterly Journal of Studies on Alcohol, 17*(2), 198–224.

Rankin, J. (1978). Etiology. In L. Phillips, G. Ramsey, L. Blumenthal, & P. Crawshaw (Eds.), *Core knowledge in the drug field.* Health and Welfare Canada.

Rapp, C., & Goscha, R. (2006). *The strengths model: Case management with people with psychiatric disabilities.* Oxford University Press.

Rasmussen, N. (2014). Stigma and the addiction paradigm for obesity: Lessons from 1950s America. *Addiction, 110*(2), 217–225.

Rathore, S., & Uma, J. (2019). Alienation, attachment style, and alcohol addiction: A study of young women habitual drinkers. *Indian Journal of Public Health Research and Development, 10*(3), 9–14.

Ray, W., Taylor, J., Meador, K., Lichtenstein, M., Griffin, M., Fought, R., Adams, M., & Blazer, D. (1993). Reducing antipsychotic drug use in nursing homes: A controlled trial of provider education. *Archives of Internal Medicine, 153*(6), 713–721.

Redmond, C., Spoth, R., Shin, C., & Lepper, H. (1999). Modeling long-term parent outcomes of two universal family-focused preventive interventions: One year follow-up results. *Journal of Consulting and Clinical Psychology, 67*(6), 975–984.

Reed, D. (2015). Ultra-violet indoor tanning addiction: A reinforcer pathologies interpretation. *Addictive Behaviors, 41*(4), 247–251.

Refuge Recovery. (2019). *What is the refuge recovery program?* https://refugerecovery.org/about#toggle-id-8

Reich, T. (1988). Beyond the gene. *Alcohol Health and Research World, 12*(4), 104–108.

Reilly, M., Noronha, A., Goldman, D., & Koob, G. (2017). Genetic studies of alcohol dependence in the context of the addiction cycle. *Neuropharmacology, 122*(1), 3–21.

Reinares, M., Rosa, A., Franco, C., Goikolea, J., Fountoulakis, K., Siamouli, M., Gonda, X., Franqou, S., & Vieta, E. (2013). A systematic review on the role of anticonvulsants in the treatment of acute bipolar depression. *The International Journal of Neuropsychopharmacology, 16*(2), 485–496.

Reinarman, C. (2005). Addiction as accomplishment: The discursive construction of disease. *Addiction Research and Theory, 13*(4), 307–320.

Remes, H., Moustgaard, H., Kestilä, L., & Martikainen, P. (2019). Parental education and adolescent health problems due to violence, self-harm and substance use: What is the role of parental health problems? *Journal of Epidemiology and Community Health, 73*(3), 225–231.

Resnicow, K., & Botvin, G. (1993). School-based substance use prevention programs: Why do effects decay? *Preventive Medicine, 22*(4), 484–490.

Resnicow, K., Soler, R., Braithwaite, R., Ahluwalia, J., & Butler, J. (2000). Cultural sensitivity in substance use prevention. *Journal of Community Psychology, 28*(3), 271–290.

Reus, V., Fochtmann, L., Eyler, A., Hilty, D., Horvitz-Lennon, M., Jibson, M., ... Wills, C. D. (2016). The American Psychiatric Association practice guideline on the use of antipsychotics to treat agitation or psychosis in patients with dementia. *American Journal of Psychiatry, 173*(5), 543–546.

Riba, J., Valle, M., Urbana, M., Yritia, M., Morteand, M., & Barbonoj, M. (2011). Human pharmacology of ayahuasca: Subjective and cardiovascular effects, monoamine metabolite excretion and pharmacokinetics. *The Journal of Pharmacology and Therapeutics, 306*(1), 73–83.

Richards, J., & Rodgers, T. (2001). *Approaches to methods in language and teaching* (2nd ed.). Cambridge University Press.

Richards, M., Jarvis, M., Thompson, N., & Wadsworth, M. (2003). Cigarette smoking and cognitive decline in midlife: Evidence from a prospective birth cohort study. *American Journal of Public Health, 93*(6), 994–998.

Rickards, L., McGraw, S., Araki, L., Casey, R., High, C., Hombs, M., & Raysor, R. (2010). Collaborative initiative to help end chronic homelessness: Introduction. *Journal of Behavioral Health Services & Research, 37*(2), 149–166.

Riley, D. (1998). *Drugs and drug policy in Canada: A brief review and commentary.* Canadian Foundation for Drug Policy & International Harm Reduction Association.

Riley, D., Sobell, L., Leo, G., Sobell, M., & Klajner, F. (1985). *Behavioural treatment of alcohol problems: A review and a comparison of behavioural studies.* Addiction Research Foundation.

Rioux, C., Castellanos-Ryan, N., Parent, S., Vitaro, F., Tremblay, R., & Séguin, J. (2018). Age of cannabis use onset and adult drug abuse symptoms: A prospective study of common risk factors and indirect effects. *Canadian Journal of Psychiatry, 63*(7), 457–464.

Ritz, B., Ascherio, A., Checkoway, H., Marder, K., Nelson, L., Rocca, W., … Gorell, J. (2007). Pooled analysis of tobacco use and risk of Parkinson disease. *Archives of Neurology, 64*(7), 990–997.

Roberto, M., Cruz, M., Gilpin, N., Sabino, V., Schweitzer, P., Baio, M., … Parsons, L. (2010). Corticotropin releasing factor-induced amygdala gamma-aminobutyric acid release plays a key role in alcohol dependence. *Biological Psychiatry, 67*(9), 831–839.

Roberts, D. (2019). How epic is the opioid epidemic? *ASBBS Proceedings, 26,* 462.

Roberts, G., McCall, D., Stevens-Lavigne, A., Anderson, J., Paglia, A., Bollenbach, S., … Gliksman, L. (2001). *Preventing substance use problems among young people: A compendium of best practices.* Health Canada.

Roberts, G., Ogborne, A., Leigh, G., & Adam, L. (1999). *Profile of substance abuse treatment and rehabilitation in Canada.* Health Canada.

Roberts, L., Shaner, A., & Eckman, T. (1999). *Overcoming addictions: Skills training for people with schizophrenia.* W. W. Norton.

Roberts, N., Roberts, P., Jones, N., & Bisson, J. (2015). Psychological interventions for post-traumatic stress disorder and comorbid substance use disorder: A systematic review and meta-analysis. *Clinical Psychology Review, 38,* 25–38.

Robins, L., Helzer, J., Hesselbrock, M., & Wish, E. (2010). Vietnam veterans three years after Vietnam: How our study changed our view of heroin. *American Journal on Addictions, 19*(3), 203–211.

Robinson, D., & Henry, S. (1977). *Self-help and health.* Chaucer Press.

Roche, A., Watt, K., & Fischer, J. (2001). General practitioners' views of home detoxification. *Drug & Alcohol Review, 20*(4), 395–406.

Rodríguez-Cintas, L., Daigre, C., Grau-Lopez, L., Barral, C., Perez-Paros, J., Voltes, N., Braquehais, M., Casas, M., & Roncero, C. (2016). Impulsivity and addiction severity in cocaine and opioid dependent patients. *Addictive Behaviors, 58*(1), 104–109.

Rodu, B., & Jansson, C. (2004). Smokeless tobacco and oral cancer: A review of the risks and determinants. *Critical Reviews in Oral Biology and Medicine, 15*(5), 252–263.

Roerecke, M., & Rehm, J. (2013). Alcohol use disorders and mortality: A systemic review and meta-analysis. *Addiction, 108*(9), 1562–1578.

Roffman, R. (1976). Addiction concepts and the Vietnam experience. *Urban and Social Change Review, 9*(2), 16–18.

Rogers, C. (1959). *Psychology: A study of a science.* McGraw-Hill.

Rogers, G., Elston, J., Garside, R., Roome, C., Taylor, R., Younger, P., … Somerville, M. (2009). The harmful health effects of recreational ecstasy: A systematic review of observational evidence. *Health Technology Assessment, 13*(6), 1–315.

Rojas, M. (2015). Suffering ailments and addiction problems in the family. *World Suffering and Quality of Life: Social Indicators Research Series, 56,* 203–216.

Rollnick, S., & Miller, W. (1995). What is motivational interviewing? *Behavioural and Cognitive Psychotherapy, 23*(4), 325–334.

Rollnick, S., Miller, W., & Butler, C. (2008). *Motivational interviewing in health care: Helping patients change behavior.* Guilford Press.

Romeder, J. (1990). *The self-help way: Mutual aid and health.* Canadian Council on Social Development.

Rømer, T., Callesen, M., Hesse, M., Kvamme, T., Pedersen, M. M., Pedersen, M. U., & Voon, V. (2018). Impulsivity traits and addiction-related behaviors in youth. *Journal of Behavioral Addictions, 7*(2), 317–330.

Ronsley, R., Scott, D., Warburton, W., Hamdi, R., Louie, D., Davidson, J., & Panagiotopoulos, C. (2013). A population-based study of antipsychotic prescription trends in children and adolescents in British Columbia from 1996–2011. *Canadian Journal of Psychiatry, 58*(6), 361–369.

Room, R. (2015). Cultural aspects and responses to addiction. In N. el-Guebaly, G. Carrà, & M. Galanter (Eds.), *Textbook of addiction treatment: International perspectives* (pp. 107–114). Springer.

Room, R., Stoduto, G., Demers, A., Ogborne, A., & Giesbrecht, N. (2006). Alcohol in the Canadian context. In N. Giesbrecht, A. Demers, & E. Lindquist (Eds.), *Sober reflections: Commerce, public health, and the evolution of alcohol policy in Canada, 1980–2000* (pp. 14–42). McGill-Queen's University Press.

Roozen, H., Waart, R., & Van Der Kroft, P. (2010). Community reinforcement and family training: An effective option to engage treatment-resistant substance-abusing individuals in treatment. *Addiction, 105*(10), 1729–1738.

Rose, J., Behm, F., Salley, A., Bates, J., Coleman, R., Hawk, T., & Turkington, T. (2007). Regional brain activity correlates of nicotine dependence. *Neuropsychopharmacology, 32*(12), 2441–2452.

Rose, R., Dick, D., Viken, R., Pulkkinen, L., & Kaprio, J. (2001). Drinking or abstaining at age 14? A genetic epidemiological study. *Alcoholism, Clinical and Experimental Research, 25*(11), 1594–1604.

Rosecrance, J. (1985). Compulsive gambling and the medicalization of deviance. *Social Problems, 32*(3), 275–284.

Rosengren, D., & Wagner, C. (2001). Motivational interviewing: Dancing, not wrestling. In R. Coombs (Ed.), *Addiction recovery tools: A practice handbook.* Safe Publications.

Rosenthal, R. (1992). Pathological gambling. *Psychiatric Annals, 22*(2), 72–78.

Rösner, S., Hackl-Herrwerth, A., Leucht, S., Lehert, P., Vecchi, S., & Soyka, M. (2010). Acamprosate for alcohol dependence. *Cochrane Database of Systematic Reviews*, Issue 9, Art. No. CD004332. https://doi.org/10.1002/14651858.CD004332.pub2

Ross, E., Graham, D., Money, K., & Stanwood, G. (2015). Developmental consequences of fetal exposure to drugs: What we know and what we still must learn. *Neuropsychopharmacology Reviews, 40*, 61–87.

Ross, E., Reisfield, G., Watson, M., Chronister, C., & Goldberger, B. (2012). Psychoactive "bath salts" intoxication with methylenedioxypyrovalerone. *Amercian Journal of Medicine, 125*(9), 854–858.

Ross, S., Bossis, A., Guss, J., Agin-Liebes, G., Malone, T., Cohen, B., ... Su, Z. (2016). Rapid and sustained symptom reduction following psilocybin treatment for anxiety and depression in patients with life-threatening cancer: A randomized controlled trial. *Journal of psychopharmacology, 30*(12), 1165–1180.

Rossow, I., & Norström, T. (2012). The impact of small changes in bar closing hours on violence: The Norwegian experience from 18 cities. *Addiction, 107*(3), 530–537.

Roterman, M. (2020). *What has changed since cannabis was legalized?* https://www150.statcan. gc.ca/n1/pub/82-003-x/2020002/article/00002-eng.htm

Roth, A., & Fonagy, P. (2005). *What works for whom? A critical review of psychotherapy research.* Guilford Press.

Roth, B., Gibbons, S., Arunotayanun, W., Huang, X., Setola, V., Treble, R., & Iversen, L. (2013). The ketamine analogue methoxetamine and 3- and 4-nethoxy analogues of phencyclidine are high affinity and selective ligands for the glutamate NMDA receptor. *PLoS One, 8*(3), e59334.

Rothenberg, J., Sullivan, M., Church, S., Seracini, A., Collins, E., Kleber, H., & Nunes, E. (2002). Behavioral naltrexone therapy: An integrated treatment for opiate dependence. *Journal of Substance Abuse Treatment, 23*(4), 351–360.

Rotunda, R. J., Scherer, D. G., & Imm, P. S. (1995). Family systems and alcohol misuse: Research on the effects of alcoholism on family functioning and effective family interventions. *Professional Psychology: Research and Practice, 26*(1), 95–104.

Rowe, W., & Rapp, L. (2017). Supervised injection sites: Harm reduction and health promotion. In R. Csiernik & W. Rowe (Eds.), *Responding to the oppression of addiction: Canadian social work perspectives* (3rd ed., pp. 48–59). Canadian Scholars' Press.

Rugle, L. (1993). Initial thought on viewing pathological gambling from a physiological and intrapsychic structural perspective. *Journal of Gambling Studies, 9*(1), 3–16.

Ruisoto, P., & Contador, I. (2019). The role of stress in drug addiction. An integrative review. *Physiology and Behavior, 202*(1), 62–68.

Rush, B. (1823). *An inquiry into the effects of ardent spirits upon the human body and mind: With an account of the means of preventing, and of the remedies for curing them.* James Loring.

Rush, B., & Ogborne, S. (1992). Alcoholism treatment in Canada: History, current status, and emerging issues. In H. Klingemann, J.-P. Takala, & G. Hunt (Eds.), *Cure, care, or control: Alcoholism treatment in sixteen countries* (pp. 253–267). SUNY Press.

Russell, M. (1984). *Handbook of feminist therapy.* Springer Publishing.

Rutman, D., & Van Bibber, M. (2010). Parenting with fetal alcohol spectrum disorder. *International Journal of Mental Health and Addiction, 8*(3), 351–361.

Rydell, C., Caulkins, J., & Everingham, S. (1996). Enforcement or treatment? Modeling the relative efficacy of alternatives for controlling cocaine. *Operations Research, 44*(1), 1–9.

Ryding, F., & Kaye, L. (2018). "Internet addiction": A conceptual minefield. *International Journal of Mental Health and Addiction, 16*(1), 225–232.

Saal, D., Dong, Y., Bonci, A., & Malenka, R. (2003). Drugs of abuse and stress trigger: A common synaptic adaptation in dopamine neurons. *Neuron, 37*(4), 577–582.

Sachdev, R., Garg, D., & Singh, G. (2018). Nicotine replacement therapy—effective tool in smoking cessation: A short review. *Dental Science, 7*(7), 47–48.

Sachs, D. (2009). A psychological analysis of the 12 Steps of Alcoholics Anonymous. *Alcoholism Treatment Quarterly, 27*(2), 199–212.

Sacks, S., Skinner, D., Sacks, J., & Peck, A. (2002). *Manual for engaging homeless mentally ill chemical abusers in a modified TC shelter program.* National Development and Research Institutes.

Sagar, K. (2019). Smartphone Addiction: Nomophobia. *Asian Journal of Nursing Education and Research, 9*(4), 583–587.

Sah, S., Neupane, N., Pradhan, A., Shah, S., & Sharma, A. (2020). Prevalence of glue-sniffing among street children. *Nursing Open, 7*(1), 206–211.

St. Pierre, T., & Kaltreider, D. (1997). Strategies for involving parents of high-risk youth in drug prevention: A three-year longitudinal study in boys & girls clubs. *Journal of Community Psychology, 25*(5), 473–485.

Sale, E., Sambrano, S., Springer, J., & Turner, C. (2003). Risk protection and substance use in adolescents: A multi-site model. *Journal of Drug Education, 33*(1), 91–105.

Saleh, S., Vaughn, T., Levey, S., Fuortes, L., Uden-Holmen, T., & Hall, J. (2006). Cost-effectiveness of case management in substance abuse treatment. *Research on Social Work Practice, 16*(1), 38–47.

Salehi, L., & Alizadeh, L. (2018). Efficacy of a cognitive-behavioral relapse prevention model in the treatment of opioid dependence in Iran: A randomized clinical trial. *Shiraz E-Medical Journal, 19*(5), e14170.

Salling, M., & Martinez, D. (2016). Brain stimulation in addiction. *Neuropsychopharmacology, 41*(12), 2798–2890.

Salloum, I., Cornelius, J., Daley, D., Kirisci, L., & Himmelhoch, J. (2005). Efficacy of valproate maintenance in patients with bipolar disorder and alcoholism. *Archives of General Psychiatry, 62*(1), 37–45.

Salmon, R., & Salmon, S. (1977). The causes of heroin addiction: A review of the literature. *The International Journal of the Addictions, 12*(5), 679–696.

Samaan, Z. (2014). Testosterone suppression and methadone treatment in men and women treated for opioid dependence with methadone. *Journal of Child Psychology and Psychiatry, 38*(4), 457–469.

Sanches, M., & John, V. (2019). Treatment of love addiction: Current status and perspectives. *European Journal of Psychiatry, 33*(1), 38–44.

Sánchez-Borges, M., Martin, B., Muraro, A., Wood, R., Agache, I., Ansotegui, I., Casale, T., Fleisher, T., Hellins, P., Papadopoulos, N., Peden, D., Sublett, J., Tilles, S., & Rossenwasser, L. (2018). The importance of allergic disease in public health: An iCAALL statement. *World Allergy Organization Journal, 11*(1), 8.

Santamarina-Rubio, E., Perez, K., Ricart, I., Rodriguez-Sanz, A., Rodriguez-Martos, M., Brugal, T., … Suelves, J. (2009). Substance use among road traffic casualties admitted to emergency departments. *Injury Prevention, 15*(1), 87–94.

Santos, K., Palmini, A., Radziuk, A., Rotert, R., & Bastos, F. (2013). The impact of methylphenidate on seizure frequency and severity in children with attention-deficit–hyperactivity disorder and difficult-to-treat epilepsies. *Developmental Medicine & Child Neurology, 55*(7), 654–660.

Sargent, J., Beach, M., Adachi-Mejia, A., Gibson, J., Titus-Ernstoff, L., Carusi, C., … Dalton, M. (2005). Exposure to movie smoking: Its relation to smoking initiation among US adolescents. *Pediatrices, 116*(5), 1183–1191.

Sartor, C., Grant, J., Bucholz, K., Madden, P., Heath, A., Agrawal A., … Lynskey, M. (2009). Common genetic contributions to alcohol and cannabis use and dependence symptomatology. *Alcoholism: Clinical and Experimental Research, 34*(3), 545–554.

Satre, D., Leibowitz, A., Sterling, S., Lu, Y., Travis, A., & Weisner, C. (2016). A randomized clinical trial of Motivational Interviewing to reduce alcohol and drug use among patients with depression. *Journal of Consulting and Clinical Psychology, 84*(7), 571–579.

Saucier, G., & Goldberg, L. (1996). Evidence for the big five in analyses of familiar English personality adjectives. *European Journal of Personality, 10*(1), 61–77.

Scala, L., Muscatello, M., Pangallo, N., Bruno, A., & Zoccali, R. (2017). Neurobiological and psychopathological mechanisms underlying addiction-like behaviors: An overview and thematic synthesis. *Mediterranean Journal of Clinical Psychology, 5*(2), 1–31.

Schaps, E., DiBartolo, R., Moskowitz, J., Palley, C., & Churgin, S. (1981). A review of 127 drug abuse prevention program evaluations. *Journal of Drug Issues, 11*(1), 17–43.

Scheim, A. (2017). *Discrimination and health: Measurement and impacts on Ontario's transgender communities* [Doctoral dissertation, Wetsern University]. Electronic Thesis and Dissertation Repository, 4737. https://ir.lib.uwo.ca/etd/4737

Schembri, E. (2019). Are opioids effective in relieving neuropathic pain? *SN Comprehensive Clinical Medicine 1*(1), 30–46.

Schenk, S., Hunt, T., Klukowski, G., & Amit, Z. (1987a). Isolation housing decreases the effectiveness of morphine in the conditioned taste aversion paradigm. *Psychopharmacology, 92*(1), 48–51.

Schenk, S., Lacelle, G., Gorman, K., & Amit, Z. (1987b). Cocaine self-administration in rats influenced by environmental conditions: Implication for the etiology of drug abuse. *Neuroscience Letters, 81*(3), 227–231.

Schiff Jr., P. (2006). Ergot and its alkaloids. *American Journal of Pharmaceutical Education, 70*(5), 98.

Schilder, P. (1941). The psychogenesis of alcoholism. *Quarterly Journal of Studies on Alcoholism, 2*(3), 277–292.

Schiller, L. (1997). Rethinking stages of development in women's groups: Implications for practice. *Journal of Social Work with Groups, 20*(3), 3–19.

Schindler, A., Thomasius, R., Ack, P., Gemeinhardt, B., Kustner, U., & Echert, J. (2005). Attachment and substance use disorders: A review of the literature and a study of drug dependent adolescents. *Attachment and Human Development, 7*(3), 207–228.

Schinke, S., Di Noia, J., & Glassman, J. (2004). Computer-mediated intervention to prevent drug abuse and violence among high-risk youth. *Addictive Behaviors, 29*(1), 225–229.

Schinke, S., Orlandi, M., Botvin, G., Gilchrist, L., Trimble, J., & Locklear, V. (1988). Preventing substance abuse among American-Indian adolescents: A bicultural competence skills approach. *Journal of Counseling Psychology, 35*(1), 87–90.

Schinke, S., & Schwinn, T. (2005). Gender-specific computer-based interventions for preventing drug abuse among girls. *The American Journal of Drug and Alcohol Abuse, 31*(4), 609–616.

Schinke, S., & Schwinn, T. (2017). Computer-based prevention and intervention to reduce substance use in youth. *Current Addiction Reports, 4*(4), 410–421.

Schloesser, R., Huang, J., Klein, P., & Manj, H. (2007). Cellular plasticity cascades in the pathophysiology and treatment of bipolar disorder. *Neuropsychopharmacology, 33*(1), 110–133.

Schmidt, C. (1992). Changes in terminology for sexual disorders in DSM-IV. *Psychiatric Medicine, 10*(2), 247–255.

Schmidt, W., & Popham, R. (1978). The single distribution theory of alcohol consumption. *Journal of Studies on Alcohol, 39*(3), 400–419.

Schooler, N., Goldberg, S., Boothe, H., & Cole, J. (1967). One year after discharge: Community adjustment of schizophrenic patients. *American Journal of Psychiatry, 123*(8), 986–995.

Schutten, M., & Eijnden, R. (2003). *Alcohol and the workplace: A European comparative study on preventive and supportive measures for problem drinkers in their working environment.* European Commission on Employment and Social Affairs.

Schwarz, A. (2013, February 2). Drowned in a stream of prescriptions. *The New York Times.* http://www.nytimes.com/2013/02/03/us/concerns-about-adhd-practices-and-amphetamine-addiction.html?_r=0

Schwarzinger, M., Pollock, B., Hasan, O., Dufouil, C., & Rehm, J. (2018). Contribution of alcohol use disorders to the burden of dementia in France 2008–13: A nationwide retrospective cohort study. *Lancet Public Health, 3*(3), e124–e132. https://doi.org/10.1016/S2468-2667(18)30022-7

Scott, D., Gignac, M., Kronfli, R., Ocana, A., & Lorberg, G. (2016). Expert opinion and recommendations for the management of attention-deficit/hyperactivity disorder in correctional facilities. *Journal of Correctional Health Care, 22*(1), 46–61.

Scott, W., Kaiser, D., Othmer, S., & Sideroff, S. (2005). Effects of an EEG biofeedback protocol on a mixed substance abusing population. *American Journal of Drug and Alcohol Abuse, 31*(3), 455–469.

Scwinn, T., Schinke, P., Keller, B., & Hopkins, J. (2019). Two- and three-year follow-up from a gender-specific, web-based drug abuse prevention program for adolescent girls. *Addictive Behaviors, 93*(1), 86–92.

Secular Organization for Sobriety. (2014). *Who we are.* http://sossobriety.org/about.html

Segal, B., & Stewart, J. (1996). Substance use and abuse in adolescence: An overview. *Child Psychiatry and Human Development, 26*(4), 193–210.

Self-Help Canada. (1992). *Self-help groups in Canada.* Self-Help Canada.

Self-Help Clearinghouse of Toronto. (1991). *Directory of self-help/mutual aid groups in Metropolitan Toronto.* Self-Help Clearinghouse of Toronto.

Sessa, B. (2018). Why MDMA therapy for alcohol use disorder? And why now? *Neuropharmacology, 142,* 83–88.

Seto, A., Einarson, T., & Koren, G. (1997). Pregnancy outcome following first trimester exposure to antihistamines: Meta-analysis. *American Journal of Perinatology, 14*(3), 119–124.

Sewell, R., Halpern, J., & Pope Jr., H. (2006). Response of cluster headache to psilocybin and LSD. *Neurology, 66*(12), 1920–1922.

Seymour, R., & Smith, D. (2011). *The physician's guide to psychoactive drugs.* Routledge.

Shadur, J. (2013). Parent emotion socialization and emotion regulation in substance abusing families. *Alcoholism: Clinical & Experimental Research, 37.*

Shaham, Y., Alvares, K., Nespor, S., & Grunberg, N. (1992). Effect of stress on oral morphine and fenatyl self-administration in rats. *Pharmacology, Biochemistry, and Behavior, 41*(3), 615–619.

Shapiro, S., & Carlson, L. (2009). *The art and science of mindfulness: Integrating mindfulness into psychology and the helping professions.* American Psychological Association.

Sharma, M., & Branscum, P. (2010). Is Alcoholics Anonymous effective? *Journal of Alcohol & Drug Education, 54*(3), 3.

Sharma, R. (2016). Role of family relationship in child rearing of drug addiction afflicted vs. normal families. *Indian Journal of Health & Wellbeing, 7*(8), 807–809.

Sharp, B., & Chen, H. (2018). Neurogenetic determinants and mechanisms of addiction to nicotine and smoked tobacco. *European Journal of Neuroscience, 50*(3), 2164–2179. https://doi.org/10.1111/ejn.14171

Sharpe, L., & Tarrier, N. (1993). Towards a cognitive-behavioural theory of problem gambling. *British Journal of Psychiatry, 162*(3), 407–412.

Shell, A., & Firmin, M. (2017). Binge eating disorder and substance use disorder: A case for food addiction. *Psychological Studies, 62*(4), 370–376.

Shenassa, E. (2002). Delivering the goods: The importance of screening accuracy for effective community intervention and prevention. *Journal of Community Psychology, 30*(2), 197–210.

Shepard, D., Lwin, A., Barnett, N., Mastroleo, N., Colby, S., Gwaltney, C., & Monti, P. (2016). Cost-effectiveness of motivational intervention with significant others for patients with alcohol misuse. *Addiction, 111*(5), 832–839.

Shepard, J., & Carlson, J. (2003). An empirical evaluation of school-based prevention programs that involve parents. *Psychology in Schools, 40*(6), 641–656.

Shier, M., & Turpin, A. (2017). A multi-dimensional conceptual framework for trauma-informed practice in addictions programming. *Journal of Social Service Research, 43*(5), 609–623.

Shin, S., McDonald, S., & Conley, D. (2018). Patterns of adverse childhood experiences and substance use among young adults: A latent class analysis. *Addictive behaviors, 78*(2), 187–192.

Shope, J., Elliot, M., Raghunathan, T., & Waller, P. (2001). Long-term follow-up of a high school alcohol misuse prevention program's effect on students' subsequent driving. *Alcoholism: Clinical and Experimental Research, 25*(3), 403–410.

Short, M., Black, L., Smith, A., Wetterneck, C., & Wells, D. (2012). A review of Internet pornography use research: Methodology and content from the past 10 years. *Cyberpsychology, Behavior, and Social Networking, 15*(1), 13–23.

Shuckit, M. (1999). New findings on the genetics of alcoholism. *Journal of the American Medical Association, 281*(20), 1875–1876.

Shumway, S., Bradshaw, S., Harris, K., & Baker, A. (2013). Important factors of early addiction recovery and inpatient treatment. *Alcoholism Treatment Quarterly, 31*(1), 3–24.

Siciliano, C., Fordahl, S., & Jones, S. (2016). Cocaine self-administration produces long-lasting alterations in dopamine transporter responses to cocaine. *The Journal of Neuroscience, 36*(30), 7807–7816.

Siegal, H., Lane, D., Falck, R., Wang, J., Carlson, R., Rahman, A., & Chambers, D. (2001). Constructing a consensus-based prevention outcome measurement instrument. *Journal of Drug Education, 31*(2), 139–152.

Silverman, P. (1980). *Mutual aid groups.* Sage.

Simon, R., & West, R. (2015). Models of addiction and types of interventions: An integrative look. *International Journal of Alcohol and Drug Research, 4*(1), 13–20.

Singer, M. (2006). *Something dangerous: Emergent and changing illict drug use and community health.* Wavelength Press.

Singh, J., Fedgchin, M., Daly, E., Xi, L., Melman, C., De Bruecker, G., Tadic, A., Sienaert, P., Wiegand, F., Manji, H., Drevets, W., & Van Nueten, L. (2016). Intravenous esketamine in adult treatment-resistant depression: A double-blind, double-randomization, placebo-controlled study. *Biological Psychiatry, 80*(6), 424–431.

Singh, M., Keer, D., Klimas, J., Wood, E., & Werb, D. (2016). Topiramate for cocaine dependence: A systematic review and meta-analysis of randomized controlled trials. *Addiction, 111*(8), 1337–1346.

Single, E., Brewster, J., MacNeil, P., Hatcher, J., & Trainor, C. (1995). *Alcohol and drug use: Results from the 1993 General Social Survey.* Canadian Centre on Substance Abuse.

Sisson, R., & Azrin, N. (1986). Family-member involvement to initiate and promote treatment of problem drinking. *Journal of Behavior Therapy and Experimental Psychiatry, 17*(1), 15–21.

Siu, A., Fung, M., Cheung, P., Shea, C., & Lau, B. (2019). Vocational evaluation and vocational guidance for young people with a history of drug abuse. *Work, 62*(2), 327–336.

Skara, S., & Sussman, S. (2003). A review of 25 long-term adolescent tobacco and other drug use prevention program evaluations. *Preventive Medicine, 37*(5), 451–474.

Skinner, B. F. (1953). *Science and human behavior.* Free Press.

Skog, O. (1980). Total alcohol consumption: Rates of excessive use. *British Journal of Addictions, 75*(3), 133–145.

Slaker, M., Blacktop, J., & Sorg, B. (2016). Caught in the net: Perineuronal nets and addiction. *Neural Plasticity, 2016,* Article 7538208. https://doi.org/10.1155/2016/7538208

Sleiman, M., Logue, J., Montesinos, V., Russell, M., Litter, M., Gundel, L., & Destaillats, H. (2016). Emissions from electronic cigarettes: Key parameters affecting the release of harmful chemicals. *Environmental science & technology, 50*(17), 9644–9651.

Slemon, A., Jenkins, E., Haines-Saah, R., Daly, Z., & Jiao, S. (2019). "You can't chain a dog to a porch": A multisite qualitative analysis of youth narratives of parental approaches to substance use. *Harm Reduction Journal, 16*(1). doi.org/10.1186/s12954-019-0297-3

SMART Recovery. (2015). *Self management for addiction recovery.* http://www.smartrecovery.org/

Smart, R., Gray, G., Finley, J., & Carpen, R. (1977). A comparison of recidivism rates for alcohol detox residents referred to hospitals, halfway houses, and outpatient facilities. *American Journal of Drug and Alcohol Abuse, 4*(2), 223–232.

Smart, R., Storm, T., Baker, E., & Solursh, L. (1967). *Lysergic Acid Dietyhlamine in the treatment of alcoholism.* Addiction Research Foundation.

Smedslund, G., Berg, R., Hammerstrøm, K., Steiro, A., Leiknes, K., Dahl, H., & Karlsen, K. (2011). Motivational interviewing for substance abuse. *Cochrane Database of Systematic Reviews,* Issue 5, Art. No. CD008063. https://doi.org/10.1002/14651858.CD008063.pub2

Smith, R., & Feigenbaum, K. (2012). Maslow's intellectual betrayal of Ruth Benedict? *Journal of Humanistic Psychology, 53*(3), 307–321.

Snyder, L., Milici, F., Slater, M., Sun, H., & Strizhakova, Y. (2006). Effects of alcohol advertising exposure on drinking among youth. *Archives of Pediatrics & Adolescent Medicine, 160*(1), 18–24.

Snyder, S. (1977). Opiate receptors and internal opiates. *Scientific American, 236*(3), 44–56.

So, M., Bozzo, P., & Inoue, M. (2010). Safety of antihistamines during pregnancy and lactation. *Canadian Family Physician, 56*(5), 427–429.

Soar, K., Kimber, C., McRobbie, H., & Dawkins, L. (2019). Nicotine absorption from e-cigarettes over 12 months. *Addictive Behaviors, 91*(1), 102–105.

Sobeck, J., Abbey, A., & Agius, E. (2006). Lessons learned from implementing school-based substance abuse prevention curriculum. *Children and Schools, 28*(2), 77–85.

Sobell, M., & Sobell, L. (1973). Individualized behavior therapy for alcoholics. *Behavior Therapy, 4*(1), 49–72.

Sobell, M., & Sobell, L. (1974). Alternatives to abstinence: Time to acknowledge reality. *Addictions, 2*(1), 2–29.

Society for the Study of Addiction. (2016). *Novel psychoactive substances.* https://www.addiction-ssa.org/images/uploads/Clin_111_Novel_Psychoative_SubstancesupdatedAug16.pdf

Solomon, R., Richmond, J., & Usprich, S. (1989). *Overview of alcohol and drug law.* Addiction Research Foundation.

Southeast Asian Tobacco Control Alliance (2013). *Child labour in tobacco cultivation in the Asean region.* SEATCA.

Spas, J., & Weyandt, L. (2015). Alcohol and its effect on adolescent brain development and executive functioning: Some results from neuroimaging. *Journal of Alcohol and Drug Dependency, 3*(5). https://doi.org/10.4172/23296488.1000220

Specht, H., & Courtney, M. (1994). *Unfaithful angels: How social work has abandoned its mission.* Maxwell Macmillan Canada.

Special Advisory Committee on the Epidemic of Opioid Overdoses. (2019). *National report: Opioid-related harms in Canada.* Public Health Agency of Canada. https://health-infobase. canada.ca/substance-related-harms/opioids

Special Committee on Non-Medical Use of Drugs. (2002). *Policy for the new millennium: Working together to redefine Canada's drug strategy.* Public Works and Government Services Canada.

Spielmans, G., & Parry, P. (2010). From evidence-based medicine to marketing-based medicine: Evidence from internal industry documents. *Journal of Bioethical Inquiry, 7*(1), 13–29.

Spinella, M. (2001). *The psychopharmacology of herbal medicine: Plant drugs that alter mind, brain, and behavior.* MIT Press.

Spithoff, S. (2019). Addressing rising alcohol-related harms in Canada. *Canadian Medical Association Journal, 191*(29), E802–E803.

Spivack, A., & McKelvie, A. (2018). Entrepreneurship addiction: Shedding light on the manifestation of the "dark side" in work-behavior patterns. *Academy of Management Perspectives, 32*(3), 358–378.

Spoth, R., & Redmond, C. (2000). Research on family engagement in preventive interventions: Toward improved use of scientific findings in primary prevention practice. *Journal of Primary Prevention, 21*(2), 267–284.

Sproule, B. (2004). *Pharmacology and drug abuse* (2nd ed.). Centre on Addiction and Mental Health.

Sproule, B., Brands, B., Li, S., & Catz-Biro, L. (2009). Changing patterns in opioid addiction: Characterizing users of oxycodone and other opioids. *Canadian Family Physician, 55*(1), 68–69.

Srey, C., Maddux, J., & Chaudhri, N. (2015). The attribution of incentive salience to Pavlovian alcohol cues: A shift from goal-tracking to sign-tracking. *Frontiers of Behavioral Neuroscience, 9*, 54. https://doi.org/10.3389/fnbeh.2015.00054

Srisurapanont, M., & Jarusuraisin, N. (2005). Naltrexone for the treatment of alcoholism: A meta-analysis of randomized controlled trials. *International Journal of Neuropsychopharmacology, 8*(2), 267–280.

Srivastava, A., & Kahan, M. (2006). Buprenorphine: A potential new treatment option for opioid dependence. *Canadian Medical Association Journal, 174*(13), 1835.

Srivastava, R. (2008). The ABC (and DE) of cultural competence in clinical care. *International Journal of Human Rights in Healthcare, 1*(1), 27–33.

Stamou, V., Clerveaux, R., Stamou, L., Le Rocheleuil, S., Berejnoi, L., Romo, L., & Graziani, P. (2017). The therapeutic contribution of music in music-assisted systematic desensitization for substance addiction treatment: A pilot study. *Arts in Psychotherapy, 56*(1), 30–44.

Standing Committee on Health. (2016). *Report and recommendations on the opiate crisis in Canada.* Standing Committee on Health.

Standing Committee on National Health and Welfare. (1987). *Booze, pills and dope: Reducing substance abuse in Canada.* Queen's Printer for Canada.

Stanger, L., & Weber, L. (2018). *The definitive guide to addiction interventions: A collective strategy.* Routledge.

Stanton, C., & Hatsukami, D. (2019). Nicotine standards in the United States. *Nicotine and Tobacco Research, 21*(Supplement1), S1–S4.

Starcevic, V., & Aboujaoude, E. (2017). Internet gaming disorder, obsessive-compulsive disorder, and addiction. *Current Addiction Reports, 4*(3), 317–322.

Statistics Canada. (2019a). *Control and sale of alcoholic beverages, year ending March 31, 2018.* https://www150.statcan.gc.ca/n1/daily-quotidien/190423/dq190423a-eng.htm

Statistics Canada. (2019b). *Prevalence of cannabis consumption in Canada. Table 36-10-0597-01* https://www150.statcan.gc.ca/t1/tbl1/en/tv.action?pid=3610059701

Stein, M., Conti, M., Kenney, S., Anderson, B., Flori, J., Risi, M., & Bailey, G. (2017). Adverse childhood experience effects on opioid use initiation, injection drug use, and overdose among persons with opioid use disorder. *Drug and Alcohol Dependence, 179,* 325–329.

Stein, U., Greyer, H., & Hentscehl, H. (2001). Nutmeg (myristicin) poisoning: Report on a fatal case and a series of cases recorded by a poison information centre. *Forensic Science International, 118*(1), 87–90.

Steinglass, P. (1992). Family systems approaches to the alcoholic family. In S. Saitoh, P. Steinglass, & M. Schuckit (Eds.), *Alcoholism and the family* (pp. 155–171). Brunner/Mazel.

Stevens, A. (2010). *Drugs, crime and public health: The political economy of drug policy.* Routledge-Cavendish.

Stevens, M., Hubbard, E., & Leutwyler, H. (2019). Tools you'll have for the rest of your life: A qualitative evaluation of a fitness and vocational training program for substance use recovery. *Substance Use & Misuse, 55*(4), 628–635. https://doi.org/10.1080/10826084.2019.1691599

Stimson, G. (1995). AIDS and injecting drug use in the United Kingdom, 1987–1993: The policy response and the prevention of the epidemic. *Social Science Medicine, 41*(5), 699–716.

Stockwell, T., Bolt, E., & Hooper, J. (1986). Detoxification from alcohol at home managed by general practitioners. *British Medical Journal, 292*(6522). https://doi.org/10.1136/bmj.292.6522.733

Stockwell, T., Bolt, L., Milner, I., Pugh, P., & Young, I. (1990). Home detoxification for problem drinkers: Acceptability to clients, relatives, general practitioners and outcome after 60 days. *British Journal of Addiction, 85*(1), 61–70.

Stockwell, T., Pauly, B., Chow, C., Vallance, K., & Perkin, K. (2013). *Evaluation of a managed alcohol program in Vancouver, BC: Early findings and reflections on alcohol harm reduction* (CARBC Bulletin #9). University of Victoria.

Stockwell, T., Zhao, J., Macdonald, S., Vallance, K., Gruenwald, P., Ponicki, W., Holder, H., & Treno, A. (2011). Impact on alcohol-related mortality of a rapid rise in the density of private liquor outlets in British Columbia: A local area multi-level analysis. *Addiction, 106*(4), 768–776.

Stohl, M. (1988). The case of the missing gene: Hereditary protection against alcoholism. *Alcohol Health and Research World, 12*(4), 130–136.

Strasser, A., Lerman, C., Sanborn, P., Pickworth, W., & Feldman, E. (2007). New lower nicotine cigarettes can produce compensatory smoking and increased carbon monoxide exposure. *Drug and alcohol dependence, 86*(2–3), 294–300.

Stratton, K., Kwan, L., & Eaton, D. (Eds.). (2018). *Public health consequences of e-cigarettes.* The National Academy Press.

Strohschein, L. (2007). Prevalence of methylphenidate use among Canadian children following parental divorce. *Canadian Medical Journal, 176*(12), 1711–1714.

Stuart, P. (1998). Home detox reaches more women, older adults. *Addictions News for Professionals, 27*(2), 6.

Substance Abuse and Mental Health Services Administration (SAMHSA). (2013). *The DAWN report: Emergency department visits involving accidental ingestion of drugs by children aged 5 or younger.* SAMHSA.

Substance Abuse and Mental Health Services Administration. (2014). Concept of trauma and guidance for a trauma-informed approach. HHS Publication No. 14-4884 (SMA). SAMHSA.

Sue, D., Sue, D., Sue, D., & Sue, S. (2011). *Understanding abnormal behaviour* (10th ed.). Houghton Mifflin.

Sumnall, H., & Brotherhood, A. (2012). *Social reintegration and employment: Evidence and interventions for drug users in treatment* (No. 13). Publications Office of the European Union.

Sumnall, H., Woolfall, K., Cole, J., Mackridge, A., & McVeigh, J. (2008). Diversion and abuse of methylphenidate in light of new guidance. *British Medical Journal, 337*, a2287. https://doi.org/10.1136/bmj.a2287

Sun, H., Li, X., Chow, E., Li, T., Xian, Y., Lu, Y., … Zhang, L. (2015). Methadone maintenance treatment programme reduces criminal activity and improves social well-being of drug users in China: A systematic review and meta-analysis. *BMJ Open, 5*, e005997. https://doi.org/10.1136/bmjopen-2014-005997

Sundquist, J., Sjöstedt, C., Winkleby, M., Li, X., Kendler, K., & Sundquist, K. (2016). Neighborhood linking social capital as a predictor of drug abuse: A Swedish national cohort study. *Addictive Behaviors, 63*(1), 37–44.

Sussman, S., & Sussman, A. (2011). Considering the definition of addiction. *International Journal of Environmental Resarch and Public Health, 8*(10), 4025–4038.

Swanson, J., Arnold, L., Molina, B., Sibley, M., Hechtman, L., Hinshaw, S., … Nichols, Q. (2017). Young adult outcomes in the follow-up of the multimodal treatment study of attention-deficit/hyperactivity disorder: Symptom persistence, source discrepancy, and height suppression. *Journal of Child Psychology and Psychiatry, 58*(6), 663–678.

Syal, R. (2009, December 13). Drug money saved banks in global crisis, claims UN advisor. *The Guardian.* http://www.theguardian.com/global/2009/dec/13/drug-money-banks-saved-un-cfief-claims

Szabó, J., Tóth, S., & Pakai, A. (2014). Narrative group therapy for alcohol dependent patients. *International Journal of Mental Health and Addiction, 12*(4), 470–476.

Szasz, T. (1967). Alcoholism: A socio-ethical perspective. *Washburn Law Journal, 6,* 255–268.

Szasz, T. (2007). *The medicalization of everyday life.* Syracuse University Press.

Tabuchi, T., Fujiwara, T., Nakayama, T., Miyashiro, I., Tsukuma, H., Ozaki, K., & Kondo, N. (2015). Maternal and paternal indoor or outdoor smoking and the risk of asthma in their children: A nationwide prospective birth cohort study. *Drug and alcohol dependence, 147*(2), 103–108.

Tang, J., & Dani, J. (2009). Dopamine enables in vivo synaptic plasticity associated with the addictive drug nicotine. *Neuron, 63*(5), 673–682.

Tannenbaum, C., Paquette, A., Hilmer, S., Holroyd-Leduc, J., & Carnahan, R. (2012). A systemic review of amnestic and non-amnestic mild cognitive impairment induced by anticholinergic, antihistamine, GABAergic and opioid drugs. *Drugs and Aging, 29*(8), 639–658.

Tanner, G., Bordon, N., Conroy, S., & Best, D. (2011). Comparing methadone and Suboxone in applied treatment settings: The experiences of maintenance patients in Lanarkshire. *Journal of Substance Abuse, 16*(3), 171–178.

Tayler, P. (2003). *The heart of the community: The best of the Carnegie Community Newsletter.* New Star Books.

Ternes, J., & O'Brien, C. (1990). The opioids: Abuse liability and treatments for dependence. *Advances in Alcohol and Substance Abuse, 9*(1–2), 27–45.

Tervalon, M., & Murray-Garcia, J. (1998). Cultural humility versus cultural competence: A critical distinction in defining physician training outcomes in multicultural education. *Journal of Health Care for the Poor and Underserved, 9*(2), 117–125.

Thacker, E., O'Reilly, S., Weisskopf, M., Chen, H., Schwarzschild, M., McCullough, M., ... Ascherio, A. (2007). Temporal relationship between cigarette smoking and risk of Parkinson disease. *Neurology, 68*(10), 764–768.

Thapar, A., Fowler, T., Rice, F., Scourfield, J., van den Bree, M., Thomas, H., ... Hay, D. (2003). Maternal smoking during pregnancy and attention deficit hyperactivity disorder symptoms in offspring. *American Journal of Psychiatry, 160*(11), 1985–1989.

Thomas, G. (2005). *Harm reduction policies and programs for persons involved in the criminal justice system.* Canadian Centre on Substance Abuse.

Thomas, J. (1989). An overview of marital and family treatments with substance abusing populations. *Alcoholism Treatment Quarterly, 6*(3–4), 91–102.

Thombs, D. (2009). Moral model. In G. Fisher & N. Roget (Eds.), *Encyclopedia of substance abuse prevention, treatment, & recovery* (pp. 561–562). Sage.

Thomson, J., Draguleasa, M., & Tan, M. (2015). Flowers with caffeinated nectar receive more pollination. *Arthropod-Plant Interactions, 9*(1), 1–7.

Thorberg, F., & Lyvers, M. (2006). Attachment, fear of intimacy and differentiation of self among clients in substance disorder treatment facilities. *Addictive Behaviors, 31*(4), 732–737.

Thornton, C., Gottheil, E., Weinstein, S., & Kerachsky, R. (1998). Patient-treatment matching in substance abuse: Drug addiction severity. *Journal of Substance Abuse Treatment, 15*(6), 505–511.

Thorsteinsson, E., & Davey, L. (2014). Adolescents' compulsive Internet use and depression: A longitudinal study. *Open Journal of Depression, 3*(1), 13–17.

Throsby, K. (2019). Pure, white and deadly: Sugar addiction and the cultivation of urgency. *Food, Culture & Society,* 1–19.

Ticku, M. (1990). Alcohol and GABA-benzodiazepine receptor function. *Annals of Medicine, 22*(4), 241–246.

Timmons, S. (2010). A Christian faith-based recovery theory: Understanding God as sponsor. *Journal of Religion and Health, 51*(4), 1152–1164.

Tinghog, M. (2014). The workplace as an arena for universal alcohol prevention—what can we expect? An evaluation of a short educational intervention. *Work, 47*(4), 543–551.

Tintera, J. (1966). Hypoglycaemia and alcoholism. *Journal of the American Geriatric Society, 16*(2), 28–34.

Tobler, N. (1993*). Meta-analysis of adolescent drug prevention programs: Results of the 1993 meta-analysis.* State University of New York.

Tobler, N. (2000). Lessons learned. *The Journal of Primary Prevention, 20*(4), 261–274.

Tobler, N., & Stratton, H. (1997). Effectiveness of school-based drug prevention programs: A meta-analysis of the research. *Journal of Primary Prevention, 18*(1), 71–128.

Todd, T. (1991). Evolution of family therapy approaches to substance abuse. *Contemporary Family Therapy, 13*(5), 471–495.

Tomie, A., Grimes, K., & Pohorecky, L. (2008). Behavioral characteristics and neurobiological substrates shared by Pavlovian sign-tracking and drug abuse. *Brain Research Reviews, 58*(1), 121–135.

Toomey, T., Williams, C., Perry, C., Murray, D., Dudovitz, B., & Veblen-Mortenson, S. (1996). An alcohol primary prevention program for parents of 7th graders: The Amazing Alternatives! Home Program. *Journal of Child and Adolescent Substance Abuse, 5*(4), 35–53.

Topalli, V. (2005). When good is bad: An explanation of neutralization theory. *Criminology, 43*(3), 797–827.

Tragler, G., Caulkins, J., & Feichtinger, G. (2001). Optimal dynamic allocation of treatment and enforcement in illicit drug control. *Operations Research, 49*(3), 352–362.

Trauma Informed Oregon. (2016). Roadmap to trauma informed care. https://traumainformedoregon.org/roadmap-trauma-informed-care/

Trescot, A., Datta, S., Lee, M., & Hansen, H. (2008). Opioid pharmacology. *Pain Physician, 11*(2S), S133–S153.

Trimpey, J. (1992). *The small book.* Delacorte Press.

Tuckman, B., & Jensen, M. (1977). Stages of small-group development revisited. *Groups and Organizational Studies, 2*(4), 419–427.

Turner, E., Matthews, A., Linardardatos, E., Tell, R., & Rosthenthal, R. (2008). Selective publication of antidepressant effectiveness and its influence on apparent efficacy. *New England Journal of Medicine, 358*(3), 252–260.

Turner, W. (2000). Cultural considerations in family-based primary prevention programs in drug abuse. *Journal of Primary Prevention, 21*(2), 285–303.

Turner, W., Wieling, E., & Allen, W. (2004). Developing culturally effective family-based research programs: Implications for family therapists. *Journal of Marital and Family Therapy, 30*(3), 257–270.

UKATT Research Team. (2005). Cost effectiveness of treatment for alcohol problems: Findings from the randomised UK alcohol treatment trial. *British Medical Journal, 331*(7516), 544. https://doi.org/10.1136/bmj.331.7516.544

UKATT Research Team. (2008). UK alcohol treatment trial: Client-treatment matching effects. *Addiction, 103*(2), 228–238.

Ulmer, R. (1977). Behaviour therapy: A promising drug abuse treatment and research approach of choice. *International Journal of the Addictions, 12*(6), 777–784.

Unger, J., Baezconde-Garbanati, L., Shakib, S., Palmer, P., Nezami, E., & Mora, J. (2004). A cultural psychology approach to "drug abuse" prevention. *Substance Use & Misuse, 39*(10–12), 1779–1820.

United Nations Office for the Coordination of Humanitarian Affairs. (2008). *Cambodia: Ecstasy labs destroying forest wilderness.* United Nations.

United Nations Office on Drug and Crime. (2004). *Schools: School-based education for drug abuse prevention.* United Nations.

United Nations Office on Drugs and Crime. (2005). *Drug treatment courts work!* United Nations. http://www.unodc.org/pdf/drug_treatment_courts_flyer.pdf

United Nations Office on Drugs and Crime. (2009). *Guide to implementing family skills training programmes for drug abuse prevention.* United Nations.

United Nations Office on Drugs and Crime. (2011). *Estimating illicit financial flows resulting from drug trafficking and other transnational organized crimes.* United Nations.

United Nations Office on Drugs and Crime. (2013). *The challenge of new psychoactive drugs.* United Nations.

United Nations Office on Drugs and Crime. (2017). *Global synthetic drugs assessment.* United Nations.

United Nations Office on Drugs and Crime. (2019). *2019 world drug report.* United Nations.

United States Department of Health and Human Services. (2014). *National survey on drug use and health, 2013.* Inter-university Consortium for Political and Social Research.

United States Department of Health and Human Services. (2016a). *Facing addiction in America: The Surgeon General's report on alcohol, drugs and health.* United States Department of Health and Human Services.

United States Department of Health and Human Services. (2016b). *E-cigarette use among youth and young adults. A report of the Surgeon General.* United States Department of Health and Human Services.

United States Department of Justice. (2003a). *Rohypnol (flunitrazepam).* National Drug Intelligence Center.

United States Department of Justice. (2003b). *GBL (gamma butyrolactone).* National Drug Intelligence Center.

United States Department of Justice. (2003c). *Methamphetamine.* National Drug Intelligence Center.

United States Department of State. (2019). *International narcotics control strategy report.* United States Department of State.

United States National Cancer Institute and World Health Organization. (2016). *The economics of tobacco and tobacco control.* Department of Health and Human Services.

Uzarska, A., Czerwiński, S., & Atroszko, P. (2019). Shopping addiction is driven by personal focus rather than social focus values but to the exclusion of achievement and self-direction. *International Journal of Mental Health and Addiction.* https://doi.org/10.1007/s11469-019-00193-z

Vaaramo, K., Puljula, J., Tetri, S., Juvela, S., & Hillbom, M. (2012). Mortality of harmful drinkers increased after reduction of alcohol prices in Northern Finland: A 10-year follow-up of head tauma subjects. *Neuroepidemiology, 39*(2), 156–162.

Vakalahi, H. (2001). Adolescent substance use and family-based risk and protective factors: A literature review. *Journal of Drug Education, 31*(1), 29–46.

Valverde, M. (1998). *Diseases of the will: Alcohol and dilemmas of freedom.* Cambridge University Press.

van Boekel, L., Brouwers, E., Van Weeghel, J., & Garretsen, H. (2013). Stigma among health professionals towards patients with substance use disorders and its consequences for healthcare delivery: Systematic review. *Drug and Alcohol Dependence, 131*(1–2), 23–35.

van den Berg, N. (1995). *Feminist practice in the 21st century.* National Association of Social Workers Press.

van den Bree, M., Johnson, E., & Neale, M. (1998). Genetic analysis of diagnostic systems of alcoholism in males. *Biological Psychiatry, 43*(2), 139–145.

van der Vorst, H., Engels, R., & Burk, W. (2010). Do parents and best friends influence the normative increase in adolescents' alcohol use at home and outside the home? *Journal of Studies on Alcohol and Drugs, 71*(2), 105–114.

van Ours, J., & Williams, J. (2009). Cannabis use and mental health problems. *VOX: CEPR's Policy Portal.* http://www.voxeu.org/article/cannabis-use-and-mental-health-problems

Van Skike, C., Goodlett, C., & Matthews, D. (2019). Acute alcohol and cognition: Remembering what it causes us to forget. *Alcohol, 79*(1), 105–125.

van Well, J., Spronk, D., Kuypers, K., Theunissen, E., Toennes, S., Verkes, R., & Ramaekers, J. (2015). Psychedelic symptoms of cannabis and cocaine use as a function of trait impulsivity. *Journal of Psychopharmacology, 29*(3), 324–334.

van Wormer, R., & van Wormer, K. (2009). Non-abstinence-based supportive housing for persons with co-occurring disorders: A human rights perspective. *Journal of Progressive Human Services, 20*(2), 152–165.

Vanderplasschen, W., Rapp, R., Wolf, J., & Broekaeert, E. (2004). The development and implementation of case management for substance use disorders in North America and Europe. *Psychiatric Services, 55*(8), 913–922.

Vandrey, R., Budney, A., Hughes, J., & Liguori, A. (2008). A within subject comparison of withdrawal symptoms during abstinence from cannabis, tobacco and both substances. *Drug and Alcohol Dependence, 92*(1–3), 48–54.

Vasilaki, E., Hosier, S., & Cox, W. (2006). The efficacy of motivational interviewing as a brief intervention for excessive drinking: A meta-analytic review. *Alcohol and Alcoholism, 41*(3), 328–335.

Vedel, E., Emmelkamp, P., & Schippers, G. (2008). Individual cognitive-behavioral therapy and behavioral couples therapy in alcohol use disorders: A comparative evaluation in community-based addiction treatment centers. *Psychotherapy and Psychosomatics, 77*(5), 280–288.

Vega, V. (2017). Music therapy with addiction and co-occurring disorders. *Music and Medicine, 9*(1), 45–49.

Verdejo-Garcia, A., Chong, T., Stout, J., Yücel, M., & London, E. (2018). Stages of dysfunctional decision-making in addiction. *Pharmacology Biochemistry and Behavior, 164*(1), 99–105.

Vermeulen-Smit, E., Verdurmen, J., Engels, R., & Vollebergh, W. (2015). The role of general parenting and cannabis-specific parenting practices in adolescent cannabis and other illicit drug use. *Drug and Alcohol Dependence, 147*(2), 222–228.

Vertefeuille, J., Marx, A., Tun, W., Huettner, S., Strathdee, S., & Vlahov, D. (2000). Decline in self-reported high-risk injection-related behaviors among HIV-seropositive participants in the Baltimore needle exchange programs. *AIDS & Behavior, 4*(4), 381–388.

Victor, S., Glenn, C., & Klonsky, E. (2012). Is non-suicidal self-injury an "addiction"? A comparison of craving in substance use and non-suicidal self-injury. *Psychiatry research, 197*(1–2), 73–77.

Victorian Aboriginal Child Care Agency. (2008). *Aboriginal cultural competence framework.* Victorian Government Department of Human Services.

Vieweg, W., Lipps, W., & Fernandez, A. (2005). Opioids and methadone equivalents for clinicians. *The Primary Care Companion to the Journal of Clinical Psychiatry, 7*(3), 86–88.

Vimpani, G. (2005). Getting the mix right: Family, community and social policy interventions to improve outcomes for young people at risk of substance misuse. *Drug and Alcohol Review, 24*(2), 111–125.

Voepel-Lewis, T., Boyd, C., McCabe, S., Zikmund-Fisher, B., Malviya, S., Grant, J., Weber, M., & Tait, A. (2018). Deliberative prescription opioid misuse among adolescents and emerging adults: Opportunities for targeted interventions. *The Journal of Adolescent Health, 63*(5), 594–600.

Vogel, W. (2017). A qualitative and semi-quantitative combined theory of addiction. *Medical Research Archives, 5*(9), 1–19.

Volkow, N., & Morales, M. (2015). The brain on drugs: From reward to addiction. *Cell, 162*(4), 712–725.

Wagenaar, A., Salois, M., & Komro, K. (2009). Effects of beverage alcohol price and tax levels on drinking: A meta-analysis of 1003 estimates from 112 studies. *Addiction, 104*(2), 179–190.

Wagenaar, A., Tobler, A., & Komro, K. (2010). Effects of alcohol tax and price policies on morbidity and mortality: A systematic review. *American Journal of Public Health, 100*(11), 2270–2278.

Wagner, E., Tubman, E., & Gil, A. (2004). Implementing school-based substance abuse interventions: Methodological dilemmas and recommended solutions. *Addiction, 99*(S2), 106–119.

Wahba, M., & Bridgewell, L. (1976). Maslow reconsidered: A review of research on the need hierarchy theory. *Organizational Behavior and Human Performance, 15*(2), 212–240.

Waiters, S., Clark, M., Gingerich, R., & Meitzer, M. (2007). *Motivating offenders to change: A guide for probation and parole.* National Institute of Correction.

Wakefield, J. (2020, September 17). Addicted: How meth hooked Edmonton—again. *Edmonton Journal.* https://edmontonjournal.com/news/crime/addicted-how-meth-hooked-edmonton-again

Waldorf, D., Reinarman, C., & Murphy, S. (1991). *Cocaine changes: The experience of using and quitting.* Temple University Press.

Waldron, H., & Kaminer, Y. (2004). On the learning curve: The emerging evidence supporting cognitive-behavioral therapies for adolescent substance abuse. *Addiction, 99*(2), 93–105.

Walker, D., Stephens, R., Towe, S., Banes, K., & Roffman, R. (2015). Maintenance check-ups following treatment for cannabis dependence. *Journal of Substance Abuse Treatment, 56*(1), 11–15.

Waller, D., & Mahony, J. (Eds.). (2002). *Treatment of addiction: Current issues for arts therapists.* Routledge.

Walsh, S., Nuzzo, P., Lofwall, M., & Holtman Jr., J. (2008). The relative abuse liability of oral oxycodone, hydrocodone and hydromorphone assessed in prescription opioid abusers. *Drug and Alcohol Dependence, 98*(3), 191–202.

Walter, J., & Peller, J. (1992). *Becoming solution-focused in brief therapy.* Taylor & Francis.

Walters, G. (2000). Spontaneous remission from alcohol, tobacco, and other drug abuse: Seeking quantitative answers to qualitative questions. *American Journal of Drug and Alcohol Abuse, 26*(3), 443–460.

Walton, M., & Hall, M. (2016). The effects of employment interventions on addiction treatment outcomes: A review of the literature. *Journal of Social Work Practice in the Addictions, 16*(4), 358–384.

Wampold, B., Mondin, G., Moody, M., Stich, F., Benson, K., & Ahn, H. (1997). A meta-analysis of outcome studies comparing bona fide psychotherapies: Empirically, "All must have prizes." *Psychological Bulletin, 122*(3), 203–215.

Wand, G., Mangold, D., El Deiry, S., McCaul, M., & Hoover, D. (1998). Family history of alcoholism and hypothalamic opioidergic activity. *Annals of General Psychiatry, 55*(12), 1114–1119.

Wang, G., Volkow, N., Logan, J., Pappas, N., Wong, C., Zhu, W., & Fowler, J. (2001). Brain dopamine and obesity. *Lancet, 357*(9253), 354–357.

Wang, G., Wiers, C., Shumay, E., Tomasi, D., Yuan, K., Wong, C., Logan, G., Fowler, J., & Volkow, N. (2019). Expectation effects on brain dopamine responses to methylphenidate in cocaine use disorder. *Translational Psychiatry, 9*(1), 1–11.

Wang, P., Wang, X., Wu, Y., Xie, X., Wang, X., Zhao, F., Ouyang, M., & Lei, L. (2018). Social networking sites addiction and adolescent depression: A moderated mediation model of rumination and self-esteem. *Personality and Individual Differences, 127*, 162–167.

Wang, T., Moosa, S., Dallapiazza, R., Elias, W., & Lynch, W. (2018). Deep brain stimulation for the treatment of drug addiction. *Neurosurgical Focus, 45*(2), E11.

Warner, C., Bobo, W., Warner, C., Reid, S., & Rachal, J. (2006). Antidepressant discontinuation syndrome. *American Family Physician, 74*(3), 449–456.

Watt, W., Saunders, S., Chaudron, C., & Soden, T. (1988). *Detox in Ontario*. Addiction Research Foundation.

Watters, E. (2010). *Crazy like us: The globalization of the American psyche*. Free Press.

Wechsler, H., Lee, J., Kuo, M., & Lee, H. (2000). College binge drinking in the 1990s: A continuing problem—results of the Harvard School of Public Health 1999 College Alcohol Study. *Journal of American College Health, 48*(5), 199–210.

Weegman, M. (2002). Motivational interviewing and addiction: A psychodynamic appreciation of psychodynamic practice. *Psychodynamic Practice, 8*(2), 179–185.

Weinberg, B., & Bealer, B. (2001). *The world of caffeine: The science and culture of the world's most popular drug*. Routledge.

Weldy, D. (2010). Research letter: Risks of alcoholic energy drinks for youth. *Journal of the American Board of Family Medicine, 24*(4), 555–558.

Wellman, R., Wilson, K., O'Loughlin, E., Dugas, E., Montreuil, A., & O'Loughlin, J. (2018). Secondhand smoke exposure and depressive symptoms in children: A longitudinal study. *Nicotine & Tobacco Research, 22*(1), 32–39.

Werb, D., Kerr, T., Zhang, R., Montaner, J., & Wood, E. (2010). Methamphetamine use and malnutrition among street-involved youth. *Harm Reduction Journal, 7*(5). https://doi.org/10.1186/1477-7517-7-5

Werb, D., Rowell, G., Guyatt, G., Kerr, T., Montaner, J., & Wood, E. (2010). *Effect of drug law enforcement on drug-related violence: Evidence from a scientific review*. International Centre for Science in Drug Policy.

Werch, C., Owen, D., Carlson, J., DiClemente, C., Edgemon, P., & Moore, M. (2001). One-year follow-up results from the STARS for Families alcohol prevention program. *Health Education Research Theory & Practice, 18*(1), 74–87.

West, S., & O'Neal, K. (2004). Project D.A.R.E outcome effectiveness revisited. *American Journal of Public Health, 94*(6), 1027–1029.

Wested. (2007). *California healthy kids survey*. State of California.

Westover, N., & Nakonezny, P. (2010). Aortic dissection in young adults who abuse amphetamines. *American Heart Journal, 160*(2), 315–321.

Wettlaufer, A., Florica, R. O., Asbridge, M., Beirness, D., Brubacher, J., Callaghan, R., ... McKiernan, A. (2017). Estimating the harms and costs of cannabis-attributable collisions in the Canadian provinces. *Drug and alcohol dependence, 173*, 185–190.

Whitaker, R. (2005). Anatomy of an epidemic: Psychiatric drugs and the astonishing rise of mental illness in America. *Ethical Human Psychology and Psychiatry, 7*(1), 23–35.

White Bison. (2002). *The red road to wellbriety in the Native American way*. White Bison.

White, D., & Pitts, M. (1998). Educating young people about drugs: A systematic review. *Addiction, 93*(10), 1475–1487.

White, I., Altmann, D., & Nanchahal, K. (2002). Alcohol consumption and mortality: Modelling risks for men and women at different ages. *British Medical Journal, 325*. https://doi.org/10.1136/bmj.325.7357.191

White, M. (1995). *Re-authoring lives: Interviews and essays*. Dulwich Centre Publications.

White, M., & Epston, D. (1990). *Narrative means to therapeutic ends*. W. W. Norton.

White, V., Azar, D., Faulkner, A., Coomber, K., Durkin, S., Livingston, M., Chikritzhs, T., Room, R., & Wakefield, M. (2017). Adolescents' exposure to paid alcohol advertising on television and their alcohol use: Exploring associations during a 13-year period. *Addiction, 112*(10), 1742–1751.

White, W. (2012). *The history of Secular Organizations for Sobriety—Save Our Selves: An interview with James Christopher*. http://www.williamwhitepapers.com/pr/James%20Christopher%20Interview%202012.pdf

White, W., Boyle, M., & Loveland, D. (2002). Alcoholism/addiction as chronic disease: From rhetoric to clinical reality. *Alcoholism Treatment Quarterly, 20*(3), 107–129.

White, W., & McLellan, A. (2008). Addiction as a chronic disease: Key messages for clients, families and referral sources. *Counselor, 9*(3), 24–33.

White, W., & Miller, W. (2007). The use of confrontation in addiction treatment: History, science and time for change. *Counselor, 8*(4), 12–30.

Whitehead, P., & Harvey, C. (1974). Explaining alcoholism: An empirical test and reformulation. *Journal of Health and Social Behavior, 15*(1), 57–64.

Whitten, L. (2005). Disulfiram reduces cocaine abuse. *NIDA Research Findings, 20*(2), 1–4.

Wicki, M., Kuntsche, E., & Gmel, G. (2010). Drinking at European universities? A review of students' alcohol use. *Addictive Behaviors, 35*(11), 913–924.

Wieland, D. (2019). Food addiction: A new mental health disorder? *Journal of Psychosocial Nursing and Mental Health Services, 57*(12), 3–5.

Wieland, D., Halter, M., & Levine, C. (2012). Bath salts: They are not what you think. *Journal of Psychosocial Nursing and Mental Health Services, 50*(2), 17–21.

Wild, C., Wolfe, J., Wang, J., & Ohinmaa, A. (2014). *Gap analysis of public mental health and addictions programs (GAP-MAP) final report*. Government of Alberta.

Wildman, R. (1997). *Gambling: An attempt at an integration*. Wynne Resources.

Wilkinson, A. (1998). Addiction is a brain disease, but we need more research. *The Journal, 27*(4), 5.

Wilkinson, A., Spitz, M., Prokhorov, A., Bondy, M., Shete, S., & Sargent, J. (2009). Exposure to smoking imagery in the movies and experimenting with cigarettes among Mexican heritage youth. *Cancer Epidemiology, Biomarkers & Prevention, 18*(12), 3435–3443.

Williams, S. (2001). Introducing an in-patient treatment for alcohol detoxification into a community setting. *Journal of Clinical Nursing, 10*(5), 635–642.

Wills, F., & Sanders, D. (2013). *Cognitive behaviour therapy: Foundations for practice.* Sage.

Wilsnack, S. (1973). Sex role identity in female alcoholism. *Journal of Abnormal Psychology, 82*(2), 253–261.

Wilsnack, S. (1974). The effects of social drinking on women's fantasy. *Journal of Personality, 42*(1), 43–61.

Wilsnack, S., & Beckman, L. (1984). *Alcohol problems in women.* Guilford Press.

Wilson, G. (1988). Alcohol use and abuse: A social learning analysis. In C. Chaudron & D. Wilkinson (Eds.), *Theories on addiction* (pp. 239–287). Addiction Research Foundation.

Wilson, G. (2000). Eating disorders and addiction. *Drugs and Society, 15*(1–2), 87–101.

Winn, J., Shealy, S., Kropp, G., Felkins-Dohm, D., Gonzales-Nolas, C., & Francis, E. (2013). Housing assistance and case management: Improving access to substance use disorder treatment for homeless veterans. *Psychological Services, 10*(2), 233–240.

Witbrodt, J., Bond, J., Kaskutas, L., Weisner, C., Jaeger, G., Pating, D., & Moore, C. (2007). Day hospital and residential addiction treatment: Randomized and nonrandomized managed care clinics. *Journal of Consulting and Clinical Psychology, 75*(6), 947–959.

Witkiewitz, K., & Bowen, S. (2010). Depression, craving, and substance use following a randomized trial of mindfulness-based relapse prevention. *Journal of Consulting and Clinical Psychology, 78*(3), 362–374.

Witkiewitz, K., Pearson, M. R., Hallgren, K. A., Maisto, S. A., Roos, C. R., Kirouac, M., Wilson, A., Montes, K., & Heather, N. (2017). Who achieves low risk drinking during alcohol treatment? An analysis of patients in three alcohol clinical trials. *Addiction, 112*(12), 2112–2121.

Woloshin, S., Schwartz, L., & Welch, H. (2008). The risk of death by age, sex and smoking status in the United States: Putting health risks in context. *Journal of the National Cancer Institute, 100*, 845–853.

Wolter, M., Huff, E., Speigel, T., Winters, B., & Leri, F. (2019). Cocaine, nicotine, and their conditioned contexts enhance consolidation of object memory in rats. *Learning & Memory, 26*(2) 46–55.

Woo, A. (2014, November 22). Vancouver addicts soon to receive prescription heroin. *The Globe and Mail.* http://www.theglobeandmail.com/news/british-columbia/vancouver-heroin-addicts-authorized-to-get-drug/article21717642/

Wood, E., Kerr, T., Montaner, J., Strathdee, S., Wodak, A., Hankins, C., ... Tyndall, M. (2004a). Rationale for evaluating North America's first medically supervised safer-injecting facility. *The Lancet Infectious Diseases, 4*(5), 301–306.

Wood, E., Kerr, T., Small, W., Li, K., Marsh, D., Montaner, J., & Tyndall, M. (2004b). Changes in public order after the opening of a medically supervised safer injecting facility for illicit injection drug users. *Canadian Medical Association Journal, 171*(7), 731–734.

Wood, E., Tyndall, M., Lai, C., Montaner, J., & Kerr, T. (2006). Impact of a medically supervised safer injecting facility on drug dealing and other drug-related crime. *Substance Abuse Treatment, Prevention, and Policy, 1*(13). https://doi.org/10.1186/1747-597X-1-13

Woods, J. (1978). Behavioral pharmacology of drug self-administration. In M. Lipton, A. DiMascio, & K. Killam (Eds.), *Psychopharmcology: A generation of progress* (pp. 595–607). Raven Publishing.

Woods, J., & Schuster, C. (1971). Opiates as reinforcing stimuli. In T. Thompson & R. Pickens (Eds.), *Stimulus properties of drugs* (pp. 163–175). Appleton-Century-Crofts.

Woody, G. (2003). Research findings on psychotherapy of addictive disorders. *The American Journal on Addictions, 12*(1), 19–26.

World Economic Forum. (2015). *State of the illicit economy: Briefing paper.* World Economic Forum.

World Health Organization. (1964). *Thirteenth report of the WHO Expert Committee on Addiction-Producing Drugs.* WHO.

World Health Organization. (2014). *Letter from the World Society of Intravenous Anaesthesia to the WHO Expert Committee on Drug Dependence (agenda item 6.2).* Thirty-sixth WHO Expert Committee on Drug Dependence.

World Health Organization. (2017a). *WHO report on the global tobacco epidemic.* WHO.

World Health Organization. (2017b). *Depression and other common mental disorders.* WHO.

World Health Organization. (2017c). *The bill China cannot afford: Health, economic and social costs of China's tobacco epidemic.* WHO.

World Health Organization. (2019a). *International classification of diseases* (11th rev.). https://icd.who.int/en

World Health Organization. (2019b). *Tobacco.* https://www.who.int/news-room/fact-sheets/detail/tobacco

World Health Organization. (2019c). *WHO report on the global tobacco epidemic: Offer help to quit tobacco use.* WHO.

Wu, S., Leung, A., & Yew, D. (2016). Acupuncture for detoxification in treatment of opioid addiction. *East Asian Archives of Psychiatry, 26*(2), 70–76.

Xiao, S., Yang, M., Zhou, L., & Hao, W. (2015). Transition of China's drug policy: Problems in practice. *Addiction, 110*(2), 193–194.

Yalom, I. (2005). *The theory and practice of group psychotherapy* (5th ed.). Basic Books.

Yang, Y., Perkins, D. R., & Stearns, A. E. (2019). "I started to feel better now": Qualitative findings from client narratives on early recovery in inpatient substance use treatment. *International Journal of Mental Health and Addiction, 18*, 1048–1066. https://doi.org/10.1007/s11469-019-00107-z

Yeager, K., & Roberts, A. (2003). Differentiating among stress, acute stress disorder, crisis episodes, trauma, and PTSD: Paradigm and treatment goals. *Brief Treatment & Crisis Intervention, 3*(1), 3–25.

Young, L. (2007). Sowing the seeds of health: Plants and clients thrive with horticultural therapy. *Crosscurrents, 10*(4), 4–5.

Young-Wolff, K., Enoch, M., &. Prescott, C. (2011). The influence of gene–environment interactions on alcohol consumption and alcohol use disorders: A comprehensive review. *Clinical Psychology Review, 31*(5), 800–816.

Zack, M., George, R., & Clark, L. (2019). Dopaminergic signaling of uncertainty and the aetiology of gambling addiction. *Progress in Neuro-Psychopharmacology and Biological Psychiatry, 99.* https://doi.org/10.1016/j.pnpbp.2019.109853

Zakzanis, K., & Young, D. (2001). Esctasy use and long term memory loss. *Neurology, 56*(7), 966–969.

Zalewska-Kaszubska, J., & Obzejta, D. (2004). Use of low-energy laser as adjunct treatment of alcohol addiction. *Lasers in Medical Science, 19*(2), 100–104.

Zaric, G., Brennan, A., Varenbut, M., & Daiter, J. (2012). The cost of providing methadone maintenance treatment in Ontario, Canada. *American Journal of Drug and Alcohol Abuse, 38*(6), 559–566.

Zarkin, G., Dunlap, L., Hicks, K., & Mamo, D. (2005). Benefits and costs of methadone treatment: Results from a lifetime simulation model. *Health Economics, 14*(11), 1133–1150.

Zemore, S., & Kaskutas, L. (2008). Services received and treatment outcomes in day-hospital and residential programs. *Substance Abuse Treatment, 35*(3), 232–244.

Zgierska, A., Rabago, D., Chawla, N., Kushner, K., Koehler, R., & Marlatt, A. (2009). Mindfulness meditation for substance use disorders: A systematic review. *Substance Use, 30*(4), 266–294.

Zhang, H., Zheng, W., Ouyang, Y., Yang, M., Wang, F., Jin, T., Zhang, J., & Wang, Z. (2016). CYP gene family variants as a potential risk factors in drug addiction in Han Chinese. *Journal of Gene Medicine, 18*(8), 147–153.

Zhang, S., Lee, I.-M., Manson, J., Cook, N., Willett, W., & Buring, J. (2007). Alcohol consumption and breast cancer risk in the Women's Health Study. *American Journal of Epidemiology, 165*(6), 667–676.

Zhao, J., Stockwell, T., Martin, G., Macdonald, S., Vallance, K., Treno, A., Ponicki, W., Tu, A., & Buxton, J. (2013). The relationship between changes to minimum alcohol prices, outlet densities, and alcohol attributable deaths in British Columbia in 2002–2009. *Addiction, 108*(6), 1059–1069.

Zhao, J., Stockwell, T., Roemer, A., & Chikritzhs, T. (2016). Is alcohol consumption a risk factor for prostate cancer? A systematic review and meta-analysis. *BMC Cancer, 16*(1), 845. https://doi.org/10.1186/s12885-016-2891-z

Zhao, Z., Gao, Y., Sun, Y., Zhao, C., Gereau, R., & Chen, Z. (2007). Central serotonergic neurons are differently required for opioid analgesia but not for morphine tolerance or morphine reward. *Proceedings of the National Academy of Sciences, 104*(36). https://doi.org/10.1073/pnas.0705740104

Zhu, W., Zhang, Y., Huang, Y., & Lu, L. (2017). Chinese herbal medicine for the treatment of drug addiction. *International Review of Neurobiology, 135,* 279–295.

Zinn, L. (1997). The home detox alternative. *Behavioral Health Management, 17*(6), 24–27.

Zubieta, J., Heitzeg, M., Smith, Y., Bueller, J., Xu, K., Xu, Y., ... Goodman, G. (2003). COMT *val[158] met* genotype affects μ-opioid neurotransmitter responses to a pain stressor. *Science, 299*(5610), 1240–1243.

Copyright Acknowledgements

Index